FUCKED

ELEMENTARY
BIOCHEMISTRY

by

EDWIN T. MERTZ Ph.D.

Professor of Biochemistry

Purdue University

Third Edition

Burgess Publishing Company

426 South 6th Street • Minneapolis, Minn. 55415

This book is dedicated

to my wife, daughter and son and

to the memory of my parents

PREFACE

The third edition of ELEMENTARY BIOCHEMISTRY marks the author's twentieth year as a teacher of biochemistry to college sophomores. During these years, the volume of knowledge has increased so tremendously that it is difficult to cover the subject of biochemistry adequately in a one semester course. Proper introduction to the field depends increasingly on the judgment of the individual professor. New students of biochemistry can be overwhelmed by the sheer mass of information now contained in an introductory textbook. The professor's lectures must chart a course, and point out which biochemical facts need to be retained as a foundation for future education.

In preparing the third edition, special attention has been given to those areas of knowledge that have developed most rapidly. Electron microscopy has revealed the fine structure of the intact cell, thus providing information for a discussion of the relation of structure to function (Chapter 1). Recent advances in the study of protein structure have been outlined in Chapter 5 (proteins). Chapter 6 (enzymes) has been expanded to include elementary discussions of enzyme kinetics and mechanisms of action, and an outline (in Appendix 3) of the International Union of Biochemistry classification system. The chapter on vitamins has been deleted, and its contents placed in the chapter on animal nutrition. In the chapter on nucleic acids, information on nucleic acid biosynthesis and composition of viruses has been added. The exciting new developments in biosynthesis of proteins and its control by genes are outlined in a separate chapter (Chapter 8). Finally, an extensive revision of the chapter on metabolism (Chapter 11) provides the latest information on synthetic and degradative pathways in the living cell.

A special note of thanks is due to the staff of Burgess Publishing Company for their many years of friendly cooperation, and to Purdue University for allowing me to take time from my research and administrative duties to prepare this revision.

Edwin T. Mertz

TABLE OF CONTENTS

Chapter 1 | INTRODUCTION

Biochemistry (Greek, *bios*, life) may be defined as a science which is concerned with the chemical nature and chemical behaviour of living matter. Modern biochemistry can be divided into two parts, descriptive biochemistry and dynamic biochemistry. Descriptive biochemistry deals with the chemical nature of cell components, whereas dynamic biochemistry encompasses the various aspects of metabolism, chemical regulation, and structural changes occurring within and between living cells.

Biochemistry was not recognized as a separate discipline until the beginning of the present century. The first scientific journal published in this area was *Zeitschrift fur physiologische Chemie*, founded in 1879 in Germany. Three more biochemical journals were established in 1903: *Biochemische Zeitschrift* in Germany, *Biochemical Journal* in England, and the *Journal of Biological Chemistry* in the United States. During the same period the first professorships in biochemistry were established in England, France and the United States.

This relatively new field of science has expanded so rapidly in recent years that it is now the major division of chemistry. More abstracts are published on biochemical research in *Chemical Abstracts* than on any other subject (inorganic, organic, analytical or physical). Recent discoveries in the biochemical field have markedly enhanced our understanding of the nature of life, and dynamic biochemistry is fast becoming the language of biology. For these reasons, a working knowledge of this branch of chemistry is absolutely essential for those in agriculture, medicine or related areas of the life sciences.

The chemical nature of cell components. The cell is, of course, the basic unit of which all living organisms are constructed. The most complex living organism, man, may contain one trillion of them, whereas many microorganisms consist of a single cell. Although animal, plant and microbial cells differ in size, morphology and function, they are quite similar in chemical composition. All contain water, carbohydrates, lipids, proteins, nucleic acids and minerals as major components. Several chapters of this book will be concerned with the chemical nature of these biochemically important classes of compounds.

Location of chemical components in the cell. With the development of methods for the fractionation of cells into their structural and functional components, and the use of the electron microscope to show the fine details of the intact cell, the chemical nature and function of specialized structures in the cell are being clarified. Figure 1 is a drawing based on the more recent findings. It can be seen that the major parts of the cell are the nucleus and the surrounding cytoplasm. Each is contained in and confined by a membrane. Both membranes contain pores and the walls are capable of regulating the passage of ions and molecules. The membrane probably consists of a complex of lipids and proteins. Plant cells, unlike animal cells, normally have relatively massive walls of cellulose reinforcing the cytoplasmic membrane (not shown in Fig. 1).

In the cytoplasm, the electron microscope has revealed the presence of numerous structural bodies, which have been isolated from the nucleus and from each other by differential centrifugation of disintegrated cells. In green plant cells, the two major bodies are *chloroplasts* (not shown in Figure 1, but shown in Figure 2), and *mitochondria*. The

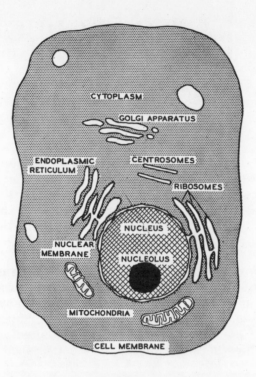

Figure 1.   Schematic representation of a
generalized living cell.

Figure 2.   Starch-free chloroplast from fully expanded leaf of Nicotiana
rustica, fixed in 2.5 per cent $KMnO_4$ (about X 7500).   The
compartmented structures are grana and the chlorophyll is thought
to be associated with the darkened partitions.   A precursor of
starch may form in the electron-transparent space between the
partitions.   The grana are embedded in a granular stroma and
are connected by anastomosing channels or frets.   (Electron
micrograph by T. E. Weier, University of California.   From
Science cover, Vol. 138 No. 3543, Nov. 23, 1962).

latter are found in both plant and animal cells. Chloroplasts are rich in proteins, lipids, and the green pigment, chlorophyll, and utilize the radiant energy of the sun to form compounds needed to convert water and carbon dioxide into carbohydrates. The mitochondria (Fig. 1) are basically fluid-filled vessels with an involuted wall. The wall consists of a double membrane made up of single layers of lipid and protein molecules. In the protein layers are found an orderly array of special respiratory enzymes, vitamins and minerals needed for the oxidative metabolism of foodstuffs.

The *lysosome* is an organized structural element of the cell cytoplasm. It contains digestive enzymes (proteins) which break down large nutrient molecules into smaller molecules which can be oxidized by the mitochondrial enzyme system. If the lysosomal membrane is ruptured, release of its contents causes rapid lysis of the cell. The lysosome is about one-third the size of a mitochondrion and more globular in shape.

Another organized structural element of the cytoplasm is the *centrosome*. The centrosomes become plainly visible by light microscopy only when the cell is beginning to divide. They are replicated during mitosis (cell division) and appear to have a directive function in this process. Since they are made up of fibers and resemble cilia and bacterial flagella, it is possible that they are composed of contractile proteins.

In addition to the particulate bodies described above, the cytoplasm contains a system of internal membranes which are not visible in the ordinary light microscope. This membrane system, called the *endoplasmic reticulum*, carries on its surface a large number of small granules, named *ribosomes* (Fig. 1). They are roughly spherical in shape and contain protein and a relatively high proportion of one form of nucleic acid, ribonucleic acid (RNA). The ribosomes are commonly assumed to be the primary sites of protein synthesis within the cell. Some workers believe that the membrane may be synthesized by the *Golgi bodies*, which apparently do not have ribosomes attached to their surfaces (Fig. 1).

The cytoplasm can be centrifuged at a speed sufficient to sediment the chloroplasts, mitochondria, and other particulate forms. The supernatant remaining is called the *cell sap*, or *soluble fraction*. It is a very complex mixture of large and small organic and inorganic molecules, including the six major types of cell compounds, which are not integrated into any preformed structural element.

The *nucleus* of the cell (Fig. 1) contains the vitally important filaments of *chromatin*, to which one form of nucleic acid (deoxyribonucleic acid or DNA) of the cell is confined with its characteristic proteins. These filaments are rather indistinct in the interval between cell divisions, but become much more compact and visible during division. Here they appear as distinct bodies called *chromosomes*.

In the nucleus can be seen another type of preformed granule, the *nucleolus*. This body undergoes cyclic changes in appearance, disappearing during cell division and reappearing at the end of division. The nucleolus is rich in proteins and in RNA, and may be the site of protein and RNA synthesis.

The next six chapters of this book will contain information on the chemical nature of water and of organic compounds which are either precursors of components, or are components of the living cell.

The remaining chapters will deal with metabolism, chemical regulation, and structural changes in the cell's components.

Chapter 2 | WATER

The living cell can be distinguished from the lifeless cell because the former has the ability to reproduce itself, to metabolize nutrients, to grow in size, to respond to stimuli, and to move. In living tissue, each cell in itself possesses the essential properties we call "life". We, at least theoretically, can dissect a single cell out of the whole organism, and, if it is placed in an appropriate medium (cell culture), it will live, and have the properties described above. In order to maintain these vital characteristics, the cell must constantly take in food and excrete end-products. Six major classes of nutrients serve as food for all living cells, namely, water, carbohydrates, lipids, proteins, vitamins, and minerals. Of these six, water is required in the largest amounts, and is the major component of most living cells.

Water is a compound whose properties are strikingly different from those of most other compounds. Hydrogen bonding between water molecules is so strong that the observed value of the melting point is 100° greater, and the boiling point 180° greater, than would be expected for water if it were a normal substance. The abnormally large dielectric constant of water is responsible for the striking power of water to dissolve ionic substances, with which it then reacts to form hydrogen bonds. Water also forms hydrogen bonds with proteins and other biopolymers. This is called *"bound water"* (see p. 5).

Pure water does not consist simply of H_2O molecules, but also contains hydrogen ions in a concentration of about 1×10^{-7} moles per liter (at 25°), as well as hydroxide ions in the same concentration. The hydrogen ion concentration of the living cell cytoplasm is maintained very near the value for pure water. Moderate deviations from this value produce marked changes. To simplify discussion of hydrogen ion changes in biological systems, the Danish biochemist, Sørensen, introduced the symbol, pH. The pH of a water solution is equal to the logarithm to the base 10 of the reciprocal of the hydrogen ion concentration. The pH of pure water is then $\log 1/1 \times 10^{-7}$ or 7.0. In man, the pH within cells has been found to vary from a low of 4.5 in the cells of the prostate gland to a high of 8.5 in the osteoblasts of bone tissue. These extremes are exceptions, most cells having a pH near that of blood plasma. The pH of the blood plasma is maintained normally at 7.4 within 0.1 pH unit. Life cannot be maintained in the body cells of the human if the pH of the plasma rises above 7.8, or falls below 7.0. This is indeed a narrow range of hydrogen ion concentration, less than 1/14 of the pH Scale.

WATER CONTENT OF VARIOUS ORGANISMS. The water content of various organisms ranges from 99.8% in the jelly fish to 40% in a very fat pig. In a given animal species, the water content is the highest in the embryo and decreases with age. Thus, the pig embryo at 15 days of development contains about 97% water, and this steadily drops to about 89% at birth, about 65% at 6 months of age, and then to as low as 40% in a fat animal about 2 years of age. Plants at the seedling stage contain about 90% water, and this drops to a value of approximately 50% at maturity.

Specialized tissues in a particular animal vary widely in water content, the more active the tissue, the higher its water content. In man and the higher animals, for example, gray matter (brain) contains approximately 84%, liver and muscle tissue 73-76%, adipose tissue 10-30%, and dentine of teeth, 10%.

In addition to its function as a major and integral part of all living protoplasm, water serves as a medium for the transfer of food materials in the form of sap in plants, in the form of blood and lymph in animals, and in the form of a nutrient solution for microorganisms. It also serves as a medium and chemical reactant in digestion, and (in animals) as a heat regulator and a lubricant in joints and muscles.

THE CELL CONTAINS TWO FORMS OF WATER. The water in an organism may exist as free *water*, i.e., liquid water containing the truly dissolved solutes, and serving as a dispersion medium for the colloidal particles in the protoplasm. However, a large part of the water is "bound" to the colloidal particles, and in this bound condition exhibits entirely different properties from water in the bulk (i.e., "free" water). In order to understand the nature of this binding, a brief discussion of the colloidal state is presented below.

TYPES OF COLLOIDAL SYSTEMS. There are many types of colloidal systems. All are obtained when one material is finely subdivided to a particle size of 1-200mμ(1 mμ or millimicron equals 0.000001 millimeter) and dispersed in a second material. Gortner lists the following colloidal systems: liquid-in-liquid (emulsoids), solid-in-liquid (suspensoids), gas-in-solids, gas-in-liquids (foam), liquid-in-gas (fog), solid-in-gas (smoke), liquid-in-solid (natural pearl gem: water dispersed in calcium carbonate), and solid-in-solid (black diamond: amorphous carbon dispersed in crystalline carbon).

The liquid-in-liquid and the solid-in-liquid types are called *colloidal solutions*. The liquid-in-liquid type of colloidal solution is also called an *emulsoid*. The "liquid-in-liquid" terminology is not strictly accurate. A better definition proposed by Martin Fischer is "a system in which the disperse phase and the dispersions medium are mutually more or less soluble one in the other". To illustrate, all proteins possess the power of becoming hydrated. Even in the dry crystalline form they may bind one third or more of their weight of water. When gelatin, a highly hydrated protein, is added to water, it takes up more water. Some of the gelatin disperses in the water, and some of the water "dissolves" in the gelatin, giving a "liquid-in-liquid" type of colloidal solution. Proteins and certain other organic compounds (polysaccharides, soaps, etc.,) that bind water are called

Table 1. A comparison of the size of particles in true
solutions, colloidal solutions, and suspensions.

State of Matter	Type of Particles (Dispersed Phase)	Size of Particles (Dispersed Phase)	Diffusibility of Particles (Dispersed Phase)
True solution	Molecules and ions	Less than 1 mμ*	Will pass through membranes
Colloidal solution	Molecular aggregates	1-200 mμ	Will not pass through membranes
Suspension	Molecular aggregates	Over 200 mμ	Will not pass through membranes
* 1 mμ (millimicron) = 0.000001 mm. (millimeter).			

lyophilic (water-loving) colloids and their solutions are called emulsoids. The colloidal particles in emulsoid solutions have a high affinity for the dispersion medium. This increases the viscosity of the solution. The particles carry a definite charge and are hydrated. Large amounts of electrolytes are required for their precipitation, and the precipitate usually can be brought back into solution by the addition of fresh solvent. The precipitation of emulsoids is therefore reversible, provided the aggregates have not passed a critical size (see Table 1).

The solid-in-liquid type of colloidal solution (suspensoid) is one in which there is little or no affinity between the colloidal particles and the dispersion medium. The colloidal particles are called *lyophobic* (water-hating). The particles carry a definite electric charge, and are precipitated from solution by the addition of very small quantities of electrolytes (such as sodium chloride), which neutralize the charge. When the particles are once precipitated from solution, it is difficult to bring them into solution again. The precipitation of suspensoids is therefore considered to be irreversible.

Most of the properties of a lyophilic colloid (emulsoid) may be explained by assuming that it is a *hydrated* suspensoid. This relationship is shown in Figure 3.

Emulsoids are of great biological importance. The large amount of water which is present in living organisms is held mainly through the affinity of the emulsoid colloids for water. Emulsoids have the property of imbibing large quantities of water and setting into semi-rigid gels. The gel-like consistency of protoplasm may be explained on the basis of its content of emulsoid colloids (mainly proteins).

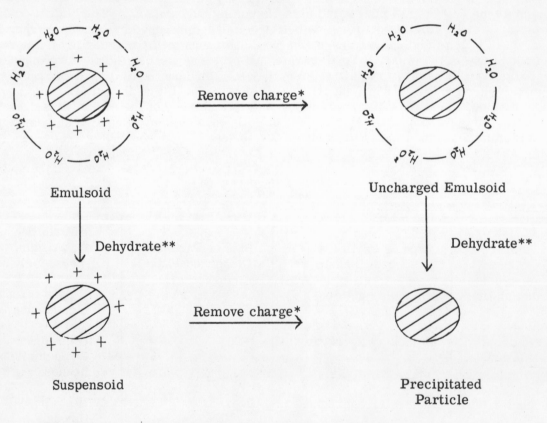

* Charge can be removed by addition of electrolytes, change in pH, electrolysis, etc.
** Remove water with alcohol or high concentrations of electrolytes.

Figure 3.   Colloidal particles.

FUNCTIONS OF BOUND WATER. The cell activities in plants, animals, and microorganisms are regulated to an important extent by the bound-free water equilibrium in the organisms. Under certain conditions of stress, it is possible for the organism to shift this equilibrium in one direction or the other in order to provide for preservation of the species. Thus, Newton has shown that winter hardiness in wheat occurs in those wheat strains which are capable of shifting the equilibrium towards larger amounts of bound water at the onset of cold weather; bound water, unlike free water, does not form ice crystals at freezing temperatures; Klotz has recently proposed that bound water is actually a *form of ice* arranged in an orderly pattern. In contrast to ordinary ice crystals, bound water "ice" does not injure cell tissues.

Bound water can be determined by comparing the freezing point depression of the plant sap or animal serum before and after addition of sucrose, for bound water does not act as a solvent for sucrose, yet can be quantitatively released in a total moisture determination in a drying oven.

Robinson has found that the ratio of bound to free water in insects regulates to a large degree the rate of water loss from the insect. The clothes moth and the granary weevil feed on wool and grain, respectively, which have moisture contents of only 5-12 per cent. With no outside source of water, these insects must rely on *metabolic* water (water released by the burning of carbohydrates, fats, and proteins in their bodies) to supplement the small amount derived from their food. Robinson showed that the granary weevil has a high bound water content (about 35 per cent). However, the granary weevil, though "drought resistant", is not "winter hardy", for lowering the temperature causes a rapid shift in the equilibrium, with an increase in *free* water and death of the weevil before the freezing point is reached. In contrast, the winter-hardy pupa of *Telea polyphemus* (a moth) shows a hardening-off period analogous to that observed in winter-hardy wheat, when the temperature is lowered gradually over a one month period. In one experiment, the insect pupae in the non-hardy condition at the start contained only 9-10 per cent of bound water. With the reduction of environmental temperature from 30°C. to 8°C., the bound water increased to 50 per cent.

Desert plants, such as the cactus, hold their water mainly in the bound form (bound to colloidal gum polysaccharides, see p. 23). This prevents, in the hot desert air, excessive loss of water by evaporation from the aerial parts of the plant.

WATER BALANCE. The water requirements of animals, plants, and microorganisms vary widely among species. In the animal kingdom, the different forms of marine life need the largest amounts for survival, excreting relatively toxic end-products of metabolism, such as ammonia and trimethylamine oxide, directly into the surrounding water for dilution, and even obtaining their oxygen from this medium. The terrestrial forms of animal life

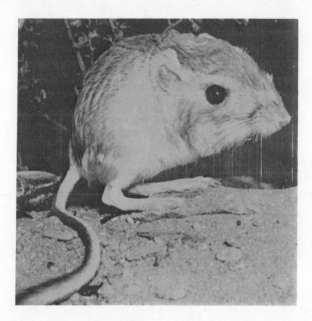

Figure 4. Kangaroo rat (Rodentia dipodomys). Photo courtesy of George M. Bradt.

have made adaptations which help to conserve ingested water. One of these adaptations is the conversion of ammonia, the toxic end-product of protein metabolism, into the relatively non-toxic water-soluble urea (mammals), or water-insoluble uric acid (birds). Only small amounts of water are needed for their excretion.

The minimum requirement for water in man and most mammals is about 2 per cent of the body weight per day. In contrast to other mammals, the desert rat (kangaroo rat) (Fig. 4) will remain in positive water balance when dry barley is given as the only food, and no water is provided. Three factors are responsible for this remarkable economy of water: (1) the kangaroo rat makes efficient use of the water gained from oxidation of the food (metabolic water) (Fig. 5), (2) there is a remarkably low rate of evaporation of water from the body, and (3) the kidneys are able to secrete a very concentrated urine solution containing unusually high levels of urea (a maximum of 24% urea compared with a maximum of 6% in human urine). The desert rat's power to concentrate salts is so great that it can use sea water as drinking water with no harmful effects. The water requirement of birds is intermediate between that of the desert rat and man.

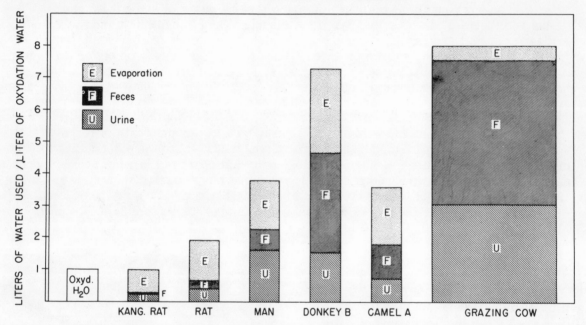

Figure 5. A comparison of the water expenditures in various mammals as related to the same metabolic level (indicated as the formation of 1 liter of oxidation water). In the kangaroo rat the total water expenditure is about equal to the oxidation water. This shows the unique ability of the kangaroo rat to cover all its needs for water without drinking. In all the other mammals shown here the minimal water expenditure exceeds the oxidation water. (Schmidt-Nielsen, B. et al. Am. J. Physiol. 185, pp. 185-194 (1956)).

Microorganisms multiply most efficiently in a medium containing about 95 per cent water. They differ in the extent to which they can be dried and still remain alive. Many microorganisms can be quick-frozen, dried from the frozen state (lyophilized), and remain alive, but dormant, for years. The well-known survival under dry conditions of certain microorganisms in the form of spores is an example of the adaptation of this form of life to drought.

Chapter 3 | CARBOHYDRATES

Carbohydrates may be defined as the aldehyde or ketone derivatives of the higher polyhydroxy alcohols, or anhydrides of such derivatives. They perform many vital functions in living organisms, serving as skeletal structures in plants, insects and crustacea, and as the outer structure of microorganisms. In the storage organs of plants, and in the liver and muscles of animals, they are an important food reserve. Most of the energy for the metabolic activities of the cell in all organisms is derived from oxidation of carbohydrates. Humans and all animals except carnivores derive the major portion of their food calories from the carbohydrates in their diets. The diverse functions listed above cannot all be assigned to one type of carbohydrate, but each function can be assigned to a particular *class* of carbohydrates. These classes are discussed below.

Classes of Carbohydrates

MONOSACCHARIDES. These are the simplest sugars and contain a single carbon chain. They are aldehyde or ketone derivatives of polyhydroxy alcohols containing 3 or more carbon atoms; thus, glycerol may be considered the parent of the simplest monosaccharides, glyceraldehyde and dihydroxyacetone.

$$
\begin{array}{ccc}
\text{H} & \text{H} & \text{H} \\
| & | & | \\
\text{C}=\text{O} & \text{H}-\text{C}-\text{OH} & \text{H}-\text{C}-\text{OH} \\
| & | & | \\
\text{H}-\text{C}-\text{OH} & \text{H}-\text{C}-\text{OH} & \text{C}=\text{O} \\
| & | & | \\
\text{H}-\text{C}-\text{OH} & \text{H}-\text{C}-\text{OH} & \text{H}-\text{C}-\text{OH} \\
| & | & | \\
\text{H} & \text{H} & \text{H} \\
\text{Glyceraldehyde} & \text{Glycerol} & \text{Dihydroxyacetone}
\end{array}
$$

Glyceraldehyde is an *aldotriose* (three-carbon sugar containing an aldehyde group). Aldotetroses, aldopentoses, aldohexoses, and aldoheptoses are also found in nature. Dihydroxyacetone is a *ketotriose* (three carbon sugar containing a ketone group). Ketone sugars are not as common in nature as aldehyde sugars, but a ketohexose (fructose) is one important exception.

DISACCHARIDES. When two molecules of the same or different monosaccharides react together with the splitting out of a molecule of water, a *disaccharide* is formed. A disaccharide is therefore the *anhydride* of two monosaccharide molecules. In an analogous fashion, a *trisaccharide* is the anhydride of three monosaccharide molecules, a tetrasaccharide of four, and a *polysaccharide* of approximately *30* or more monosaccharide molecules.

OPTICAL ACTIVITY AND ITS RELATION TO CARBOHYDRATE STRUCTURE. Carbohydrates contain asymmetric carbon atoms (carbon atoms with four dissimilar atoms or groups attached). A compound which contains one asymmetric carbon atom exists in two isomeric forms which are mirror images of each other. This is the case for most of the amino acids (see p. 54). This is also the case for glyceric aldehyde, the simplest sugar. The following formulas show the space relationships of the two mirror image isomers, D- and L-glyceric aldehyde.

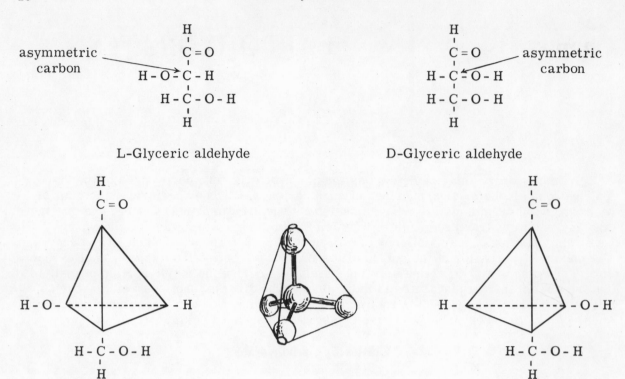

In the space formulas shown above, the asymmetric carbon atom is at the center of the tetrahedron diagrams. By using actual molecular models, it can be shown that the mirror image isomers cannot be made to coincide by superimposing one upon the other.

Effect of optically active compounds on polarized light. If light vibrating in only one plane (polarized light) is passed through a carbohydrate solution, the plane of light will be rotated to the right or to the left (unless equal amounts of the mirror image isomers are present; in this case, no rotation will occur). For example, if all other conditions are held constant, a 10% solution of L-glyceric aldehyde will rotate polarized light to the left, and a 10% solution of D-glyceric aldehyde will rotate polarized light the *same number* of degrees to the right. Since the rotation of a compound is affected by its concentration in the solvent, by the temperature, etc., an instrument has been developed for the precise measurement of the optical rotation. It is called a *polarimeter*. The working parts of a polarimeter are shown in Figure 6.

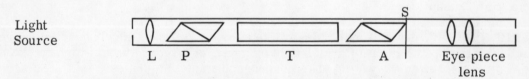

Figure 6.   Working parts of a polarimeter. A: Nicol prism (two pieces of calcite cemented together with Canada Balsam) fastened to center of circular scale S ruled off in angular degrees; prism A is called the analyzing prism. T: glass tube with flat removable glass ends to hold the sugar solution. P: Nicol prism to polarize entering light. Prism P is called the polarizing prism. L: glass lens transmitting parallel monochromatic light to P.

Light of one wave length (usually sodium light -D line of spectrum) is passed through L, and the polarizing prism P transmits only polarized light to T. If T contains only distilled water, no rotation of the plane of the beam will occur, and the light passes through A.

With the polarizer prism P fixed, there will be one position of the analyzing prism A which will allow maximum transmission of the polarized light beam, and another position 90 angular degrees away, which will give extinction. The person looking through the eyepiece, by rotating scale S, can use as a zero reading either maximum transmission of the beam, or complete extinction.

After the operator has made the zero reading, the optically active solution is placed in T, and the analyzing prism A is turned until the condition of the beam at the zero reading is again established. The total number of angular degrees of rotation of the scale (designated as alpha or α), and the direction of rotation (to the right-dextro, or to the left-levo) are then recorded. Alpha is then the observed rotation obtained, and is a measure of the ability of the optically active solution tested to rotate the beam of polarized light passing through it from prism P.

Inasmuch as the observed rotation of a compound will vary with concentration, length of tube T, temperature, and source of light, comparison of the optical rotation of different compounds must be made with these factors constant. This can be done by converting observed rotations for compounds to the *specific rotation* of the compound.

The specific rotation ($[\alpha]_D^t$) is related to the observed rotation, α, by the following equation:

$$[\alpha]_D^t = \frac{\alpha}{WL}$$

In this equation, $[\alpha]_D^t$ is the specific rotation, when the sugar solution is at the temperature, t, and the D line of the spectrum (sodium line) is used as the source of light; α is the observed rotation in angular degrees, W is the weight of solute in grams per milliliter of solution, and L is the length of the polarimeter tube in *decimeters* (1 decimeter = 10 centimeters). If a solvent other than water is used, this must be specified. The specific rotation of a compound is thus the rotation observed when a solution containing 1 gm. of the compound per milliliter of solution, in a tube one decimeter long at the temperature, t, is analyzed in the polarimeter. In practice, these conditions are never fulfilled experimentally, for it is very difficult to prepare solutions of such great concentration for analysis. Lower concentrations of the compounds are therefore tested, and the values substituted in the equation to give the specific rotation.

The specific rotation of a compound is an important constant that can be used to identify the compound, or can be used in its quantitative determination. If the specific rotation of a sugar is known, the concentration of solutions of the sugar can be quickly determined in the polarimeter. Thus, the lactose content of deproteinized skim milk and the sucrose content of beet and cane sirups can be determined quickly and accurately in the polarimeter. In this case, W becomes the unknown quantity, and the equation is as follows:

$$W = \frac{\alpha}{L[\alpha]_D^t}$$

The specific rotations of several carbohydrates are shown in Table 2.

Table 2.   The specific rotations of several carbohydrates

Carbohydrate	Specific rotation (D line, 20°)	Carbohydrate	Specific rotation (D line, 20°)
D-Glyceric aldehyde	+ 13.5	D-Galactose	+ 81.5
L-Arabinose	+104	D-Fructose	- 92.0
D-Xylose	+ 19	Maltose	+138.5
D-Ribose	- 23.7	Lactose	+ 52.5
D-Glucose	+ 52.7	Sucrose	+ 66.5
D-Mannose	+ 14.2	Starch (CaCl$_2$ solution)	+200.0

TOTAL NUMBER OF ISOMERS OF THE MONOSACCHARIDES; THE LE BEL-VAN'T
HOFF RULE. As asymmetric carbons are added to glyceric aldehyde, the number of possible isomeric forms increases. For example, the conversion of D-glyceric aldehyde into
an aldotetrose yields *two* aldotetroses which are diastereoisomers (isomers but not *mirror*
images of each other).

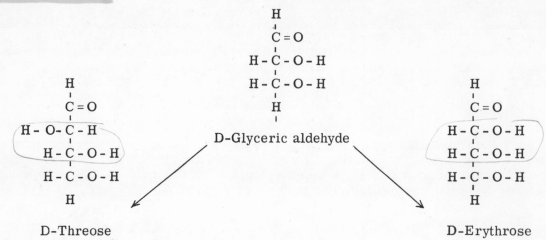

In a like manner, L-glyceric aldehyde, when converted to the aldotetrose, yields
two aldotetroses which are diastereoisomers, and also mirror images of the D-aldo-
tetroses shown above.

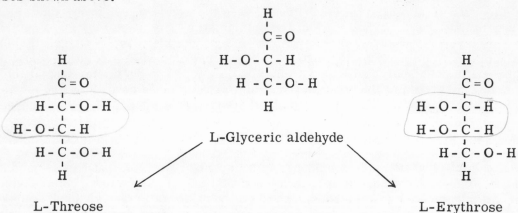

Each of the four aldotetroses shown above is capable of yielding, upon the synthesis
of a new asymmetric carbon center, *two* aldopentoses. In this manner, a total of four
D-aldopentoses and four L-aldopentoses are obtained. In turn, each of the eight aldopentoses, upon the addition of a new asymmetric carbon atom, yields a pair of aldohexoses; this gives a total of 8 D-aldohexoses and 8 L-aldohexoses, or *16* isomers for
the 6-carbon aldehyde formula for a monosaccharide.

The mathematical relationship between the total number of asymmetric carbons and
the number of optical isomers for a given monosaccharide formula was first recognized
independently by the chemists, LeBel, and van't Hoff. Their rule (called the LeBel-van't
Hoff rule) states that the total number of optically active forms of a monosaccharide will
equal 2^n, where n represents the number of asymmetric carbon atoms in the monosaccharide.

Table 3 lists the number of optically active isomers possible for monosaccharides
containing three to six carbon atoms. Optical isomers which have been both isolated from

animal or plant material and also synthesized are in italics; the other isomers listed have been synthesized in the laboratory. The list does not include all of the monosaccharides which have been synthesized.

Table 3. Isomeric monosaccharides*

Monosaccharide	Type	n**	2^n	Name of Isomers
Triose	Aldose	1	2	D-glyceric aldehyde, L-glyceric aldehyde
Tetrose	Aldose	2	4	D and L-erythrose, D and L-threose
Pentose	Aldose	3	8	D-*arabinose, ribose, xylose*, lyxose; L-*arabinose*, ribose, xylose, lyxose.
Hexose	Aldose	4	16	D-*glucose, galactose, mannose*; L-glucose, galactose, mannose; D and L-allose, altrose, gulose, idose, talose.
Hexose	Ketose	3	8	D-*fructose*, L-fructose; D and L psicose, sorbose and tagatose.

* The aldoheptoses, D-mannoheptulose and L-perseulose, occur in nature. In photosynthesis (see p. 175) it is also evident that two intermediates are present in small amounts, a ketopentose, ribulose, and a ketoheptulose, sedoheptulose.

** The number of asymmetric carbon atoms in the monosaccharide.

DETERMINATION OF THE STRUCTURE OF MONOSACCHARIDES. In 1886, glucose (with a previously proved empirical formula of $C_6H_{12}O_6$) was converted into the penta-acetate by Kiliani, thus proving that this monosaccharide is a pentahydroxyl aldehyde or ketone. Conversion of glucose via the cyanohydrin (see p. 32) to the polyhydroxy heptylic acid, followed by reduction with HI to n-heptylic acid, proved that glucose has a *straight chain structure*. In the cyanohydrin synthesis, a molecule of HCN is added to the glucose molecule, and since this was hydrolyzed to a terminal -COOH group in n-heptylic acid, the carbonyl group of glucose must occupy a *terminal* position, and must therefore be an *aldehyde* group. Since glucose has a straight chain structure, only one alcoholic -OH group can be present on each of the remaining five carbon atoms, for a carbon atom with two -OH groups attached would spontaneously lose a molecule of water and be converted to a ketone group. These considerations would lead to the following formula:

$$
\begin{array}{c}
H \\
| \\
C = O \\
| \\
(H - C - OH)_4 \\
| \\
H - C - OH \\
| \\
H
\end{array}
$$

Glucose

The demonstration by Kiliani that glucose is a straight chain polyhydroxy aldehyde was an important advance in the understanding of the structure of monosaccharides. The next great advance was the assignment of the correct configurations to the asymmetric carbon atoms in glucose. This was completed by the noted chemist, Emil Fischer, ten years later. The spatial relationships are shown in the formula on the following page.

```
              H
              |
              C = O
              |
          H - C - OH
              |
         HO - C - H
              |
          H - C - OH
              |
          H - C - OH
              |
          H - C - OH
              |
              H
```
Glucose (Fischer formula)

Naturally occurring glucose was shown by the chemist, Rosanoff, to be related to D-glyceric aldehyde, i. e., glucose can be degraded to this aldotriose.

```
      H
      |
      C = O
 - - -|- - - -
  H - C - OH                  H
      |                       |
 HO - C - H                   C = O
      |                  - - -|- - - - -
  H - C - OH             HO - C - H                 H
      |                       |                     |
  H - C - OH     →        H - C - OH                C = O
      |                       |                - - -|- - - - -
  H - C - OH               H - C - OH           H - C - OH              H
      |                       |                     |                   |
      H                    H - C - OH           H - C - OH              C = O
                              |                     |              - - -|- - - - -
   Glucose                    H                     H                H - C - OH
                                                                        |
                          D-Arabinose          D-Erythrose    →      H - C - OH
                                                                        |
                                                                        H

                                                                   D-Glyceraldehyde
```

All monosaccharides which can be degraded to D-glyceraldehyde are called "D"-sugars. D-glyceraldehyde actually has a dextro rotation (specific rotation of +13.5°). However, several D-monosaccharides have a levo (negative) rotation, as shown in Table 2. The D- prefix for monosaccharides which are related to D-glyceraldehyde, and the L-prefix monosaccharides which are related (can be degraded to) L-glyceraldehyde are therefore not related to the direction of rotation of the monosaccharide.

Using methods analogous to those used in the determination of the structure and configuration of glucose, Fischer and other chemists have established the straight chain structures of all of the monosaccharides which are found in significant amounts in plants and animals. These formulas are shown below.

Straight chain structures of the pentoses

```
      H                  H                  H                  H
      |                  |                  |                  |
      C = O              C = O              C = O              C = O
      |                  |                  |                  |
  H - C - OH         H - C - OH         H - C - H          H - C - OH
      |                  |                  |                  |
 HO - C - H         H - C - OH         H - C - OH        HO - C - H
      |                  |                  |                  |
 HO - C - H         H - C - OH         H - C - OH         H - C - OH
      |                  |                  |                  |
  H - C - OH         H - C - OH         H - C - OH         H - C - OH
      |                  |                  |                  |
      H                  H                  H                  H

  L-Arabinose        D-Ribose          2-Desoxy           D-Xylose
                                        D-Ribose
```

L-arabinose can be isolated in good yield from the polysaccharide, gum arabic, *D-ribose* and *2-Desoxy D-Ribose* are important constituents of nucleic acids (see p. 109), and *D-xylose* is obtained by hydrolysis of the polysaccharide, xylan, in corn cobs, straw, and wood.

Straight chain structures of the hexoses

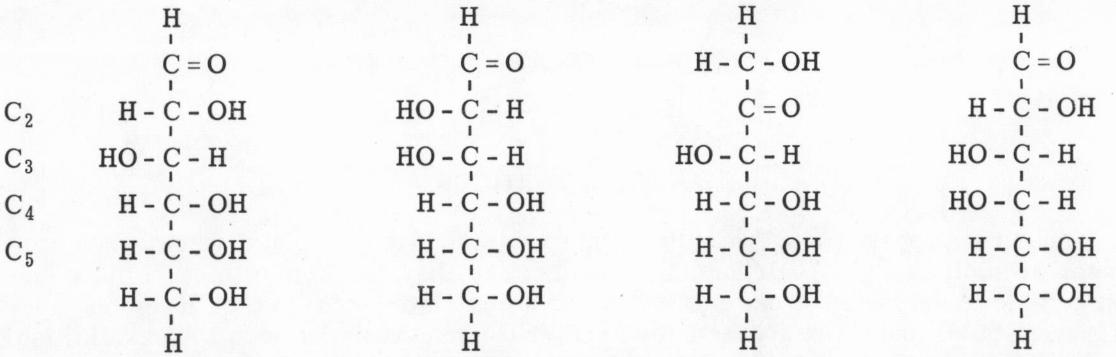

	D-Glucose	D-Mannose	D-Fructose	D-Galactose
	H	H	H	H
	C = O	C = O	H - C - OH	C = O
C_2	H - C - OH	HO - C - H	C = O	H - C - OH
C_3	HO - C - H	HO - C - H	HO - C - H	HO - C - H
C_4	H - C - OH	H - C - OH	H - C - OH	HO - C - H
C_5	H - C - OH	H - C - OH	H - C - OH	H - C - OH
	H - C - OH	H - C - OH	H - C - OH	H - C - OH
	H	H	H	H

In the structural formulas for the hexoses, it should be noted that the asymmetric centers C_3, C_4, and C_5 are identical in D-glucose, D-mannose, and D-fructose. Because of this similarity, all three of these monosaccharides form the *same osazone* (see p. 33).

D-glucose, which is also called dextrose or grape sugar, is manufactured from corn sirup. It is also present as one of the main sugars in honey and the juice of many plants and fruits. In animals, glucose is a vital constituent of the blood (see p. 256); fasting blood contains about 90 milligrams of glucose per 100 ml. of blood.

D-mannose can be prepared by hydrolyzing the polysaccharide, mannan, found in the ivory nut.

D-fructose (also called levulose and fruit sugar) is usually prepared by hydrolyzing its polysaccharide, inulin, the starch of the Jerusalem artichoke, dandelion, and dahlia. Like glucose, it is a constituent of honey and the juice of many plants and fruits.

D-galactose is usually prepared by hydrolyzing its polysaccharide, agar-agar, a mucilage from Asiatic seaweeds; D-galactose is also a constituent of the disaccharide, lactose, and of certain pectins, gums, and of galactolipids (see p. 48).

Discovery of ring structures in monosaccharides. Fischer, in 1893, wanted to convert D-glucose into the methyl acetal by treatment with methyl alcohol in the presence of dry hydrogen chloride gas. If D-glucose was actually an aldehyde compound, he could expect to obtain an acetal derivative containing two methoxy groups:

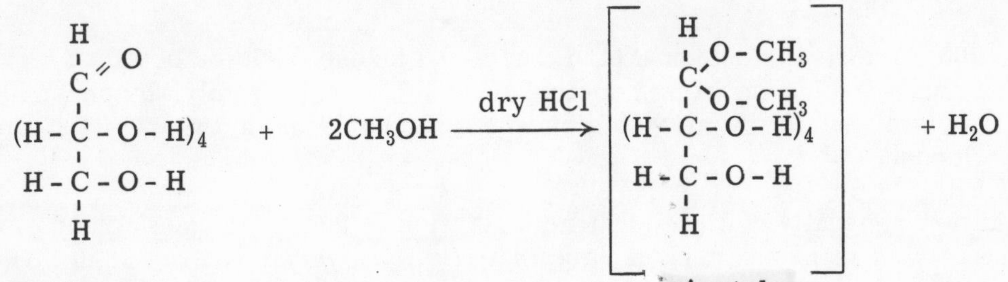

Much to his surprise, only *one* methoxy group entered the molecule, and he reasoned that the derivative must have a structure similar to an acetal, but that it contained in place of one of the $-OCH_3$ groups, an oxygen linkage which extended to one of the carbon atoms in the monosaccharide chain:

$$
\begin{array}{l}
\text{H} \\
| \\
\text{C*} \underline{\qquad} \text{O - CH}_3 \\
| \qquad\qquad\qquad\qquad | \\
\text{(H - C - O - H)n} \qquad\quad \text{O} \\
| \\
\text{H - C} \underline{\qquad\qquad\qquad} \\
|
\end{array}
$$

Possible ring structure

Since the proposed ring structure contains an additional asymmetric carbon atom, Fischer predicted that two mirror image isomers of the ring form of methyl glucoside must be able to exist. He isolated the dextrorotatory isomer (α-methylglucoside, specific rotation, +159°), and about a year later another German chemist, von Eckenstein, isolated the levorotatory isomer (β-methyl glucoside, specific rotation, - 34°).

$$
\begin{array}{l}
\text{CH}_3\text{- O} \diagdown \quad \diagup \text{H} \\
\qquad\qquad \text{C} \\
\qquad | \\
\text{(H - C - OH)}_3 \qquad \text{O} \\
\qquad | \\
\text{H - C} \underline{\qquad\qquad} \\
\qquad | \\
\text{H - C - OH} \\
\qquad | \\
\qquad \text{H}
\end{array}
\qquad\qquad
\begin{array}{l}
\text{H} \diagdown \quad \diagup \text{O - CH}_3 \\
\qquad \text{C} \\
\qquad | \\
\text{(H - C - OH)}_3 \qquad \text{O} \\
\qquad | \\
\text{H - C} \underline{\qquad\qquad} \\
\qquad | \\
\text{H - C - OH} \\
\qquad | \\
\qquad \text{H}
\end{array}
$$

β-methyl glucoside α-methyl glucoside

The finding of ring structures in these glucose derivatives solved the mystery of the phenomenon called *mutarotation*, or changing rotation, which had been observed by chemists for fifty years in freshly prepared glucose solutions.

A freshly prepared solution of commercial D-glucose has a specific rotation of about +112°. However, on standing, the specific rotation gradually drops to a value of +52.7°. In contrast to these relatively high positive rotations, a form of glucose isolated in 1897 by Tanret has a rotation of +18.5°. He obtained this form of glucose by crystallizing ordinary commercial (see p. 295) D-glucose at a temperature of 110°C. Conversely, recrystallization of commercial D-glucose from alcohol-water solutions increased the specific rotation to a maximum of +113°. It was concluded that the two mirror image isomers of the ring forms of D-glucose had been prepared. The ring form with a specific rotation of +113° was named α-D-glucose, and the ring form with a specific rotation of +18.5° was named β-D-glucose. Mutarotation, then, was the change of almost pure α-D-glucose to an equilibrium mixture of α- and β-D-glucose, when the monosaccharide was dissolved in water.

In 1903, Armstrong demonstrated that α-D-glucose could be obtained from α-methyl glucoside, and β-D-glucose from β-methyl glucoside, respectively, by enzymatic hydrolysis. This established the relationship between Fischer's methyl glucosides, and the ring forms of glucose.

It is now generally accepted that mutarotation is due to an opening and closing of the ring structures of monosaccharides, and that *all monosaccharides* exist in three forms in nature: (1) the aldehyde form (traces), (2) the α-ring form, and (3) the β-ring form.

<u>Location of the oxide ring in glucose</u>. The point of attachment of the oxide ring to the carbon chain of glucose was established in 1926 by Haworth and Hirst, and is indicated in the following Fischer formulas.

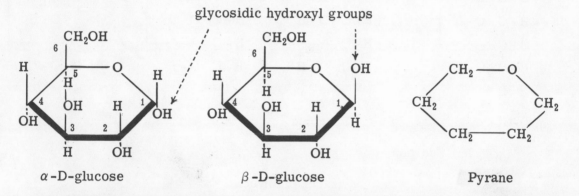

The spatial arrangement of the groups around the asymmetric carbon atoms in the ring forms of the monosaccharides is more accurately portrayed by a ring formula first proposed by the English chemist, Haworth. These are shown for α- and β-D-glucose.

glycosidic hydroxyl groups

α-D-glucose   β-D-glucose   Pyrane

   It is apparent from the Haworth ring formulas that the ring forms of **D**-glucose are derived from the six-membered ring of the heterocyclic compound, *pyrane*. Monosaccharides containing this ring form are called *pyranose* sugars. *With no exceptions*, all of the monosaccharides form the six-membered ring in water solution. This appears to be the most stable ring form. Evidence for the transitory formation of a five-membered ring (furanose ring, connecting carbons 1 and 4) has been obtained, and in one case, (fructose), the furanose ring is found in its *anhydrides*, such as the disaccharide, sucrose.

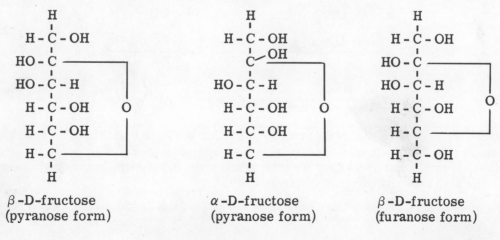

β-D-fructose   α-D-fructose   β-D-fructose
(pyranose form)   (pyranose form)   (furanose form)

STRUCTURE OF THE DISACCHARIDES. The simplest anhydrides of the monosaccharides are formed by the splitting out of one molecule of water from the ring forms of two molecules of the same or different monosaccharides. These are called *disaccharides*. Only three disaccharides are found free in reasonable quantities in natural products; these are *sucrose* (ordinary table sugar-prepared from cane, or from sugar beets), *lactose* (milk sugar), and *maltose* (prepared from germinating grains). A fourth disaccharide, *cellobiose*, is released by the action of microbial cellulases on cellulose; it is usually prepared by the partial acid hydrolysis of cellulose.

<u>Sucrose.</u> (α-glucopyranosido-β-fructofuranoside) This disaccharide, ordinary table sugar, is considered to be the least expensive pure (99.9% sucrose) carbon compound available commercially. It is formed in plants by the splitting out of the elements of water from the glycosidic hydroxyl groups of *alpha*-D-glucose and *beta*-D-fructose. The actual synthesis, of course, involves the formation of phosphate esters and the mediation of specific enzymes.

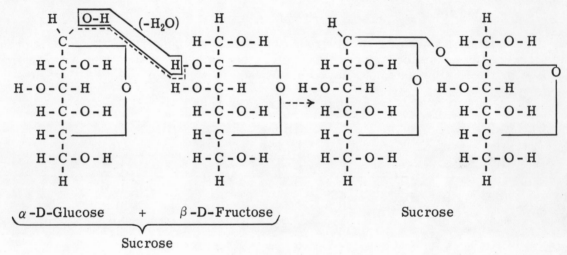

(Fischer formula)

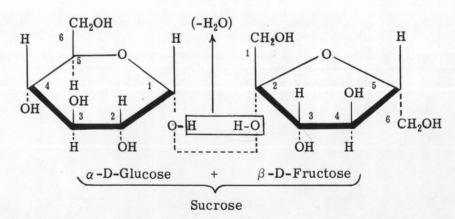

(Haworth formula)

It can be seen from the structural formula for sucrose that it has *no free* glycosidic hydroxyl groups, aldehyde groups, or ketone groups, and therefore *cannot mutarotate.** The beta-D-fructose exists in the *furanose* ring form rather than in the pyranose form found in the alpha-D-glucose part of the molecule.

---

* Trehalose, the principal sugar of insect "blood" (hemolymph) is like sucrose, with β-D-fructose replaced by α-D-glucose in the C_1-O-C_1 linkage. Thus, it is a disaccharide of glucose which cannot mutarotate.

Lactose. (4-β-galactosido glucose) Lactose is found free in the milk of mammals, where it occurs in a concentration of about 5 gm. per 100 ml of milk (see Table 41, p. 268). It is a unique product of the mammary gland, and is not produced in plants* or in other parts of the animal body. One may consider this disaccharide to be formed by the splitting out of the elements of water from the glycosidic hydroxyl group of *beta*-D-galactose and the *alcoholic hydroxyl* group on carbon number four of D-glucose (any one of the three forms):

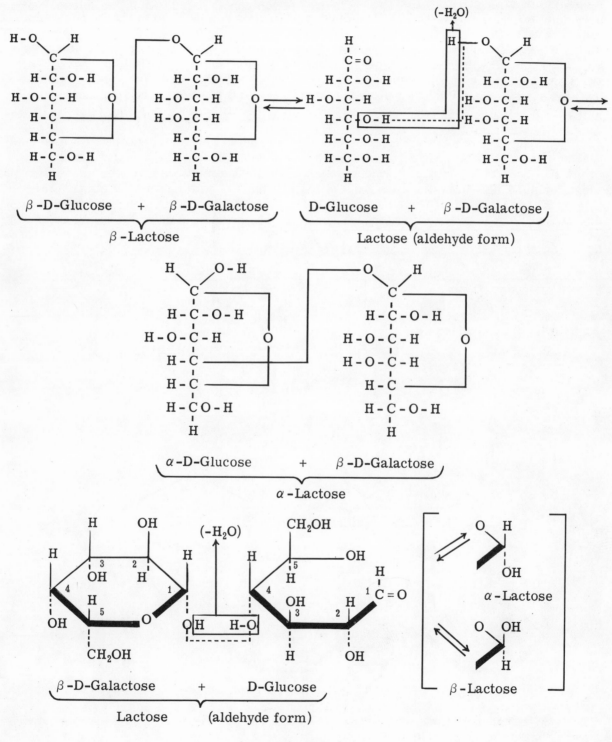

β-D-Glucose   +   β-D-Galactose   D-Glucose   +   β-D-Galactose

β-Lactose   Lactose (aldehyde form)

α-D-Glucose   +   β-D-Galactose

α-Lactose

β-D-Galactose   +   D-Glucose   α-Lactose

Lactose   (aldehyde form)   β-Lactose

(Haworth formula)

* Kuhn (Ber. **82**, 479 (1949)) found lactose in the pollen of the Forsythia plant.

It is apparent from the Fischer and Haworth formulas for lactose that this disaccharide exists in three forms, the aldehyde form (probably present only in traces, but always present), the alpha form, and the beta form.   The alpha and beta forms have been isolated and found to have specific rotations (20°C., D line) of +90° and +35° respectively.   The equilibrium mixture (Table 2, p. 11) has a specific rotation of +52.5°.   It is thus obvious that lactose exhibits *mutarotation* (if the equilibrium mixture of the alpha and beta forms is not present), just like the monosaccharides do.   This, of course, is due to the presence of a potentially free aldehyde group on carbon number one of the glucose unit.

<u>Maltose</u>.   (4-α-glucopyranosido-glucose) Sprouting cereal grains have a high content of amylases, which split the starch present to dextrins and maltose.   Malt, prepared from sprouting barley, is an excellent source of maltose.   Starches are also split to maltose by the amylases present in human saliva, and in the pancreatic secretion of man and all animals.

The partial hydrolysis of starch with mineral acids releases dextrins, maltose and glucose.   Commercial corn sirup, which is made by the hydrolysis of corn starch with dilute HCl, contains significant amounts of maltose.   One may consider this disaccharide as originating from the splitting out of the elements of water from the glycosidic hydroxyl group of alpha-D-glucose, and the alcoholic hydroxyl group on carbon number 4 of D-glucose.   In order to save space, only the aldehyde form of maltose will be shown with the Fischer formula.

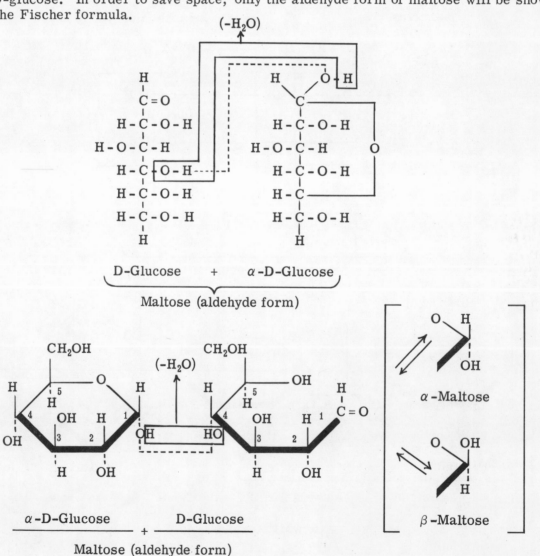

D-Glucose   +   α-D-Glucose

Maltose (aldehyde form)

α-D-Glucose   D-Glucose

Maltose (aldehyde form)

α-Maltose

β-Maltose

It can be seen from the formulas that maltose exists in the aldehyde form and in an alpha and beta ring form.   It is also apparent that maltose is a mutarotating disaccharide.

<u>Cellobiose</u>. (4-β-glucopyranosido-glucose) Cellobiose is probably present in only trace amounts in nature.   It is apparently released during the digestion of cellulose by the cellulases of microorganisms.   It can also be prepared by the careful fractionation of acid hydrolysates of cellulose.   This disaccharide may be considered as originating by the splitting out of the elements of water from the glycosidic hydroxyl group of beta-**D**-glucose and the alcoholic hydroxyl group on carbon number 4 of **D**-glucose.   In order to save space, only the aldehyde form of cellobiose will be shown with the Fischer formula.

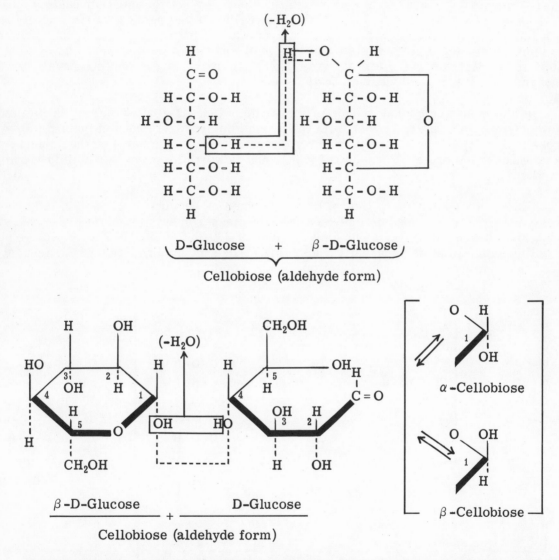

D-Glucose   +   β-D-Glucose

Cellobiose (aldehyde form)

β-D-Glucose   +   D-Glucose

Cellobiose (aldehyde form)

α-Cellobiose

β-Cellobiose

It can be seen from the formulas for cellobiose that this disaccharide can exist in the aldehyde form, an alpha ring form, and a beta ring form.   It is also apparent that cellobiose is capable of mutarotation in water solution.

POLYSACCHARIDES. Polysaccharides may be defined as the polymeric anhydrides of monosaccharides.   Those found in nature contain either five- or six-carbon monosaccharide units.   For a more advanced discussion of the distribution and composition of naturally occurring polysaccharides, the student is referred to a monograph on this subject by Whistler and Smart (see p. 306, Appendix).

Polysaccharides may be roughly divided into two groups based on their availability as nutrients to monogastric animals. The indigestible group includes the *celluloses, hemicelluloses,* and *chitin.* The digestible group includes *glycogen, inulin,* and *starch.* In their formation in nature, the elements of water are split out from the *glycosidic hydroxyl* group of one monosaccharide unit and the *alcoholic hydroxyl* on carbons number *four* or *six* on the adjacent monosaccharide unit, leaving an oxygen bridge analogous to that in the mutarotating disaccharides. This process then repeats itself until approximately 30 to 5,000 monosaccharide molecules have been added.

Cellulose. (4-β-glucopyranosido-glucose) Cellulose is the major skeletal material in plants. It exists in several forms, of which the *alpha form* is the most abundant (alpha here does not refer to a ring form). Pure alpha-cellulose is prepared commercially from cotton linters, from flax, and from wood. Careful acid hydrolysis of cellulose followed by column chromatography permits the isolation of a series of *"oligosaccharides"* such as cellobiose, cellotriose, cellotetrose, etc. Complete hydrolysis permits recovery of about 95% of the weight of the cellulose as D-glucose.

Cellulose may be considered as an anhydride of beta-D-glucose units. In its formation the elements of water are lost from the glycosidic hydroxyl group of one beta-D-glucose molecule and the alcoholic hydroxyl group on carbon number 4 of the adjacent beta-D-glucose molecule. Condensed Fischer and Haworth formulas for cellulose are shown below.

It is estimated that the cellulose molecule contains between 1,600 and 2,700 beta-D-glucose units. This is based on molecular weight measurements (osmotic pressure, viscosity, and ultracentrifugation) which give values of 300,000 to 500,000 for cellulose. The cellulose molecule is apparently a long thread-like molecule, which would account for the fiber nature of its products (cotton, linen, ramie, etc.)

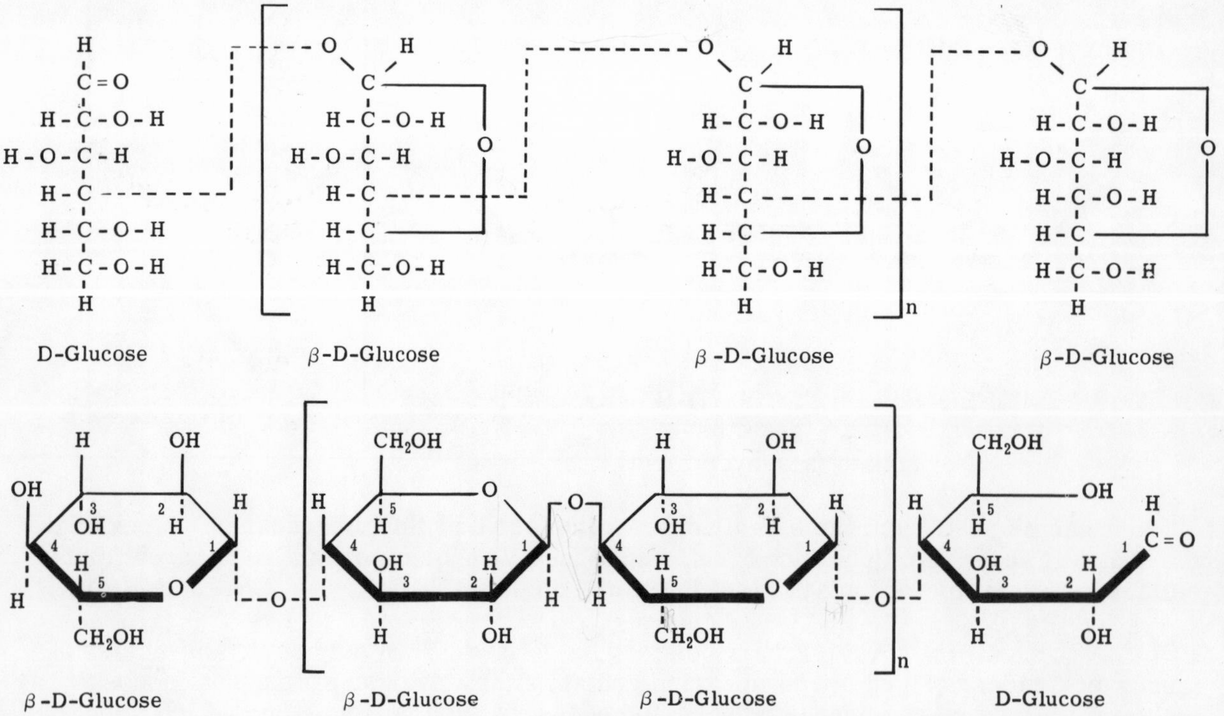

Cellulose

Hemicelluloses. Hemicelluloses may be defined as water-insoluble compounds which are extractable from plant cells with 4-5% sodium hydroxide solution. They can be hydrolyzed with hot dilute mineral acids, and yield one or more of the following products: L-arabinose, D-galactose, D-glucose, and D-xylose; they also yield uronic acids (see p. 32) such as glucuronic and galacturonic acids.

It is possible to divide the hemicelluloses into two groups, those which contain no uronic acids, and those which contain significant proportions of one or more of these monosaccharide derivatives. The former group includes the *pentosans*, and the latter group is called the *polyuronides*. The Haworth formulas for a segment of the chain of a pentosan, xylan (major constituent of corn cobs), and for a segment of the chain of a polygalacturonic acid, are shown below. The important jelling agent, *pectin*, is a polysaccharide of α-D-galacturonic acid, in which some of the free carboxyl groups (see the formula below) are esterified with methyl alcohol, and others are combined with calcium or magnesium ions. *Gum arabic* is a useful plant gum which is a polysaccharide made of D-galactose and L-arabinose units; the plant mucilage present in Asiatic seaweeds, *agar-agar*, is a polysaccharide containing D-galactose and D-galacturonic acid units.

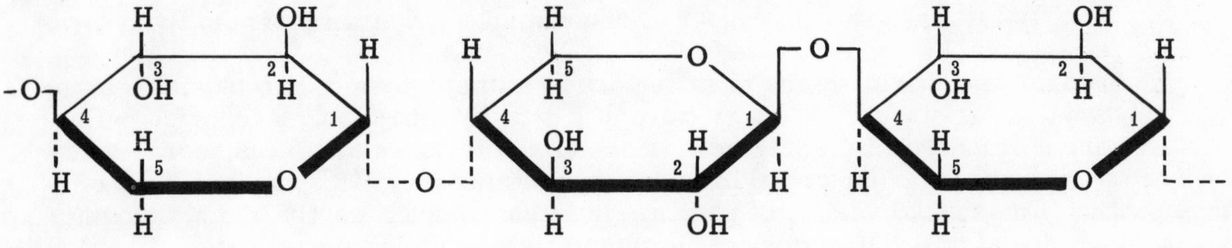

Xylan

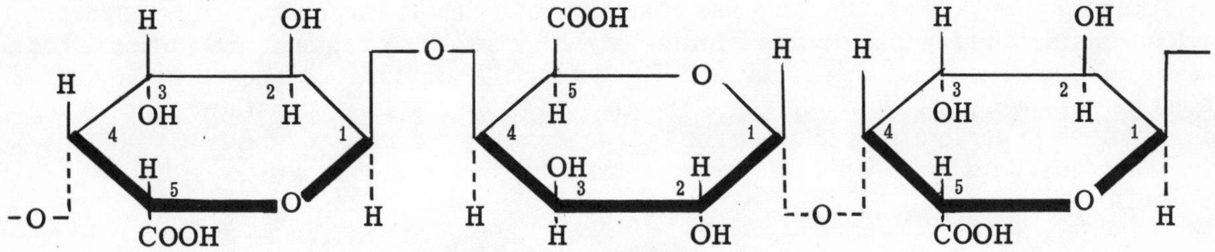

α-Polygalacturonic acid

Chitin. Chitin is the major constituent of the exoskeleton of insects and *Crustacea* (Crabs, lobsters, etc.). It is a polysaccharide closely related to cellulose, in which the alcoholic hydroxyl group on carbon number 2 of the beta-D-glucose units is replaced with an *N-acetyl group*:

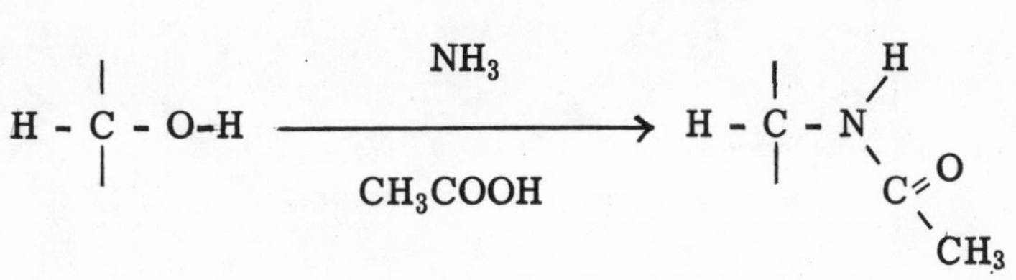

When chitin is hydrolyzed with mineral acids, it yields as final end-products, acetic acid and *glucosamine*. Glucosamine is also an important constituent of certain glyco-proteins (for example, mucin of saliva), (see p. 282). Two other important amino sugars are D-galactosamine (in galactolipids and polysaccharides), and neuraminic acid (in galactolipids).

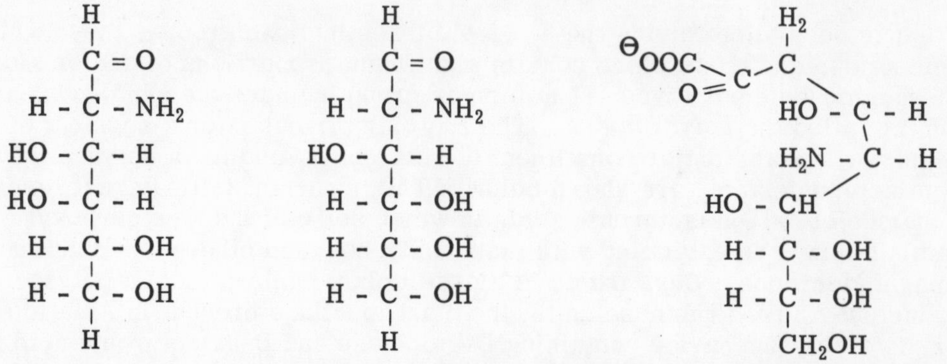

D-2-Galactosamine   D-2-Glucosamine   Neuraminic acid (keto form)

Starch. This polysaccharide is the most important storage form of carbohydrate in the plant kingdom. Most starches are a mixture of a straight-chain polysaccharide called *amylose*, and a branched-chain polysaccharide called *amylopectin*. Thus, corn starch prepared from ordinary commercial hybrid corn contains about 20% amylose, and 80% amylopectin. One special variety of corn has been developed recently which yields a starch containing almost 100% amylopectin; this variety is called *waxy maize*. Waxy maize starch has superior thickening properties. Plant geneticists are also trying to develop a *high amylose* corn for film and fiber applications. Strains have been developed which contain 65 per cent amylose.

Both amylose and amylopectin are composed of alpha-D-glucose units; however, amylose is a straight chain polymer similar to cellulose. The osmotic pressure method gives a molecular weight range of 10,000-50,000 for the amylose molecule, and end-group assay proves that the molecule is linear. Additional evidence that amylose resembles cellulose in structure is found in the fact that amylose acetate, a derivative of this polysaccharide, can be spun into fibers that are comparable in strength to cellulose acetate fibers.

A condensed structure for amylose is shown below. One may consider that amylose is formed in the plant by the splitting out of the elements of water from the glycosidic hydroxyl group of one alpha-D-glucose molecule, and the alcoholic hydroxyl group on carbon number 4 of the adjacent alpha D-glucose molecule.

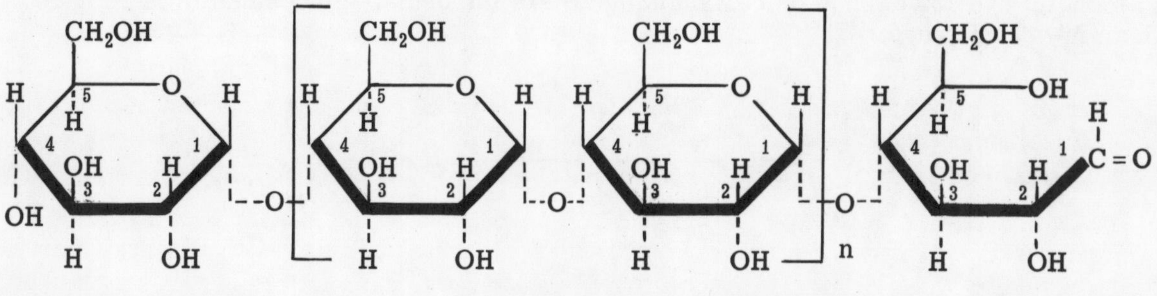

Amylose

Amylopectin.   The amylopectin molecule is much larger than the amylose molecule; the osmotic pressure method indicates a molecular weight range of 50,000 to 1,000,000. This would correspond to 280-5,500 alpha-D-glucose units per molecule. In contrast to amylose, which contains only one end-group (glucose unit with 4 free hydroxyl groups) per 55-280 glucose units, amylopectin contains one end-group per 24-30 glucose units. Inasmuch as this denotes 10-200 end-groups per molecule (280-5500/24-30), amylopectin must have a branched chain structure to accommodate all of the end-groups.   This means that some of the glucose molecules must have 3 points of attachment in order to serve as a point of branching.   The structural formula of amylopectin can be visualized from the segment of the molecule shown below.   One may consider that amylopectin is formed in the plant by the splitting out of the elements of water from the glycosidic hydroxyl group of one molecule of alpha-D-glucose, and the alcoholic hydroxyl group on carbon number 4 (*or 6*) of the adjacent alpha-D-glucose molecule.   At the points of branching, the glucose unit has attachments at *both* carbon numbers 4 and 6, and also, of course, at carbon number 1.

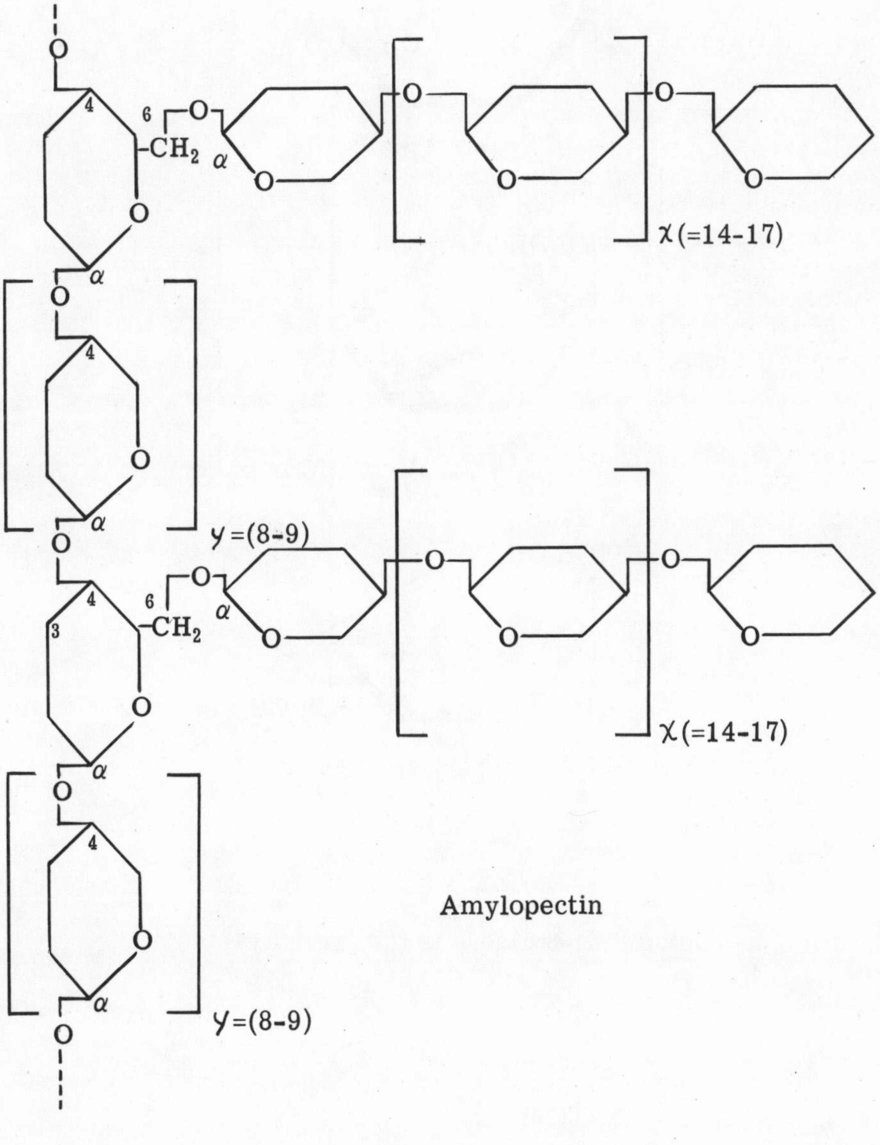

Amylopectin

<u>Inulin</u>. This polysaccharide is the storage form of carbohydrate in the *Compositae* family (artichokes, dahlias, dandelions, etc.). The Jerusalem artichoke is used as a commercial source of inulin. Complete hydrolysis of inulin yields D-fructose as the end-product. The molecular weight of inulin is approximately 5,000 if we assume no branching, and use the end-group assay factor of 1 end-group to 30 fructose units (30 x 180).

The probable structure of inulin is shown in condensed form below. One may consider that inulin is formed in the plant by a splitting out of the elements of water from the glycosidic hydroxyl on carbon number 2 of one beta-D-fructose unit, and the alcoholic hydroxyl on carbon number 1 of the adjacent beta-D-fructose unit. Again, as in the sucrose molecule, fructose has a 5-membered or *furanose* ring structure.

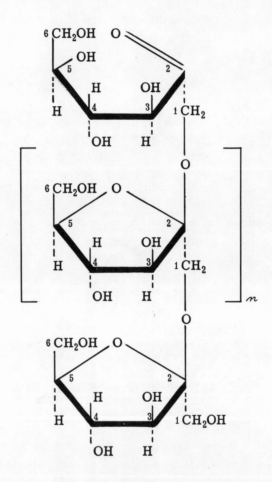

Inulin
(assuming β-D-fructose is the structural unit)

Glycogen. This polysaccharide is the storage form of carbohydrate in animals, and is often called "animal starch". Glycogen is stored in the liver and muscles of animals, is split to glucose in the liver to maintain the proper concentration of this monosaccharide in the blood, and to pyruvic and lactic acids in the muscles to furnish the energy for muscle contraction (see p. 157). Glycogen resembles amylopectin in structure, except that the molecular weight is lower, and the chains are shorter (average value for x = 5 - 6, y = 3). One may consider that this polysaccharide is formed in the animal by the splitting out of the elements of water from the glycosidic hydroxyl group on carbon number 1 of one alpha-D-glucose molecule and the alcoholic hydroxyl group on carbon number 4 (or 6) of an adjacent alpha-D-glucose molecule. At the points of branching, the alpha-D-glucose molecule will have points of attachment at carbons number 1, 4, and 6.

A SUMMARY OF THE STRUCTURES OF THE DISACCHARIDES. Table 4 supplies basic information which is useful in learning to write the structural formulas of the common disaccharides. It is assumed that the student knows the straight chain structures of the monosaccharides (p. 14), and can convert these to the alpha and beta ring forms (p. 17).

Table 4. A key to the structures of the disaccharides

Monosaccharides Involved*	Reactive Group Entering Linkage	Oxide Linkage Formed Between Monosaccharides	Disaccharide Produced
Beta-D-glucose	Glycosidic -OH on C_1	C_1	
D-glucose	Alcoholic -OH on C_4	$\overset{O}{C_4}$	Cellobiose
Beta-D-galactose	Glycosidic -OH on C_1	C_1	
D-glucose	Alcoholic -OH on C_4	$\overset{O}{C_4}$	Lactose
Alpha-D-glucose	Glycosidic -OH on C_1	C_1	
D-glucose	Alcoholic -OH on C_4	$\overset{O}{C_4}$	Maltose
Alpha-D-glucose	Glycosidic -OH on C_1	C_1	
Beta-D-fructose	Glycosidic -OH on C_2	$\overset{O}{C_2}$	Sucrose

* All of the ring forms of the monosaccharides are pyranose, except fructose, which has a furanose ring.

A SUMMARY OF THE STRUCTURES OF THE POLYSACCHARIDES. Table 5 supplies basic information which is useful in learning the structural details which distinguish the individual polysaccharides. All of the oxide linkages between the monosaccharides in polysaccharides are formed by the splitting out of the elements of water from the *glycosidic hydroxyl group* of one monosaccharide, and the *alcoholic hydroxyl group* of an adjacent monosaccharide.

Table 5. A key to the structures of polysaccharides*

Monosaccharide Unit	Number in Polysacch. Mol.	Groups Entering Linkage	Type(s) of Oxide Linkages Between Monosacch.	Polysacch. Formed
Alpha-D-glucose	280–5,500	Glycosidic –OH(C_1) Alcoholic –OH(C_4) Alcoholic –OH(C_6)	$\begin{matrix} C_1 \\ O \\ C_4 \end{matrix}$ and $\begin{matrix} C_1 \\ O \\ C_6 \end{matrix}$	Amylopectin
Alpha-D-glucose	55–280	Glycosidic –OH(C_1) Alcoholic –OH(C_4)	$\begin{matrix} C_1 \\ O \\ C_4 \end{matrix}$	Amylose
Beta-D-glucose	1,600–2,700	Glycosidic –OH(C_1) Alcoholic –OH(C_4)	$\begin{matrix} C_1 \\ O \\ C_4 \end{matrix}$	Cellulose
Beta-D-(N-acetyl) 2-glucosamine	----	Glycosidic –OH(C_1) Alcoholic –OH(C_4)	$\begin{matrix} C_1 \\ O \\ C_4 \end{matrix}$	Chitin
Alpha-D-glucose	----	Glycosidic –OH(C_1) Alcoholic –OH(C_4) Alcoholic –OH(C_6)	$\begin{matrix} C_1 \\ O \\ C_4 \end{matrix}$ and $\begin{matrix} C_1 \\ O \\ C_6 \end{matrix}$	Glycogen
Beta-D-fructose	30	Glycosidic –OH(C_2) Alcoholic –OH(C_1)	$\begin{matrix} C_2 \\ O \\ C_1 \end{matrix}$	Inulin
Beta-D-xylose	---	Glycosidic –OH(C_1) Alcoholic –OH(C_4)	$\begin{matrix} C_1 \\ O \\ C_4 \end{matrix}$	Xylan

* All monosaccharide rings are in the pyranose form, except fructose, which is in the furanose ring form.

Chemical Reactions of the Carbohydrates

Carbohydrates have reactive groups which are responsible for their chemical behaviour. These are (1) the glycosidic hydroxyl group, (2), the alcoholic hydroxyl group, and (3), the free aldehyde or ketone group. Most of the reactions of carbohydrates are carried out in an aqueous solution, which means that all three types of groups will be present and available for reaction in *mutarotating* mono and disaccharides. When chemical reagents react specifically with (1) or (3) in mono and disaccharides, the equilibrium (alpha $\rightleftharpoons$ aldehyde $\rightleftharpoons$ beta) or (alpha $\rightleftharpoons$ ketone $\rightleftharpoons$ beta) is shifted in favor of the group which is being used up. Some reagents react with more than one group. Typical reactions of each group are listed below.

GROUP (1). GLYCOSIDIC HYDROXYL GROUP. The glycosidic hydroxyl group of mutarotating sugars reacts with alcoholic hydroxyl groups (including Group (2) in nature) to form alpha and beta-glycosides. Thus, glucose forms glucosides (see p. 180), fructose forms fructosides, etc. Di- and higher saccharides are examples of natural glycosides.

dry HCl gas

-OH   +   ROH   -------------->   -OR   + H₂O

Glycosidic hydroxyl   Alcohol   Alpha or beta
                                                          glycoside

This reaction is specific for the glycosidic hydroxyl group in mono and disaccharides. Glycosides are easily hydrolyzed with dilute mineral acids like HCl, H_2SO_4, etc.

REACTION SHARED BY GROUPS (1) AND (2). ESTERIFICATION. The glycosidic and alcoholic hydroxyl groups of mono and disaccharides, and the alcoholic hydroxyl groups of polysaccharides, can be converted to esters by treatment with the appropriate acylating agents. An example is the conversion of alpha-D-glucose to the pentaacetate with acetic anhydride in pyridine. Here the reaction is carried out in a non-aqueous medium, and only the alpha-ring form is involved.

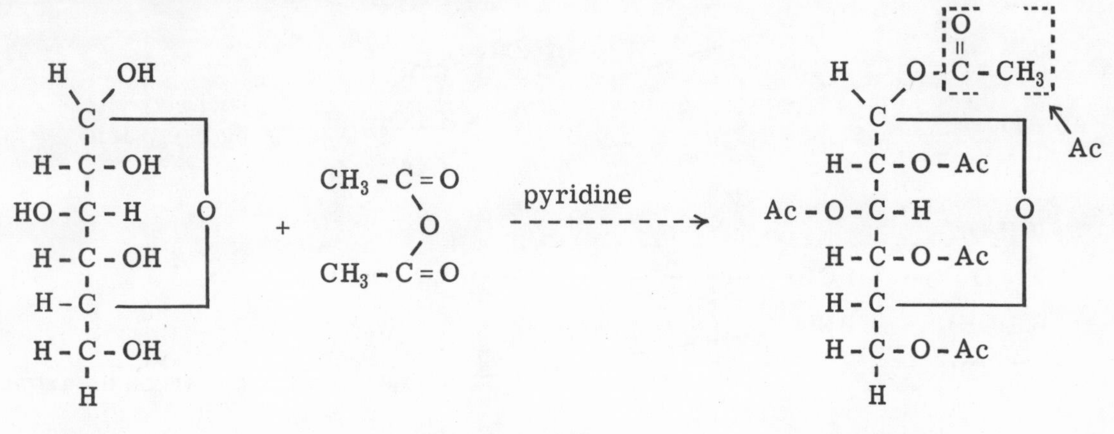

Alpha-D-glucose   Acetic anhydride   Alpha-D-glucose
                                               penta-acetate

The esters of simple sugars are valuable for sugar identification, and the esters of polysaccharides have important commercial uses (see p. 296).

REACTIONS OF GROUP (2). ALCOHOLIC HYDROXYL GROUP. If the glycosidic hydroxyl group of mono- or disaccharides is protected with an R group (by conversion of the sugar to a glycoside) the alcoholic groups can be converted to *ether* groups. No protection is necessary in the case of polysaccharides.

Preparation of methyl ether. The glycoside or polysaccharide is reacted with a methylating agent (methyl iodide + silver oxide, dimethyl sulfate, methyl chloride, etc.). The tetramethyl ether is obtained.

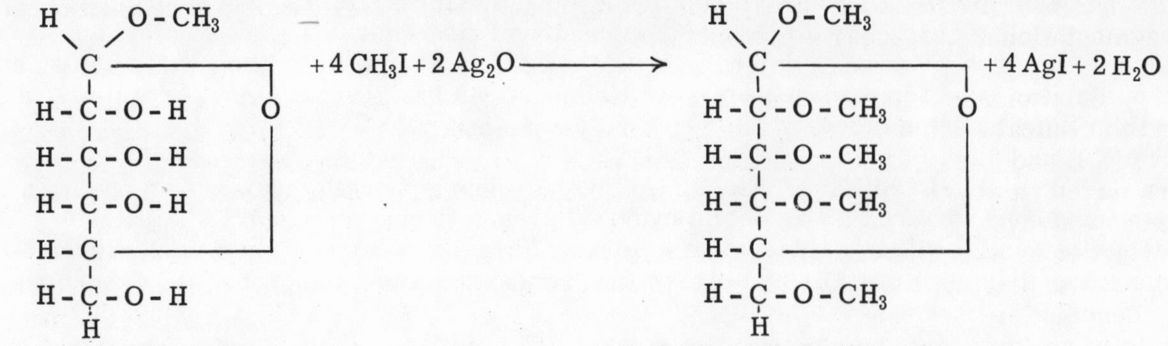

$$\text{α- or β- Methyl glycoside} \quad +4\,CH_3I + 2\,Ag_2O \longrightarrow \quad \text{Tetramethyl ether of α- or} \quad +4\,AgI + 2\,H_2O$$

α - or β - Methyl glycoside

Tetramethyl ether of α - or
β - methyl glycoside

The ethers of simple sugars are also valuable for sugar identification, and the ethers of polysaccharides have important commercial uses (see p. 297).

REACTIONS INVOLVING GROUPS (2) AND (3). Alcoholic hydroxyl and free aldehyde or ketone groups are oxidized to carboxyl groups by certain reagents. In acid solution, weak oxidants affect only aldehyde groups, whereas strong oxidants oxidize aldehyde, ketone, and primary (terminal) alcohol groups.

<u>With acidic oxidants.</u>

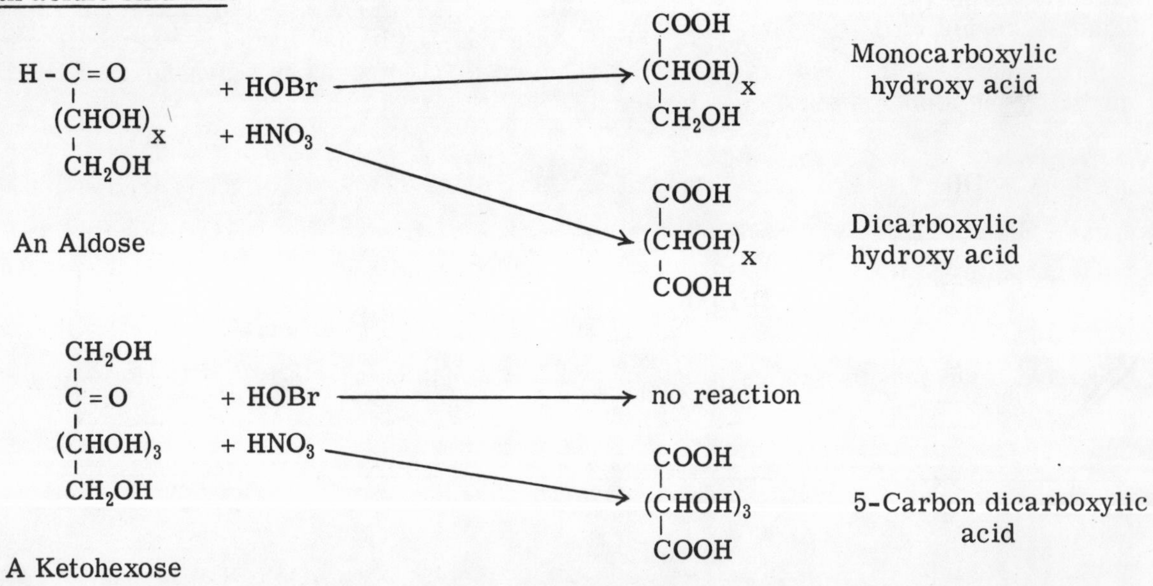

An Aldose   + HOBr $\longrightarrow$ Monocarboxylic hydroxy acid

+ HNO$_3$ $\longrightarrow$ Dicarboxylic hydroxy acid

A Ketohexose   + HOBr $\longrightarrow$ no reaction

+ HNO$_3$ $\longrightarrow$ 5-Carbon dicarboxylic acid

Oxidation of D-glucose with a halogen acid like HOBr (a weak oxidant) yields *D-gluconic acid;* oxidation with a strong acid like HNO$_3$ yields *D-saccharic acid.* Oxidation of D-galactose with HOBr gives *D-galactonic acid,* and with HNO$_3$, *mucic acid,* a water-insoluble dicarboxylic acid useful in the identification of galactose and lactose.

REACTIONS OF GROUP (3). FREE ALDEHYDE AND KETONE GROUPS. These groups respond to metal oxidants, catalytic, electrolytic and metallic reduction, alkali, hydrogen cyanide, amines, phenyl hydrazine, etc. These reactions will be discussed below.

<u>Metal oxidants.</u> Valuable qualitative and quantitative tests for reducing sugars depend upon the ability of certain metal hydroxides (hydrated oxides) to oxidize free aldehyde or ketone groups of sugars. Cu(OH)$_2$, AgOH, and Bi(OH)$_3$ oxidize mutarotating mono and disaccharides, and at the same time are reduced to the lower oxide, in the case of copper, and to the free metal, in the case of silver and bismuth. The carbohydrate oxidation

products are mixtures of hydroxy acids of different chain length (the alkali present causes fragmentation of the sugar - see below).

Solutions containing copper hydroxide are widely used in carbohydrate chemistry and in clinical laboratories. Fehling's Solution A contains 7% $CuSO_4$; Solution B contains 25% KOH and 35% sodium potassium tartrate. When equal volumes of the two solutions are mixed, a clear blue solution results, for the tartrate forms a soluble complex with the copper hydroxide produced. This solution is used as the oxidizing reagent, and is preferred for quantitative sugar determinations. In medicine, a modification of Fehling's solution is preferred for qualitative detection of glucose in the urine. This was devised by Benedict, and is called *Benedict's solution**. It is a single solution in which the tartrate is replaced with sodium citrate, and the KOH is replaced with sodium carbonate; this reduces the alkalinity of Fehling's Solution B to such an extent that the copper sulfate (Fehling's Solution A) can be mixed with Solution B, and the mixture stored indefinitely as one solution, Benedict's solution. *Barfoed's* test is a copper oxidation test carried out in weakly acid solution. The reagent contains 7% cupric acetate, and 1% acetic acid. Monosaccharides are more active reducing agents than disaccharides, and give a cuprous oxide precipitate in dilute acid more quickly than the disaccharides. This can be used to distinguish between mono- and di- saccharides.

Reduction. Free aldehyde and ketone groups are reduced to alcoholic hydroxyl groups by metallic reduction (for example, sodium-mercury amalgam), electrolytic reduction, and catalytic reduction. Thus D-glucose can be reduced to a mixture of the polyhydroxy alcohols, *sorbitol* and *mannitol*, by any one of these three methods. Examination of the

α-D-glucose   Sorbitol   Mannitol

structures of these two alcohols shows that one is derived from glucose, the other from D-mannose; in the reduction, a partial racemization of the C_2 asymmetric center occurs, which results in the formation of some mannitol. Sorbitol and mannitol were prepared commercially by electrolytic reduction of D-glucose for many years, but are now prepared by the catalytic reduction of D-glucose using hydrogen and a nickel catalyst. Mannitol is used in the manufacture of explosives, and sorbitol is used to prepare surface-active agents, as a humectant, etc.

Formation of glucuronic acid by reduction. Glucuronic acid is an acid derivative of D-glucose in which the aldehyde group is intact, and the primary alcohol group on carbon number 6 has been oxidized to a carboxyl group. This change takes place with ease in the animal body, where glucuronic acid is synthesized and combined with hormones, and also with toxic chemicals such as phenols, camphor, etc., and the conjugation products excreted in the urine. Glucuronic acid can be made in the laboratory by first converting

---

* Both Benedict's test and an enzymatic (glucose oxidase) test are used in clinical laboratories.

D-saccharic acid (see below) to the gamma-lactone, and then reducing the lactone to glucuronic acid with sodium-mercury amalgam.

```
        COOH                              C         O              H
                                            ⫽                      C = O
      H - C - O - H                    H - C - O - H
                                                                 H - C - O - H
      H - O - C - H    (-H₂O)        H - O - C - H    O    Na(Hg)x
                        ────►                                    H - O - C - H
      H - C - O - H                    H - C
                                                                 H - C - O - H
      H - C - O - H                    H - C - O - H
                                                                 H - C - O - H
        COOH                              COOH                     COOH

      D-saccharic acid                  Gamma-lactone              Glucuronic acid
```

Glucuronic acid is not only important in detoxification reactions in the animal body, but it is also a major constituent of hyaluronic acid (cementing substance in skin, component of vitreous humor of eye, etc.), heparin (blood anticoagulant - see p. 259), and chondroitin and mucoitin sulfate (cartilage, mucosa, etc. - see p. 282).

REACTION WITH HCN. Hydrogen cyanide adds to free aldehyde or ketone groups to form a cyanohydrin. Addition of HCN to mutarotating sugars creates a new asymmetric carbon atom, giving two new compounds, cyanohydrin A and cyanohydrin B.

```
        H                              C ≡ N                        C ≡ N
        C = O      +     HCN ───► H - C - O - H         +      H - O - C - H
      H - C - O - H                H - C - O - H                H - C - O - H

        Aldose                       Cyanohydrin A              Cyanohydrin B
```

The cyanide groups of cyanohydrin A and cyanohydrin B can be converted to carboxyl groups by hydrolysis with dilute mineral acids. The new hydroxy acids formed can be converted to the gamma lactones and reduced (see glucuronic acid), preferably by acid reduction, to two new sugars with one more carbon than the starting sugar.

FORMATION OF SCHIFF'S BASE. Aldehyde groups of carbohydrates condense with primary amines to form a Schiff's base. The reaction of glucose with the amino acid, alanine, is given as an example.

```
      H                                        CH₃          H      CH₃
      C = O                            H                    C = N - C - H
                                         N - C - H
      H - C - OH                      H                     H - C - OH  COOH
                                             COOH
     HO - C - H                                            HO - C - H

      H - C - OH                                            H - C - OH

      H - C - OH           +                                H - C - OH

      H - C - OH                                            H - C - OH
      H                                                     H

      D-glucose                     Alanine                 Schiff's base
```

The browning reaction (Maillard's reaction) which occurs during the baking of bread and other mixtures of carbohydrates and proteins, is believed to be due to the formation of Schiff's base structures between free alpha- and epsilon-amino groups in the proteins, and free aldehyde groups in the carbohydrates, followed by polymerization.

REACTION WITH PHENYL HYDRAZINE. FORMATION OF OSAZONES AND HYDRA-ZONES. The reaction of phenylhydrazine with free aldehyde and ketone groups of sugars may be considered to be an example of the formation of a special type of Schiff's base, a *hydrazone,* followed by the formation of a double Schiff's base, the *osazone.*

$$
\begin{array}{cccc}
\text{H} & & & \text{H} \quad \text{H}\\
| & & & | \quad\quad | \\
\text{C}=\text{O} \;\;+\;\; \text{C}_6\text{H}_5\text{NHNH}_2 \;\longrightarrow\; & \text{C}=\text{N}-\text{N}-\text{C}_6\text{H}_5 \;\;+\;\; \text{H}_2\text{O}\\
| & & & | \\
\text{H}-\text{C}-\text{O}-\text{H} & & & \text{H}-\text{C}-\text{O}-\text{H}\\
| & & & | \\
\text{Aldose} & \text{Phenyl hydrazine} & \text{Phenyl hydrazone}
\end{array}
$$

$$
\xrightarrow{\;2\text{C}_6\text{H}_5\text{NHNH}_2\;}
\begin{array}{l}
\text{H} \quad\quad \text{H}\\
| \quad\quad\quad |\\
\text{C}=\text{N}-\text{N}-\text{C}_6\text{H}_5 \;\;+\;\; \text{C}_6\text{H}_5\text{NH}_2 \;\;+\;\; \text{NH}_3 \;\;+\;\; \text{H}_2\text{O}\\
|\\
\quad\quad\quad \text{H}\\
\quad\quad\quad |\\
\text{C}=\text{N}-\text{N}-\text{C}_6\text{H}_5\\
\\
\text{Phenylosazone} \quad\quad \text{Aniline} \quad\quad \text{Ammonia}
\end{array}
$$

$$
\begin{array}{cccc}
\text{H} & & \text{H} \\
| & & | \\
\text{H}-\text{C}-\text{O}-\text{H} \;\;+\;\; \text{C}_6\text{H}_5\text{NHNH}_2 & \text{H}-\text{C}-\text{O}-\text{H} \;\;+\;\; \text{H}_2\text{O}\\
| & & | \\
\text{C}=\text{O} & & \quad\quad \text{H}\\
| & & \quad\quad | \\
& & \text{C}=\text{N}-\text{N}-\text{C}_6\text{H}_5\\
& & |\\
\text{Ketose} & \text{Phenyl hydrazine} & \text{Phenyl hydrazone}
\end{array}
$$

$$
\xrightarrow{\;2\text{C}_6\text{H}_5\text{NHNH}_2\;}
\begin{array}{l}
\text{H} \quad\quad \text{H}\\
| \quad\quad\quad |\\
\text{C}=\text{N}-\text{N}-\text{C}_6\text{H}_5 \;\;+\;\; \text{C}_6\text{H}_5\text{NH}_2 \;\;+\;\; \text{NH}_3 \;\;+\;\; \text{H}_2\text{O}\\
|\\
\quad\quad\quad \text{H}\\
\quad\quad\quad |\\
\text{C}=\text{N}-\text{N}-\text{C}_6\text{H}_5\\
|\\
\text{Phenylosazone} \quad\quad \text{Aniline} \quad\quad \text{Ammonia}
\end{array}
$$

The osazones of the reducing (mutarotating) sugars are yellow, crystalline, compounds which are very insoluble in water; they are used frequently in carbohydrate chemistry to identify the individual mutarotating mono and disaccharides.

It should be pointed out that the osazones of glucose, fructose, and mannose are *identical;* examination of the structures of these three monosaccharides (see p. 15) shows that they have identical configurations below carbon number two. In the formation of the osazone, the asymmetry at carbon number two is destroyed, hence the osazones from these three sugars are identical.

Carbohydrate Analysis

In recent years, carbohydrate chemists have developed excellent chromatographic methods for the detection and identification of the soluble carbohydrates. Mono, di, tri and tetra saccharides can be separated and identified qualitatively by one or two-dimensional paper chromatography (see p. 80). To determine quantitative levels, the sugar solutions are placed on a charcoal column (see p. 78), which separates the oligosaccharides from each other (i.e. would separate di from tri, mono from di, etc. "Oligo" means "small" or soluble saccharides). To separate and measure quantitatively two different saccharides containing the same number of monosaccharide units (for example, maltose and lactose), or to separate two different monosaccharides, a powdered cellulose column is used. The principle of chromatographic analysis is briefly described below. Not only is this method used extensively for analysis and separation of soluble carbohydrates, but also for pigments (p. 311) and amino acids (p. 78). In a modified form (gas-liquid chromatography) it is used for the analysis and separation of fatty acids (p. 43) and essential oils (p. 53).

CHROMATOGRAPHIC ANALYSIS. Gordon, Martin and Synge * define chromatography as "the technical procedure of analysis by percolation of fluid through a body of comminuted or porous rigid material irrespective of the nature of the physico-chemical processes that may lead to the separation of substances in the apparatus". This rather ambiguous definition was dictated by the observation that the mechanism of separation is different with different types of chromatographic columns. Originally, the name chromatography was applied by the Polish botanist Tswett, in 1906, to a procedure for separating a mixture of different-colored pigments (chlorophylls and xanthophylls) from each other. A petroleum ether solution of the pigments was poured onto the top of a column of calcium carbonate firmly packed in a narrow glass tube. By adding fresh solvent to the top of the column, the individual pigments moved as distinct colored bands down the tube at different rates, and could thus be separated. Tswett ascribed the difference in behaviour of the pigments to differences in absorbability on calcium carbonate. However, when a mixture of sugars or amino acids in water solution is placed on a moist starch or moist powdered cellulose column, and an organic solvent immiscible with water is passed down the column, a similar separation of the sugars or amino acids is obtained. In this case, as much as 20 per cent by weight of water is held by the washed starch or cellulose column; the sugars or amino acids dissolve in the water of the column, and are extracted from it by the flowing immiscible solvent in proportion to their *relative solubilities* in the two phases (partition chromatography). Paper chromatography is an important extension of cellulose column chromatography, with this same partition principle applying.

A third form of chromatography is obtained with columns containing ion-exchange resins such as (a) Dowex 50, Amberlite IR100, and Permutit H, which are highly insoluble synthetic polymers containing freely accessible carboxyl or sulfonic acid groups, and (b) Dowex 1, Amberlite IR4, and Permutit S, which are highly insoluble synthetic polymers containing freely accessible amine or substituted amine groups. It is believed that the functional or accessible groups of the resin react directly with the various substances placed on the column, but to a different degree. For example, a resin with acidic groups may be expected to combine with a mixture of bases (placed on the column) in the same way that an acid in solution distributes itself between various bases present. The bases will be moved along the column in the same order, when fresh solvent is added to the top of the column. Using ion-exchange columns, it is possible to separate and determine quantitatively the individual amino acids in protein hydrolyzates (see p. 78).

* Biochem. J. 38: 65 (1944).

Chapter 4 | LIPIDS

The term "lipid"* was proposed by the biochemist Bloor to denote that group of substances which is insoluble, or nearly insoluble, in water, but soluble in such solvents as ether, chloroform, carbon disulfide, hot alcohol, etc. In addition, to belong to this class, a substance must occur in, or be a product of, living organisms. Bloor divided lipids into three major classes:

1. Simple lipids. This class includes the most abundant of all lipids, the fats, or triglycerides, and the less abundant waxes.

2. Compound lipids. This class includes the phosphorus-containing *phospholipids*, and the galactose-containing galactolipids.

3. Derived lipids. This class includes the hydrolysis products of the first two classes, and in addition, other compounds such as the sterids, fatty aldehydes, ketones, alcohols, hydrocarbons, essential oils, fat-soluble vitamins, etc. which are produced by living cells.

General Chemistry of the Lipids

Chemistry of Fats (Triglycerides). The true fats (if liquid at ordinary temperatures, they are referred to as "oils") are the most abundant of all lipids. Chemically, they are esters of fatty acids and glycerol. In nature, three fatty acid molecules combine with one glycerol molecule with the splitting out of three molecules of water.

$$CH_3CH_2CH_2\,COO\,[H \qquad HO]\,-\,C\,-\,H$$
$$CH_3CH_2CH_2\,COO\,[H \qquad HO]\,-\,C\,-\,H$$
$$CH_3CH_2CH_2\,COO\,[H \qquad HO]\,-\,C\,-\,H$$

Butyric Acid   Glycerol

$$\longrightarrow$$

$$CH_3CH_2CH_2\,\overset{O}{\overset{\|}{C}}\,-\,O\,-\,C\,-\,H$$
$$CH_3CH_2CH_2\,\overset{O}{\overset{\|}{C}}\,-\,O\,-\,C\,-\,H$$
$$CH_3CH_2CH_2\,\overset{O}{\overset{\|}{C}}\,-\,O\,-\,C\,-\,H$$

Tributyrin
(A fat (oil) in butter)

Most of the triglycerides which occur in nature are mixed triglycerides, that is, they contain two or three different fatty acids in the molecule. Since all of the true fats contain glycerol, their chemical and physical properties are determined by the nature of the fatty acid components. Some of the fatty acids are saturated with hydrogen, others are partially unsaturated. A few have branched chains, or contain hydroxyl groups, or have a cyclic structure at the end of the chain. All have one property in common in addition to the terminal carboxyl group: they contain an even number of carbon atoms if derived from a naturally occurring fat. Fatty acids with odd numbers of carbons are rare in nature, probably because of the mode of synthesis of fatty acids from 2-carbon fragments (see p. 184).

The most important of the naturally occurring fatty acids are listed below, along with their abbreviated structures and a good source (Table 6).

---

* Chemical Abstracts and some biochemical journals use the spelling "lipide".

Table 6.   Structure and source of fatty acids

SATURATED FATTY ACIDS

Name	Formula	Number of Carbons	Good Source
Butyric acid (butanoic)	$CH_3(CH_2)_2COOH$	4	Butter
Caproic acid (hexanoic)	$CH_3(CH_2)_4COOH$	6	Butter, coconut oil, palm oil
Caprylic acid (octanoic)	$CH_3(CH_2)_6COOH$	8	Coconut oil, palm oil
Capric acid (decanoic)	$CH_3(CH_2)_8COOH$	10	Coconut oil, palm oil
Lauric acid (dodecanoic)	$CH_3(CH_2)_{10}COOH$	12	Laurel, coconut, palm oils
Myristic acid (tetradecanoic)	$CH_3(CH_2)_{12}COOH$	14	Butter, wool fat
Palmitic acid (hexadecanoic)	$CH_3(CH_2)_{14}COOH$	16	Animal, plant fats
Stearic acid (octadecanoic)	$CH_3(CH_2)_{16}COOH$	18	Animal, plant fats
Arachidic acid (eicosanoic)	$CH_3(CH_2)_{18}COOH$	20	Peanut oil

UNSATURATED FATTY ACIDS

Name	Formula	Number of Carbons	Good Source
Palmitoleic acid (9-hexadecenoic)	$CH_3(CH_2)_5CH=CH(CH_2)_7COOH$	16	Sardine oil
Oleic acid (9-octadecenoic acid)	$CH_3(CH_2)_7CH=CH(CH_2)_7COOH$	18	Olive oil
Linoleic acid (9, 12-octadecenoic acid)	$CH_3(CH_2)_4CH=CHCH_2CH=CH(CH_2)_7COOH$	18	Cottonseed, soy bean oils
Linolenic acid (9, 12, 15-octa-decatrienoic acid)	$CH_3CH_2CH=CHCH_2CH=CHCH_2CH=CH(CH_2)_7COOH$	18	Linseed oil
Eleostearic acid (9, 11, 13-octa-decatrienoic acid)	$CH_3(CH_2)_3CH=CHCH=CHCH=CH(CH_2)_7COOH$	18	Tung oil
Arachidonic acid (5, 8, 11, 14-tetraeicosenoic acid)	$CH_3(CH_2)_4CH=CHCH_2CH=CHCH_2CH=CHCH_2CH=CH(CH_2)_3COOH$ 14 11 8 5	20	Animal fats, adrenal phosphatides
Erucic acid (13-docosenoic acid)	$CH_3(CH_2)_7CH=CH(CH_2)_{11}COOH$	22	Rapeseed oil

OTHER FATTY ACIDS

Name	Formula	Number of Carbons	Good Source
Tuberculostearic acid (10-methyl heptadecanoic acid)	$CH_3-(CH_2)_6-CH(-CH_2)_8-COOH$ CH_3	18	Tubercle bacilli
Ricinoleic acid (12-hydroxy 9-octa-decenoic acid)	$CH_3-(CH_2)_5-CH-CH_2-CH=CH-(CH_2)_7-COOH$ OH	18	Castor oil
Chaulmoogric acid (13-cyclopentenol tridecanoic acid)	$CH=CH$ CH_2-CH_2 $CH-(CH_2)_{12}-COOH$	18	Chaulmoogra oil

Physical Properties of the Triglycerides

Tryglycerides are solids or oils at room temperature, and have a specific gravity of less than one (about 0.86). They are therefore lighter than water. The melting point of fats is dependent on two factors: the chain length of the component fatty acids, and their degree of unsaturation. Fatty acids which are saturated and contain 4 to 8 carbon atoms are liquids at ordinary temperatures. Saturated fatty acids containing more than 8 carbon atoms are solids, their melting points increasing with increasing chain length. These properties carry over to the fats containing these fatty acids.

The introduction of one carbon-carbon double bond into the fatty acid molecule lowers the melting point so markedly that even fatty acids with 18 carbon atoms become liquids (oils) at room temperature. The triglycerides containing unsaturated fatty acids thus have melting points which are lower than those containing only saturated fatty acids. Most plant fats contain high proportions of the unsaturated fatty acids oleic and linoleic acids, and are therefore oils at ordinary temperatures. Conversely, animal fats have higher levels of the saturated fatty acids, and are usually solids at room temperature. Table 7 shows the relative proportions of the various fatty acids in fats from different sources.

Table 7. Distribution of fatty acids in fats

Fat	Saturated fatty acids (%) C_4	C_6	C_8	C_{10}	C_{12}	C_{14}	C_{16}	C_{18}	C_{20-24}	Palmitoleic	Oleic	Linoleic	Linolenic	Other unsaturated fatty acids	Iodine value*
Butterfat	3	2	1	3	6	15	27	6	1	4	30	4		$1(C_{20, 22})$	33
Castor oil								2			8	3		87(ricinoleic)	--
Cocoa butter							24	35			38	2			37
Coconut oil		1	9	7	45	18	9	1	1		7	2			9
Corn oil						1	8	3	1	1	46	40			127
Cottonseed oil						2	23	1	1	2	23	48			109
Lard						1	28	12		3	48	6		$2(C_{20, 22})$	64
Linseed oil							6	2	1		19	24	48		--
Rapeseed oil						1	1	1	3		20	15	2	57(erucic)	--
Sardine oil						5	15	3		12	18			$48(C_{20-24})$	--
Soybean oil							10	2	1	1	30	50	6		133
Tallow (beef)						6	27	14			50	2			47

* See page 42

The values in Table 7 are simply examples of fatty acid composition of different fats and oils. Variations due to variety of plant, climate, etc. are appreciable. The variations in content of low molecular weight saturated fatty acids, high molecular weight saturated fatty acids, and high molecular weight unsaturated fatty acids (Table 7), can be used to explain the differences in melting points observed among these fats.

Chemical Properties of Triglycerides

HYDROLYSIS AND SAPONIFICATION. Triglycerides are split to glycerol and fatty acids by enzymes (lipases) and by alkali. Water must be present, three molecules adding to one triglyceride molecule. Lipases split the triglycerides at a *slightly* alkaline pH (7.5-8.5) in a stepwise fashion. Diglycerides containing two fatty acids are first formed, part of these are then split to monoglycerides containing one fatty acid, and finally part of the monoglycerides are split to free glycerol and fatty acid. In the lumen of the intestine, absorption of soluble or emulsified mono-, di-, and triglyceride is so rapid that very little free glycerol is formed.

$$
\begin{array}{llcll}
\underset{\text{Triglyceride}}{\begin{array}{l} \text{R-C-O-CH}_2 \\ \text{R-C-O-CH} \\ \text{R-C-O-CH}_2 \end{array}} & + \; \underset{\text{Water}}{\text{HOH}} & \xrightarrow{\text{lipase, 0-40}^\circ\text{C.}} & \underset{\text{Diglyceride}}{\begin{array}{l} \text{R-C-O-CH}_2 \\ \text{R-C-O-CH} \\ \text{HO-CH}_2 \end{array}} & + \; \underset{\text{Fatty acid}}{\text{R-C} \overset{O}{\underset{OH}{}}}
\end{array}
$$

$$
\begin{array}{llcll}
\underset{\text{Diglyceride}}{\begin{array}{l} \text{R-C-O-CH}_2 \\ \text{R-C-O-CH} \\ \text{HO-CH}_2 \end{array}} & + \; \underset{\text{Water}}{\text{HOH}} & \xrightarrow{\text{lipase, 0-40}^\circ\text{C.}} & \underset{\text{Monoglyceride}}{\begin{array}{l} \text{R-C-O-CH}_2 \\ \text{HO-CH} \\ \text{HO-CH}_2 \end{array}} & + \; \underset{\text{Fatty acid}}{\text{R-C} \overset{O}{\underset{OH}{}}}
\end{array}
$$

$$
\begin{array}{llcll}
\underset{\text{Monoglyceride}}{\begin{array}{l} \text{R-C-O-CH}_2 \\ \text{HO-CH} \\ \text{HO-CH}_2 \end{array}} & + \; \underset{\text{Water}}{\text{HOH}} & \xrightarrow{\text{lipase, 0-40}^\circ\text{C.}} & \underset{\text{Glycerol}}{\begin{array}{l} \text{HO-CH}_2 \\ \text{HO-CH} \\ \text{HO-CH}_2 \end{array}} & + \; \underset{\text{Fatty acid}}{\text{R-C} \overset{O}{\underset{OH}{}}}
\end{array}
$$

The splitting of triglycerides by alkali is called *saponification*. Here the free fatty acids formed by the hydrolysis of the fat are immediately neutralized by the alkali (which furnishes OH ion as the catalyst) to form metallic salts called *soaps*. Sodium and potassium soaps are soluble in water, but other metal salts such as calcium, magnesium, barium, etc., are water-insoluble. (see p. 298, Chapter 15).

$$
\begin{array}{llcll}
\underset{\text{Triglyceride}}{\begin{array}{l} \text{R-C-O-CH}_2 \\ \text{R-C-O-CH} \\ \text{R-C-O-CH}_2 \end{array}} & + \; \underset{\text{Alkali}}{\text{3NaOH}} & \xrightarrow{\text{H}_2\text{O, OH}^-,\ 40\text{-}120^\circ\text{C.}} & \underset{\text{Glycerol}}{\begin{array}{l} \text{HO-CH}_2 \\ \text{HO-CH} \\ \text{HO-CH}_2 \end{array}} & + \; \underset{\text{Soap}}{\text{3R-C} \overset{O}{\underset{ONa}{}}}
\end{array}
$$

Hydrolytic rancidity. When butter or other fats are stored, they often become rancid. One type of rancidity is called *hydrolytic rancidity*, and is caused by the growth of microorganisms in the fat. These microorganisms secrete lipases (enzymes) which split the triglycerides into mono and diglycerides, glycerol, and free fatty acids. If any fatty acids of low molecular weight (4 to 10 carbons) are released, they impart off-flavors and odors to the fat. Hydrolytic rancidity can be reduced by refrigeration (butter is stored at low temperatures), by exclusion of water, or by destroying the microorganisms.

Chemical reactions of the olefinic bonds; oxidative rancidity. Unsaturated fatty acids, either free or combined in lipids, react with hydrogen, oxygen, and halogens. These elements add at the carbon-carbon double bond.

$$CH_3(CH_2)_7CH=CH(CH_2)_7COOH + H_2 \longrightarrow CH_3(CH_2)_7CH_2CH_2(CH_2)_7COOH$$

Oleic acid   Hydrogen   Stearic acid

$$CH_3(CH_2)_4CH=CH-CH_2-CH=CH(CH_2)_7COOH + I_2 \longrightarrow CH_3(CH_2)_4\overset{I}{\underset{H}{C}}-\overset{I}{\underset{H}{C}}-CH_2-\overset{I}{\underset{H}{C}}-\overset{I}{\underset{H}{C}}-(CH_2)_7COOH$$

Linoleic acid   Iodine

Tetraiodostearic acid

$$CH_3CH_2(CH=CHCH_2)_3-(CH_2)_6COOH + O_2 \longrightarrow CH_3\overset{H}{\underset{\overset{O}{\underset{\overset{O}{H}}{|}}}{C}}(CH=CHCH_2)_3(CH_2)_6COOH$$

Linolenic acid   Oxygen

Hydroperoxide (see below)

The reaction of hydrogen with fats and oils is used commercially to produce hydrogenated shortenings and oleomargarine.

Vegetable oils (soybean, cottonseed, etc.) $\dfrac{H_2 \text{ gas}}{Ni \text{ catalyst, pressure}}$ solid fats

In this process, the melting point of the oil is raiśed, due to the conversion to stearic acid of the unsaturated fatty acids such as oleic, linoleic, and linolenic acids. If the process is continued until all of the olefinic bonds are saturated with hydrogen, a high-melting fat resembling beef tallow, and suitable for making candles, is obtained. In the manufacture of vegetable shortenings and of oleomargarine, the addition of hydrogen is stopped when a semi-solid fat is obtained.

Oxidative rancidity. Oxygen adds to the olefinic bonds of unsaturated fatty acids to produce either cleavage, or polymerization. The slow oxidation of unsaturated fatty acids in edible fats is associated with a cleavage type of reaction. The products formed are short-chain acids, aldehydes, etc., which give a rancid taste and odor to the fat. This type of rancidity is called "oxidative rancidity", and is due to autoxidation.

Probable mechanism of autoxidation. According to Holman*: "Autoxidation of all unsaturated substances proceeds by a free radical mechanism in which the primary point of attack is the α-methylene group. The oxidation proceeds by a chain reaction initiated by removal of a hydrogen atom from an α-methylene group."

It is thought by some that the first chain must be initiated by a non-peroxide free radical, or by stray radiation giving a free radical.

$$-\overset{H}{\underset{}{C}}-\overset{H}{\underset{}{C}}=\overset{H}{\underset{}{C}}- \quad + \quad O_2 \longrightarrow -\overset{H}{\underset{\overset{O}{\underset{O\cdot}{|}}}{C}}-\overset{H}{\underset{}{C}}=\overset{H}{\underset{}{C}}-$$

Free radical   Peroxy radical

* Holman, R. T., in Progress in The Chemistry of Fats and Other Lipids. Vol. 2. Academic Press, N. Y. (1954)).

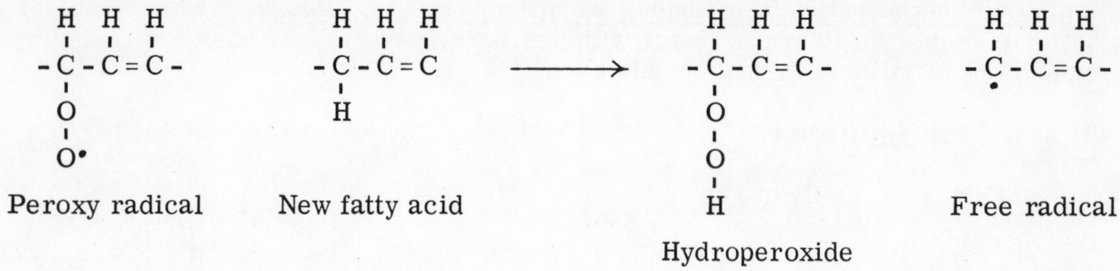

$$
\begin{array}{cccc}
\overset{\displaystyle H}{\underset{\displaystyle|}{}}\ \overset{\displaystyle H}{}\ \overset{\displaystyle H}{} &
\overset{\displaystyle H}{}\ \overset{\displaystyle H}{}\ \overset{\displaystyle H}{} & &
\overset{\displaystyle H}{}\ \overset{\displaystyle H}{}\ \overset{\displaystyle H}{} &
\overset{\displaystyle H}{}\ \overset{\displaystyle H}{}\ \overset{\displaystyle H}{}
\end{array}
$$

Peroxy radical   New fatty acid $\longrightarrow$ Hydroperoxide   Free radical

-C - C = C -   -C - C = C   -C - C = C -   -C - C = C-
 | | | •
 O   H   O
 | |
 O•   O
                                     |
                                     H

Linoleate oxidation:

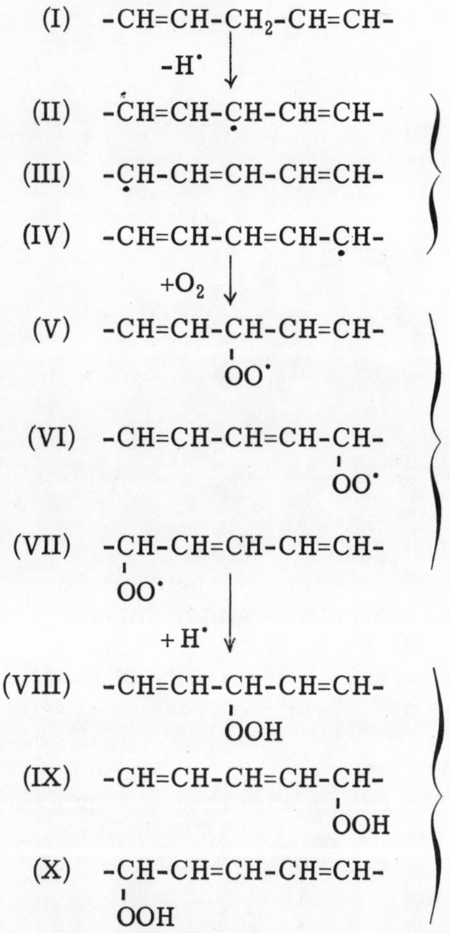

(I) $-CH=CH-CH_2-CH=CH-$ removal of a hydrogen atom
                              (by non-peroxide free radical or stray
      $-H•\downarrow$ radiation)

(II) $-\overset{\bullet}{C}H=CH-\overset{\bullet}{C}H-CH=CH-$

(III) $-\overset{\bullet}{C}H-CH=CH-CH=CH-$ resonance hybrid free radical

(IV) $-CH=CH-CH=CH-\overset{\bullet}{C}H-$

      $+O_2\downarrow$

(V) $-CH=CH-CH-CH=CH-$
                $|$
                $OO•$

(VI) $-CH=CH-CH=CH-CH-$ three possible peroxy radicals
                      $|$
                      $OO•$

(VII) $-CH-CH=CH-CH=CH-$
       $|$
       $OO•$

      $+H•\downarrow$ addition of hydrogen atom obtained from
                                  another linoleate molecule

(VIII) $-CH=CH-CH-CH=CH-$
                $|$
                OOH

(IX) $-CH=CH-CH=CH-CH-$ three possible hydroperoxides, two of which
                      $|$ are conjugated.
                      OOH

(X) $-CH-CH=CH-CH=CH-$
       $|$
       OOH

The hydroperoxides are cleaved to aldehydes as shown below for oxidized linolenic acid.

Linolenate oxidation:

Removal of a hydrogen atom from the linolenate at position 17 will yield two resonating forms of free radical ester:

(I) $CH_3-\overset{\bullet}{C}H-CH=CH-CH_2-CH=CH-CH_2-CH=CH-(CH_2)_7COOR$

(II) $CH_3-CH=CH-\overset{\bullet}{C}H-CH_2-CH=CH-CH_2-CH=CH-(CH_2)_7-COOR$

When form (I) reacts with a molecule of active oxygen, a peroxidic free radical is formed which can remove a hydrogen from a nearby ester to form 17-hydroperoxide linolenate.

(III)   CH$_3$-CH-CH=CH-CH$_2$-CH=CH-CH$_2$-CH=CH-(CH$_2$)$_7$-COOR
　　　　　｜
　　　　　O
　　　　　｜
　　　　　O
　　　　　｜
　　　　　H

The homolytic scission of the O-O bond and the simultaneous cleavage of the adjacent C-C bond will yield *acetaldehyde* and an unidentified fragment. Form II would yield *crotonaldehyde*.

The autoxidation of soybean oil results in the formation of volatile carbonyl compounds. Some of these that have been positively identified are hexanal, α-pentenal, propionaldehyde, and acetaldehyde.

Termination of reaction: The autocatalytic oxidation is terminated either by the reaction

-CH=CH-CH-   +   -CH=CH-CH-   ⟶   -CH=CH-CH-
　　　　　·　　　　　　　　　｜　　　　　　　　　　　｜
　　　　　　　　　　　　　　OO°　　　　　　　　　　O
　　　　　　　　　　　　　　　　　　　　　　　　　　｜
　　　　　　　　　　　　　　　　　　　　　　　　　　O
　　　　　　　　　　　　　　　　　　　　　　　　　　｜
　　　　　　　　　　　　　　　　　　　　　　　　　-CH-CH=CH-

-CH=CH-CH-   +   AH   ⟶   -CH=CH-CH-   +   A
　　　　　｜　　　antioxidant　　　　　　　　｜
　　　　　O　　　　　　　　　　　　　　　　　O
　　　　　｜　　　　　　　　　　　　　　　　　｜
　　　　　O·　　　　　　　　　　　　　　　　O
　　　　　　　　　　　　　　　　　　　　　　　｜
　　　　　　　　　　　　　　　　　　　　　　　H

of a free radical with a peroxy compound (to give a polymeric nucleus), or by reaction with an antioxidant which readily gives up a hydrogen atom to yield a hydroperoxide.

Oxidative rancidity is observed more often in animal fats than in vegetable oils, inasmuch as the latter contain natural "antioxidants", such as the tocopherols (see p. 229), which break the autocatalytic chain of reactions leading to smaller fatty acid derivatives. Commercial animal shortenings such as lard are now protected against oxidative rancidity by the addition of synthetic antioxidants such as nordihydroguiaretic acid (NDGA), tertiary butyl hydroxy anisole (BHA), or di-tertiary butyl para-cresol.

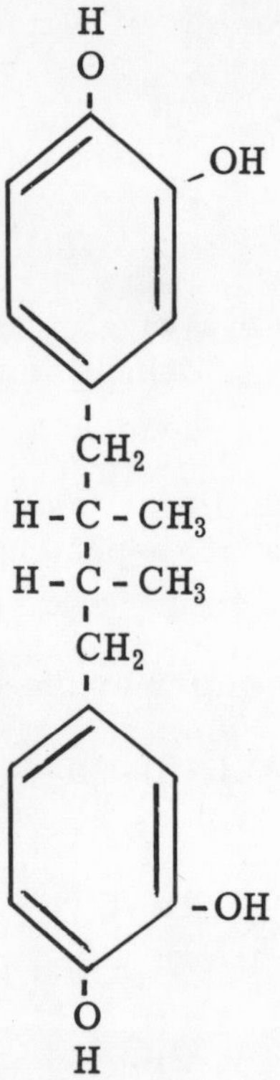

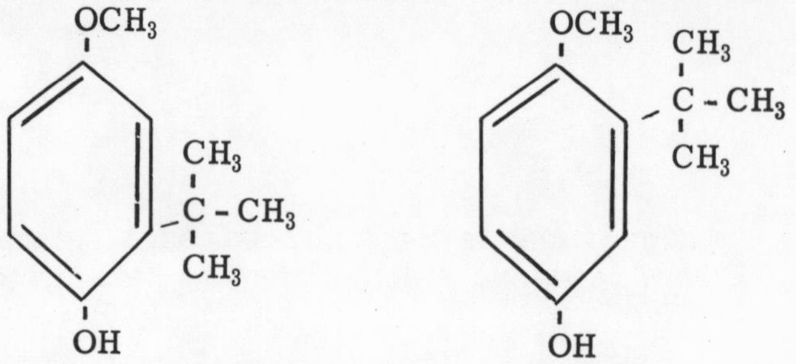

BHA (mixture of two isomers of tertiary butyl hydroxy anisole)

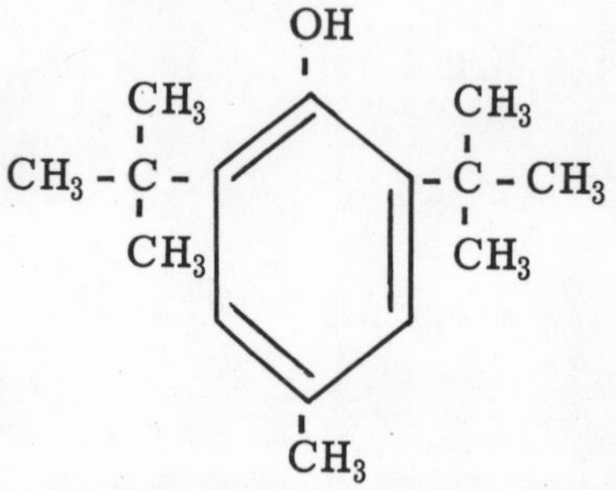

Nordihydroguiaretic acid (NDGA)   Ditertiary butyl para cresol

<u>Oxidative polymerization of unsaturated fatty acids</u>. The addition of oxygen to the olefinic bonds of highly unsaturated triglycerides such as linseed oil, tung oil, dehydrated castor oil, etc. (see p. 301 and Table 7), leads to a polymerization of the addition products with the formation of a plastic film, a three-dimensional polymer, which is the impervious film of paints and other surface coatings.

<u>Quantitative tests based on the above reactions</u>. Using the reactions described above, it is possible to learn something about the nature of the fatty acids in fats from different sources. Thus, the *acid value* tells how much free fatty acid is present in a fat. In the case of fats exposed to bacterial rancidity, it measures the degree of hydrolytic rancidity. The *saponification number* provides information on the average chain length of the fatty acids in the fat, and the *iodine number* is a measure of the degree of unsaturation of the fatty acids in a sample of fat.

1. <u>Acid Value of a fat</u>. The number of milligrams of KOH required to neutralize the free fatty acids in *one* gram of fat.

2. <u>Saponification Number of a fat</u>. The number of milligrams of KOH required to saponify *one* gram of fat. The higher the number, the shorter the average chain length of the fatty acids.

3. <u>Iodine Number of a fat</u>. The number of *grams* of iodine absorbed by *100* grams of fat. (see Table 7, p. 37).

Tests have also been devised to measure in triglycerides the quantity of short-chain fatty acids (up to capric acid inclusive)(Reichert-Meissl method), and to determine the number of hydroxyl groups (acetyl number method).

ISOLATION AND PURIFICATION OF FATTY ACIDS. Commercially, fatty acids are separated (after saponification or methanol exchange) by fractional distillation *in vacuo* (see p. 300, Chapter 15). In the laboratory, the fat is saponified with alcoholic potassium hydroxide and extracted with ether. The soaps are insoluble in ether. The soaps are acidified to yield free fatty acids, then subjected to steam distillation. The fatty acids up to capric acid inclusive are volatile with steam. The volatile and non-volatile fractions are then dissolved in hot alcohol and treated with an alcoholic solution of lead chloride. Saturated fatty acids form insoluble lead salts and precipitate, thus separating them from unsaturated fatty acids whose lead salts are soluble. Both fractions are then converted to free fatty acids with HCl, the fatty acids extracted with ether, and converted to their methyl esters. The methyl esters are more volatile than the free fatty acids, and are separated and purified by fractional distillation *in vacuo*.

Other methods of separation are the Craig counter current distribution method (partition between two immiscible solvents), and the gas chromatography method.

Gas Chromatography. The principle of this method is the stepwise elution of a volatile mixture of carbon compounds (such as the methyl esters of fatty acids) from a column "packed" with a high boiling (non-volatile) liquid like silicone oil. The method is therefore actually "gas-liquid chromatography". Figure 7 shows a diagram of the essential parts of this apparatus. Helium gas is introduced at a constant rate of flow through valve V, passing through the detector, D, then through the column S. P. (stationary phase)

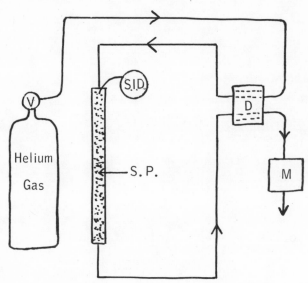

Figure 7. Diagram of chromatography apparatus

filled with silicone or other non-volatile liquid, then through the lower part of the detector, D, then through a wet gas-flow meter, M, where the exact rate of flow of gas is measured. The sample to be analyzed is dissolved in a carrier solvent and "injected" at the top of the column with the sample introducing device, S. I. D.

The detector, D, is a thermal conductivity cell called a double katharometer. The principle of this detector is shown in Figure 8.

Heat is conducted away from a hot body by passing a gas over the hot body. The rate of heat removal will depend on the nature of the gas, other factors being constant. Thus, the inert gas, freon, has only about one-fifth of the heat conductivity of air, whereas hydrogen gas is seven times more effective than air. In Figure 8, the identical gas chambers C_1 and C_2 contain identical pieces of platinum wire. These are heated by identical

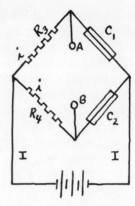

Figure 8. Bridge circuit of D.
(thermal conductivity cell)

quantities of electrical current. The resistance of the two wires will be identical *if* the same gas passes through C_1 and C_2 at a constant rate. However, if pure inert gas such as helium, passes over C_1 and the methyl ester of a fatty acid is mixed with it in S. P. (Fig. 7) and *this* mixture passes over wire C_2, C_2 will be surrounded by a gas with different thermal conductivity (probably a lower conductivity in this case), the C_2 wire will not lose as much heat as the C_1 wire so will have a *higher* resistance. If the resistance of C_1 and C_2 were first just balanced with R_3 and R_4 resistances of a wheatstone bridge with only helium flowing, then a potential would develop between A and B (Fig. 8) when the methyl ester was introduced. This could be measured and taped with an electrical paper tracing recorder. An example of such a tracing is shown in Figure 9.

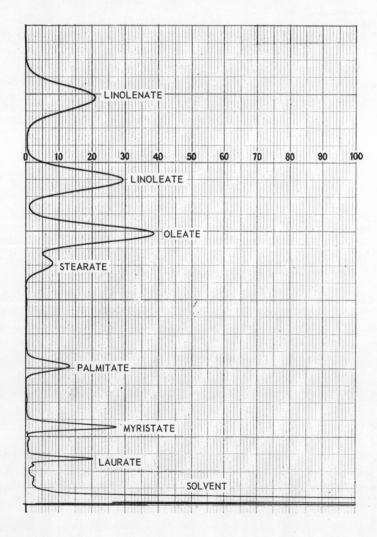

Figure 9. Separation and quantitative determination of fatty acid methyl esters by gas chromatography. Peak locations were identified first by using pure samples of the individual methyl esters of the fatty acids.

Twenty microliters of mixed methyl esters of C_{10}-C_{20} fatty acids dissolved in methyl caproate were injected into a column operating at $208^{\circ}C$ and a flow rate of 75 ml. helium per minute. The separation of the esters was recorded with a 10 millivolt full scale sensitivity recorder, a filament current of 260 milliamps and chart speed of 15 inches per hour. The C_{20} (arachidonate) peak was ahead of the linolenate peak and is not shown in the figure. The apparatus used was an Aerograph A-100-C (Wilkens Instrument and Research, Inc., Walnut Creek, California).

Waxes

Waxes are found in numerous locations in animals, plants and microorgranisms, where they form a protective covering (leaves, fruits) or are present in oily secretions (animals, microorganisms). Examples of true (lipid) waxes are beeswax, carnauba wax (from the carnauba plant) and sperm whale wax. Waxes are simple lipids containing one molecule of fatty acid esterified with one molecule of a high molecular weight monohydroxy alcohol. Thus, beeswax and spermaceti (sperm whale wax) are composed mainly of palmitic acid esterified with either hexacosonol ($C_{26}H_{53}OH$) or triacontanol ($C_{30}H_{61}OH$). Carnauba wax, the hardest known wax, consists of fatty acids esterified with tetracosanol

$$CH_3(CH_2)_{14}COOH \quad\quad HOCH_2(CH_2)_{24}CH_3 \longrightarrow CH_3(CH_2)_{14}\overset{\displaystyle O}{\overset{\|}{C}}-O-CH_2(CH_2)_{24}CH_3$$

Palmitic acid	Hexacosanol	Hexacosyl palmitate (one of the major constituents of beeswax and spermaceti)

($C_{24}H_{49}OH$) and tetratriacontanol ($C_{34}H_{69}OH$). Waxes are quite inert chemically, but they can be split slowly with hot alcoholic KOH. They are insoluble in water, and are very resistant to atmospheric oxidation. Because of these properties, they are used in furniture and automobile polishes, and in wax-coated paper used to wrap perishable food products.

Compound Lipids

PHOSPHOLIPIDS. From the biological standpoint, phospholipids are probably the most important of the lipids. They are present in all living cells, and are essential for their proper functioning. Among the many vital functions of this class of lipids may be mentioned their regulation of plant and animal cell permeability, their participation in the transport and metabolism of synthesized and dietary fat, and their important role in blood coagulation.

Folch and Sperry propose the following classification of phospholipids:

1. Phosphoglycerides

    a. Lecithins (and Lysolecithins)
    b. Cephalins
    c. Plasmalogens

2. Phosphoinositides

3. Phosphosphingosides

The products obtained on hydrolysis of each of these compounds and solubility characteristics which are helpful in their separation are shown in Table 8.

Table 8. Components and solubility of phospholipids

Phospholipid	Components Obtained on Hydrolysis	Solubility Characteristics
Lecithins	Fatty acids, glycerol, choline, phosphoric acid	Soluble ether, alcohol, insol. acetone
Cephalins	Fatty acids, glycerol, ethanol-amine, serine, phosphoric acid	Same as lecithin, except insol. in alcohol at 60°C.
Plasmalogens	Fatty aldehyde, glycerol, ethanol-amine, choline, phosphoric acid	Soluble in lipid solvents
Phosphoinositides	Fatty acids, glycerol, inositol, phosphate	Soluble in lipid solvents
Phosphosphingosides	Fatty acid, sphingosine, phosphoric acid, choline	Insol. acetone, cold ether, cold alcohol; sol. warm ether, $CHCl_3$, pyr., HAc

PHOSPHOGLYCERIDES. Lecithins. Lecithins are widely distributed in nature. A good plant source is the oil of seeds. Most of the lecithin sold commercially is a by-product of the soybean oil industry. Commercial lecithin is actually a crude phosphatide mixture containing less than 50% lecithin. Glandular tissues and nervous tissues of animals also contain appreciable amounts of this lipid. Lecithins have the following general formula:

$$
\begin{array}{c}
\quad\quad\quad\quad\quad\quad\quad O \\
\quad\quad\quad\quad\quad\quad\quad \parallel \\
\quad\quad\quad H_2C - O - C - R_1 \\
O \quad\quad\quad | \\
\parallel \quad\quad\quad | \quad\quad\quad\quad\quad\quad CH_3 \\
R_2 - C - O - C - H \quad O \quad\quad\quad\quad / \\
\quad\quad\quad | \quad\quad\quad \uparrow \quad\quad\quad\quad CH_3 \\
\quad\quad H_2C - O - P - OCH_2CH_2N - CH_3 \\
\quad\quad\quad\quad\quad\quad | \quad\quad\quad\quad + \quad\quad\backslash \\
\quad\quad\quad\quad\quad\quad O - (H,OH) \quad\quad CH_3
\end{array}
$$

α-Lecithin
(Phosphatidyl Choline)

The fatty acids most commonly found in lecithins are palmitic, stearic, oleic, linoleic, linolenic and arachidonic acids. Only two fatty acid molecules are present in a lecithin molecule. If esterification with fatty acids occurs on the first and second, or on the second and third carbons of glycerol, an *alpha*-lecithin is obtained; if esterification with fatty acids occurs on the first and third carbons of glycerol, a *beta*-lecithin is obtained. The nitrogenous base (choline) attached by ester linkage to phosphoric acid is unusual in that it is also a vitamin in animals. The absence of this compound, choline (trimethylhydroxy ethyl ammonium hydroxide) from the diet of chicks causes perosis (slipped tendon), and its absence from the diet of all animals causes fatty livers (see p. 234). Choline is an important agent for the methylation of various biologically important compounds such as adrenaline (page 269), creatine (page 166), etc. Its acetyl derivative, *acetyl choline,* is believed to be the agent for transmission of nerve impulses.

$$
\begin{array}{c}
\quad\quad\quad\quad CH_3 \\
\quad\quad\quad\quad / \\
HOCH_2CH_2 N - CH_3 \\
\quad\quad\quad + \quad\backslash \\
\quad\quad\quad\quad CH_3
\end{array}
\quad\quad\quad\quad\quad
\begin{array}{c}
O \quad\quad\quad\quad\quad CH_3 \\
\parallel \quad\quad\quad\quad\quad / \\
CH_3 - C - OCH_2CH_2 N - CH_3 \\
\quad\quad\quad\quad\quad\quad + \quad\backslash \\
\quad\quad\quad\quad\quad\quad\quad CH_3
\end{array}
$$

Choline   Acetyl Choline

Lysolecithins. Lysolecithins are produced from lecithins by certain lecithinases which are the active principle in venoms such as that of the bee and cobra. These lecithinases remove an unsaturated fatty acid residue from lecithin, leaving an unesterified hydroxyl group on the glycerol part of the molecule. When injected into the blood stream by sting, bite, or needle, lysolecithins cause rapid hemolysis (rupture, see p. 257) of the red blood cells.

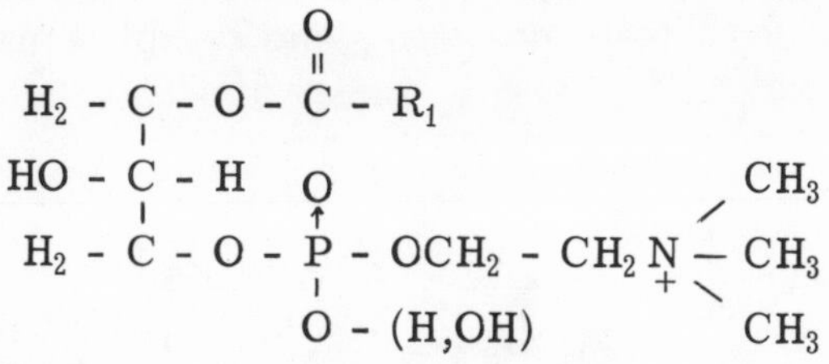

$$
\begin{array}{l}
\quad\quad\quad\quad\quad\quad \overset{O}{\overset{\|}{}} \\
H_2 - C - O - C - R_1 \\
HO - C - H \quad O \\
H_2 - C - O - \overset{\uparrow}{P} - OCH_2 - CH_2\,\overset{+}{N} \begin{array}{l} CH_3 \\ CH_3 \\ CH_3 \end{array} \\
\quad\quad\quad\quad O - (H,OH)
\end{array}
$$

A Lysolecithin

Cephalin. The cephalins (also spelled kephalins) are closely associated with lecithins in animal tissues; they have also been identified as a constituent of one plant lipid, soybean oil. The primary difference between lecithins and cephalins is the nature of the nitrogenous base. Cephalins contain ethanolamine (and in some cases, serine) in place of choline.

HO $CH_2CH_2NH_2$

$$
\begin{array}{l}
H \quad H \\
| \quad\, | \\
H - C - C - COOH \\
| \quad\, | \\
OH \ NH_2
\end{array}
$$

Ethanolamine   Serine

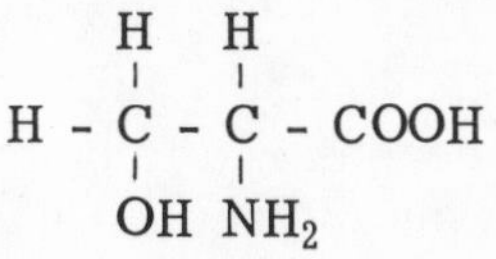

Cephalins exist in alpha and beta forms, depending upon the relative positions of the two substituting fatty acids (see lecithins). In contrast to lecithins, they contain fewer different fatty acids. They usually contain stearic, oleic, linoleic, and arachidonic acids. Venoms containing lecithinases also split off fatty acids from cephalins, leaving hemolytic lysocephalins.

Cephalins are components of certain lipoproteins; the lipoprotein, thromboplastin (see p. 259) is an important factor in blood coagulation. It contains a relatively high level of cephalins.

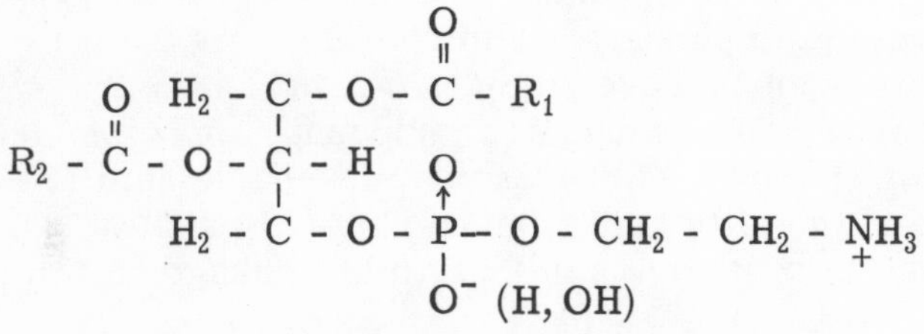

$$
\begin{array}{l}
\quad\quad\quad\quad\quad \overset{O}{\overset{\|}{}} \\
\overset{O}{\overset{\|}{}} \ H_2 - C - O - C - R_1 \\
R_2 - C - O - C - H \quad O \\
\quad\quad H_2 - C - O - \overset{\uparrow}{P} - O - CH_2 - CH_2 - \overset{+}{N}H_3 \\
\quad\quad\quad\quad\quad O^- (H, OH)
\end{array}
$$

Phosphatidyl Ethanolamine
(A Cephalin)

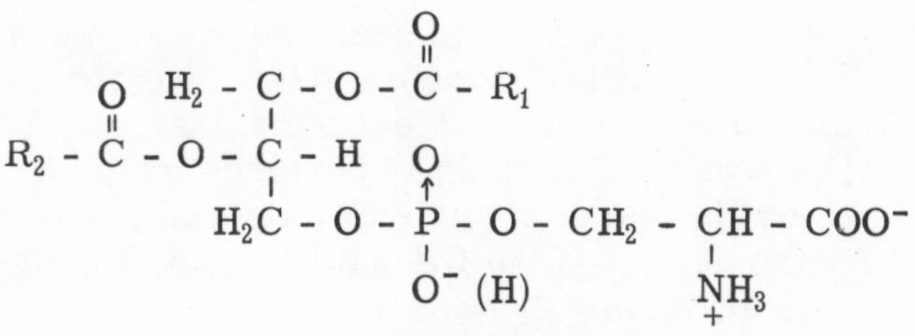

$$
\begin{array}{l}
\quad\quad\quad\quad\quad \overset{O}{\overset{\|}{}} \\
\overset{O}{\overset{\|}{}} \ H_2 - C - O - C - R_1 \\
R_2 - C - O - C - H \quad O \\
\quad\quad H_2C - O - P - O - CH_2 - CH - COO^- \\
\quad\quad\quad\quad\quad O^- (H) \quad\quad\quad \overset{+}{N}H_3
\end{array}
$$

Phosphatidyl Serine
(A Cephalin)

Plasmalogens. The most recent evidence indicates that these phosphoglycerides contain the enol form of a long chain aldehyde connected by ether linkage and replacing one of the fatty acids found in lecithins and cephalins.

$$
\begin{array}{l}
\quad\quad \overset{O}{\overset{\|}{}} \quad H_2C - O - CH=CH-R_1 \\
R_2 - C - O - C - H \quad O \\
\quad\quad H_2C - O - \overset{\uparrow}{P} - O - CH_2 - CH_2 - \overset{+}{N}H_3 \text{ (or choline)} \\
\quad\quad\quad\quad O^- (H, OH)
\end{array}
$$

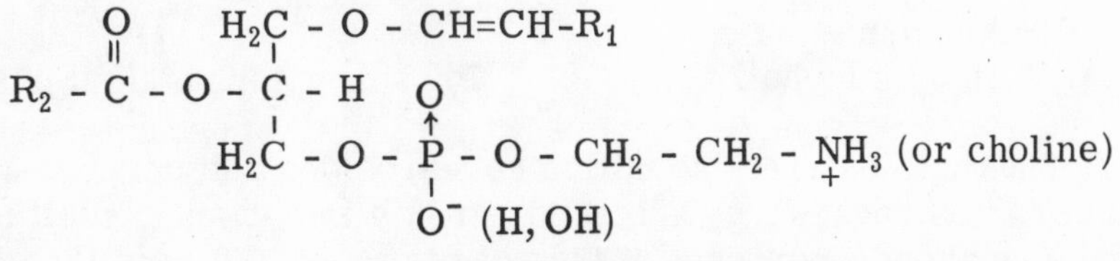

A Plasmalogen

PHOSPHOINOSITIDES. Folch has shown the presence of inositol-containing phospholipids in plant and animal tissues. These yield on hydrolysis glycerol, fatty acids, inositol, and phosphate. The name, lipositol, was proposed by Folch and Woolley for these substances. There are nine stereoisomers of inositol, two of which are mirror images. Myoinositol, a meso form, is the most abundant of the four isomers which are found in nature. These phospholipids may be divided into mono-, di-, and complex phosphoinositides.

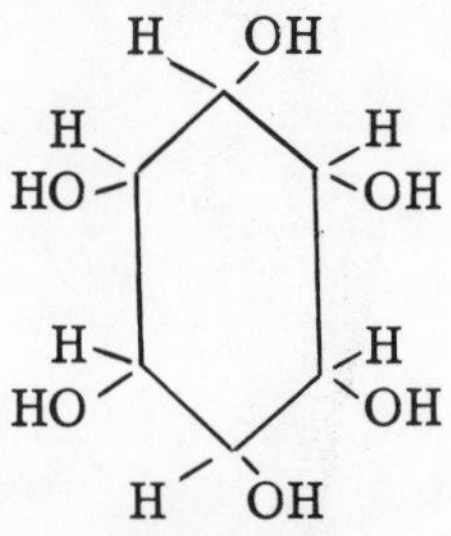

Inositol

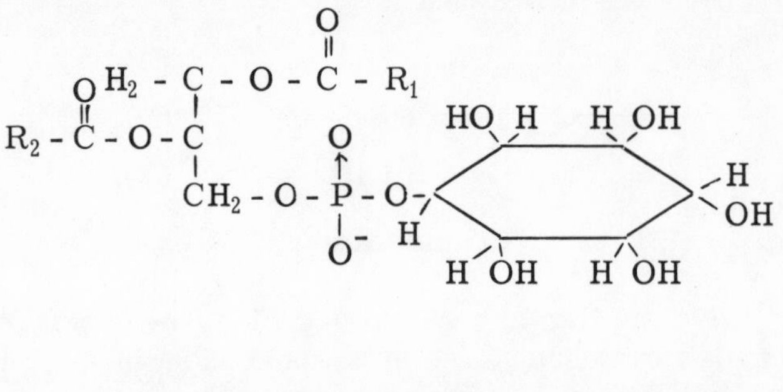

Monophosphoinositide
(Inositol phosphatide)

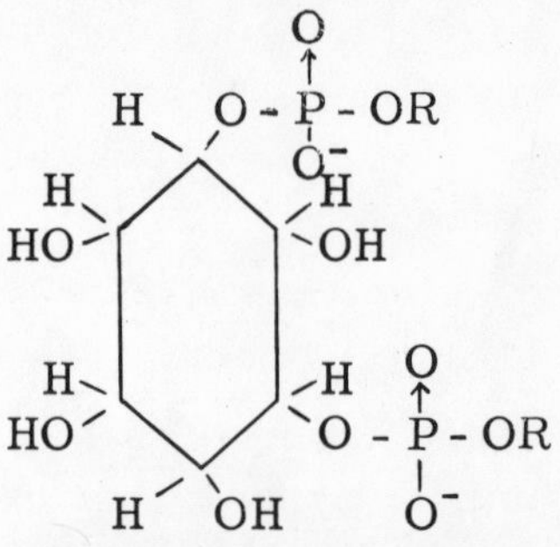

Diphosphoinositide
(R = glycerol, fatty acid)

Inositol is considered to be a vitamin for animals (see p. 235). It also occurs in combination with six molecules of phosphoric acid as *phytic acid*. The mixed calcium and magnesium salt of phytic acid, called phytin, is a constituent of the leaf, stem and seed of most plants.

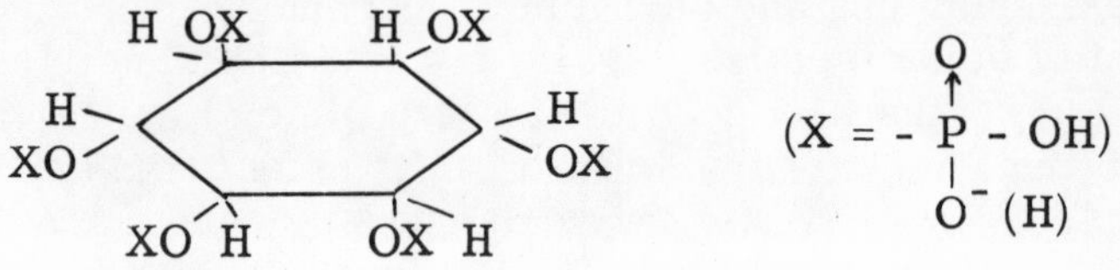

Phytic Acid (Inositol Hexaphosphate)

PHOSPHOSPHINGOSIDES. (Sphingomyelins). These compounds, which are especially abundant in nervous tissue, and apparently lacking in plants and microorganisms, differ from phosphoglycerides in the nature of the nitrogenous base component, and in their lack of glycerol. Two bases are present, choline, and an unusual compound, *sphingosine* (sphingol). The sphingosine takes the place of glycerol, carrying the phosphoric acid in ester linkage on its primary alcohol group, and the fatty acid (lignoceric, $CH_3(CH_2)_{22}COOH$, nervonic, $CH_3(CH_2)_7CH=CH(CH_2)_{13}COOH$, or hydroxystearic acid) by amide linkage on its primary amine group.

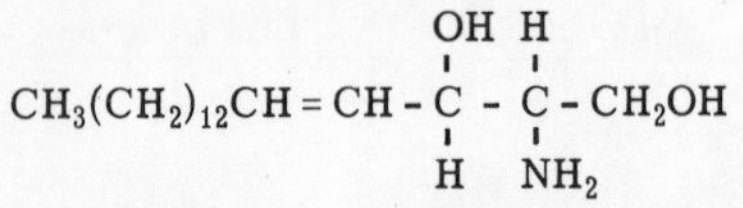

Sphingosine
(An amino dialcohol)

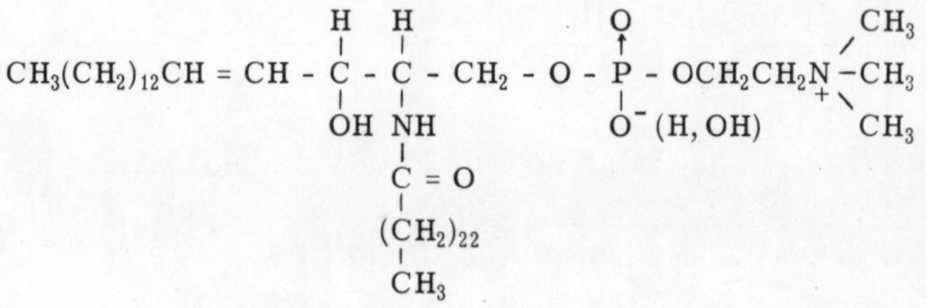

Phosphosphingoside (Sphingomyelin)

Galactolipids. These lipids are also called cerebrosides and cerebro-galactosides. As the alternate names suggest, galactolipids are an important constituent of the brain, where they make up about 8 per cent of the solid matter. Two of the relatively well characterized galactolipids of the brain are called *kerasin* and *cerebron* (phrenosin). Galactolipids are widely distributed in animal organs, those in the spleen containing both galactose and glucose. There is evidence that they also occur in some plant structures.

Galactolipids have a structure which is somewhat similar to that of the phosphosphingosides. They contain galactose, sphingosine, and one of four different fatty acids: cerebronic ($CH_3(CH_2)_{21}CHOHCOOH$), lignoceric, nervonic, and oxynervonic ($CH_3(CH_2)_7CH=CH(CH_2)_{12}-CHOHCOOH$) acids. Here again, the sphingosine takes the place of glycerol, carrying the galactose by glycosidic (see p. 16) linkage on its primary alcohol group, and the fatty acid by an amide linkage on its primary amine group.

Klenk has isolated a new type of galactolipid from brain tissue which he has named *ganglioside*. Gangliosides contain an extra lactose, neuraminic acid, and in some cases N-acetyl galactosamine (see p. 24).

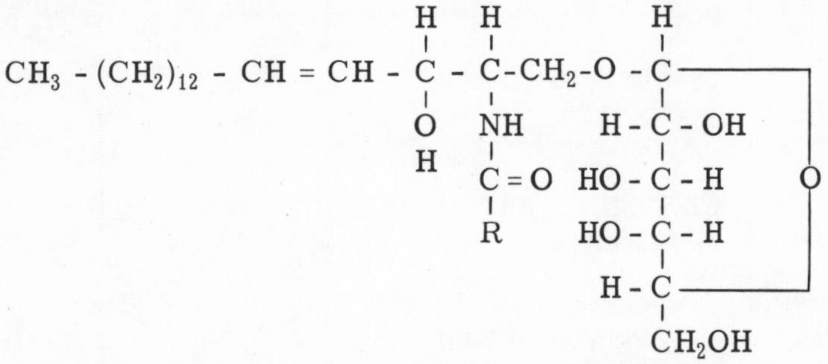

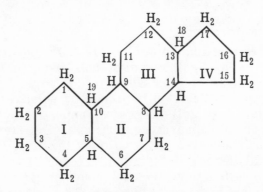

General formula of a galactolipid

Derived Lipids, Including Sterids

The derived lipids group is a "catch all" group in the Bloor classification (p. 35). It includes the hydrolysis products of simple and compound lipids, and in addition other compounds such as sterids, fatty aldehydes, ketones, alcohols, essential oils, hydrocarbons, etc. The most abundant, and also the most important group of derived lipids is the *sterid* group.

STERIDS. This term is used as a general term to include both sterols and steroids. Sterids are widely distributed in animals, plants and microorganisms. They are waxlike lipids found both in the free form and as fatty acid esters. In contrast to most lipids, sterids contain a ring structure, the cyclopentanoperhydrophenanthrene nucleus.

Cyclopentanoperhydrophenanthrene (sterane),
with carbon atoms numbered

In the structure shown above, ring IV is a cyclopentane ring, and rings I, II, and III fused together, constitute a perhydrophenanthrene ring. In most sterids, a side chain (saturated or unsaturated aliphatic) is attached to *carbon atom 17*.

Classification. It is possible to classify sterids on the basis of (a) the nature of the side chain attached to carbon 17, (b) the hydrocarbon which could be obtained by complete reduction of the sterid, and (c) whether ring I is cis or trans to the fixed orientation of rings II, III and IV. Methyl groups are usually present at positions 18 and 19. Table 9 gives a classification on this basis.

Table 9. General classification of sterids

Hydrocarbon Parent	Naturally Occurring Sterids	Orientation of Ring I	C_{17} Side Chain
Allopregnane ($C_{21}H_{36}$)	Allopregnandiol (urine)	trans	$-CH_2CH_3$
Androstane ($C_{19}H_{32}$)	Androgenic hormones	trans	none
Cholane ($C_{24}H_{42}$)	Cholic acid (bile)	cis	$-CHCH_2CH_2CH_3$ $\quad\ \|$ $\quad CH_3$
Cholestane ($C_{27}H_{48}$)	Cholesterol and its derivatives	trans	$-CH(CH_2)_3CHCH_3$ $\quad\ \| \qquad\quad \|$ $\quad CH_3 \qquad CH_3$
Coprostane ($C_{27}H_{48}$)	Coprosterol (feces)	trans	$-CH(CH_2)_3CHCH_3$ $\quad\ \| \qquad\quad \|$ $\quad CH_3 \qquad CH_3$
Ergostane ($C_{28}H_{50}$)	Ergosterol and its derivatives	trans	$-CH(CH_2)_2CHCHCH_3$ $\quad\ \| \qquad\ / \ \ \backslash$ $\quad CH_3 \qquad CH_3\ CH_3$
Estrane ($C_{18}H_{30}$)	Estrogenic hormones	cis	None-also no-CH_3 at position 18.
Pregnane ($C_{21}H_{36}$)	Progesterone, adrenal cortex hormones	cis	$-CH_2CH_3$
Sitostane ($C_{29}H_{52}$)	Sitosterols, stigmasterols, in plants	trans	$-CH(CH_2)_2CHCHCH_3$ $\quad\ \| \qquad / \ \backslash$ $\quad CH_3 \qquad CH_2\ CH_3$ $\qquad\qquad\quad \|$ $\qquad\qquad\ CH_3$

STEROLS. The sterols are wax-like solid alcohols which occur free, and esterified with fatty acids, in most living cells. Examples of sterols are *ergosterol* from yeasts and fungi, and *stigmasterol, spinasterol,* and *sitosterol,* from various plants. The best known animal sterol is *cholesterol.* Cholesterol is present in relatively high concentration in nervous tissues and in bile. Most gallstones are composed of cholesterol, which crystallizes from the bile under certain abnormal conditions. Two sterols serve as precursors of the antirachitic vitamins D_2 and D_3. Irradiation of the plant sterol, ergosterol, converts it into vitamin D_2 (calciferol). Irradiation of 7-dehydrocholesterol, a derivative of cholesterol, which is present in animal tissues, converts the former into vitamin D_3. The function of these vitamins is discussed on page 229. Formulas for ergosterol, stigmasterol, cholesterol, 7-dehydrocholesterol, vitamin D_3, and calciferol (vitamin D_2) are shown on the following page. Other non-sterid vitamins belonging to the derived lipids group are vitamins K_1 and K_2 (p. 230) and provitamins A (carotenes, p. 226). Non-vitamin carotenoid pigments (p. 311) also belong to the derived lipids class, but are not sterids.

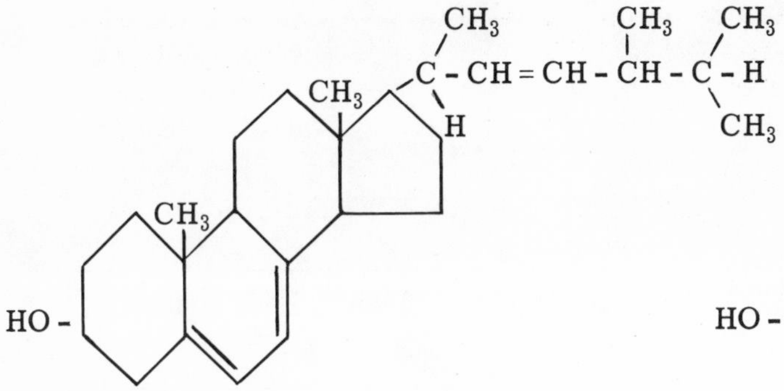

Ergosterol

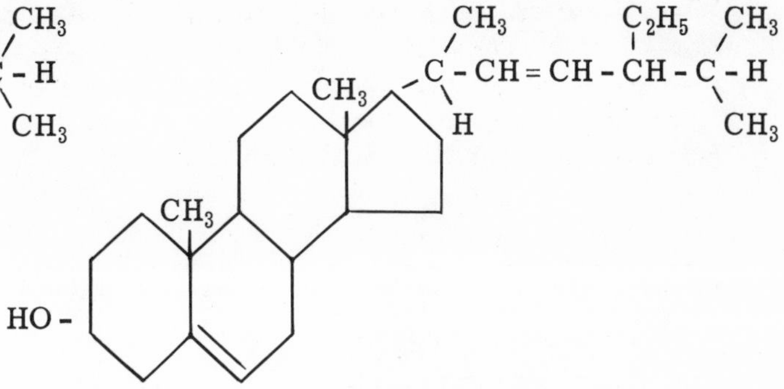

Stigmasterol

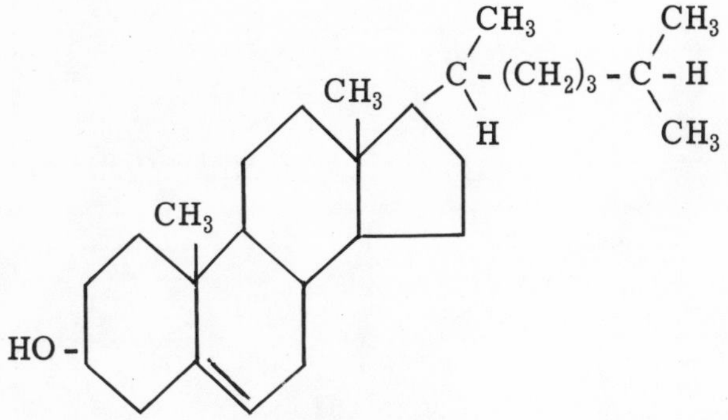

Cholesterol

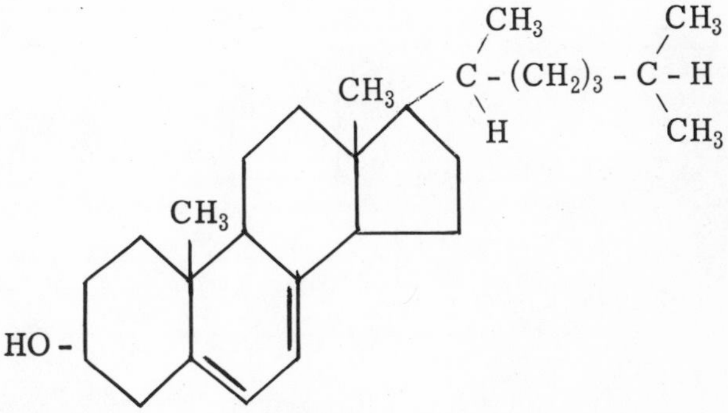

7-Dehydrocholesterol

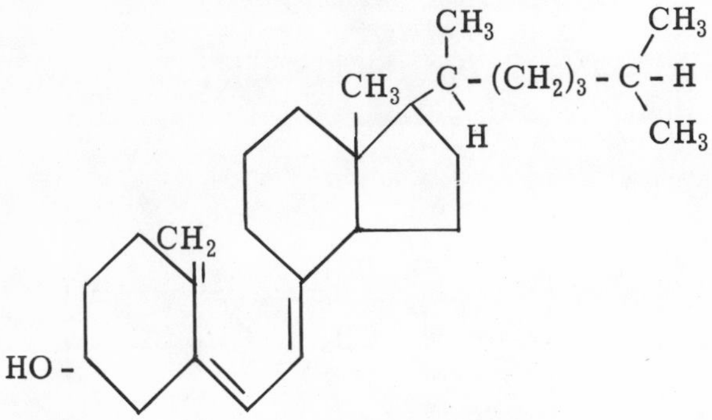

Vitamin D_3

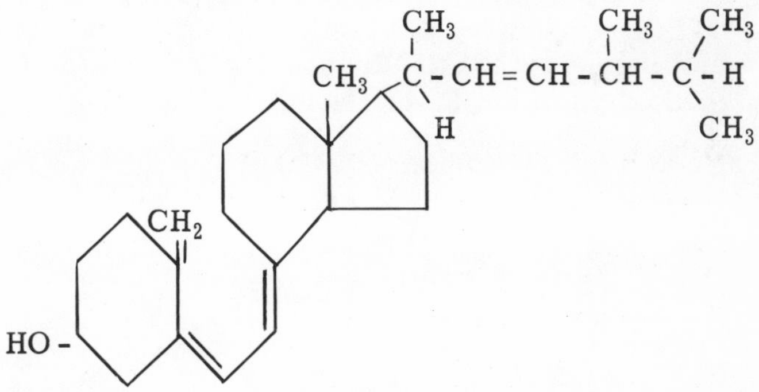

Vitamin D_2 (Calciferol)

<u>Steroid hormones.</u> Steroid hormones (see page 269 for a discussion of physiological activity) are secreted by the adrenal cortex and the male and female gonads. The mixture of adrenal cortex hormones known as "cortin" contains corticosterone, desoxycorticosterone, 11-dehydro-17-hydroxy corticosterone, adrenosterone, and possibly other steroids.

The male gonads (testes) secrete testosterone, androsterone, dehydroandrosterone, and adrenosterone. The female gonads (ovaries) secrete two types of steroid hormones (1) the estrogenic hormones, estradiol, estrone (theelin), estriol (theelol), equilin and equilinin, and (2) progesterone.

Formulas for corticosterone, testosterone, estradiol and progesterone are given on the following page.

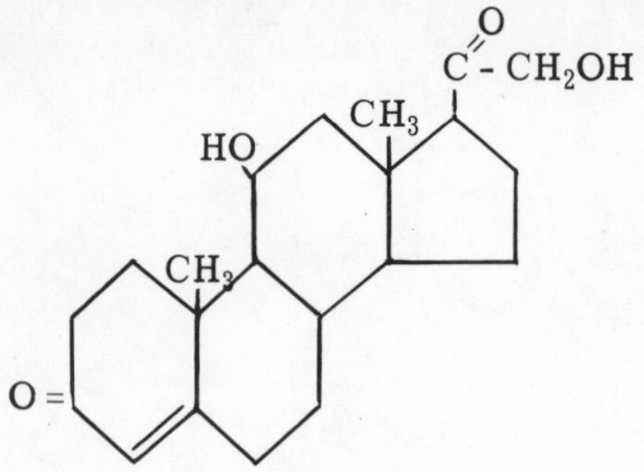

Corticosterone

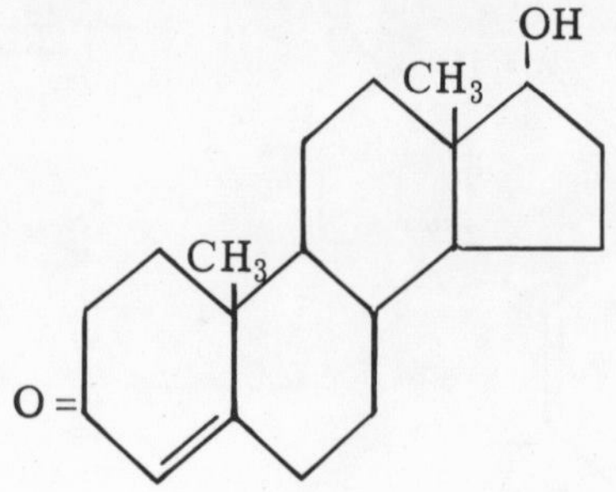

Testosterone

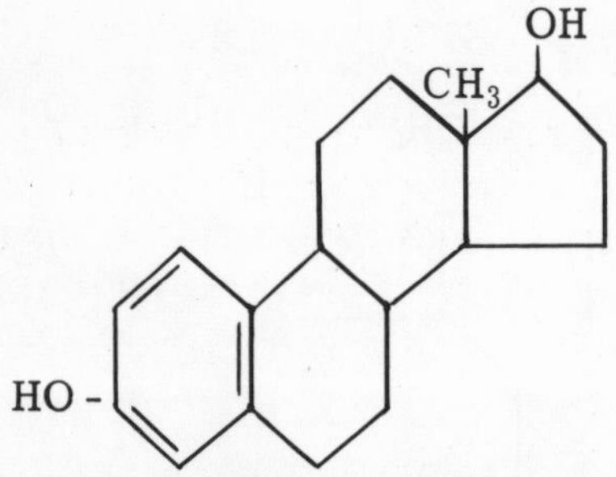

Estradiol (dihydrotheelin)

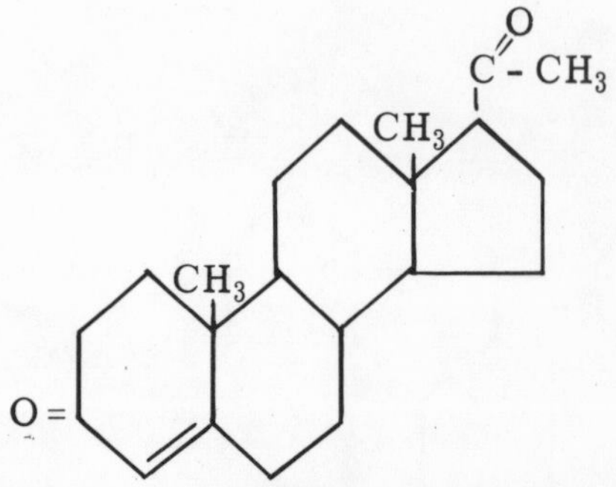

Progesterone

FATTY ACIDS; MONO AND DIGLYCERIDES. Fatty acids, mono and diglycerides, and glycerol are all classed as derived lipids. Table 10 shows that the melting point increases as fatty acids are split from the triglyceride molecule, the monoglyceride having a higher melting point than the diglyceride, etc. It is of interest to note that the melting point of the free fatty acid is lower than that of any of its combinations with glycerol.

Table 10.   Melting points of certain glycerides and fatty acids

Lipid	Type	M. P. °C.
Tricaprin	Triglyceride	31.5
Dicaprin	Diglyceride	44.5
Monocaprin	Monoglyceride	53.0
Capric acid	Fatty acid	-3.4
Tristearin	Triglyceride	71.5
Distearin	Diglyceride	78.0
Monostearin	Monoglyceride	81.5
Stearic acid	Fatty acid	69.6

Free fatty acids, as well as *mono* and *di* glycerides, are never found in large amounts in plant or animal tissues. They are found in leaves, in the intestines of animals following a meal containing fats, and in various oily seeds (see p. 147) during germination. The chemical and physical properties of the fatty acids have been discussed previously (p. 35). Derivatives of the free fatty acids used in industry will be discussed later (p. 301).

GLYCEROL. Free glycerol is found in small quantities in various plant and animal tissues, wherever lipids containing this alcohol are being metabolized. It is present in the intestines following a meal containing fats, and in germinating oily seeds.

Glycerol is readily metabolized by the body, going via glycerol phosphate into the metabolic pool of the body (see p. 185). Its esterification to form various lipids has been discussed. Glycerol undergoes in the test tube a unique reaction involving dehydration. This reaction, known as the *"acrolein test"* is often used as a qualitative test for glycerol, either free or combined in lipids. Acrolein has a characteristic, acrid odor which is used to identify it (acrolein is produced when fat meat is fried at too high a temperature).

$$
\begin{array}{c}
\text{H} \\
| \\
\text{H - C - OH} \\
| \\
\text{H - C - OH} \\
| \\
\text{H - C - OH} \\
| \\
\text{H}
\end{array}
\qquad
\xrightarrow{\text{KHSO}_4,\ \text{heat}}
\qquad
\begin{array}{c}
\text{H} \\
| \\
\text{H - C} \\
\| \\
\text{H - C} \\
| \\
\text{H - C = O}
\end{array}
\qquad + \qquad 2\,\text{H}_2\text{O}
$$

Glycerol   Acrolein   Water
                                          (Acrylic aldehyde)

ALCOHOLS, KETONES, AND HYDROCARBONS. Most plant and animal species secrete waxy compounds which are not true waxes, but are free high molecular weight hydrocarbons or their derivatives. These, along with the true waxes, play a protective role, providing an impervious surface for the cuticle of fruits, for the outside of leaves, and (as a secretion) for the hair and skin of all fur-bearing animals. Table 11 lists the names, empirical formulas, and sources of some of these derived lipids.

Table 11. Lipid hydrocarbons and other wax-like compounds

Compound	Formula	Source
Carnaubyl alcohol	$C_{22}H_{45}OH$	Wool fat (lanolin)
n-Hentriacontane	$C_{31}H_{64}$	Tomato skin, wax of Chinese insect
n-Hexacosanol	$C_{26}H_{53}OH$	Cuticle, apple skin, bent grass
n-Nonacosan-15-one	$C_{29}H_{58}O$	Cuticle, cabbage, Brussel Sprout leaf
n-Nonacosane	$C_{29}H_{60}$	Cuticle, apple, grapefruit skin
n-Octacosanol	$C_{28}H_{57}OH$	Cuticle, apple, wheat leaf
n-Pentatriacontane	$C_{35}H_{72}$	Cuticle, sugar cane
Squalene (an oil)	$C_{30}H_{50}$	Shark liver oil, also trace, olive oil
n-Triacontanol	$C_{30}H_{61}OH$	Beeswax, carnauba wax, cuticle, alfalfa, sugar cane

ESSENTIAL OILS. Essential oils such as peppermint, rose, lemon, pine, etc. may be defined as volatile plant oils. They are classed as lipids because of their solubility characteristics and their origin in the living plant. The chemical structures of about 500 constituents of essential oils have been studied. On the basis of these analyses, essential oils can be divided into four main groups:

1. Terpenes related to isoprene or isopentene.
2. Straight chain carbon compounds, not containing any side branches.
3. Benzene derivatives.
4. Essential oils not included above. Valuable information about the composition of essential oils is now being obtained using *gas chromatography* (see p. 43).

Chapter 5 | PROTEINS

No compounds have a more important role in living organisms than those for which Berzelius in a letter to Mulder in 1838 suggested the name *proteins* (from the Greek word *proteios* meaning "first"). These nitrogen compounds are the most abundant solids in cell protoplasm. One component of protoplasm, the cell nucleus, contains proteins (nucleoproteins) which are intimately associated with cell division and heredity. Another part, the cell cytoplasm, contains a thousand or more separate proteins, called enzymes, which catalyze the many chemical changes required for the maintenance of cell life. In addition, animals, plants, and microbes produce extracellular enzymes which split complex dietary proteins, lipids, and carbohydrates to simple diffusible nutrients which are easily absorbed and utilized within the cell. Proteins also serve as major components of the blood, epithelial tissues and connective tissues in animals, and when fed in excess, as a source of energy and fat. In the seeds of many plants, proteins are stored as a reserve of amino acids and energy. It is indeed unlikely that any chemical reaction is carried out in living tissues without the participation of proteins.

Amino Acids: Building Stones of Protein

Proteins are high molecular weight polymers of a group of low molecular weight monomers called amino acids. Amino acids derived from animal, plant, and microbial proteins are organic acids which all contain either an amino or an imino group on the alpha-carbon atom. A total of 18 amino acids has been isolated from the proteins of all major classes of living organisms. These amino acids are apparently common to all living organisms. In addition, there are more than 80 amino acids which have been isolated from the proteins or extracts of a single class of plant, animal, or microorganism. Examples are citrulline from watermelon juice, hydroxylysine from collagen, and lanthionine from wool hydrolyzates. Several antibiotics contain amino acids of unusual structure. The names and structures of the 18 amino acids which are common to the proteins of all three classes of living matter are listed below. The formula for hydroxyproline, an important constituent of collagen, is also listed. It can be seen from the structural formulas that the first 17 amino acids contain the terminal -CH-COOH group. The characteristic

$$\underset{NH_2}{-CH-COOH}$$

part of these amino acids is the R group to the left of the vertical dotted line. The last two amino acids listed, proline and hydroxyproline, do not have the -CH-COOH grouping.

$$\underset{NH_2}{-CH-COOH}$$

This has become part of a ring structure, and these amino acids are actually *imino* acids. Since they are an integral part of the protein molecule, and their reactions are in most cases the same as those of amino acids, they are usually referred to as amino acids.

All of the amino acids except glycine contain at least one asymmetric carbon atom. These atoms have four dissimilar groups attached, and are starred in the amino acid formulas given below. Molecules containing one asymmetric carbon atom exist in two optically active forms, those containing two asymmetric carbon atoms in four optically active forms, the total number following the Le Bel-van't Hoff rule (see page 12). The amino acids found in proteins are (with the exception of glycine) optically active, and belong to the L-series (related to L-glyceraldehyde - see page 14). Most of the naturally occurring L-amino acids rotate polarized light (page 10) to the left, but some rotate polarized light to the right, for example, L(+) alanine and L(+) lysine.

$$
\begin{array}{ccc}
\text{COOH} & & \text{CHO} \\
| & & | \\
\text{H}_2\text{N} - \text{C} - \text{H} & \longrightarrow & \text{HO} - \text{C} - \text{H} \\
| & & | \\
\text{R} & & \text{CH}_2\text{OH} \\
\text{L-Amino acid} & & \text{L-Glyceraldehyde}
\end{array}
$$

The amino acids are colorless, crystalline compounds which have, in the bulk, the appearance of a white powder. The crystal forms are quite characteristic, varying from tufts of slender needles (tyrosine) to thick hexagonal plates (cystine). The taste varies from sugar-sweet (glycine, alanine) through tasteless (tyrosine) to bitter (arginine). The ten amino acids whose names are italicized are required for optimum growth in all mammalian, avian and fish species tested to date (see page 222). A convenient way to remember the first letters of the names of these ten amino acids is to memorize the name of the vice-president of a mythical feed company - T. T. HALLIM, V. P.

Names and Structures of Amino Acids Common to Animal, Plant and Microbial Proteins

I. Mono-amino-mono-carboxylic acids

(R = characteristic group to left of vertical dotted line)

1. (R)
$$
\begin{array}{c}
\text{COOH} \\
| \\
\text{H} - \text{C} - \text{H} \\
| \\
\text{NH}_2
\end{array}
$$
Glycine (aminoacetic acid)

2.
$$
\begin{array}{c}
\text{COOH} \\
| \\
\text{CH}_3 - \overset{*}{\text{C}} - \text{H} \\
| \\
\text{NH}_2
\end{array}
$$
Alanine (α-amino-propionic acid)

3.
$$
\begin{array}{c}
\quad\;\; \text{COOH} \\
| \\
\text{CH}_2 - \overset{*}{\text{C}} - \text{H} \\
| \quad\quad | \\
\text{OH} \quad \text{NH}_2
\end{array}
$$
Serine (α-amino-β-hydroxy propionic acid)

4.
$$
\begin{array}{c}
\quad\quad\quad\;\; \text{COOH} \\
* \qquad | \\
\text{CH}_3 - \text{CH} - \overset{*}{\text{C}} - \text{H} \\
| \qquad\quad | \\
\text{OH} \quad\; \text{NH}_2
\end{array}
$$
Threonine (α-amino-β-hydroxy butyric acid)

5.
$$
\begin{array}{c}
\text{CH}_3 \quad\quad\; \text{COOH} \\
\diagdown \qquad\;\; | \\
\text{CH} - \overset{*}{\text{C}} - \text{H} \\
\diagup \qquad\;\; | \\
\text{CH}_3 \quad\quad\; \text{NH}_2
\end{array}
$$
Valine (α-amino-isovaleric acid)

6.
$$
\begin{array}{c}
\quad\quad\quad\quad\quad\quad \text{COOH} \\
| \\
\text{CH}_3\text{-S} - \text{CH}_2\text{-CH}_2 - \overset{*}{\text{C}} - \text{H} \\
| \\
\text{NH}_2
\end{array}
$$
Methionine (α-amino-γ-methylthiol butyric acid)

                                                    COOH
                                        S - CH$_2$ - C*- H
7.   NH$_2$ Cystine (di-α-amino-β-thio propionic
                                        | acid; dicysteine)
                                                    COOH
                                        S - CH$_2$ - C*- H
                                                    NH$_2$

                                                    COOH
7a.   HS - CH$_2$ - C*- H   Cysteine (α-amino-β-thio propionic
                                                    NH$_2$ acid)

                                                    COOH
                                CH$_3$
8.   CH - CH$_2$ - C*- H   *Leucine* (α-amino-isocaproic acid)
                                CH$_3$ NH$_2$

                                                    COOH
9.   CH$_3$CH$_2$ - CH - C*- H   *Isoleucine* (α-amino-β-methyl
                                        CH$_3$ NH$_2$ valeric acid)

II. Mono-amino-dicarboxylic acids

                                                    COOH
10. (R)   HOOC - CH$_2$ - C*- H   Aspartic acid (α-amino-succinic acid)
                                                    NH$_2$

                                                    COOH
11.   HOOC - CH$_2$ - CH$_2$ - C*- H   Glutamic acid (α-amino-glutaric acid)
                                                    NH$_2$

III. Diamino-mono-carboxylic acids

                                                    COOH
12.   H$_2$N - CH$_2$ - CH$_2$ - CH$_2$ - CH$_2$ - C*- H   *Lysine* (α, ϵ -diamino caproic acid)
                                                    NH$_2$

              NH   COOH
13. H$_2$N - C - NH - CH$_2$ - CH$_2$ - CH$_2$ - C*- H   *Arginine* (α-amino-δ -guanidine
                                                    NH$_2$ valeric acid)

IV. <u>Aromatic amino acids</u>

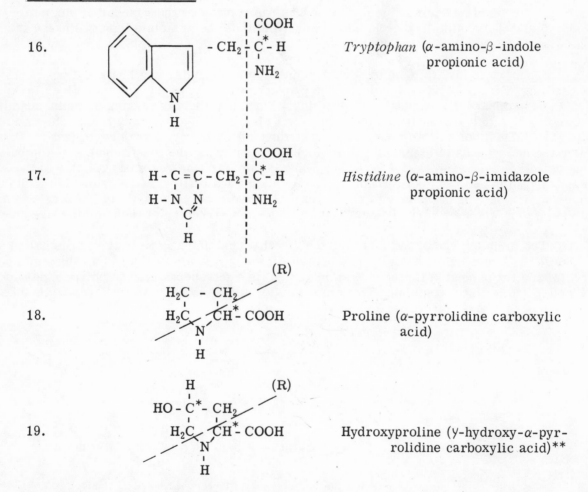

14. *Phenylalanine* (α-amino-β-phenyl propionic acid)

15. Tyrosine (α-amino-β-hydroxy phenyl propionic acid)

V. <u>Heterocyclic amino acids</u>

16. *Tryptophan* (α-amino-β-indole propionic acid)

17. *Histidine* (α-amino-β-imidazole propionic acid)

18. Proline (α-pyrrolidine carboxylic acid)

19. Hydroxyproline (γ-hydroxy-α-pyrrolidine carboxylic acid)**

* Asymmetric carbon atom.

** L-Hydroxyproline is found in the collagen of animal connective tissue, where it appears to be synthesized in situ from L-proline. It is also widely distributed in the seed coat and pericarp of seeds as a component of the structural proteins. L-Delta hydroxy lysine, a unique constituent of connective tissue protein, is formed in situ from lysine.

It can be seen from the structural formulas that the first 17 amino acids contain the terminal $-\underset{\underset{NH_2}{|}}{C}H-COOH$ group. The characteristic part of these amino acids is the (R) group to the left of the dotted line. The last two amino acids listed, proline and hydroxyproline, do not have the $-\underset{\underset{NH_2}{|}}{C}H-COOH$ grouping. This has become part of a ring structure, and these amino acids have a secondary amino group.

Structure of Proteins

In 1902, Fischer, and Hofmeister, independently proposed that proteins are formed by the splitting out of the elements of water from the α-amino (or α-imino) group of one amino acid and the terminal carboxyl group of the adjacent amino acid (see amino acid formulas 1-19 above); the resulting linkage is called a peptide linkage. Experimental evidence accumulated during the past 50 years has confirmed the Fischer-Hofmeister theory, and the peptide linkage is now considered to be the principle type of linkage in the protein molecule.

Fischer, in his attempts to verify the peptide hypothesis, synthesized a polypeptide containing 18 amino acid molecules. The product was an amorphous, non-diffusible solid which had some of the properties of proteins. Since naturally occurring proteins contain 50-150,000 amino acid residues per molecule, Fischer was a long way from achieving the goal of synthesis of a protein molecule. The difficulties involved are great indeed. Protein-like compounds of high molecular weight, containing a single amino acid as the building unit have been synthesized recently, using polymerization reactions similar to those employed in making synthetic rubber. To duplicate a naturally occurring protein with this method, it would be necessary to carry out a directed copolymerization of several amino acids, which would be very difficult, even if the exact structure of the protein were known.*

The simplest combination of amino acids that contains a peptide linkage is called a *dipeptide*. A molecule containing two peptide linkages (3 amino acids) is a tripeptide, one containing three peptide linkages (4 amino acids) is a tetrapeptide. The polypeptide which Fischer synthesized (containing 18 amino acids) would be called an *octadecapeptide*. Examples of di-, tri-, and tetrapeptides are shown below.

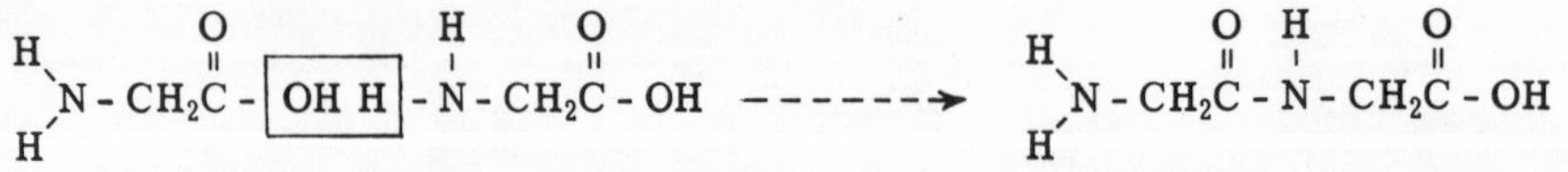

Glycine + Glycine → Glycyl glycine (dipeptide)

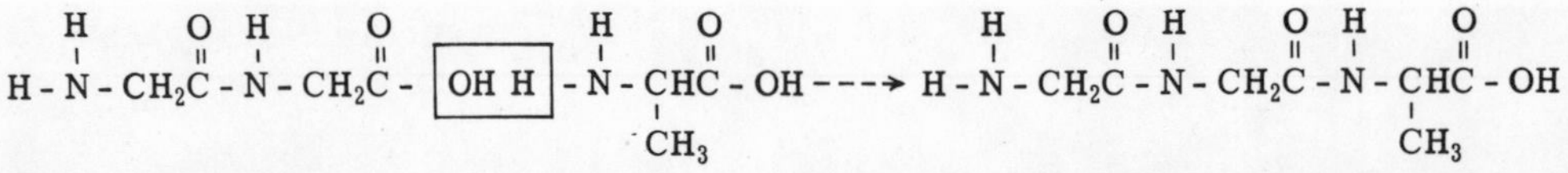

Glycyl glycine + Alanine → Glycyl glycyl alanine (tripeptide)

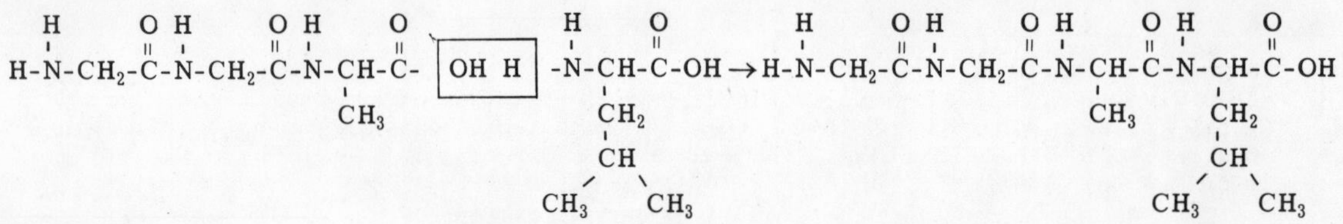

Glycyl glycyl alanine + Leucine → Glycyl glycyl alanyl leucine (tetrapeptide)

*See p. 73

It can be seen that each peptide contains a free, terminal carboxyl group at the right-hand end of the chain, and a free, terminal amino group at the left-hand end of the chain. If the process of adding amino acids to the chain were continued until the chain consisted of about 100 amino acids, the resulting polypeptide would have the molecular weight of some of the smallest protein molecules.

A simple general formula for proteins would be as follows:

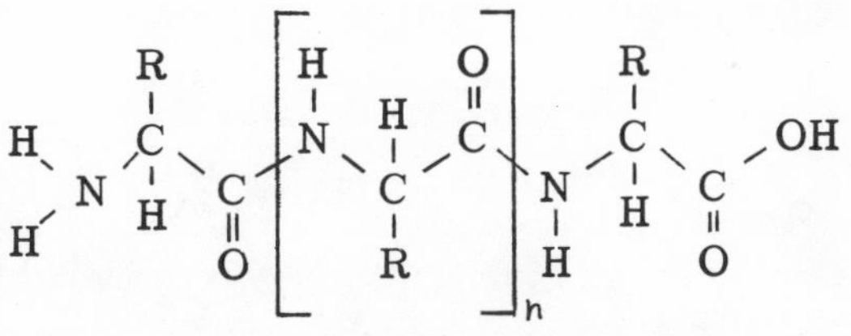

General Formula for Proteins

The value for n in the general formula is 51 for the hormone, insulin (see p. 272), about 100 for simple proteins such as pepsin, and about 150,000 for complex nucleoproteins such as tobacco mosaic virus. In the formula, R represents the distinctive aliphatic or aromatic radical of any one of the first 17 amino acids whose structures are listed on pp. 55-57. Proline and hydroxyproline fit into the general formula as follows:

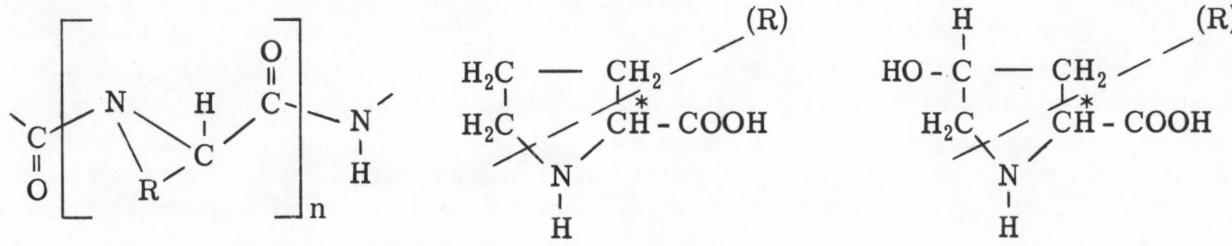

The general formula for proteins given above does not portray adequately their exceedingly complex structure. Most of the proteins are molecules of great size, complexity and diversity. Each type of protein appears to be designed with high specificity for its particular task in the cell of a plant, animal or microorganism. This specificity is achieved by the *folding* of the long polypeptide chain (or chains) of the protein in a unique configuration. When this configuration is altered, the protein loses its biological activity and its function in the cell.

To locate each group and each atom in the configuration of the folded polypeptide chain of a biologically active protein is a Herculean task. For example, the exact sequence of amino acids has been worked out for the simple protein*, insulin (51 amino acid residues). The sequence is shown in Figure 10. This pioneer achievement was made by Sanger in England. Nevertheless, we do not know what the insulin molecule looks like in "3-D," i.e., in three dimensions. We can be quite confident that the biological activity of insulin is dependent on its "3-D" configuration. To date, several proteins have been pictured in three dimensions, for example, hemoglobin, myoglobin, and lysozyme.

In spite of our inability to date to completely visualize the three-dimensional structure of proteins, great progress has been made in determining the nature of the polypeptide "backbones" of these giant molecules. Our first insight into the nature of these

_____

* The molecular weight of insulin is 6,000, and for that reason it should be classified as a peptide. However, in solution, especially when metal ions (for example, zinc ions) are present, it aggregates to form molecules with molecular weights of 12,000, also 36,000, and even 48,000, all classed as proteins.

polypeptide chains came from the x-ray study of fibrous proteins. These proteins are characterized by their insolubility in water and in other solvents which do not decompose them.

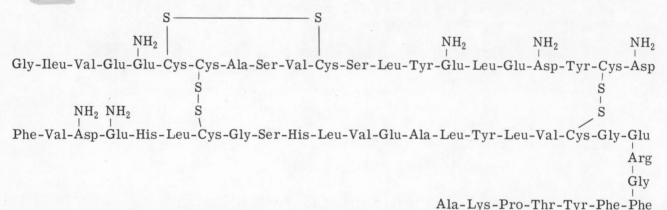

Figure 10. The sequence of amino acids in insulin. Ala=alanine, Arg=arginine, Asp-NH$_2$=asparagine, Cys-S-S-Cys=cystine, Glu=glutamic acid, Glu-NH$_2$=glutamine, Gly=glycine, His=histidine, Ileu=isoleucine, Leu=leucine, Lys=lysine, Phe=phenylalanine, Pro=proline, Ser=serine, Thr=threonine, Tyr=tyrosine, and Val=valine. Top peptide is "A" chain, bottom peptide is "B" chain.

They serve as structural materials for animals and certain insects in much the same way that cellulose and hemicellulose serve as structural materials for plants. Examples of fibrous proteins (see p. 64) are (1) the keratins, (2) collagen, (3) elastin, and (4) fibroin.

The pioneer studies of Astbury in England showed that three distinctive x-ray diffraction patterns were obtained with (a) keratins and elastin, (b) collagen and (c) fibroin. In this country, Pauling and others showed that the x-ray pattern for keratins and elastin is created by the twisting of the polypeptide chain into a helix (spiral). This has been named the *alpha helix*. In the alpha helix chain (Fig. 11) the atoms in a repeating unit

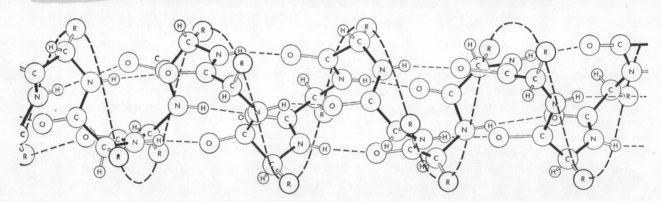

Figure 11. Diagram of alpha helix. (From P. Doty, Scientific American 197 p. 176 (1957)).

(C - C - N - C) lie in the same plane. The change in angle between one unit and the next occurs at the carbon to which the side group (R) is attached. The spiral configuration of the polypeptide chain is held rigidly in place by the hydrogen bond (broken black lines, Fig. 11) between the hydrogen atom attached to the nitrogen atom in one unit and the oxygen atom attached to a carbon atom three units along the chain. Four turns of the helix can be traced in Figure 11 by following the dotted black lines connecting the "backbone" atoms.

Recently, the Indian x-ray crystallographer Ramachandran showed that the collagen pattern is caused by the twisting of *three* helixes around one another to form a three-strand fiber (Fig. 12). Other details were worked out by Crick, Rich and Cowan in England. The

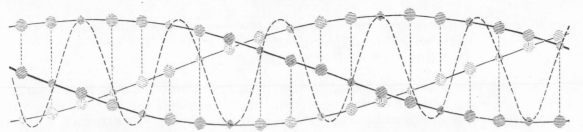

Figure 12.   Collagen molecule.   Triple strand helix.   (From P. Doty, Scientific American *197* p. 178 (1957)).

collagen molecule consists of three polypeptide chains, each containing three different amino acid units - proline, hydroxyproline and glycine, as the major units.   The unique design of collagen is attributed to the occurrence of glycine, the smallest amino acid unit, at every third position on each chain.   This permits the bulky proline and hydroxyproline units to fit into the three-helix strand, and for hydrogen bonding to occur between glycine units.   The triple strand is strengthened further by hydrogen bonding between hydroxyproline units, and it has been found by Doty in this country that the higher the hydroxyproline content of collagen, the more resistant it is to heat.   Thus, the collagen in human skin, with a relatively high hydroxyproline content, is irreversibly broken down at 145 degrees Fahrenheit, whereas the collagen in the skin of the codfish, which is low in hydroxyproline, cannot withstand a temperature above 100 degrees*.   Fibrils of collagen enlarged 47,000 diameters with the electron microscope are shown in Fig. 13.   Each fibril has been

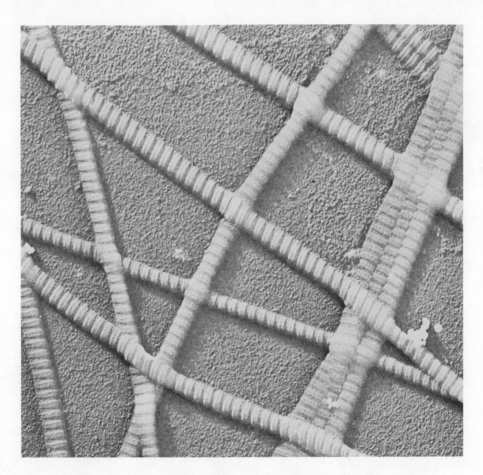

Figure 13.   Fibrils of collagen enlarged 47,000 diameters.   (Photomicrograph courtesy of Jerome Gross, Massachusetts General Hospital).

* This may explain why the codfish is found only in very cold northern waters.

shown by x-ray diffraction methods to consist of thirty or more parallel chains of triple strand collagen molecules. The molecular strands are held together by hydrogen bonding through the hydroxyproline units, and by other forces.

The third distinctive x-ray pattern, namely, that of fibroin, was shown by Astbury and others to be due to the tieing together of two or more "stretched" or fully extended polypeptide chains to give a more crystalline structure. This type of structure is shown in Fig. 14. Known as the *beta* configuration, it consists of fully extended polypeptide chains in which the hydrogen bonds link the hydrogen atoms of one chain to the oxygen

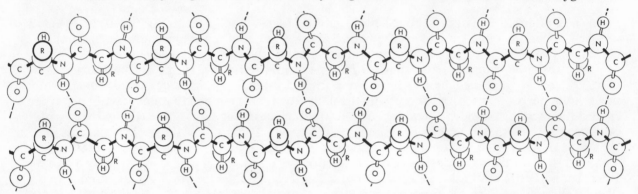

Figure 14.   Beta configuration (stretched chain). (From P. Doty, Scientific American, 197 p. 176, (1957)).

atoms in the adjoining chain. Thus, hydrogen bonds do not contribute to the internal organization of the chain as they do in the alpha helix, but only bind chain to chain.

Conversion of the beta configuration to the alpha helix configuration would result in contraction of the molecule. Some workers believe that contractile fibers such as muscle fibers contract and elongate because their proteins can make reversible transition from alpha to beta configuration.

STRUCTURE OF GLOBULAR PROTEINS. Our discussion of protein structure has been confined so far to fibrous proteins. The number of fibrous proteins isolated and identified is small compared with the total number of proteins recognized as constituents of animal, plant and microbial cells. Most proteins are members of a second class known as the soluble or *globular* proteins. These proteins are soluble in at least one of the following: water, dilute salt solution, dilute acids, or dilute alkalies. It is well known that water molecules have a great affinity for hydrogen ions. Therefore, even if soluble proteins had the alpha or beta configuration, one might expect considerable disruption of the configuration due to the presence of a high ratio of water to protein.

P. Doty and E. R. Blout in this country carried out pioneer studies on soluble synthetic polypeptides (mainly polylysine). They found that the *alpha helix* was the major configuration, and that by adjusting the pH of the solution, this could be made to unwind to form a *random chain* (Fig. 15). This is a configuration assumed by the polypeptide molecule in solution, when internal hydrogen bonds are not formed. The repeating unit

$$\text{(C - } \overset{\overset{\displaystyle O}{\|}}{\text{C}} \text{ - } \overset{\overset{\displaystyle H}{|}}{\text{N}} \text{ - C)}$$

is flat (all in the same plane) as in the alpha helix, but the chain rotates freely about the carbon atoms to which the side groups are attached. The transition from the alpha helix to the random coil configuration occurs within a narrow pH range as the pH is increased in the polypeptide solution. Since the hydrogen bonds are all equivalent in bond strength in the alpha helix, they tend to let go all at once. This is analogous to an ice crystal, which melts in a narrow temperature range. Both cases are alike, for the ice crystal is also held together by hydrogen bonds. Not only is the change from

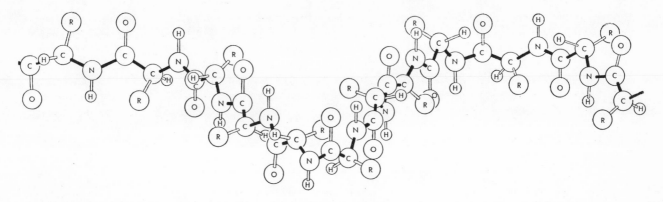

Figure 15. Random chain configuration. (From P. Doty, Scientific American, 197, p. 176, (1957)).

alpha helix to random coil obtained by changing the pH in a critical range, but the change can be induced by heat, just as with an ice crystal. This is actually a true melting process, for the alpha helix is a one-dimensional crystal and the random coil a flexible chain. Synthetic polypeptides in the solid state are mainly in the alpha helix form.

Doty, Blout and coworkers did not expect to find 100 per cent alpha helix at any pH when they started to investigate naturally occurring proteins, for the alpha helix is disrupted by either one of two types of amino acid units. Proline lacks the hydrogen atom necessary to form the crucial hydrogen bond (see Fig. 11), since it is an *imino* acid (see p. 59), the side groups form a distorting linkage in the chain. Cystine is a double unit (dicysteine), and forms somewhat distorting cross-links *between* chains, or *in* chains. (See structure of insulin, p. 60.) These two amino acid units therefore play an important role in the intricate coiling and folding of the polypeptide chains in globular proteins.

The successful determination of the relative percentages of alpha helix and random coil "backbones" in natural proteins was based on the observation that the optical rotation of proteins changed on denaturation. The amino acids, except glycine, are predominantly levorotatory (see p. 55) and impart this rotation tendency to proteins. The alpha helix is a right-handed helix (Fig. 16) and as such tends to rotate polarized light to the *right*. This tendency is so strong that it just about cancels out the leftward rotation of the constituent amino acids, giving an optical rotation of about zero. If the protein is denatured, all of the alpha helix configurations are converted to random coils, which have no rotatory powers. This leaves only the *levorotation* of the amino acids in the protein, and the specific rotation is about -100°. Thus, if the specific rotation of a particular protein at a specified temperature and pH is -50°, this would suggest that approximately one-half of the molecule is in the form of alpha-helix, and one-half in the form of random coil. Doty and coworkers have in fact found this to be the case for serum albumin at pH 7. At the same pH, the protein, ribonuclease (an enzyme), contains 15 per cent alpha helix, and the muscle protein tropomyosin, 85 per cent alpha helix. In each case, they found that the alpha helix content could be reduced to zero by the addition of a denaturing agent (see p. 75). Furthermore, the ratio of alpha helix to random coil is a function of pH, temperature, and ionic strength of the protein solution. The two forms are in equilibrium with each other, and the tendency of water to break down the alpha helix will vary with variations in the three factors listed. Doty and coworkers have also found that the biological activity of enzymes falls off with *decrease* in helical content and *increases* with increase in helical content.

These studies permit us to visualize the *dry* globular protein molecule as one or more polypeptide chains which are mainly in the alpha helix form.

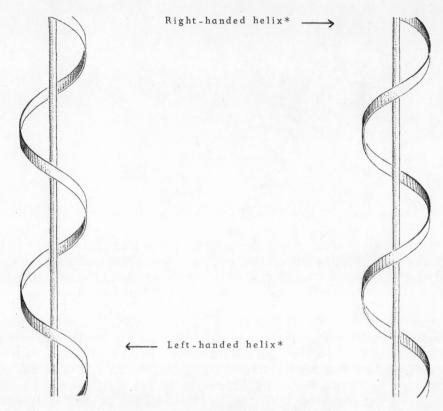

Figure 16.   Direction of rotation of helix.

When the dry protein crystal is dissolved in water, part of the alpha form is converted to random coil, the amount depending on the pH, temperature and ionic strength of
the solution, as well as on other factors.   The *unique configuration* of the protein is probably retained in those parts of the dissolved protein still retaining the alpha helix, but not
in the part containing the random coil.   This could explain the marked changes in activity
of enzymes with change in pH, temperature, and ionic strength.

Proteins can be divided into two major classes on the basis of structure and solubility.   These classes are discussed below.

I.   FIBROUS PROTEINS

A.   Simple Fibrous Proteins.   Examples of fibrous proteins are (1) the keratins which
are the major constituents of epithelial tissues such as skin, hair, feathers, horn,
hoof and nails, (2) collagen, the main protein constituent of white connective tissue
(tendons, cartilage) and of bone, (3) elastin, the main protein constituent of yellow
elastic tissue (ligaments, blood vessels) and (4) fibroin, the major constituent of
silk.

Because of their fiber-like molecular structure (see previous section), fibrous proteins are very insoluble in all common solvents such as water, dilute salt solution,
organic solvents, and dilute acids and alkalies.

B.   Conjugated Fibrous Proteins.   Very little information is available on simple fibrous
proteins which are combined with some non-protein group.   It is possible that the
pigment in chicken feathers is a conjugated fibrous protein.

* Drawings from P. Doty, Scientific American, 197 182 (1957).

II. GLOBULAR PROTEINS

A. Simple Globular Proteins. These proteins are soluble in one or more of the common solvents listed above. Their structure has been discussed in the previous section. On the basis of their solubility characteristics, the author suggests that simple globular proteins be divided into two main classes: (1) those soluble in distilled water and (2) those insoluble in distilled water, but soluble in some other aqueous or organic medium.

Globular proteins would then be classified as follows:

1. Soluble in Distilled Water

   a. Albumins. Very soluble proteins which can be precipitated from a water solution by saturating with an acid salt such as $(NH_4)_2SO_4$, or by saturating with a neutral salt such as Na_2SO_4 in slightly acid solution. Albumins are widely distributed in nature. Examples are egg white albumin, blood serum albumin, and soybean albumin. Albumins are coagulated by heat.

   b. Pseudoglobulins. Soluble proteins which can be precipitated from a water solution by one-fourth to three-fourths saturation with an acid salt such as $(NH_4)_2SO_4$. Pseudoglobulins are not widely distributed. An example is pseudoglobulin of milk whey. Pseudoglobulins are coagulated by heat.

   c. Protamines*. Very soluble proteins which are basic in nature and are not coagulated by heat. Protamines form crystalline salts with mineral acids, and insoluble salts with other more acidic proteins. An example of a protein salt is the commonly used drug, protamine-insulin (see p. 273). Protamines are the simplest proteins and may contain no more than four or five of the amino acids, with one (for example, arginine in salmin) comprising 85% or more of the total weight. Protamines have been isolated only from ripe sperm cells, and may be limited to the nuclei of animal cells. Examples are salmin from salmon sperm, and clupeine from herring sperm.

   d. Histones. Soluble proteins which are basic and are precipitated by the addition of ammonium hydroxide. Very few good examples of this class of proteins are known. They are probably limited to the nuclei of cells. Thymus histone is a classical example.

2. Insoluble in Distilled Water

   a. Euglobulins. Proteins which are insoluble in distilled water but are readily soluble in dilute salt (for example, 5% NaCl) solutions. They can be precipitated from a dilute salt solution by one-half saturation with an acid salt such as $(NH_4)_2SO_4$, or by saturating with a neutral salt such as Na_2SO_4 in neutral solution. Euglobulins are widely distributed in nature.

   Examples are edestin from hemp seed, egg white globulin, blood serum globulin, and soybean globulin. Globulins are coagulated by heat.

---

* With a molecular weight of approximately 5,000, these would be more properly called globular polypeptides.

b. Prolamins. Proteins which are insoluble in distilled water, but are soluble in dilute alkali, and in 60-80% alcohol solutions (ethyl, isopropyl,
etc.). They have been isolated only from plant seeds. Examples are
zein from corn endosperm, and gliadin from wheat endosperm.

c. Glutelins. Proteins which are insoluble in distilled water and alcohol
solutions, but are soluble in dilute alkali. They have been isolated only
from plant seeds. Examples are glutelin from corn endosperm and
glutenin from wheat endosperm.

B. Conjugated Globular Proteins. The globular proteins are also found in nature
combined with non-proteins (prosthetic groups). Thus, the protein, globin, is
combined with an iron-containing porphin compound, heme, to give hemoglobin,
the oxygen-carrying pigment of the blood (see p. 262). These complex compounds are called *conjugated proteins*, and may be divided into several classes
depending on the nature of the prosthetic group.

1. Chromoproteins. Proteins combined with pigments. Example: hemoglobin.

2. Glycoproteins. Proteins combined with carbohydrates. Example: mucin
(saliva).

3. Lipoproteins. Proteins combined with lipids. Example: serum lipo-protein,
which when present at high levels indicates arteriosclerosis.

4. Phosphoproteins. Proteins combined with phosphoric acid. Example: casein
of milk.

5. Nucleoproteins. Proteins attached to a unique class of substances known as
nucleic acids (see Chapter 7).

6. Metalloproteins. Proteins combined with metals. Example: ceruloplasmin,
a blue copper-containing protein of serum with 8 atoms of copper per molecule of protein. Ceruloplasmin may regulate the distribution of copper in
the body.

RECENT ADVANCES IN THE STUDY OF PROTEIN STRUCTURE. For purposes of
discussion, the sequence of amino acids in a polypeptide chain is called the *primary*
structure, the configuration of the chain (relative amounts of alpha-, beta-, and random)
due primarily to hydrogen bonding, plus any disulfide bridges in or between chains*, constitutes the *secondary* structure, and the final three-dimensional structure that the protein molecule assumes under normal conditions is called the *tertiary* structure. Factors
which help to determine the tertiary structure are: location of disulfide bridges, kinks in
the helix due to proline residues, hydrogen bonding between two chains, or two parts of
one chain, and salt linkages between acidic and basic side chains.

Primary structure. In addition to insulin, the primary structures of the following proteins have been determined: ribonuclease (124 amino acid residues), by Hirs, Stein and
Moore, and by Anfinsen, tobacco mosaic virus protein (158 residues) by Schramm and
coworkers, human heart cytochrome c (104 residues) by Tuppy and by Smith, and human
hemoglobin (574 residues) by Braunitzer and coworkers. The primary structure is apparently determined by a single gene for each polypeptide. Thus, the A and B chains of
insulin (see page 60) would be under the control of two separate genes. Primary structure
varies between species, and between mutants within a species. For example, alanine replaces threonine, and valine replaces isoleucine in the A chain, and alanine replaces

---

* Some workers consider disulfide bridges to be part of the tertiary structure.

threonine in the B chain of human insulin in the bovine species. Normal human hemoglobin contains two alpha chains and two beta chains, each chain having a heme group in a crevice on its surface. The alpha chain has 141 residues and the beta chain, which is more acidic, 146 residues. The alpha and beta chains are held together as a pair by ionic (salt linkages) and by hydrogen bonds. The two pairs then are attracted to each other by additional ionic bonds, hydrogen bonds and weaker hydrophobic forces such as

Table 12. Chemically active groups in the common amino acids

Name	Formula	Chemical Nature	Distribution
α-amino	$-NH_2$	primary amine	all a.a. except the prolines
α-imino	$-N-H$	secondary amine	proline, OHproline
ϵ-amino	$-NH_2$	primary amine	lysine
α-carboxyl	$-COOH$	acid carboxyl	all amino acids
γ- and δ-carboxyl	$-COOH$	acid carboxyl	aspartic, glutamic acids, respectively.
β-hydroxy	$-OH$	alcoholic hydroxyl	serine, threonine
γ-hydroxy	$-OH$	alcoholic hydroxyl	hydroxyproline
β-thio	$-S-S-$	disulfide	cystine
β-thiol	$-S-H$	mercaptan (thio-alcohol)	cysteine
δ-guanidine	$\underset{\underset{H}{\overset{\displaystyle NH}{\|}}}{H_2N-C-N-}$	strongly basic group	arginine
β-phenyl	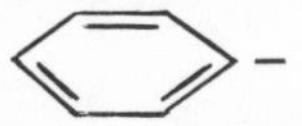 aromatic ring	phenylalanine
β-hydroxyphenyl	$HO-$ 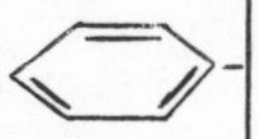	phenol (aromatic-OH)	tyrosine
β-indole	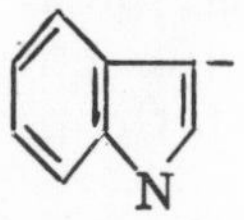 aromatic heterocycle	tryptophan
β-imidazole	$H-C=C-$ $H-N\diagdown_{\underset{H}{C}}N$	basic heterocycle	histidine

van der Waals (London dispersion) forces, to form the complete hemoglobin molecule. In a human mutation, a valine residue replaces the glutamic acid residue at position 6 of the beta-chains of hemoglobin, causing sickle cell anemia.

Secondary structure. Present evidence suggests that the primary amino acid sequence (primary structure) determines how the polypeptide chain folds into the proper native conformation. This implies that there is only one conformation of maximum stability. It also implies that the secondary structure will be determined by the amino acid sequence. In the case of hemoglobin, which contains no disulfide bonds, the folding of the chains presumably involves only secondary forces, primarily hydrogen bonding with alpha helix formation. This also holds for myoglobin and cytochrome c, which lack disulfide linkages. Since hemoglobin can be reversibly denatured, the hydrogen bonds are broken, but they must reform to take the same positions as in the original native conformation.

Even when the secondary structure contains disulfide linkages, a conformation of maximum stability apparently exists. Anfinsen and White reduced the four disulfide bridges in the enzyme, ribonuclease, and found that, under favorable conditions, the native, active enzyme was regenerated upon reoxidation. Thus, the regenerated molecule must fold in just the right way to bring the correct sulfur atoms in position.

Disulfide interchange in serum albumin. Foster has found that serum albumin contains one sulfhydryl (-SH) group as well as many disulfide linkages. A slow interchange between this group and disulfide linkages to form new -SH and new -S-S groups produces a family of serum albumin molecules all with different tertiary structures. Native serum albumin is therefore a heterogeneous protein. Other proteins containing free sulfhydryl groups may behave like serum albumin.

Chemical Reactions of Amino Acids

Chemically Active Groups. A study of the structures of the 19 amino acids whose formulas are given on pages 55-57, indicates the presence of at least ten different types of chemically active groups. These are listed in Table 12.

It can be seen from Table 12 that a wide variety of chemical activities are represented, especially in the R groups (see page 55) of the various amino acids. Thus, reagents which react with amines, or with carboxyl groups, will attack all of the amino acids; esterifying agents will attack hydroxyproline, serine, threonine and tyrosine; reagents which react with aromatic and heterocyclic rings (halogens, concentrated nitric acid, etc.) will attack histidine, phenylalanine, tyrosine, and tryptophan, and mild oxidizing and reducing agents will selectively react with cysteine and cystine, respectively. In the protein molecule, these groups will react in much the same manner; however, most of the alpha-amino and alpha-carboxyl groups are tied up in the peptide linkage (only the "end-groups" can react), part or all of the delta and gamma carboxyl groups of the dicarboxylic acids are present as amides (see insulin, p. 60), and the coiling configuration and bound water of globular native proteins often covers up many of the active groups listed in Table 12, so that they cannot react until the protein is denatured.

The important reactions of some of the groups listed in Table 12 will be discussed separately.

CHEMICAL REACTIONS OF THE ALPHA AMINO GROUP. Reaction with acid. The formation of an acid salt is observed when either free amino acids or proteins are treated with mineral acids. The amino acids alanine and lysine will be used as examples.

$$CH_3-\underset{\underset{NH_2}{|}}{\overset{\overset{COOH}{|}}{C}}-H \quad + \quad HCl \quad \longrightarrow \quad CH_3-\underset{\underset{NH_2 \cdot HCl}{|}}{\overset{\overset{COOH}{|}}{C}}-H$$

Alanine   Alanine hydrochloride

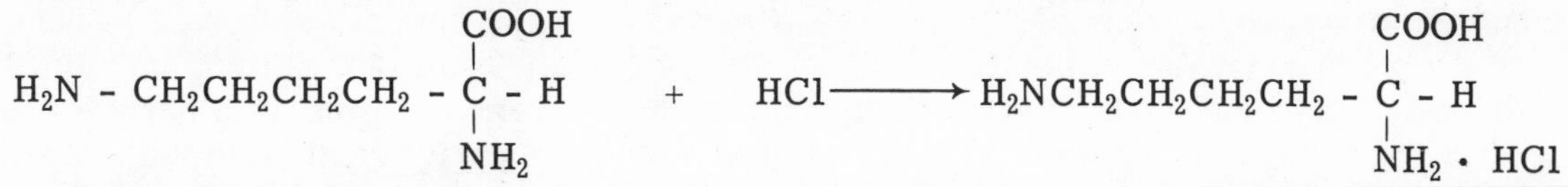

$$H_2N - CH_2CH_2CH_2CH_2 - \overset{\overset{\displaystyle COOH}{|}}{\underset{\underset{\displaystyle NH_2}{|}}{C}} - H \quad + \quad HCl \longrightarrow H_2NCH_2CH_2CH_2CH_2 - \overset{\overset{\displaystyle COOH}{|}}{\underset{\underset{\displaystyle NH_2 \cdot HCl}{|}}{C}} - H$$

Lysine   Lysine monohydrochloride

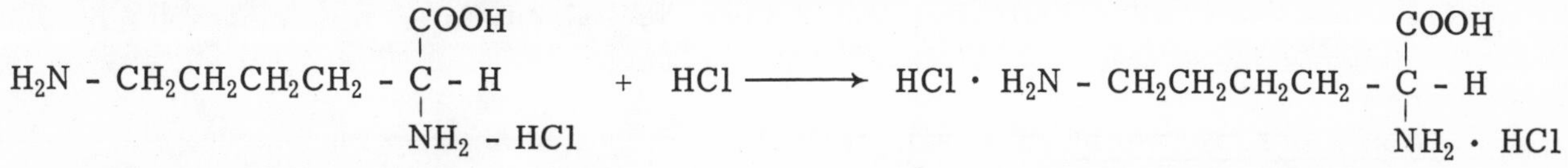

$$H_2N - CH_2CH_2CH_2CH_2 - \overset{\overset{\displaystyle COOH}{|}}{\underset{\underset{\displaystyle NH_2 - HCl}{|}}{C}} - H \quad + \quad HCl \longrightarrow HCl \cdot H_2N - CH_2CH_2CH_2CH_2 - \overset{\overset{\displaystyle COOH}{|}}{\underset{\underset{\displaystyle NH_2 \cdot HCl}{|}}{C}} - H$$

Lysine monohydrochloride   Lysine dihydrochloride

The basic amino acids, arginine and lysine, react with carbon dioxide in the air to form carbonate salts; because of this property, they are usually stored and sold commercially in the form of the monohydrochloride.

Reaction with 1-fluoro, 2, 4-dinitrobenzene (FDNB). Sanger in England found that FDNB would react with the alpha amino group of amino acids with the production of a yellow derivative (DNB-amino acid). This could be easily separated by chromatography (see p. 78), and he used this reaction to determine the N-terminal amino acid (amino acid with free amino group) in a series of peptides in an insulin hydrolysate. This task was an important factor in his successful determination of the sequence of amino acids in insulin (see p. 60).

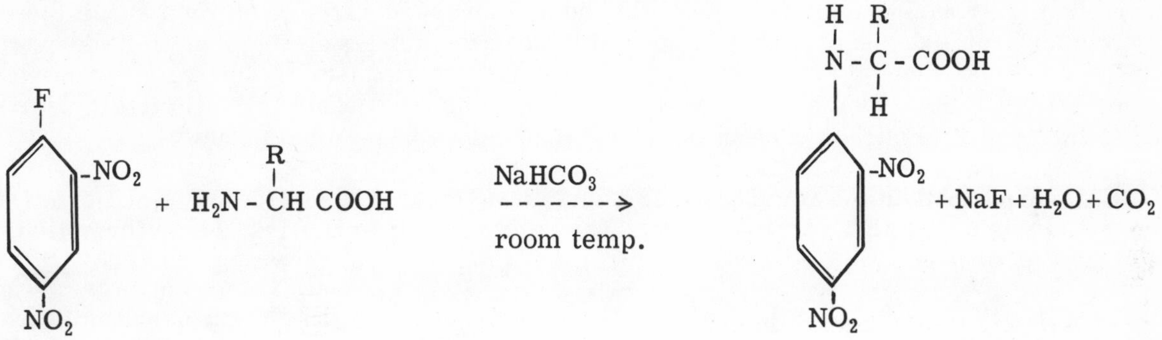

1-fluoro 2, 4-dinitrobenzene   amino acid   DNB-derivative (yellow)

The epsilon amino group of lysine, the imidazole group of histidine, the hydroxyl group of tyrosine, and the thiol group of cysteine also combine with FDNB to form a DNB derivative.

Reaction with formaldehyde. An example of this reaction is shown below.

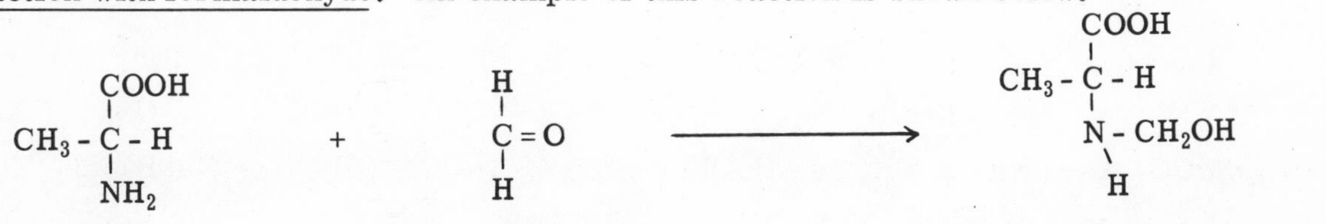

Alanine   Formaldehyde   N-monomethylol derivative

N-dimethylol derivative   N-methylene derivative

The relative proportions of these three possible formaldehyde derivatives is not known, but they effectively eliminate the alkalinity of the alpha amino, imino, and epsilon amino groups. Because of this action, the formaldehyde-treated amino acid behaves like a fatty acid, and the carboxyl group (or groups) can be quantitatively titrated with alkali, using a pH meter or an appropriate indicator to titrate to the correct final pH.

This reaction is the basis of the Sorensen titration method, which has been modified by Dunn; Dunn considers it one of the most accurate methods for determining the purity of the individual amino acids.

Reaction with nitrous acid. An example of this reaction is shown with leucine.

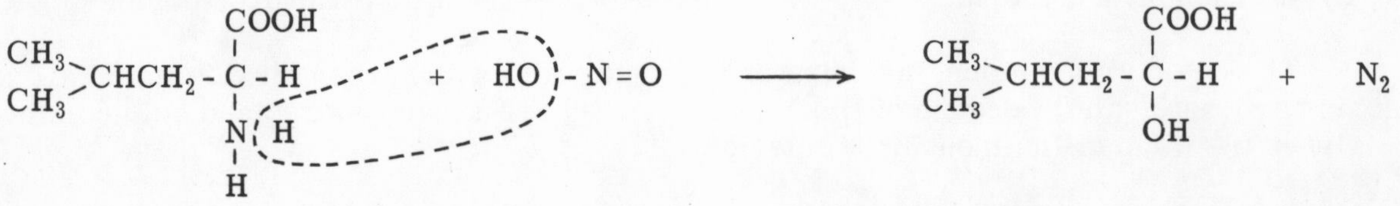

| Leucine | Nitrous acid | Alpha-hydroxy isocaproic acid | Nitrogen |

$$+ \quad H_2O$$

Water

The nitrogen of the alpha-amino (but not the alpha-imino) group is released quantitatively as nitrogen gas, and can be collected and measured accurately in a special gasometric apparatus devised by Van Slyke. This reaction serves as the basis for the quantitative Van Slyke method for determining the per cent of alpha-amino nitrogen in amino acids and proteins. The epsilon-amino group of lysine also reacts quantitatively with HNO_2, but the rate of the reaction is slower than with alpha-amino groups.

CHEMICAL REACTIONS OF THE CARBOXYL GROUP. These are not as numerous as the reactions of the alpha-amino group. They include salt formation, ester formation, and acyl formation.

Salt formation. Reaction with alkalies. An example is the formation of mono-and disodium glutamate.

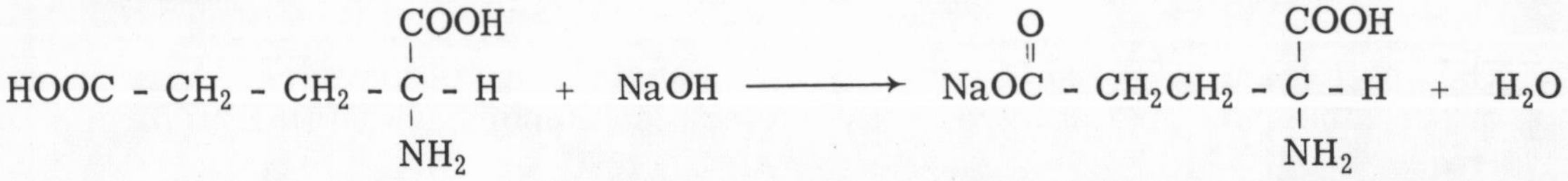

| Glutamic acid | Sodium hydroxide | Monosodium glutamate | Water |

| Monosodium glutamate | Sodium hydroxide | Disodium glutamate | Water |

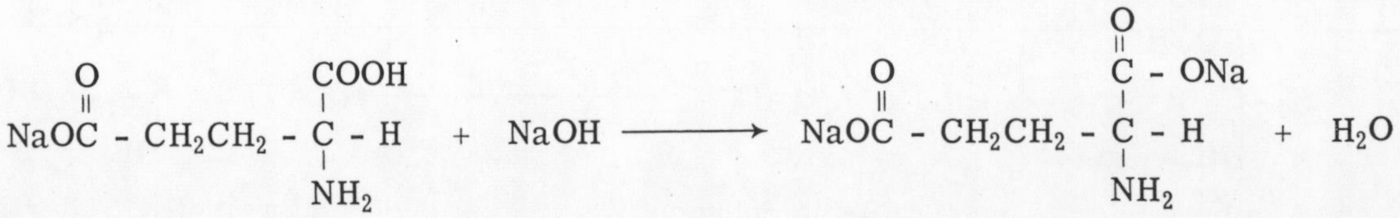

Monosodium glutamate is manufactured in large quantities as a flavor-enhancing agent (see page 302), and imparts a meat-like flavor to foods.

Ester formation.   Reaction with alcohols.   An example is the formation of glycine ethyl ester.

$$
\begin{array}{ccc}
\underset{\text{Glycine}}{\underset{\displaystyle NH_2}{\overset{\displaystyle COOH}{H-C-H}}} & + & \underset{\text{Ethyl alcohol}}{CH_3CH_2OH}
\end{array}
\quad\text{bubble in dry HCl gas} \longrightarrow\quad
\begin{array}{ccc}
\underset{\substack{\text{Glycine ethyl ester}\\ \text{hydrochloride}}}{\underset{\displaystyle NH_2-HCl}{\overset{\displaystyle \overset{\displaystyle O}{\overset{\parallel}{C}}-O-CH_2CH_3}{H-C-H}}} & + & \underset{\text{Water}}{H_2O}
\end{array}
$$

$$
\begin{array}{ccc}
\underset{\substack{\text{Glycine ethyl ester}\\ \text{hydrochloride}}}{\underset{\displaystyle NH_2-HCl}{\overset{\displaystyle \overset{\displaystyle O}{\overset{\parallel}{C}}-O-CH_2CH_3}{H-C-H}}} & + & \underset{\text{Sodium hydroxide}}{NaOH}
\end{array}
\longrightarrow\quad
\begin{array}{ccccc}
\underset{\text{Glycine ethyl ester}}{\underset{\displaystyle NH_2}{\overset{\displaystyle \overset{\displaystyle O}{\overset{\parallel}{C}}-O-CH_2CH_3}{H-C-H}}} & + & \underset{\text{Salt}}{NaCl} & + & \underset{\text{Water}}{H_2O}
\end{array}
$$

Glycine can be isolated from a gelatin hydrolysate (see page 76) by bubbling dry HCl gas into a suspension of the dry hydrolysate in ethyl alcohol. Glycine ethyl ester hydrochloride crystallizes out of the solution. Fischer isolated, for the first time, several amino acids in pure form from protein hydrolysates by the fractional distillation *in vacuo* of their ethyl esters.

Reactions shared by the alpha-amino and the alpha-carboxyl groups.   There are several important reactions which require the joint participation of *both* the alpha-amino and the alpha-carboxyl groups.

Amphoteric reaction. A compound is said to be amphoteric if it is capable of reacting with *both* acids and bases. Amino acids and proteins fulfill these requirements, readily forming salts with either acids or alkalies. If an amino acid (or protein) is dissolved in a mineral acid like HCl solution, it becomes the *cation* (positively charged ion), and will migrate to the cathode or negative pole of an electric circuit.

$$
\begin{array}{ccc}
\underset{\text{Amino acid}}{\underset{\displaystyle NH_2}{\overset{\displaystyle COOH}{R-C-H}}} & + & HCl
\end{array}
\longrightarrow\quad
\begin{array}{c}
\underset{\text{Amino acid cation}}{\underset{\displaystyle NH_2\cdot H^+\ (+\ Cl^-)}{\overset{\displaystyle COOH}{R-C-H}}} \longrightarrow \text{Cathode}
\end{array}
$$

Conversely, if the amino acid is dissolved in a solution of a base, like NaOH solution, it becomes an *anion* (negatively charged ion), and will migrate to the anode, or positive pole of an electric circuit.

$$
\begin{array}{ccc}
\underset{\text{Amino acid}}{\underset{\displaystyle NH_2}{\overset{\displaystyle COOH}{R-C-H}}} & + & NaOH
\end{array}
\longrightarrow\quad
\begin{array}{c}
\underset{\text{Amino acid anion}}{\underset{\displaystyle NH_2 \quad (+Na^+)}{\overset{\displaystyle COO^-}{R-C-H}}} \longrightarrow \text{Anode}
\end{array}
$$

At one specific pH value (the change-over point from *cation* to *anion*, or vice versa), the amino acid is combined with *neither* acid nor base. This pH value is the *isoelectric point* of the amino acid (or protein).   Amino acids and proteins have their lowest solubility at the isoelectric point.   The isoelectric points of several amino acids are given in Table 13.

Table 13.   Isoelectric points (pI) of amino acids*

Amino acid	pI	Amino acid	pI	Amino acid	pI
Alanine(DL)	6.11	Histidine(L)	7.64	Proline(L)	6.3
Arginine(L)	10.76	Hydroxyproline(L)	5.82	Sarcosine	6.00
Asparagine(L)	4.3	Isoleucine(DL)	6.04	Serine(DL)	5.68
Aspartic acid(L)	2.98	Leucine(DL)	6.04	Threonine(L)	5.59
Cystine(L)	5.02	Lysine(L)	9.47	Tryptophan(L)	5.88
Glutamic acid(L)	3.08	Methionine(DL)	5.74	Tyrosine(L)	5.63
Glycine	6.20	Phenylalanine(DL)	5.91	Valine(DL)	6.00

* Compiled by California Foundation for Biochemical Research (1954).

Inner salt (zwitter ion) form of the amino acids.   When amino acids are at the isoelectric point, the alpha-amino and alpha-carboxyl groups react with each other to form an *inner salt* or *zwitter ion*.   Aliphatic amino acids are almost completely converted to the inner salt form, whereas aromatic amino acids are converted to the extent of about 50 per cent. The formation of the inner salts (zwitter ions) of threonine and phenylalanine is shown below.

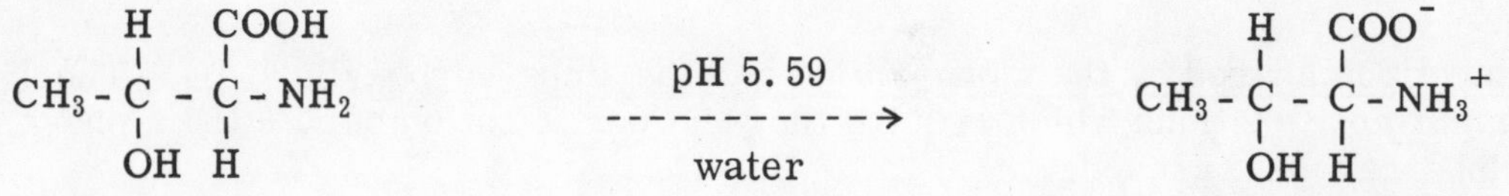

$$CH_3 - \overset{\overset{\displaystyle H}{|}}{\underset{\underset{\displaystyle OH}{|}}{C}} - \overset{\overset{\displaystyle COOH}{|}}{\underset{\underset{\displaystyle H}{|}}{C}} - NH_2 \quad \xrightarrow[\text{water}]{\text{pH 5.59}} \quad CH_3 - \overset{\overset{\displaystyle H}{|}}{\underset{\underset{\displaystyle OH}{|}}{C}} - \overset{\overset{\displaystyle COO^-}{|}}{\underset{\underset{\displaystyle H}{|}}{C}} - NH_3^+$$

Threonine   Threonine Zwitter Ion

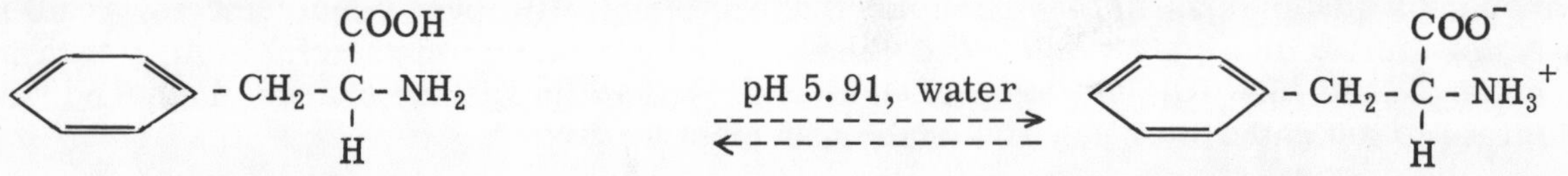

$$- CH_2 - \overset{\overset{\displaystyle COOH}{|}}{\underset{\underset{\displaystyle H}{|}}{C}} - NH_2 \quad \underset{\xrightarrow{\hspace{2cm}}}{\xleftarrow{\text{pH 5.91, water}}} \quad - CH_2 - \overset{\overset{\displaystyle COO^-}{|}}{\underset{\underset{\displaystyle H}{|}}{C}} - NH_3^+$$

Phenylalanine   Phenylalanine Zwitter Ion

   The addition of acid or base to isoelectric solutions of amino acids destroys the zwitter ion by neutralizing one of the ionic charges.

Reaction of alpha-amino and alpha-carboxyl groups with ninhydrin.   Ninhydrin (triketo hydrindene hydrate), is specifically reduced when heated in aqueous solution with free amino acids.   The amino acid is oxidized to an aldehyde with one less carbon, with the release of carbon dioxide and ammonia.   The ninhydrin is reduced to a compound which can condense with the ammonia, and with more ninhydrin, to form a blue pigment.

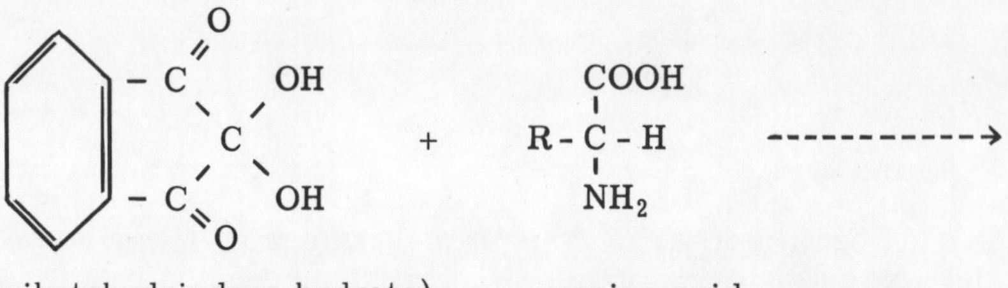

$$\overset{\displaystyle - C \overset{\displaystyle O}{\diagup} \quad OH}{\underset{\displaystyle - C \underset{\displaystyle O}{\diagdown} \quad OH}{\quad C \quad}} \qquad + \qquad R - \overset{\overset{\displaystyle COOH}{|}}{\underset{\underset{\displaystyle NH_2}{|}}{C}} - H \qquad \dashrightarrow$$

Ninhydrin (triketohydrindene hydrate)   amino acid

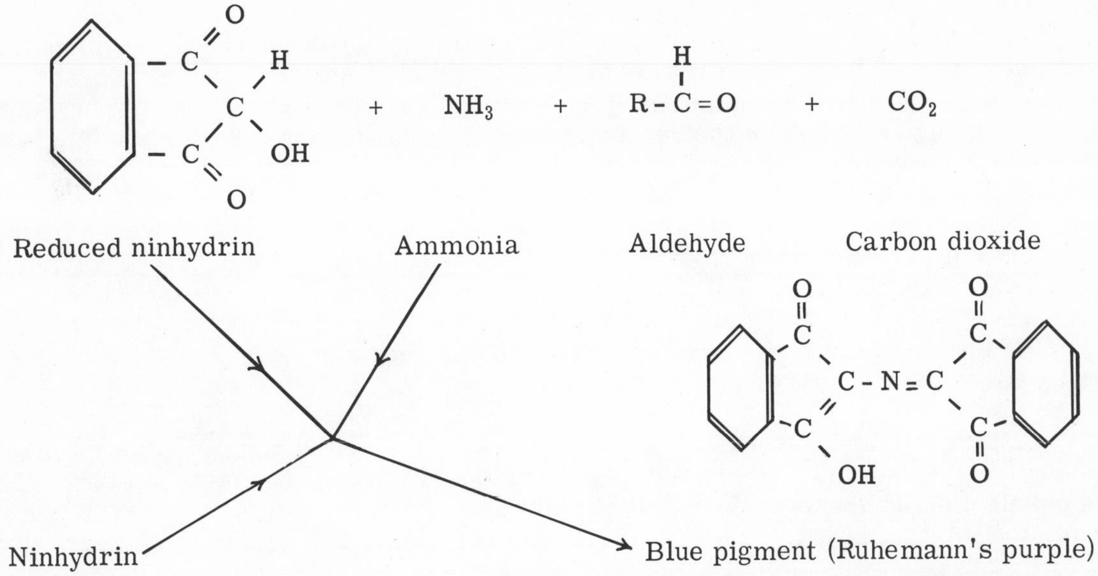

The reaction chemistry diagram showing the ninhydrin reaction is at the top of the page.

Reduced ninhydrin   +   NH₃   +   R - C = O   +   CO₂

Ammonia   Aldehyde   Carbon dioxide

Ninhydrin → Blue pigment (Ruhemann's purple)

The reaction is quite specific*. The amino group must be alpha to the carboxyl group, and both amino and carboxyl must be free. If the CO_2 released is measured quantitatively, the method is specific for *free* amino acids. It is also possible to make a colorimetric comparison of the blue color with the color produced from known amounts of pure amino acids treated in the same fashion. This colorimetric method is used extensively in paper and column chromatography of amino acids (see p. 78).

Reaction of alpha-amino and alpha-carboxyl groups to form chain peptides. Living cells contain the enzyme systems and high energy bond compounds (p. 166) to pull out water molecules between alpha-amino groups and alpha-carboxyl groups on adjacent amino acid molecules. The final product is a chain peptide, the major structural unit of the protein molecule. This reaction occurs in small particles called *ribosomes* in the cell cytoplasm (see p. 3).

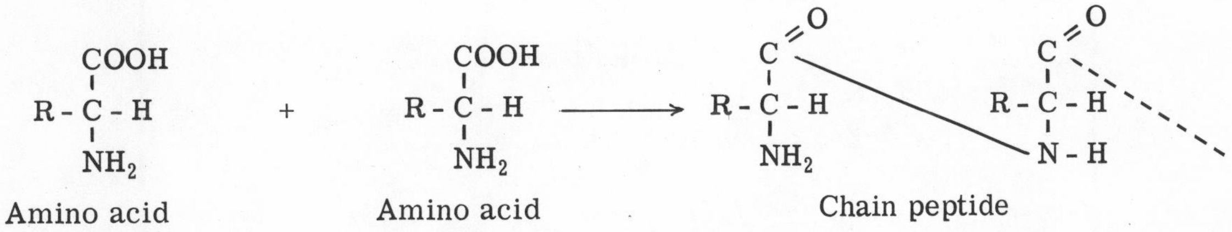

Amino acid   +   Amino acid   →   Chain peptide

Chemical synthesis of peptides and proteins. In the first part of this chapter the pioneer studies of Fischer on the synthesis of polypeptides were described. Recently a revolutionary method for controlled synthesis of a polypeptide has been devised at the Rockefeller Institute. Merrifield and coworkers have perfected a solid-phase system which involves the steps shown in Figure 17.

The first step involves attaching an amino acid with its carboxyl group free and its amino group protected by a tertiary butyl oxycarbonyl (t-BOC) group to a solid styrene polymer containing free chloro methyl benzene groups on its surface. In the second step,

* For release of carbon dioxide.

the protecting t-BOC group is removed from the amino group of the attached amino acid by treating the amino acid-polymer combination with 1 N hydrochloric acid in acetic acid.

In the third step, the first peptide bond is formed between the free amino group of the amino acid-polymer and the activated carboxyl of a second amino acid. The second amino acid must have its amino group covered with a t-BOC group. Coupling is brought about by using an excess of the second amino acid and an excess of a coupling reagent, N, N'-dicyclohexylcarbodiimide with methylene chloride or dimethylformamide as solvent.

The fourth and last step in the synthesis of the dipeptide uses hydrogen bromide in trifluoroacetic acid to remove the t-BOC group, regenerate bromomethyl polymer, and release the dipeptide.

If longer peptides are desired, step 4 is omitted, and steps 2 and 3 are repeated as many times as necessary.

Merrifield and coworkers have developed an automated apparatus which is able to incorporate six amino acids into a polypeptide in 24 hours. The potential of this method of polypeptide synthesis looks highly promising.

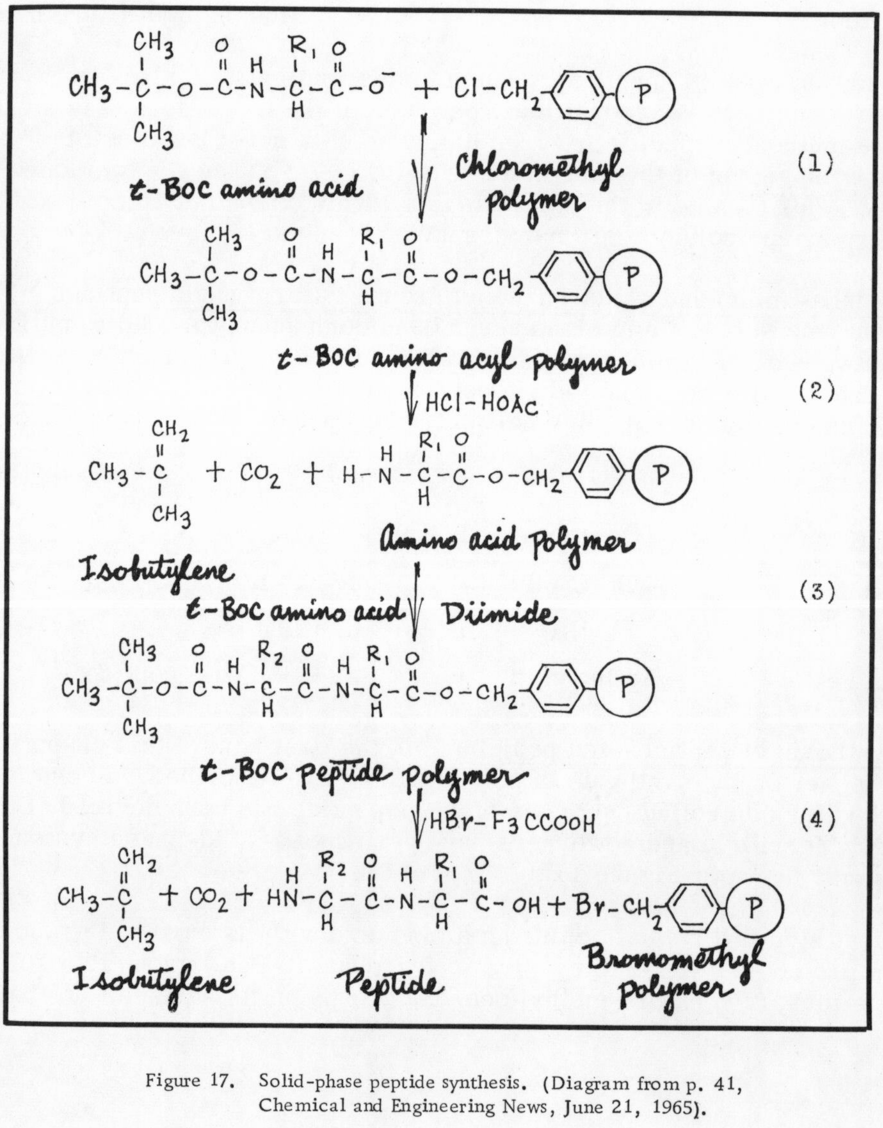

Figure 17.   Solid-phase peptide synthesis. (Diagram from p. 41, Chemical and Engineering News, June 21, 1965).

CHEMICAL REACTIONS OF PROTEINS. Proteins consist mainly of amino acid residues joined by peptide linkages. The chemical reactions of proteins are therefore very similar to those observed with the individual amino acids. Groups which do not respond to amino acid reagents are (1) those tied up in the peptide linkage or some other covalent type of linkage (ester, amide, etc.), and (2) groups "buried" in the native globular structure (see page 63).

Isoelectric points. Proteins are amphoteric. They have characteristic isoelectric points (Table 14) and form *zwitter ions* analogous to amino acid zwitter ions.

Table 14. pI values for certain proteins

Protein	pI	Protein	pI
Casein	4.6	Tetanus toxin	5.1
Avidin	10.0	Serum albumin	4.8
Lysozyme	11.0	Serum globulin	5.4
Pepsin	2.7	Edestin	6.9
Cytochrome c	9.8		

Proteins form salts with mineral acids and alkalies, and even with other more acidic or more basic proteins (e.g. protamine insulin). They can be acylated and alkylated, and deaminated with nitrous acid. FDNB reacts with all exposed alpha amino groups just as it does with free amino acids (see p. 69).

Formaldehyde reacts with the free amino groups in proteins (see page 69) to form a water-insoluble product which is resistant to attack by microorganisms. Because of this action, formaldehyde is the principal reagent in embalming fluids, and is used to harden and preserve f ibers (Aralac, Vicara, etc.) spun from globular proteins (see page 302).

The presence of certain chemically active groups from specific amino acids is used to detect proteins in biological mixtures. Thus, a positive Millon's test (red) for tyrosine, a positive Hopkins-Cole test (violet) for tryptophan, or a positive unoxidized sulfur test (black) for cysteine and cystine all serve, in the absence of the free amino acid, to prove that a protein is present.

Proteins also give the ninhydrin color test (see page 72), and the *biuret* test. In the biuret test, the protein is dissolved in dilute alkali, and a very dilute solution of copper sulfate is added. Proteins give a purple-violet to blue color, which is attributed to the presence of multiple peptide linkages in the molecule. The compound, biuret,

$$\text{(H}_2\text{N - }\overset{\text{O}}{\overset{\|}{\text{C}}}\text{ - NH - }\overset{\text{O}}{\overset{\|}{\text{C}}}\text{ - NH}_2)$$ also gives the color, hence the name, biuret test.

PROTEIN DENATURATION. Denaturation may be defined as any change in a globular protein that decreases its solubility at the isoelectric point. The rigid structure of a globular protein (see page 63) is held in shape by three main types of cross linkages: -S-S-(disulfide) linkages, (2) salt bridges (between aspartic, glutamic acids and lysine, arginine), (3) hydrogen bonds (between peptide linkages: -C=O.....H-N-, and similar "polar" groups). When a protein is denatured, some or all of these cross linkages are split, and the specific internal structure of the native protein is lost (Fig. 18). According to Klotz, denaturation reduces the amount of water bound in "ice crystal" form in the native protein.

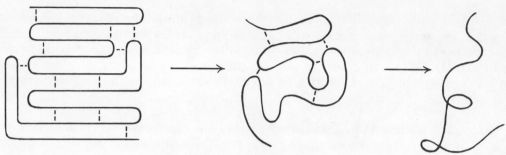

Figure 18.   Denaturation breaks bonds.

When the closely folded peptide chains of the globular protein unfold to a marked degree due to denaturation, the soluble globular protein is changed into an insoluble protein of the fibrous type.   Commercial fibers are produced in this way from globular proteins (see p. 302).

In globular proteins, chemical tests show that the chemically active groups in the amino acid residues are less reactive in the native protein than in the denatured protein. For example, only 12 epsilon-amino groups react with fluorodinitrobenzene in native lactoglobulin, whereas all 31 epsilon-amino groups react when lactoglobulin is denatured. Much stronger tests are obtained also for -S-S-, -SH, hydroxyphenyl, and indole groups in denatured proteins.   It is believed that denaturation removes a protective layer of "ice crystal" water, uncoils the peptide chains, and uncovers these groups, which are then accessible for reaction.

Denaturing agents.   It is difficult to find agents which do *not* denature globular proteins. Table 15 shows a partial list of the many agents and conditions which cause protein denaturation.   In most cases, the probable cause of denaturation is also listed.

Table 15.   Protein denaturants

Agent	Probable cause of denaturation
Heat	Thermal splitting of salt bridges, "melting" ice crystal bound water
Mineral acids and alkalies	Cleavage of salt bridges
Acetone	Cleaves hydrogen bonds
Alcohols	" " "
Urea	" " "
Tungstic, picric, trichloroacetic, acids	" salt bridges
Vigorous grinding	Unknown
Shaking or stirring	Unfolding of peptide chains (protein monolayer forms at surface and in foam)
Visible light + sensitizer	Unknown
Ultrasonic waves	Mechanical agitation, thermal effects, release of (O) from water
Ultraviolet light, also X-rays	Absorption of energy, splitting of bonds

Hydrolytic cleavage of proteins.   Proteins can be broken down stepwise, by hydrolysis, into their ultimate building stones, the amino acids.   The important catalysts bringing about these changes are the hydrogen ion, the hydroxyl ion, and certain hydrolytic enzymes.   Intermediate products released during hydrolysis are (1) denatured protein, (2) metaprotein, (3) proteoses, (4) peptones, (5) polypeptides, (6) dipeptides, and (7) amino acids.   These products are arranged in the order of their decreasing complexity and increasing solubility. The amino acids, dipeptides, and some of the smaller polypeptides are dialyzable through a semi-permeable membrane such as Visking casing. Products (1), (2), and (3) are insoluble in saturated $(NH_4)_2SO_4$ solution.

Hydrolysis with hydrogen ion as catalyst. The protein is heated for about 8 hours at 120°C. in an autoclave (or refluxed for 24 hours at the boiling point) with 4-5 parts by weight of 20% (constant boiling) HCl solution, or 25% (by weight) H_2SO_4 solution. Complete hydrolysis yields a mixture of free amino acids and their breakdown products. If tryptophan and carbohydrate are present, a black pigment, humin, is also obtained. Most of the amino acids are recovered in the L-(natural) form, although traces of the DL(racemic) form may be produced. Acid hydrolysis completely destroys tryptophan, and destroys about 10% of the serine and threonine when carried out in the manner described above.

Hydrolysis with hydroxyl ion as catalyst. The protein is usually heated in a nickel beaker at 120°C. in an autoclave with 4-5 parts by weight of 20% sodium hydroxide solution. Complete hydrolysis yields a mixture of free amino acids, with some breakdown products of amino acids, but little or no colored humin products. The amino acids are completely racemized (all DL instead of L). Threonine and serine may be partially or completely destroyed, and cystine, arginine, and lysine are partially destroyed.

Hydrolysis with enzymes as catalyst. Animals, plants, and microorganisms secrete proteases which split proteins step-wise to amino acids. The amino acids are absorbed and utilized for various purposes (see page 149). The author and other workers have tried to duplicate *in vivo* digestion using various combinations of enzymes in the test tube. To date, *complete* hydrolysis of a protein to a mixture of free amino acids has not been achieved with enzymes *outside* of the living organism (see page 149).

Although digestion with purified proteases such as pepsin, trypsin, etc. does not split proteins completely to free amino acids, such enzymes, as well as less pure preparations such as papain (page 303), and pancreatin (page 304), serve many useful purposes in the solubilization of proteins, and in the preparation of individual amino acids and special hydrolysates. Enzyme digestion is the mildest form of protein hydrolysis. The amino acids and peptides released are all of the L- or natural configuration.

ISOLATION AND SYNTHESIS OF AMINO ACIDS. The nineteen commonly recognized amino acids (page 55) have been isolated in pure form from the hydrolysates of proteins from animals, plants, and microorganisms, and have been characterized (structure determined) and synthesized in the laboratory. There is now an increasing demand for the pure individual amino acids for use in foods and medicine, and for research in nutrition and metabolism. This demand has stimulated interest in the improvement of older methods and the development of new methods for the isolation and synthesis of the various amino acids. At the present time, several commercial firms manufacture and supply purified L and DL amino acids of good quality. The commercially available amino acids vary in price from about one cent a gram, to several dollars a gram, depending on the cost of preparation. In Table 16, on the following page, the amino acids are listed on the basis of the most economical method of preparation: isolation or synthesis. The most available form (commercially) is also included.

Table 16. Preparation of amino acids

Amino acid	Practical method of preparation	Most available form
Alanine	Synthesis	DL-alanine
Arginine	Isolation (gelatin)	L-arginine·HCl
Aspartic acid	Synthesis	DL-aspartic acid
Cystine	Isolation (hair)	L-cystine
Glutamic acid	Isolation (gluten, Steffen's waste)*	L-glutamic acid
Glycine	Synthesis	Glycine
Histidine	Isolation (hemoglobin)	L-histidine·HCl·H₂O
Hydroxyproline	Isolation (gelatin)	L-hydroxyproline
Isoleucine	Synthesis	DL-isoleucine
Leucine	Isolation (gluten)	L-leucine
Lysine	Synthesis, resolution of DL form*	L-lysine·HCl
Methionine	Synthesis	DL-methionine
Phenylalanine	Synthesis	DL-phenylalanine
Proline	Isolation (gelatin)	L-proline
Serine	Synthesis	DL-serine
Threonine	Synthesis	DL-threonine
Tryptophan	Synthesis	DL-tryptophan
Tyrosine	Isolation (gelatin, gluten)	L-tyrosine
Valine	Synthesis	DL-valine

QUANTITATIVE DETERMINATION OF AMINO ACIDS. Accurate methods for the determination of the amino acid content of proteins and of plant and body fluids are a necessity in order to increase our knowledge regarding protein structure and amino acid metabolism. Some methods now available are especially suited to the determination of the exact amount of each amino acid in a highly purified protein; others are less accurate, but provide useful data with a smaller expenditure of time and with simpler laboratory equipment.

Quantitative methods for amino acids can be divided into four major groups: *gravimetric, chromatographic, colorimetric,* and *microbiological.* Only one of these methods, the chromatographic method, will be discussed here. Students interested in the other methods are referred to a book by Block and Weiss (see p. 307).

CHROMATOGRAPHIC METHOD. Column chromatography. The principle of all chromatographic methods is to first adsorb the amino acids on an insoluble material and to then differentially remove (elute) the amino acids one at a time with suitable liquid solvents. The adsorbent can be packed into a column, or can be in the form of a sheet; the former is called *column* chromatography, the latter, *paper* chromatography (see p. 34).

One of the most successful applications of column chromatography is that of Moore and Stein. The amino acids are adsorbed on a column of synthetic resin. Individual amino acids are then "eluted" from the resin by passing appropriate buffer solutions through the column. A standard curve (elution curve) can be constructed using pure known amino acids, and the quantity of each amino acid eluted from an unknown hydrolysate can be compared with the standard curve. The quantity of amino acid in a given fraction is determined by measuring color intensity at a wave length of 570 millimicrons in a photoelectric colorimeter, using the ninhydrin color reaction (page 72). The method will determine most of the amino acids with an accuracy of 100 ± 3%.

* Recently, commercial methods for preparing L-glutamic acid and L-lysine HCl by fermentation of suitable substrates have been developed. These methods use glycerol as the carbon source, and mutant strains of Micrococcus Glutamicus as the microorganism.

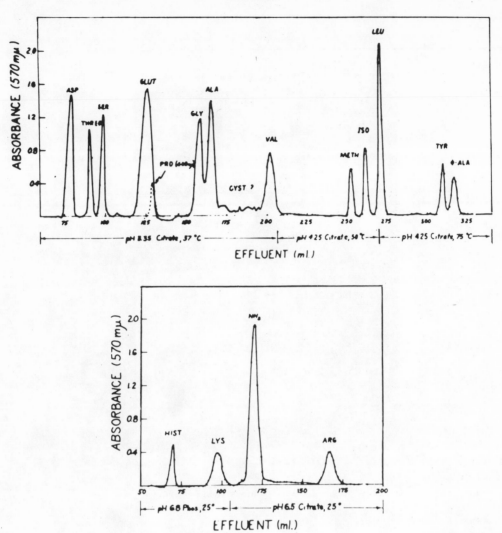

Figure 19.   Chromatograms of acid hydrolysate of purified corn glutelin (Ph. D. thesis, N. E. Lloyd, Purdue University).

In Fig. 19 are shown the elution curves for the neutral and acidic amino acids using a 100 cm. Dowex 50 column (top curve), and for the basic amino acids and ammonia using a 15 cm. Dowex column (bottom curve). A twenty milligram sample of a purified corn glutelin of unknown amino acid composition was hydrolyzed, and one fifth of the hydroly-sate placed on each of the two columns. The abscissae of the charts show the total vol-ume of eluate collected (in 1 ml fractions) and the ordinates show the color intensity of the separate fractions. Citrate buffers, pH 3.35 (37°C), pH 4.25 (50°C) and pH 4.25 (75°C) were used consecutively in the top curve, and phosphate buffer pH 6.8 (25°C) and citrate buffer pH 6.5 (25°C) were used consecutively in the bottom curve, as the eluting solutions. The amino acid composition of the corn glutelin, based on these analyses, is shown in Table 45, page 316 (Appendix).

The curves shown above were obtained using a manually operated column with auto-matic fraction collector. A completely automatic instrument based on the Moore-Stein method has been developed by Beckman Instruments, Inc. A picture of this instrument is shown in Fig. 20 on the following page. Called the Spinco Amino Acid Analyzer, it automatically analyzes a protein hydrolysate for the constituent amino acids in approxi-mately 3 hours, with a high degree of accuracy.

Figure 20.   Spinco Amino Acid Analyzer.

Paper chromatography.   Amino acids can be adsorbed and differentially eluted from a sheet of cellulose fibers (ordinary filter paper).   The method is used both as a quantitative and as a qualitative method for the detection of various amino acids in protein hydrolysates and biological fluids. The method is used widely in all branches of the biological sciences.

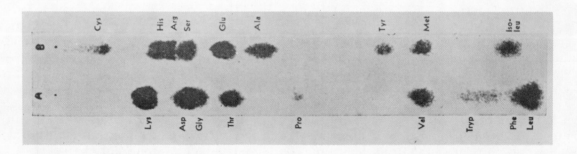

Figure 21.   One dimensional paper chromatogram of natural amino acids, using butanol, acetic acid, and water
(4:1:5) on Whatman No. 1 paper. (From A. L. Levy and D. Chung, Anal. Chem. 25 399 (1953)).

A strip of filter paper carrying a drop of the amino acid solution is allowed to hang from a trough containing the solvent, and the trough with filter paper draped down one side is enclosed in a chamber so that the atmosphere is maintained saturated with solvent vapors. The solvent is drawn into the filter paper strip by capillarity, and flows slowly down the strip. The individual amino acids move down the strip at rates determined by (a) the ratio of water to other solvent in the trough and by (b) the partition coefficient of the amino acid between the water and other solvent phases. The rate of movement of the individual amino acids down the strip is different with different solvents. It is therefore possible to "develop" the paper chromatogram in one direction for a period of time with one non-aqueous solvent, thus obtaining a *vertical* separation of the amino acids (one-dimensional chromatogram, Fig. 21), and then to turn the paper through an angle of 90° and "develop" the chromatogram with another non-aqueous solvent, in this way obtaining both vertical and horizontal separation of the amino acids. This is called a *2-dimensional* paper chromatogram.

After a one or two-dimensional paper chromatogram has been prepared as described above, the paper is dried, sprayed with ninhydrin reagent, and heated. A blue spot appears at the location of an amino acid, and the density of color will be proportional to the relative quantity of each amino acid present. The amino acids can be identified by comparing the chromatogram with a standard chromatogram "map" made with known purified amino acids. Figure 22 shows a photograph of a 2-dimensional chromatogram.

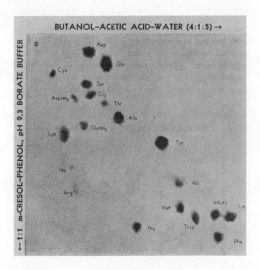

Figure 22.   Two dimensional paper chromatogram of natural amino acids (20 amino acids
in equimolar concentrations). Run first with butanol mixture, then with
cresol mixture. (From A. L. Levy and D. Chung, Anal. Chem. 25 397 (1953)).

If a radioactive atom such as C^{14} is incorporated into the various amino acids, the "undeveloped" chromatogram is placed against a photographic plate. The plate will become exposed at the spots where each radioactive amino acid is located. This method has been used with much success in the studies on the pathways of carbon in photosynthesis (page 174).

Amino Acid Composition of Proteins.   Proteins vary widely in amino acid composition. For example, casein contains 2.7% glycine and 6.3% tyrosine, whereas gelatin contains 15.7% glycine and only 0.6% tyrosine. Nearly one-half of the silk fibroin and wheat gliadin molecules can be accounted for as glycine and glutamic acid, respectively. Other important differences are apparent in the table on amino acid content of proteins shown in the Appendix (Table 46, p. 317).

In Table 46 (p. 317, Appendix), the values are expressed as grams of amino acid per 100 grams of protein. It can be seen that the total weight of the amino acids per 100 grams of protein exceeds 100 in most cases. This is due to the fact that the amino acids exist as *residues* in the protein molecule, to which water molecules are *added* on hydrolysis. The data are satisfactory for use in nutrition studies (page 219), but are not satisfactory for studies on protein structure. If the molecular weight of the protein is known, one can indicate the *number* of amino acid residues present per protein molecule. Thus, Brand expresses the amino acid composition of crystalline beta-lactoglobulin as follows:

gly_8, ala_{29}, val_{21}, leu_{50}, iso_{27}, pro_{15}, phe_9, arg_7, his_4, lys_{33}, asp_{36}, glu_{56}, ser_{20}, thr_{21}, $(cys\text{-}SH)_4$, $(cys\text{-}S\text{-}S\text{-}cys/2)_8$, met_9, tyr_9, try_4, amm_{32}.

This is actually an empirical formula for a protein, using the amino acids instead of the elements as the building stones.

ISOLATION, PURIFICATION, AND DETERMINATION OF THE PURITY OF PROTEINS. Fevold[*] has written that "the successful purification, isolation and crystallization of native proteins requires painstaking work, with strict attention to detail, under conditions most conducive to protein stability." Proteins are extremely sensitive to heat, hydrogen ion, hydroxyl ion, organic solvents, etc., and in some cases, even to distilled water. Many methods which can be used in the isolation of other biologically important carbon compounds (lipids, carbohydrates, vitamins, etc.) cannot be applied to the isolation of native globular proteins.

GENERAL METHODS OF ISOLATION. Fibrous proteins can be isolated only by extracting away all of the soluble organic and inorganic matter. The residue is the "purified" protein, and it is difficult to determine how uniform this is.

Globular (soluble) proteins can be extracted by grinding animal tissues with suitable solvents in a meat grinder or a blendor (homogenizer). Plant tissues are ground in a colloid mill with a suitable buffered solvent. The proteins can be precipitated from the plant or animal extracts by altering the concentration of salts, and, or, hydrogen ion concentration, and, or, the addition of organic solvents. Working at low temperatures minimizes the denaturation of the proteins, especially in salt-free solutions and in solutions containing organic solvents, and also reduces bacterial contamination.

General methods of purification. The purification of a crude protein generally involves one or more of the following general techniques: (1) adsorption and elution (example: purification of prothrombin), (2) crystallization from a saturated solution by cooling (example: crystallization of urease), (3) fractional "salting out" with $(NH_4)_2SO_4$ or similar salt (example: isolation of crystalline catalase), (4) isoelectric precipitation (example: purification of horse hemoglobin), (5) precipitation from an alcohol-water system at low temperature (example: isolation of blood plasma proteins (Cohn method), and (6) differential ultracentrifugation (example: purification of influenza virus (Fig. 23 on following page).

[*] H. L. Fevold. Amino Acids and Proteins. Edited by D. M. Greenberg - page 268. C. C. Thomas, Springfield, Ill. (1951).

Figure 23. Electron micrograph of purified influenza virus (magnified 30,000 times).

Principles involved.

1. Proteins are absorbed on certain materials (clays, gels such as magnesium hydroxide, $Ca_3(PO_4)_2$, diethylamino ethyl (DEAE) cellulose etc.). These can be packed in a column, and the proteins separated by column chromatography in a manner similar to that used for separation of amino acids (see page 78, and Reference 10, p. 307 (Appendix). They can also be separated by a molecular sieve effect using Sephadex, a cross-linked dextran (see p. 88).

2. The crystallization of compounds from their saturated solutions is a well known phenomenon.

3. Because of their colloidal nature, globular proteins are sensitive to high concentrations of salts. Water - or salt-soluble proteins (see page 65) can often be separated on the basis of their differential solubility in salts such as $(NH_4)_2SO_4$, Na_2SO_4, etc.

4. Isoelectric precipitation of a protein occurs because the protein exists as a zwitter ion at that pH, and exhibits minimum solubility. This property can often be used to separate a protein from its impurities, both protein and otherwise.

5. Precipitation from an alcohol-water system at low temperature has been used with great success for the separation of blood plasma proteins. In this method, careful control is maintained over five variables: protein concentration, alcohol concentration, ionic strength, pH, and temperature. Ethyl alcohol is usually employed, but methyl alcohol has also been used. Recent modifications include the fractionation of the zinc salts of the plasma proteins.

6. Ultracentrifugation is a process whereby molecules are subjected to gravitational (centrifugal) forces which are greater than the thermal forces causing them to diffuse.

Svedberg pioneered the development of two types of ultracentrifuges, a low speed type (50-8,500 x gravity), and an oil-turbine type (8,000-400,000 x gravity). The maximum speed of the former is about 40,000 r.p.m., and of the latter about 80,000 r.p.m. Efficient ultracentrifuges are now manufactured in the United States which are powered by electric motors. A "preparative" ultracentrifuge is available for the purification of proteins of relatively high molecular weight (such as viruses, plant cytoplasm proteins) and an "analytical" ultracentrifuge is available to determine the molecular weights of proteins of all sizes.

The determination of the purity of proteins. The four most important methods of determining the purity of proteins are the *solubility method, electrophoresis, chromatography, and ultracentrifugation.*

The solubility method. If increments of a pure protein are added to a solution in which the protein has limited solubility (for example, in an $(NH_4)_2SO_4$ solution), a point will be reached at which further increments of added protein will not dissolve. If the total solid protein added is plotted against the total protein dissolved, a curve similar to that shown in Figure 24 for a highly purified preparation of prothrombin (see p. 259) will be obtained.

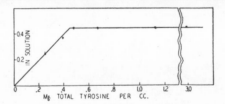

Figure 24.   Solubility Curve of Prothrombin with a Specific Activity of 15,200 Units per mg. Tyrosine.
Solvent: 37% saturated ammonium sulfate, pH 7.6, temperature 0°.
(From W. H. Seegers, E. C. Loomis and J. M. Vandenbelt, Arch. Biochem. 6 92 (1945)).

If the protein tested contains impurities, these will change the slope of the ascending curve. Figure 25 shows the general shape of the solubility curve that would be obtained if the protein contained two different impurities.

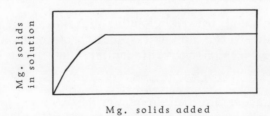

Mg. solids added

Figure 25.   Protein with two impurities.

Using solubility diagrams of this type, it is possible to detect the presence of small amounts of impurities in purified proteins.

Electrophoresis. Globular proteins carry either a positive or negative "net" charge at all pH values except at the isoelectric point. On the acid side of the isoelectric point, the net charge on the protein is *positive* (protein is a cation), and on the alkaline side of the pI the net charge on the protein is *negative* (protein is an anion). When a solution of the protein is placed in a compartment containing a positively charged anode at one end and a negatively charged cathode at the other, protein cations migrate to the cathode, and protein anions migrate to the anode. A protein at its pI (isoelectric point) will migrate to neither pole.

Tiselius devised an "electrophoresis" apparatus consisting of compartmented cells forming a U tube, connected to an anode and a cathode compartment (Fig. 26). Since each molecular species of protein will migrate at a characteristic rate *(mobility)*, depending on the pH, net charge, and shape of the molecule, it is possible to move one species of protein into a separate glass compartment (bottom section, or ascending leg of center section) ahead of all other proteins present, or vice versa, and then to slide out the compartment containing the pure protein.

It is also possible to photograph (using a shadow scanning method or a cylindrical lens) (see Fig. 27) the protein gradients (points of maximum change in density of the solution due to different zones of protein) and to thus obtain a shadow pattern corresponding to the different zones of protein in the electrophoresis cell. If a single pure protein is present, only *one* hump or peak will be obtained on the photograph. Figure 28 demonstrates the usefulness of the electrophoresis method in following the changes in the rela-

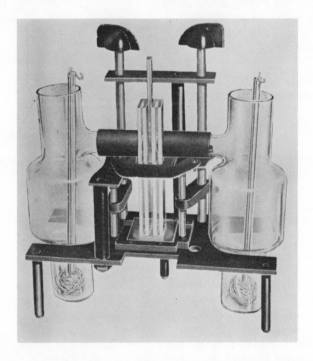

Figure 26.   Tiselius electrophoresis cell and electrode vessels. The cell is
built in three sections (top, center and bottom). The lower ground
glass square plate of the center section is shown and is in contact
with the ground glass square plate of the shallow bottom section.
Similar ground glass plates connect the top and center sections,
but are hidden in this photograph by the flat metal clip of the
holder. The cell is connected to the electrode vessels with neo-
prene tubing. The electrodes across which the potential is applied
consist of silver wire coated with silver chloride. The vessels are
filled with buffer solution. The rack and pinion device is used to
slide out the center section.

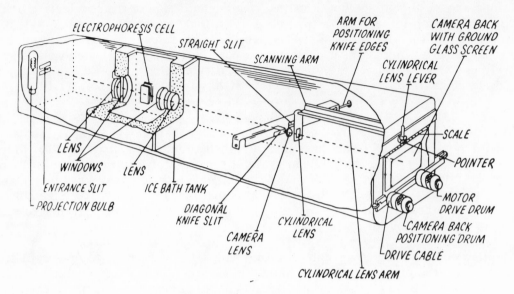

Figure 27.   Cut-away view of compact electrophoresis apparatus.
(Courtesy of Perkin-Elmer Corp., Norwalk, Conn.).

tive proportions of proteins in the cytoplasm
of alfalfa leaf when the plant is made sulfur-
deficient using the sand culture technique
(p. 136).   The δ component is a boundary
anomaly and not a protein component.   The
actual protein components present are major component I, and minor components
a and b.

<u>Starch gel electrophoresis</u>.   This method
differs from free boundary electrophoresis in that the proteins move through a
solid starch gel, giving a combination of
electrophoresis and chromatography.
Figure 29 is a diagram of a plastic electrophoresis apparatus for use with starch
gels.

     In a typical experiment for separa-
tion of the proteins in partially purified
samples of plasminogen (see page 260),
the tray was filled with a hot gel made
from partially hydrolyzed potato starch
mixed with a glycine-HCl buffer at pH
2.1 and ionic strength 0.1 (see page 96).
The plasminogen samples were prepared
by dissolving 15 mg. of lyophilized preparation in 1 ml. of pH 2.1 glycine-HCl buffer and adding unhydrolyzed starch to
make a thick paste which could still be
drawn into a 1-ml. serological pipette.

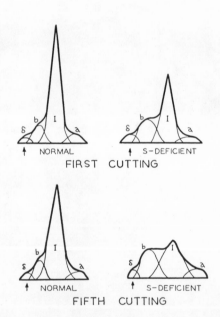

Figure 28.   Tracings of electrophoretic patterns (ascending) of
normal and sulfur-deficient alfalfa leaf cytoplasm
proteins, showing changes in relative quantities of
components with sulfur deficiency.   Fine lines indicate arbitrary division of components; arrows indicate starting boundaries.   Analysis in 0.2 ionic
strength KOH-maleate buffer, pH 7.0; time of
migration 5000 sec.   (From E. T. Mertz and
H. Matsumoto.   Arch. Biochem. Biophysics. <u>63</u>
60 (1956)).

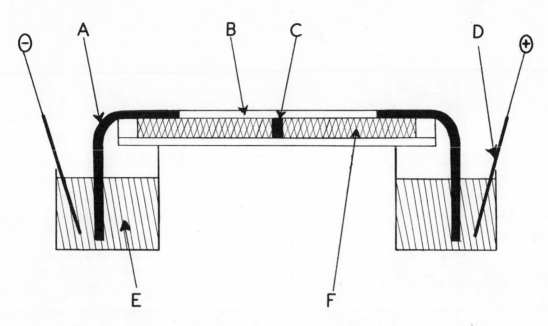

Fig. 29. Diagram of starch gel electrophoresis assembly.   A. Filter paper bridge soaked in buffer solution
B. Seal to prevent water loss during electrophoresis.   C. Position of sample insertion.   D. Platinum electrode.   E. Buffer solution-same as in starch gel.   F. Starch gel contained in plastic
tray. (Drawing by John Chan and Lynn Hoepfinger).

A 2.5 mm. slot cut out of the gel about half-way down the length of the gel tray was filled
with the paste. Electrophoresis was carried out at 3 volts/cm. for 16 hours in a 5° cold
room. Figure 30 shows the strips after the protein bands were revealed by staining with
Amido Black dye and washing out the excess dye. The leading bands are essentially pure
plasminogen in both the bovine and the human preparations.

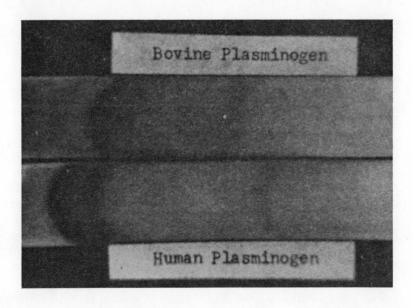

Fig. 30. Photograph of stained gel strips used for starch gel electrophoresis
of bovine and human plasminogen. Migration is to the left.
(From Cole and Mertz, Can. J. Biochem. Physiol. <u>39</u>, 1429 (1961)).

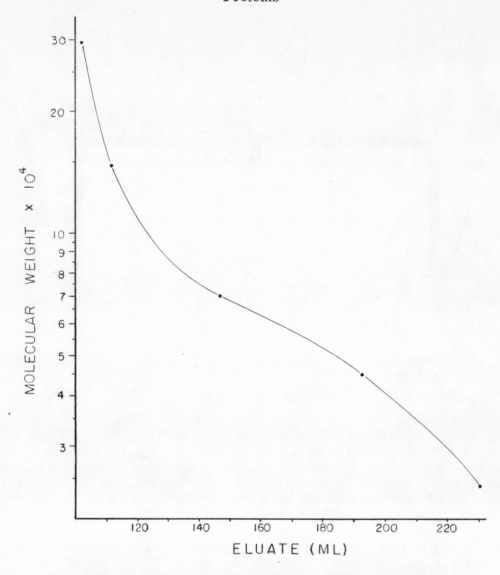

Figure 31.   Standard Curve for Molecular Weight Estimation.

<u>Chromatography</u>. The cellulose derivatives, diethylaminoethyl (DEAE) and carboxymethyl cellulose are strong resolving agents for proteins because of their charged groups and ion-exchange properties.   An even more versatile substance for separation of proteins is a cross-linked dextran (modified dextrin from starch) called *Sephadex*.   Five grades of Sephadex with different degrees of cross-linking are available.   When packed in a column and equilibrated with aqueous buffer, the expanded polysaccharide acts as a molecular sieve towards protein molecules.   Thus, Sephadex G-25 beads retain molecules with molecular weights up to 5,000.   The "exclusion limit" of G-25 is therefore 5,000.   On the same basis, the exclusion limits of G-50, G-75, G-100 and G-200 are 10,000, 50,000, 100,000, and 200,000, respectively.   Since most proteins have molecular weights in excess of 10,000, G-25 is used to desalt them.   The sodium chloride molecules are retained by G-25 and the proteins quickly pass through the column.

Sephadex 100 is very useful for the separation of proteins with different molecular weights.   In fact, Whitaker has devised a method for determining the molecular weight of a protein using Sephadex.   First, a standard curve is prepared using purified proteins of known molecular weight.   In an actual experiment in our laboratories, a glass column 1.6 cm. in diameter and 185 cm. in length was packed with Sephadex G-100.   The column was equilibrated with acetate buffer, pH 3.5 (0.20M acetic acid-0.01M sodium acetate). Four milligrams of the purified protein standard in 1 ml. of the acetate buffer was placed on top of the resin in the column, and a measured amount of acetate buffer was allowed to flow through the column. The following purified proteins were used, each in a separate experiment: γ-globulin (M.W. 147,000 and 294,000 (dimer)), bovine serum albumin (M.W. 70,000), ovalbumin (M.W. 45,000), and trypsin (M.W. 24,000). In each experiment, the total volume of eluate which corresponded to the peak of the elution curve for each protein was recorded. These values were plotted against the molecular weights of the proteins to obtain the standard curve shown in Figure 31. The molecular weight of an unknown purified protein can be determined by running it in the same manner on the Sephadex column, and interpolating the value on the standard curve.

Ultracentrifugation. The principle of the ultracentrifuge has been briefly explained in a previous section. The analytical type separates molecular species of proteins by centrifugal force in much the same way that the electrophoresis apparatus separates them by electrical force. The optical scanning devices employed to follow the protein boundaries (gradients) are similar to those used for electrophoresis, and photographs such as those shown in Figure 32 are obtained. By special calculations and the use of various associated physical properties of the protein and its solution it is possible to calculate the molecular weight of a pure protein by determining its sedimentation rate in the analytical ultracentrifuge.

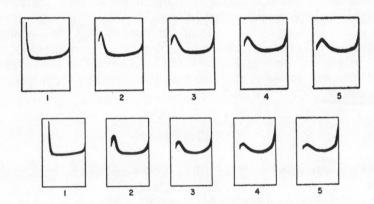

Figure 32. Ultracentrifugal analysis of gamma-glutelin, a purified protein from corn. Upper row of exposures is of 0.6% gamma-glutelin in pH 10.5 sodium glycinate-sodium chloride buffer, ionic strength 0.1. First exposure 13 minutes after a rotor speed of 59,780 r.p.m. was attained, with subsequent exposures at 16-minute intervals. Average temperature was 2.8°C. Lower row of exposures is of 0.4% gamma-glutelin in pH 8.6 sodium veronal buffer, ionic strength 0.1. First exposure 2 minutes after a speed of 59,780 r.p.m. was attained. Subsequent exposures, 32-minute intervals. Average temperature of run, 9.4°C. Direction of sedimentation is to the right. (From N. E. Lloyd and E. T. Mertz, Cereal Chem. 35 165 (1958)).

Chapter 6 | ENZYMES

General Properties

The cell protoplasm contains a thousand or more proteins, each bringing about one of the many chemical changes required for the maintenance of life. These proteins, called *enzymes*, are catalysts. Catalysts, both organic and inorganic, increase the velocity of a reaction without being consumed in the reaction. Enzymes speed up chemical reactions in biological systems so that they can take place at relatively low temperatures. In many cases, enzymes appear to *initiate* reactions. This may be due to the fact that the chemical reaction was proceeding at a rate which was too slow to measure prior to the addition of the enzyme.

It is believed that for every enzyme in the living cell there is a separate *gene* which is responsible for that enzyme's synthesis (see p. 111). Inasmuch as the genes are self-duplicating units which remain unchanged in composition as they are passed on from generation to generation, enzymes elaborated in the cells of living organisms today must be identical to those which existed in the cells of our ancestors. This would explain why the metabolism, behaviour and physical characteristics of a given species remain the same for generations. Only when there is a loss or change in one or more genes (*gene mutation*) with parallel loss or change in the enzymes produced by these genes, is a change observed in the progeny.

Chemical Nature

Repeated analyses have shown that all enzymes studied to date are proteins. They are water-soluble, and belong to either the simple globular or conjugated globular class. The chemical and physical characteristics of enzymes are the same as those of other proteins of the globular class. For example, they are readily denatured by heat and a variety of chemical agents.

Enzymes vary widely in molecular weight. Simple globular enzymes may have molecular weights of as low as 20,000; conjugated globular enzymes may have molecular weights of several million.

Enzymes can be divided into three classes on the basis of chemical composition: (1) simple globular protein, (2) globular metalloprotein and (3) globular protein (or metallo protein) attached to a non-protein prosthetic group, which, when dialyzable is called a *coenzyme*. Pepsin is an example of class (1), ascorbic acid oxidase (copper proteinate) an example of class (2), and transaminase (pyridoxalpyrophosphate-proteinate) and catalase (iron-porphyrin-proteinate) are examples of class (3). Usually the enzyme complex in class (3) is referred to as the "holoenzyme", the protein part as the "apoenzyme", and the remainder of the complex (for example, pyridoxalpyrophosphate in transaminase) as the "coenzyme".

Naming and Classification of Enzymes

The substance upon which an enzyme acts is called the *substrate*. Most enzymes are named after the substrate by changing the root ending to -ase. Thus, the enzyme which splits table sugar, sucrose, to its end-products glucose and fructose, is called *sucrase*.

The enzyme *protease* splits proteins to simpler products. Since there are several enzymes which split proteins, specific names must be given to them. Gastric juice contains a protease which splits most globular proteins. It could be called gastric protease, but it is better known by the name *pepsin,* which was given to it many years before the present system of naming enzymes was agreed upon.

Other examples of older names for some of the enzymes are given in Table 17.

Table 17.   Older names for enzymes

Old Name	Source and Type
Ptyalin	Salivary amylase
Pepsin	Gastric protease
Rennin	Gastric caseinase
Chymotrypsin	Pancreatic protease
Trypsin	Pancreatic protease
Amylopsin	Pancreatic amylase

In some cases enzymes are named for both the substrate involved and the type of reaction catalyzed. For example, the enzyme which catalyzes the oxidation of ascorbic acid is called *ascorbic acid oxidase*. In many cases it is necessary to include the source of an enzyme in its name (for example, *salivary* and *pancreatic* amylase).

Enzymes can be divided into classes by any one of several systems. Some of the possible methods of classification are listed below.

1. Site of action (extracellular or intracellular)
2. Source of enzyme (plant, animal, or microorganism)
3. Chemical composition (simple, metallo or conjugated globular protein)
4. Type of reaction catalyzed (hydrolysis, oxidation, dismutation)
5. Typical substrate affected (specific carbohydrate, lipid, etc.)

An international commission in 1961 drafted specific rules for the classification and naming of enzymes. The commission has proposed six main classes based on type of reaction catalyzed, with further subdivision on the basis of the nature of the reaction catalyzed and the type of bond formed or severed. Table 47 (p. 318, Appendix) shows further details of this new method of classification. The six main classes are: 1. *Oxidoreductases,* 2. *Transferases,* 3. *Hydrolases,* 4. *Lyases,* 5. *Isomerases,* and 6. *Ligases.* In the older system of classification, enzymes were divided into two groups, hydrolases and desmolases, then subdivided further on the basis of reaction catalyzed and type of substrate attacked. Now that the total number of known enzymes exceeds 700, and new ones are being added to the list at a steady rate, it is fortunate that we have a more efficient system for their orderly classification and naming. About 100 enzymes have been prepared in a pure state by the methods of protein chemistry.

Enzyme Kinetics and Energetics

Chemical equilibrium. It is well known that chemical and biochemical reactions tend to approach a state of equilibrium. Therefore, every reaction, even though catalyzed by an enzyme, proceeds *only until equilibrium is reached*. This same equilibrium could also be reached using some inorganic catalyst, and, theoretically, without the aid of any catalyst. If in the following equation reactants A and B form the products C and D, the law of mass action states that at equilibrium the product of C* and D*, divided by the product of A* and B* will be a constant, K (the equilibrium constant).

$$A + B \rightleftharpoons C + D \qquad\qquad K = \frac{[C] \times [D]}{[A] \times [B]}$$

In an uninhibited reaction, the more vigorously the reaction between A and B proceeds, the farther the equilibrium lies to the right (to the side of C and D), and hence the larger the equilibrium constant, K. At the start, then, the reaction mixture possesses a high potential energy, and during the course of the reaction it drops to a lower potential. Change in free energy is expressed by the symbol, ΔF. A reference or standard quantity of change in free energy is denoted by the symbol, $\Delta F°$. It equals that amount of energy that can be released when the reactants are dissolved in a pure solvent at a concentration of one mole per liter, and exactly one mole of material has reacted.

In the above example of a drop in potential energy during the course of the reaction, the drop in energy (change in free energy, ΔF) is related to the equilibrium constant as follows:

$$\Delta F = \Delta F° + RT \ln \frac{C_C \times C_D}{C_A \times C_B}$$

In this equation, C_C, C_D, C_A, and C_B are the concentrations of reactants in moles per liter, R is the gas constant, 1.987 calories per mole per degree Kelvin, T is the absolute temperature in degrees Kelvin, and ln stands for natural logarithm (to the base 2.303).

At equilibrium the change in free energy, ΔF, equals zero. Every spontaneous reaction is *exergonic***, that is, it proceeds as long as the free energy is decreasing. When no further decrease is possible, equilibrium has been reached, and ΔF is zero.

Calculation of $\Delta F°$ from equilibrium constant. In the above equation, the free energy change (ΔF) is zero at equilibrium. By substituting K, the equilibrium constant, for the quantity in the parentheses, the value at equilibrium becomes:

$$\Delta F° = -RT \ln K$$

At 37° C.,

$$\Delta F° = -1.420 \log_{10} K$$

The standard free energy of a chemical reaction can thus be calculated by measurement of the equilibrium constant. If $\Delta F°$ is negative, the reaction may proceed spontaneously; if it is positive, the reaction can proceed only if external free energy is added to the system.

Enthalpy and entropy. Free energy is related to two other thermodynamic quantities: H(enthalpy or change in internal energy of a system), and S (entropy or measure of molecular randomness and disorder). The equation relating these quantities is:

$$F = H - TS$$

Protein denaturation is an exergonic reaction that occurs at a critical temperature, and requires only a very minor temperature increment to take place with explosive rapid-

---

* Concentration in moles per liter.
** Reaction that releases energy. An endergonic reaction consumes energy.

ity. In this case, entropy increases at a much faster rate than enthalpy, giving a large negative $\triangle F$.

Equilibrium and energy of activation. In nature, equilibrium is not attained rapidly, for if this happened, we would have no carbon chemistry and no life on this planet, only the final end-products of the oxidation reaction: carbon dioxide and water.

Most carbon compounds in the cell are quite stable when isolated in pure form and stored on the shelf at room temperature, and even when stored at body temperature. The reactivity of such compounds can be raised by heating, and they will burn. At lower temperatures they are metastable; though not at equilibrium, they do not react with atmospheric oxygen. Only when a certain amount of energy has been added (called the energy of activation), will they react with the oxygen. This is the case with most chemical and biological reactions. In Figure 33, the chemical compound, X is in the metastable state. An amount of energy, E_X, the energy of activation, is needed to raise the level of energy in X to a new level, Y, so that the reaction becomes exergonic. In the change from Y to Z, E_X is recovered, and energy is made available according to the difference in enthalpy ($\triangle H$) between X and Z. The new compound has reached a state of equilibrium at Z.

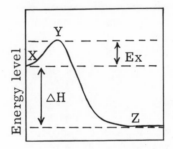

Figure 33.   Energy of activation of a metastable compound.

All catalysts appear to increase the rate of a reaction by *lowering* the energy of activation of the reaction. For example, it has been found that in the absence of a catalyst, the "average" molecule of hydrogen peroxide must have an energy level equivalent to 18,000 kilocalories per mol (6.06×10^{23} molecules) before it will decompose to oxygen and water. In the presence of the enzyme, catalase, decomposition will take place at an energy level equivalent to only 5,500 kilocalories per mol. The energy of activation is thus reduced to less than one-third of its original value by catalase. Other examples of reduction of the energy of activation are casein hydrolysis: 20,600 kilocalories with hydrogen ion, 12,000 kilocalories with trypsin; sucrose hydrolysis: 26,000 kilocalories with hydrogen ion, 11,500 with yeast sucrase (invertase), ethyl butyrate hydrolysis (cleavage of ester linkage similar to that found in triglycerides): 13,200 kilocalories with hydrogen ion, 4,200 kilocalories with pancreatic lipase.

In all of these cases, the energy of activation required would be much higher if the substrate were split with water alone. Eventually, however, some cleavage would result if these substrates were boiled for several months with pure distilled water containing no catalyst. The energy of activation may be visualized as the state of kinetic activity at which substrate molecules can react with water molecules to produce measurable amounts of end-products. The catalysts, both inorganic H^+ and organic (enzymes), permit end-products to be produced at substantially *lower* levels of average kinetic activity in the substrate. They are believed to do this by momentarily *combining* with the substrate and producing by this combination an additional strain on the bonds which need to be broken to produce end-products. This is illustrated in Figure 34. The enzyme, drawn in black, has in this example two active parts which fit the molecule (substrate) on which they act (No. 1, Fig. 34).

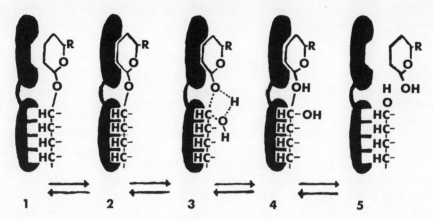

Figure 34.   Possible mechanism for enzyme action.   R = -CH₂OH.   (From J. Pfeiffer.
The Physics and Chemistry of Life. p. 172, Scientific American (1955)).

The substrate in this case is α butyl-D-glucoside, a higher analog of α-methyl-D-glucoside (see p. 15). When the enzyme combines with the molecule (No. 2, Fig. 34), its active parts deform the molecule in such a way (No. 3 and 4) that a water molecule is easily added and the intermediate product is broken down (No. 5) into two molecules, in this case, D-glucose and N-butyl alcohol.

The mechanism suggested in Figure 34 not only helps to explain why enzymes lower the energy of activation of a reaction, but also helps to explain why enzymes are so amazingly specific. An enzyme can only split those substrates that "fit" on the surface of the enzyme. This is known as the "lock and key" theory. In it the enzyme can be visualized as a "lock" with notches and indentations of a specific pattern, and the substrate molecule, in this case N-butyl-D-glucoside, as the key. Its configuration must *fit or mesh* into the enzyme pattern (No. 2, Fig. 34), or the enzyme will not be able to catalyze its breakdown.

The idea of an actual combination between the enzyme and its specific substrate dates back to 1913 when Michaelis and Menten proposed the following theory to explain enzyme action:

Enzyme (E) + Substrate (S) ⇌ Enzyme-substrate ⇌ End-products + E
                                    complex (ES)   (EP)

According to this theory, the enzyme (E) and the substrate (S) combine to form a complex (ES), and the complex then breaks down to give the end-products (EP) and the original enzyme.

Factors Which Affect Enzyme Activity

The following factors have an important effect on enzyme activity:

1. Substrate concentration
2. Enzyme concentration
3. Temperature
4. pH
5. Ionic strength
6. Oxidation-reduction potential (*Redox* potential compared with hydrogen electrode)

7. Specific activators such as *metallic ions, proenzyme activators* and *co-enzymes*.
8. Inhibitors
   a. Competitive (also called *biological antagonists,* or *antimetabolites)*
   b. Non-competitive

These eight important factors will be discussed separately.

SUBSTRATE CONCENTRATION. The concentration of substrate affects the rate of the enzyme-catalyzed reaction. Up to a certain concentration, increasing the concentration of substrate increases the rate of formation of end-products. A point is finally reached, however, where the enzyme is saturated with substrate (see equation above). When this point is reached, further increases in substrate concentration have no influence on the rate of formation of end-products. Figure 35 is a graph showing the general shape of the curve which relates substrate concentration to enzyme activity.

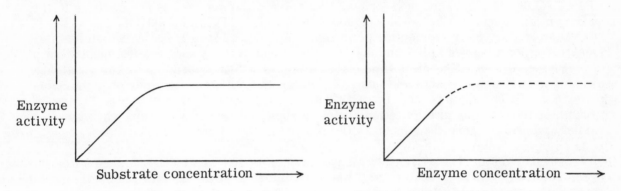

Figure 35. Relation of substrate concentration to enzyme activity.

Figure 36. Relation of enzyme concentration to enzyme activity.

ENZYME CONCENTRATION. The concentration of enzyme also affects the rate of the enzyme-catalyzed reaction. If an excess of substrate is present, doubling the enzyme concentration usually doubles the rate of formation of end-products. This usually applies only at the *start* of the reaction, for the end-products of the reaction often have an inhibitory effect on the enzyme, and decrease its efficiency. As the concentration of enzyme is increased, however, a point could (theoretically) be reached where the substrate (concentration held constant) is saturated with enzyme (all in the form of ES complex). This would require a mole to mole ratio for most enzymes. If this point could be reached, further increases in enzyme concentration would have no influence on the rate of formation of end-products. Figure 36 is a graph showing the general shape of the curve which relates enzyme concentration to enzyme activity, all other factors being held constant. The dotted part is hypothetical, and almost impossible to attain in vitro; it may occur to a limited extent in the living cell.

TEMPERATURE. A rule first formulated by the chemist van't Hoff states that a rise of 10° in temperature will double the speed of a chemical reaction. This is usually expressed as Q_{10}, the ratio of the rates of reaction at two temperatures 10° apart. If the reaction rate is doubled by a 10° rise in temperature, then $Q_{10} = 2$. If the reaction is not influenced by heat (like the decomposition of radium), $Q_{10} = 1$. For most enzyme-catalyzed reactions, Q_{10} is approximately 2 at lower temperatures, but gradually drops off until the rate is 1 (or lower) at higher temperatures. Figure 37 shows the general effect of temperatures on enzyme-catalyzed reactions. Enzymes show a temperature optimum, which is usually somewhere between 30°C. and 50°C. The enzymes in thermophilic bacteria have temperature optima above 50°C.

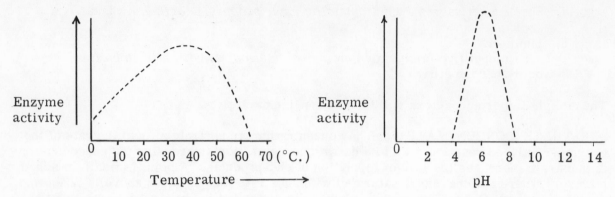

Figure 37.   Effect of temperature on enzyme activity.   Figure 38.   Relation of pH to urease activity.

EFFECT OF pH. Because of their protein nature, enzymes are very sensitive to the
hydrogen ion concentration of their aqueous solutions. Maximum activity is usually observed at or near their isoelectric point (see page 75). Thus, trypsin, which has its
isoelectric point between pH 7 and 8, shows greatest activity towards its substrates in
the pH range of 7-9. The pH optimum for pepsin is 1.5-3 (depending on the substrate
used), for enzymes of plants and fungi, 4.0-6.5, and for most enzymes of higher animals, 6.5-8. In the curve for crystalline urease in citrate buffer shown in Figure 38,
it can be seen that the activity of the enzyme drops quite rapidly to zero when the pH is
raised or lowered more than about 2 pH units from the pH optimum.

IONIC STRENGTH. The activity of many enzymes is affected by the concentration of ions
in the solution. This effect is in addition to the more specific effects of certain cation and
anion activators which will be discussed later. The sensitivity of enzymes to the concentration of ions may be due to the presence of a diffuse ionic atmosphere around each enzyme protein molecule, which attracts ions of opposite sign. This produces a double
layer, the thickness of which is inversely proportional to the ionic strength of the solution. The ionic strength of a solution is designated by the Greek letter *mu* (μ) and is
equal to one-half of the sum of the products of the squared valence and molarity of each
anion and cation present: $\mu = (Aa^2 + Cc^2 + A_1a_1^2 + C_1c_1^2 + \text{etc.})/2$. In this equation,
A = molar concentration of anion A, a = valence of anion A, C = molar concentration
of cation C, etc. According to this method of calculating ionic strength, a 0.01 M (molar)
solution of calcium chloride ($CaCl_2$) would have an ionic strength (μ) of $(0.04 + 0.02)/2$
= 0.03.

OXIDATION-REDUCTION POTENTIAL. Many enzymes are sensitive to the action of
oxidizing or reducing agents. The relative oxidizing or reducing ability of a solution is
expressed in terms of its *redox* potential. This is the electromotive force (in millivolts)
developed by the solution when it is in contact with a platinum electrode, and this half
cell is compared with the normal H_2 electrode taken as zero potential. The redox potential of a solution will be either positive or negative, depending on its relative oxidizing
or reducing power compared with hydrogen. Oxidizing enzymes (see Table 47, p. 318,
Appendix) are intimately concerned with redox potentials, and many other enzymes are
sensitive to changes in the redox potential of their solutions, presumably because of the
presence of (-SH) groups in the molecule.

SPECIFIC ACTIVATORS. Metallic ions. Metallic ions are integral parts of many enzyme systems. Since they can be reversibly removed from the apoenzyme (protein), they
may be considered as activators. Thus, arginase requires cobalt, manganese, or iron
ions, but the apoenzyme cannot be activated with other ions. Leucylpeptidase is activated
by magnesium or manganese ions; copper is required by ascorbic acid oxidase, tyrosinase,
and laccase, and carbonic anhydrase cannot function in the absence of zinc ions. The enzyme, salivary amylase, requires the presence of an anion, chloride ion, for full activity.

The commonly accepted theory for the activator properties of most metallic ions is that they form co-ordination compounds and act as bridges between substrate and enzyme. This is illustrated below with the substrate, leucyl glycine, and its enzyme, leucyl peptidase, using manganese as the activating ion.

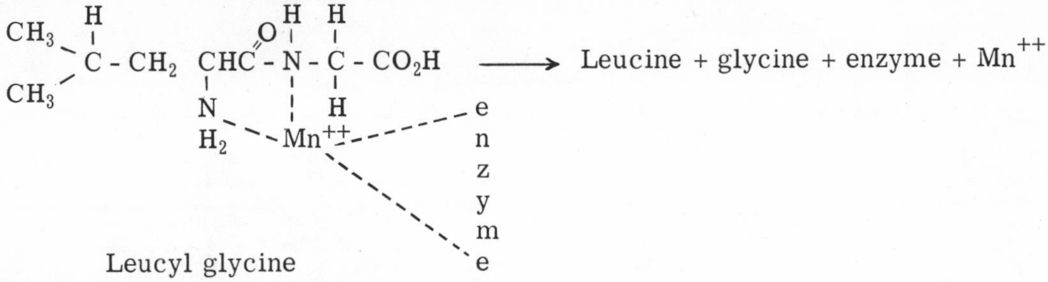

Leucyl glycine $\longrightarrow$ Leucine + glycine + enzyme + Mn^{++}

Akabori, in a study of the crystalline enzyme, taka-amylase, found that one calcium atom is required per molecule of enzyme for full activity. He believes that the calcium ion fits in a loop of the peptide structure as sketched below (Fig. 39).

Ca^{++}

Figure 39.   Proposed structure of calcium-taka-amylase.

Proenzyme activators. Many proteases are elaborated by the cells in an inactive form, called a zymogen, or proenzyme. This is nature's way of protecting the mother cell from self-digestion or autolysis. Examples of zymogens or proenzymes are pepsinogen, trypsinogen, chymotrypsinogen, and prothrombin. Pepsinogen is activated to pepsin by hydrogen ions, and more rapidly by pepsin itself (autocatalysis). Trypsinogen is activated to trypsin by an enzyme, enterokinase, and by trypsin itself. Chymotrypsinogen is activated to chymotrypsin by trypsin. Prothrombin is activated to thrombin (see page 258) by the combined action of calcium ions, thromboplastin, accelerator plasma, and platelet factors. If thrombin were not elaborated as inactive prothrombin by the liver, but secreted as active thrombin into the blood stream, it would cause the rapid death of the animal by intravascular clotting.

Coenzymes. Coenzymes might be considered special activators in that they can be removed reversibly from the protein part of the molecule, and are needed for activity of the enzyme. Coenzymes are dialyzable non-protein (prosthetic) groups which usually have as their "active" group one of the vitamins (see page 226). The structures of some of the more intensively studied coenzymes are given below. Table 18 (page 101) lists the major coenzymes, their abbreviations, the group transferred, and the corresponding vitamin (if present).

A. Coenzymes acting as hydrogen acceptors.

1. Pyridine coenzymes. These include nicotinamide-adenine dinucleotide (NAD) and nicotinamide-adenine dinucleotide phosphate (NADP). These coenzymes act as hydrogen acceptors. For example, the enzyme, alcohol dehydrogenase "dehydrogenates" (oxidizes) ethyl alcohol to acetaldehyde, provided the coenzyme NAD is present.

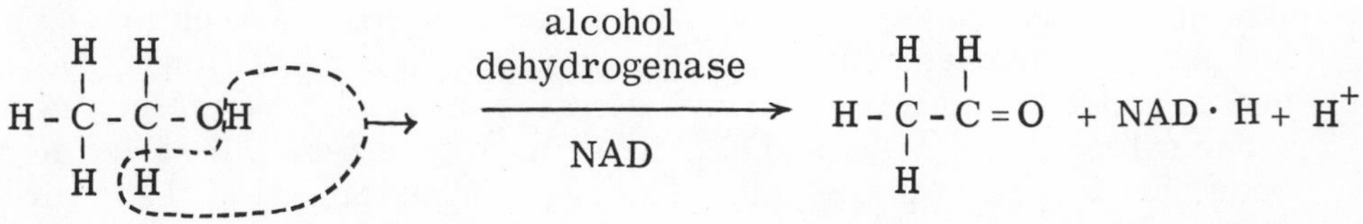

The part of the NAD molecule affected is the nicotinamide, which is reduced as follows:

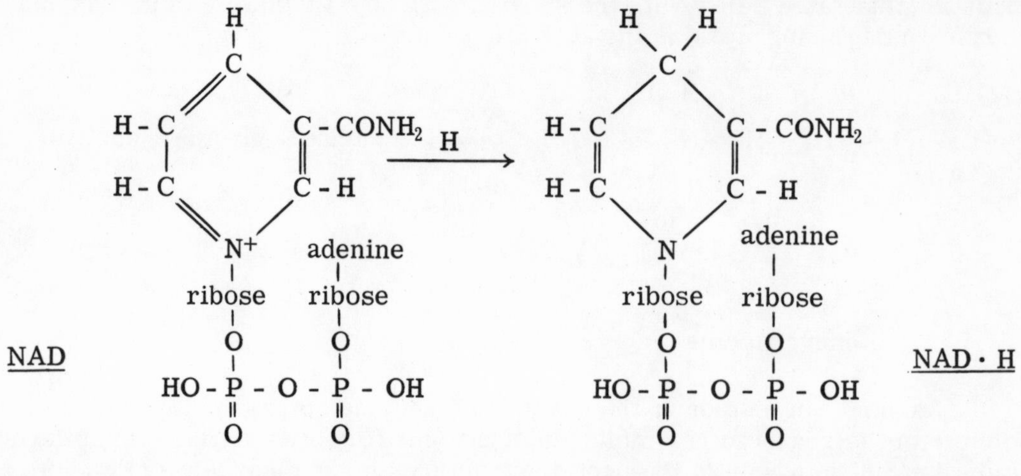

NAD   NAD·H

NADP acts in the same manner as NAD. The structures of NAD and NADP are discussed on p. 112.

2. Riboflavin coenzymes. There are two of these: flavin mononucleotide (FMN) and flavin adenine dinucleotide (FAD). They also act as hydrogen acceptors, the isoalloxazine group being affected.

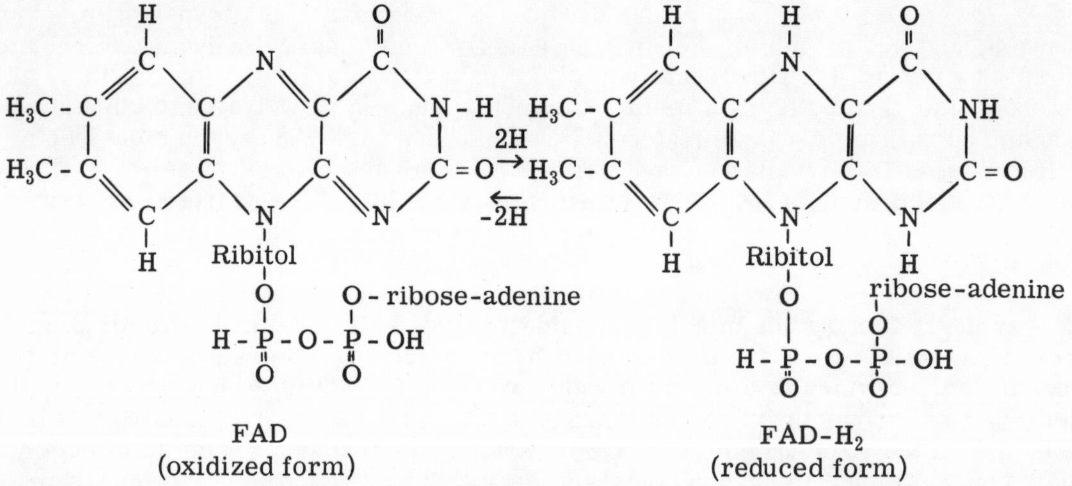

FAD   FAD-H_2
(oxidized form)   (reduced form)

FMN (see p. 113) undergoes a similar oxidation-reduction, accepting hydrogen atoms from the substrate, or giving hydrogen atoms to the substrate in the presence of a specific apoenzyme.

3. Iron porphyrin compounds. These compounds cannot be strictly classified as coenzymes because they are so tightly bound that they cannot be removed from the apoenzyme by dialysis. However, they are essential for the activity of specific apoenzymes. The iron porphyrin part (heme) is referred to as a *prosthetic* group. Examples of enzymes requiring this prosthetic group are catalase, peroxidase, and the cytochromes. Catalase speeds up the decomposition of hydrogen peroxide and peroxidase catalyzes the oxidation of substrates by hydrogen peroxide. The three cytochromes a, b, and c are respiratory enzymes involved in oxidation-reduction reactions in the cell. The best characterized of these three is cytochrome c.

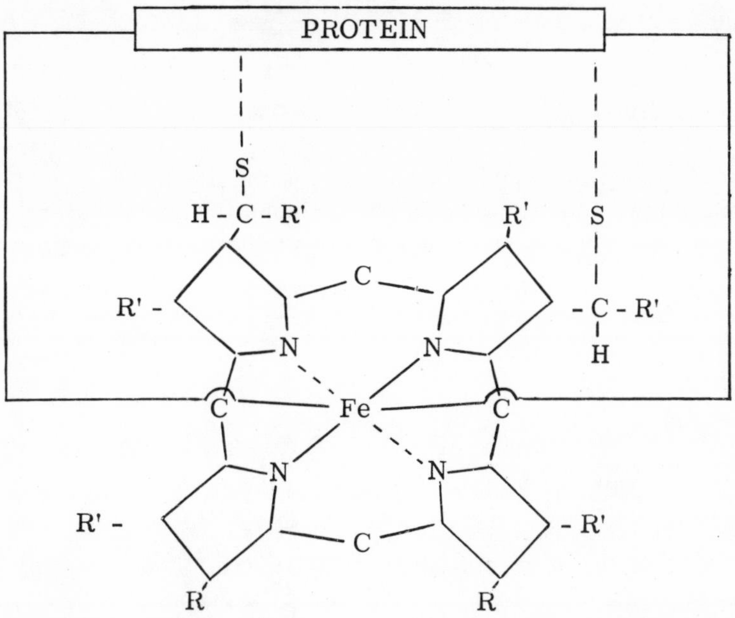

Crystalline cytochrome c has a molecular weight of 13,000 and contains 0.43 per cent iron. As can be seen from the abbreviated formula, the iron atom is attached by primary and secondary valence bonds to the porphyrin nucleus and to the specific apoenzyme (protein). Protein and porphyrin are also linked. Cytochrome c functions as an electron carrier (see p. 164) because its iron atom readily changes its valence from 3 to 2: $Fe^{+++} + e \rightleftharpoons Fe^{++}$.

B. Coenzymes acting as decarboxylases and transaminases.

These enzymes require pyridoxal or pyridoxamine phosphate as coenzymes. Specific enzymes in this group split amino acids to the corresponding primary amine and carbon dioxide (see p. 318, Appendix). The transaminases catalyze the transfer of an amino group from one amino acid to the corresponding keto acid of another amino acid (see p. 187). Pyridoxal phosphate is a "codecarboxylase", whereas both pyridoxal phosphate and the amino form, pyridoxamine phosphate, function as "co-transaminases" in bringing about transfer of the $-NH_2$ group.

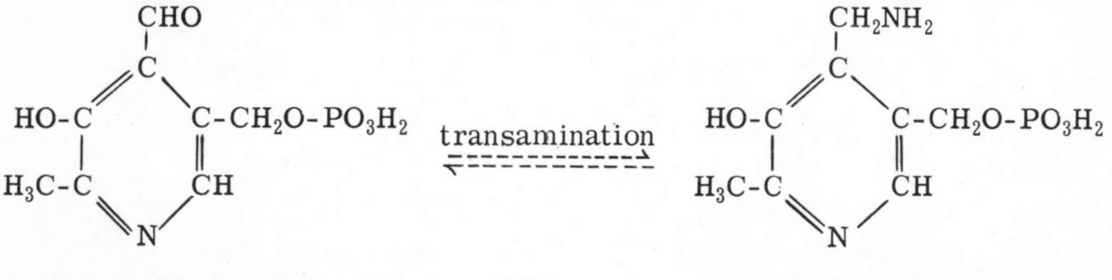

Pyridoxal phosphate   Pyridoxamine phosphate

C. Coenzyme for acetylation. Lipmann and coworkers found that a coenzyme was needed for the acetylation of sulfanilamide. This led later to its identification as a general coenzyme for acetylation reactions. The coenzyme, now called *Coenzyme A*, accepts acetyl groups from one metabolite and then donates them to another (see p. 159). If we designate two metabolites as M_1 and M_2, then Coenzyme A functions as follows:

$$\text{Acetyl-}M_1 + \text{CoA} \quad \xrightarrow{\text{Apoenzyme 1}} \quad M_1 + \text{Acetyl CoA}$$

$$\text{Acetyl CoA} + M_2 \quad \xrightarrow{\text{Apoenzyme 2}} \quad \text{Acetyl } M_2 + \text{CoA}$$

<u>Coenzyme A</u> plays an important role in the metabolism of fatty acids (see p. 182). Its formula shows that it contains thiolethanolamine, the B-vitamin pantothenic acid (p. 236), pyrophosphate, and the nucleotide adenylic acid (phosphoric acid, ribose and adenine, p. 112).

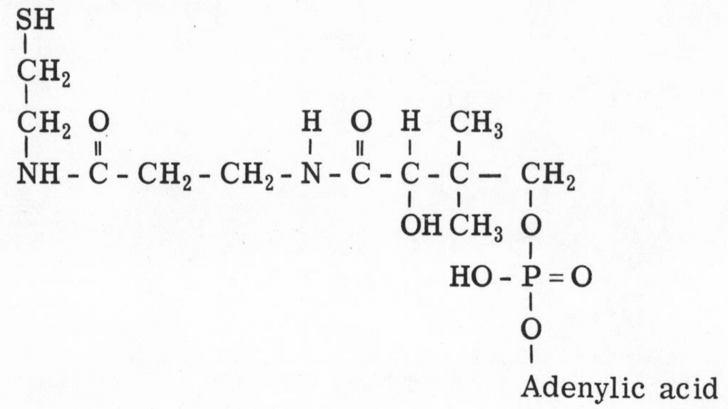

Coenzyme A

D. <u>Coenzyme for oxidative decarboxylation.</u>

An enzyme, *carboxylase*, requires thiamine pyrophosphate (cocarboxylase) as a coenzyme to split pyruvic acid into CO_2 and acetaldehyde in yeast cells. The enzymatic oxidative decarboxylation of pyruvic acid in animal cells to yield CO_2 and acetyl CoA (see above), requires a coenzyme which contains lipoic acid (thioctic acid) and thiamine pyrophosphate.

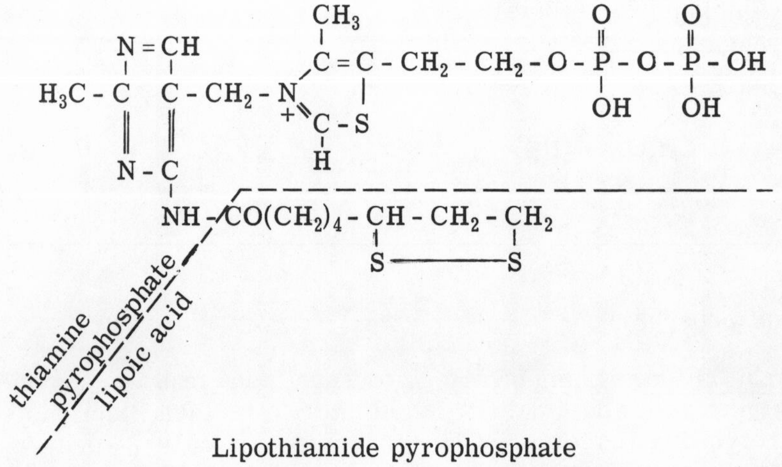

Lipothiamide pyrophosphate

E. <u>Other coenzymes.</u>

There is evidence that many other compounds function as coenzymes. Examples are glucose-1, 6-diphosphate, glyceric acid-2, 3-diphosphate and a glucose-1-phosphate-uridine nucleotide (p. 113) (carbohydrate metabolism); glutathione, ascorbic acid, (oxidation-reduction reactions); biotin (carbon dioxide fixation reactions); folic acid (formyl group transfer); and vitamin B_{12} (metabolism of methyl groups and synthesis of DNA).

Table 18. Summary of major coenzymes

Coenzymes	Abbreviation	Group Transferred	Vitamin
1. Oxidoreductase coenzymes:			
Nicotinamide-adenine dinucleotide	NAD	Hydrogen	Nicotinamide
Nicotinamide-adenine dinucleotide phosphate	NADP	Hydrogen	Nicotinamide
Flavin mononucleotide	FMN	Hydrogen	Riboflavin
Flavin adenine dinucleotide	FAD	Hydrogen	Riboflavin
Lipoic acid	$Lip(S_2)$	Hydrogen, acyl groups	-
Cell hemins (cytochromes, etc.)	--	Electrons	-
2. Transferase coenzymes:			
Adenosine triphosphate	ATP	Phosphate, AMP	-
Adenosyl methionine	-	Methyl (of methionine)	-
Phosphoadenyl sulfate	PAPS	Sulfate	-
Biotin	-	Carboxyl	Biotin
Coenzyme A	CoA	Acyl	Pantothenic acid
Cytidine diphosphate	CDP	Phosphoryl choline	-
Pyridoxal phosphate	PALP	Alpha-amino	Pyridoxine
Tetrahydrofolic acid	THF	Formyl	Folic acid
Thiamine pyrophosphate	TPP	C_2-aldehyde	Thiamine
Uridine diphosphate	UDP	Monosaccharides, uronic acid	-
3. Isomerase and lyase coenzymes.			
B_{12} coenzyme	-	Carboxyl displacement	Cobalamin
Pyridoxal phosphate	PALP	Decarboxylation	Pyridoxine
Thiamine pyrophosphate	TPP	Decarboxylation	Thiamine
Uridine diphosphate	UDP	Monosaccharide isomerization	-

INHIBITORS

Competitive inhibitors. Competitive inhibitors (biological antagonists, antimetabolites) unite with the enzyme reversibly in direct competition with the substrate. This leaves less enzyme available for reaction with the substrate, and slows down the enzyme-catalyzed reaction. An example is the reaction of the enzyme, liver histidase, with its substrate, L-histidine, in the presence of the competitive inhibitor, D-histidine.

$$\text{L-histidine} \xrightarrow{\text{liver histidase}} \text{glutamic acid} + NH_3$$

$$\text{D-histidine} \xrightarrow{\text{liver histidase}} \text{no reaction}$$

$$\text{D- + L-histidine} \xrightarrow{\text{liver histidase}} \text{yield of end-products varies with ratio D/L}$$

The higher the ratio of D/L, the lower the yield of glutamic acid and ammonia in the above reaction, for D-histidine combines with liver histidase and thus removes it from the reaction. Excess L-histidine, however, will, by displacing D-histidine, reverse the reaction.

The *sulfa drugs* are believed to be competitive inhibitors of the enzyme utilizing (as coenzyme) p-amino benzoic acid, a vitamin essential for the growth of most bacteria. It can be seen from the formulas of these two compounds that they are closely related structurally, and that the bacterial enzyme using PABA as a coenzyme might just as easily accept sulfanilamide. Since this reduces the effectiveness of the enzyme, sulfanilamide and its derivatives inhibit the growth of those bacteria which require PABA.

p-amino benzoic acid (PABA)   sulfanilamide

The "lock and key" theory can be used to explain why compounds closely related to specific substrates can inhibit enzyme action. Barron found that an enzyme which catalyzed the oxidation of acetic acid was competitively inhibited by monofluoracetate but not by monochloroacetate. These three substrates differ by one atom. In acetic acid the hydrogen atom on the alpha carbon is 1.09 angstrom units ($1 \overset{\circ}{A} = 0.00000001$ cm) from the carbon atom, in fluoroacetic acid the fluorine atom is $1.41 \overset{\circ}{A}$ from the carbon, and in chloroacetic acid the chlorine atom is $1.76 \overset{\circ}{A}$ from the carbon. Monofluoroacetate completely inhibits the oxidation, which means that it fits the enzyme molecule. Monochloroacetate, however, does not appear to fit, for it has no effect on the ability of the enzyme to oxidize acetic acid. These differences are explained by the "lock and key" diagrams in Figure 40; the greater length of the chlorine-carbon bond prevents proper "locking" of the monochloroacetate to the enzyme, whereas the fluorine derivative fits the lock.

Non-competitive inhibitors. Non-competitive inhibitors combine irreversibly with the enzyme, and the yield of end-products is inversely proportional to the concentration of inhibitor. Examples of naturally-occurring inhibitors are two polypeptides secreted by the round worm, *ascaris*, one of which inhibits pepsin, the other trypsin. This prevents the worm from being digested when it inhabits the intestinal tract of animals. Trypsin is also irreversibly inhibited by specific proteins in blood plasma, pancreas, egg white and soybeans.

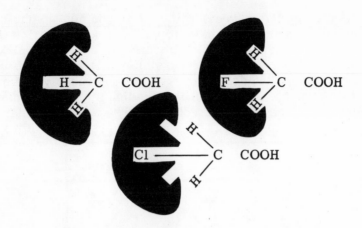

Figure 40.   A possible mechanism for competitive inhibition. (Based on drawing
by J. Pfeiffer in The Physics and Chemistry of Life, p. 171 (1955)).

Michaelis-Menten equation-kinetics of enzyme and inhibitor reactions.   The Michaelis-
Menten hypothesis briefly discussed on page 94 has been expressed mathematically and
used in studying the kinetics of enzyme and enzyme-inhibitor reactions.   Starting with the
simple equilibrium equation (1), which gives the respective velocity constants, k_1, k_2, and

$$E \; + \; S \underset{k_2}{\overset{k_1}{\rightleftharpoons}} ES \overset{k_3}{\longrightarrow} P \; + \; E \tag{1}$$

k_3 of the three assumed processes (E + S → ES, ES → E + S, and ES → P + E), where E is
the enzyme, S the substrate, ES the enzyme-substrate complex, and P the end-products,
Michaelis and Menten derived the following equation (2):

$$K_m \; = \; S \frac{V_{max} \; - \; 1}{V} \tag{2}$$

In this equation, $K_m = \frac{k_2 - k_3}{k_1}$.   This is known as the *Michaelis constant.*   S is the
substrate concentration, and V is the observed *initial* velocity of the reaction. V_{max} is
the maximum velocity of the reaction, and is obtained when the substrate concentration is
made so high in relation to the enzyme concentration that essentially all of the enzyme is
present as ES. K_m values are each characteristic for one enzyme-substrate system.   If
the same enzyme can attack several substrates, the K_m values give a useful comparison
of the relative affinities of the enzyme for the different substrates, the smaller the K_m
value, the greater the affinity.   When $V = 1/2 \; V_{max}$, in equation (2), K_m is equal to
the concentration of substrate (expressed in moles per liter).

Lineweaver and Burk rearranged equation (2) to give equation (3), which provides a
more convenient form for a linear plot of experimental data.   When S is plotted on the

$$\frac{[S]}{V} \; = \; \frac{[S]}{V_{max}} \; + \; \frac{K_m}{V_{max}} \tag{3}$$

x axis and S/V on the y axis, a straight line is obtained.   The intercept of this line with
the y axis equals K_m/V_{max}, and the slope of the line is $1/V_{max}$.   Thus, K_m can be
calculated from the slope and the intercept.

Use of linear plot to differentiate between competitive and non-competitive inhibitors. The formation of an inhibitor complex is similar to that shown in equation (1) for an enzyme-substrate complex. If we designate the inhibitor as I, then the complex is EI. As stated previously, the combination of E and I is reversible if I is a *competitive* inhibitor. If I is a *non-competitive* inhibitor, EI does not dissociate. Probably a competitive inhibitor is competing with the substrate for a particular binding site on the enzyme, whereas the non-competitive inhibitor binds at a different site. The use of a linear plot demonstrates a difference in the nature of the inhibition of the two types of inhibitors. In Figure 41,

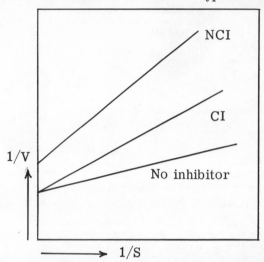

Figure 41.   A plot of 1/V against 1/S for an enzymic reaction with no inhibitor, a competitive inhibitor (CI), and a noncompetitive inhibitor (NCI).

1/S has been plotted on the abscissa or x axis, and 1/V on the ordinate or y axis. The lowest line is obtained with the enzyme alone. This resembles the Lineweaver-Burk plot, except here the intercept is $1/V_{max}$ and the slope is K_m/V_{max}. Note that the slope for the line obtained on addition of competitive inhibitor (CI) to the enzyme-substrate system is greater than that of the uninhibited system, but that the line has the *same intercept*. This shows that at very high substrate concentrations, the effect of the competitive inhibitor is wiped out. In contrast, the top line shows that with a non-competitive inhibitor (NCI), the effect of the inhibitor is to bind enzyme irreversibly, and not release it in the presence of high substrate levels.

Mechanism of activation of the proenzyme chymotrypsinogen A. This proenzyme was one of the first to be isolated in crystalline form, and the study of its activation by trypsin and by the active enzyme, chymotrypsin, has provided valuable information on the exact manner in which an active enzyme is formed from its inactive zymogen precursor. According to the studies of Neurath, Desnuelle, and others, the zymogen or proenzyme is a single long polypeptide chain (M.W. 25,000) with an N-terminal cystine and a C-terminal asparagine (N-terminal amino acid has its alpha- amino group free and is at one end of the peptide chain. C-terminal amino acid has its -COOH group free and is at the other end of the peptide chain). As shown in Figure 42, trypsin splits the peptide bond between an isoleucine and an arginine residue, giving *π-chymotrypsin*, an active enzyme. Chymotrypsin can attack the peptide bond between serine and leucine, releasing the dipeptide, seryl arginine and forming δ-chymotrypsin, an active enzyme. Chymotrypsin then attacks a peptide bond near the C-terminal end of δ-chymotrypsin, releasing threonyl asparagine, and giving a new active enzyme, α-chymotrypsin. Both π and δ-chymotrypsin are more active than α-chymotrypsin. In the latter, there are three C-terminal and three N-terminal amino acid groups. In π and δ-chymotrypsin, there are only two of each. It is astonishing that the cleavage of a single peptide bond in chymotrypsinogen yields the highly active π-chymotrypsin. Apparently, the tertiary structure of chymo-

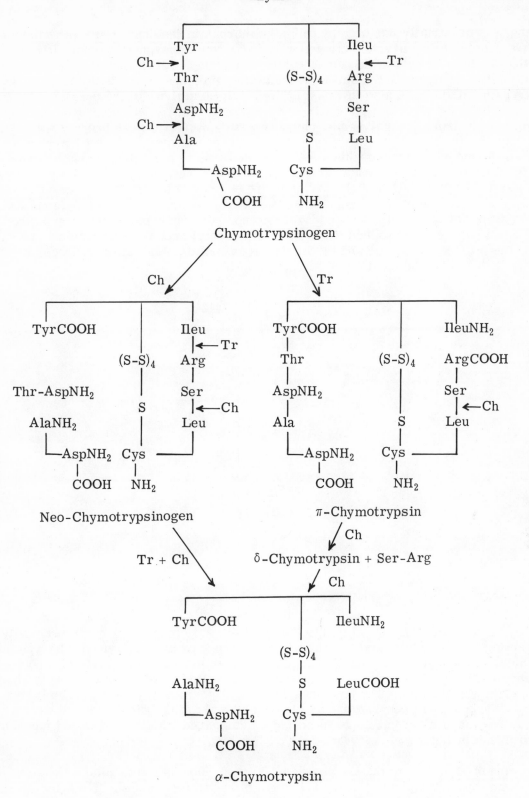

Figure 42.   Activation of chymotrypsinogen.   The activation by trypsin is discussed in the text.   An alternate pathway is also shown, in which chymotrypsin converts chymotrypsinogen to inactive neo-chymotrypsinogen.   This is then split by trypsin and chymotrypsin to yield α-chymotrypsin. Tr is trypsin and Ch is chymotrypsin in the diagram.

trypsinogen is drastically modified by this single break in the chain, with the exposure of the active center of the enzyme. Studies with diisopropyl phosphofluoridate (DIPF) have shown that serine is a part of the active center of several hydrolases, including chymotrypsin. DIPF couples with the serine at the active site, and inactivates the enzyme. In chymotrypsin, histidine is also involved in the catalytic activity of the enzyme.

Mechanism of hydrolysis catalyzed by chymotrypsin. Sturtevant has proposed the following mechanism for the action of this hydrolase on its substrates: Using para-nitrophenyl acetate as the model substance (this splits by hydrolysis to para-nitro phenol and acetic acid), the initially hydrogen-bonded active center of the enzyme (A, Fig. 43) reacts with the substrate with acetylation of the serine hydroxyl, and release of the para-nitro phenol (x^- in B). The release of the nitrophenol group is accompanied by the transfer of a proton to the imidazole of histidine. The imidazole group hydrogen bonds to a water molecule, which is then correctly positioned (C) to attack the acetyl group. Acetic acid is released (D), and the hydroxyl of serine and the imidazole of histidine can again hydrogen bond and react with another molecule of substrate as in (A).

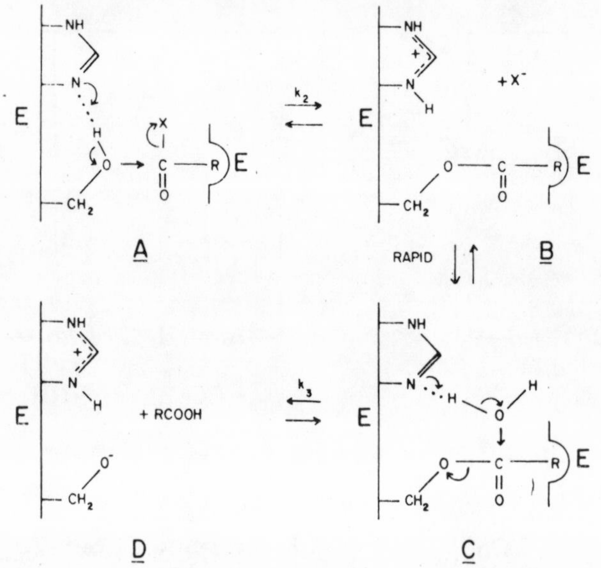

Figure 43.   Sturtevant's proposed mechanism for a hydrolysis catalyzed
by trypsin. The curved arrows represent electron shifts.

Bergmann showed many years ago (see p. 149) that chymotrypsin preferentially attacks peptide bonds containing the carboxyl group of phenylalanine, tyrosine, tryptophan or methionine. The above mechanism suggests that in proteins, the carboxyl group of these amino acids acylates the serine hydroxyl in step B (Fig. 43) and is released in Step D. This would explain why free phenylalanine is formed when a synthetic tri or tetrapeptide containing phenylalanine as the N-terminal amino acid is treated with chymotrypsin. The mechanism in Figure 43 should be compared with the suggested mechanism for hydrolases in Figure 34, p. 94.

The relation of structure to the enzymatic activity of ribonuclease. Ribonuclease is the only enzyme whose complete primary structure is known (see p. 66). The effect of modifying certain parts of the primary and secondary structure of this enzyme has been studied by Anfinsen and others. From these studies, valuable insight has been gained regarding the relation between structure and enzymatic activity. Figure 44 summarizes the effects of various treatments on the activity of the ribonuclease molecule.

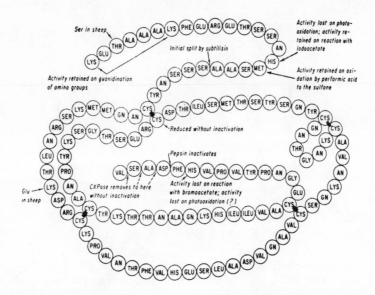

Figure 44.   The provisional primary structure of ribonuclease. (From C. Anfinsen
and F. White in The Enzymes, P. Boyer, H. Lardy, and K. Myrback
(editors), vol. 4, p. 501, Academic Press, N. Y. (1960)).

Ribonuclease consists of a single polypeptide chain which is internally linked by
four disulfide bonds.

Effect of modifying primary structure.   Two to five bonds may be split by trypsin without
loss of activity.   Evidently, the disulfide bonds together with the tertiary structure are
sufficient to maintain the active center in its proper configuration.   However, if pepsin
removes the four C- terminal amino acids, the enzyme is inactive.   Apparently, aspartic
acid is essential, for valine, serine, and alanine (Fig. 44) can be removed without loss
of activity.   An even more interesting observation was made by Richards, who removed
an N-terminal "tail" containing 20 amino acids with the hydrolytic enzyme, subtilisin.
If carried out at low temperatures, no loss of activity could be detected.   The N-terminal
"tail", which contains no cystine, was separated from the rest of the molecule by chemical fractionation.   The two separated fragments were inactive.   When combined, however,
the activity was regained.   These findings have been explained as follows: (1) The "tail"
contains an essential portion of the active site, or (2) the "tail" is needed to maintain the
native configuration of the enzyme, or (3) the "tail" is incorporated into the tertiary
structure, from which it may be detached reversibly.

As indicated in Figure 44, the imidazole group of histidine is needed, for its destruction by photooxidation inactivates the enzyme.

Effect of modifying secondary structure.   In the presence of 8 molar urea, an agent that
breaks hydrogen bonds, the full activity of ribonuclease is retained.   Ribonuclease is
estimated to contain 15-40 per cent alpha-helix, and these results suggest that the helical
parts of the structure are not essential for enzyme activity.   In an earlier chapter (p. 68),
we discussed the remarkable ability of ribonuclease to recover after reoxidation of previously reduced disulfide linkages.   Complete reduction of these bonds destroys the activity,
showing that disulfide bridges are essential.   However, the disulfide bond closest to the
N-terminal "tail" can be reduced without harmful effects.   The fact that the four essential bridge locations can be formed again after complete disruption by reductive cleavage
suggests that the active configuration of ribonuclease is also the most thermodynamically
stable one.

Chapter 7 | NUCLEOPROTEINS, NUCLEIC ACIDS AND NUCLEOTIDES

Nucleic acids are giant molecules - polymers, which contain as the monomers or "building stones" certain monosaccharides, purines, pyrimidines, and phosphoric acid. There are two kinds of nucleic acid: *deoxyribonucleic* acid (usually called DNA), and *ribonucleic* acid (usually called RNA). DNA is always found in the *nucleus* of cells, whereas RNA may be found in the nucleus, but occurs mainly in the *cytoplasm* of the cell.

Very little of the DNA and RNA are present in the free form. They are combined with specific proteins. The DNA nucleoproteins thus formed usually contain 40-60 per cent nucleic acid and the remainder is protein. The linkage of nucleic acid to protein is salt-like and is easily dissociated (for example, the two components can be separated by passing an electric current through a solution of DNA nucleoprotein).

RNA nucleoproteins usually contain about 5-20 per cent nucleic acid. One exception is tobacco ring-spot virus, which contains 40 per cent nucleic acid. The linkage of nucleic acid to protein is probably not salt-like in RNA nucleoproteins, but a more stable, less dissociable, covalent type. To separate the nucleic acid from the protein, one must either destroy the protein (by denaturation or enzymatic digestion) and recover the nucleic acid, or destroy the nucleic acid (by digestion with the enzyme ribonuclease) and recover the protein. Examples of typical DNA and RNA nucleoproteins are shown in Table 19. The molecular weights of these giant molecules lie in the range of 2 to 40 million. The presence of a histone or protamine type of protein in most of the DNA nucleoproteins may account for the salt-like linkage between nucleic acid and protein, for these proteins are very basic (see p. 65). The nature of the protein component of RNA nucleoproteins has not been determined.

Table 19. Composition of nucleoproteins

Source	Nucleic Acid %	Protein %
Calf thymus nuclei	DNA - 60	Histone - 40
Liver nuclei	DNA - 5	Lipoprotein - 95
Sperm heads (fish)	DNA - 60	Protamine - 40
Calf thymus chromosome fraction	RNA - 11	Not studied
Ribosomal nucleoprotein	RNA - 50	Unclassified - 50
Tobacco mosaic virus	RNA - 6	Unclassified - 94
Tobacco ring-spot virus	RNA - 40	Unclassified - 60

When the nucleic acid part of DNA or RNA nucleoproteins is separated from the protein part, it is found that the DNA and RNA are chemically very similar. Each consists of a long chain of monosaccharides joined by phosphate links. Attached to the sugars as side groups are either purines or pyrimidines.

The formulas for the two monosaccharides, two purines, and four pyrimidines which make up the chain are shown below. The two monosaccharides are D-ribose (see p. 14),

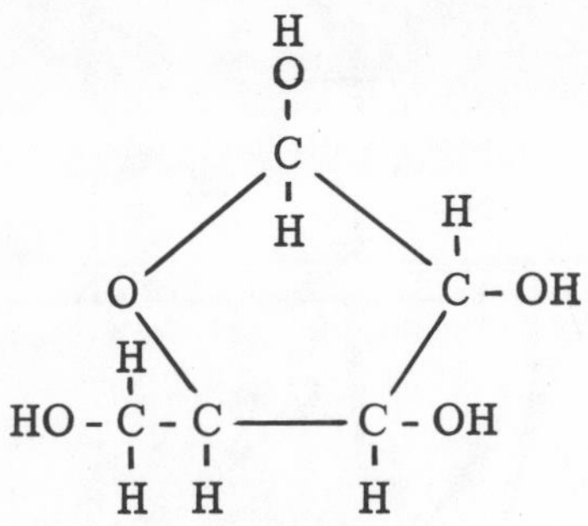

D-Ribose

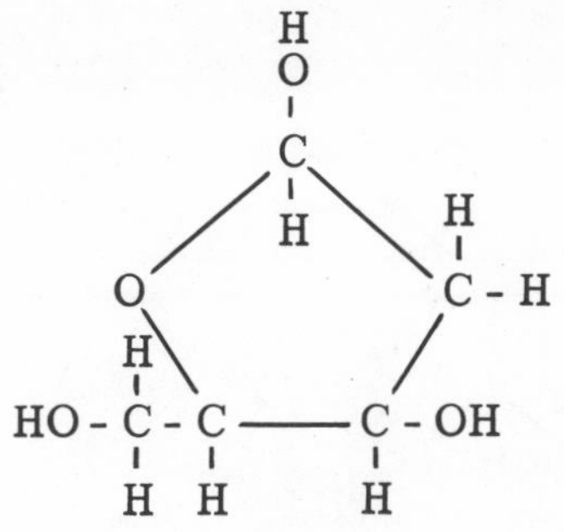

D-2-Deoxyribose

and its deoxy derivative, D-2-deoxyribose. *RNA* contains only D-ribose, whereas *DNA* contains only D-2-deoxyribose. The two types of nucleic acid are therefore named on the basis of the pentose sugar which they contain.

The two purines found in RNA and DNA are adenine and guanine. As the formulas show, these are basic heterocyclic nitrogen compounds.

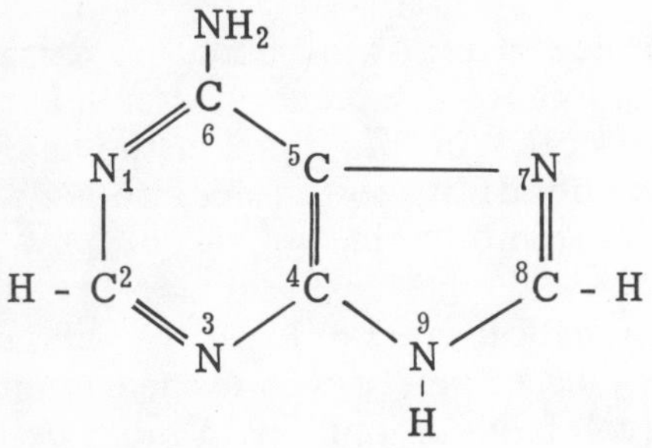

Adenine (6-aminopurine)

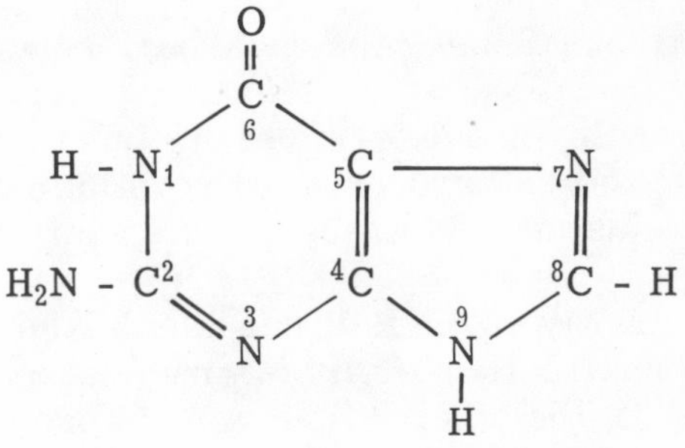

Guanine (2-amino-6-oxypurine)

The pyrimidines are structurally related to purines, containing the six-membered heterocyclic ring found in purines. Cytosine is common to both DNA and RNA. Uracil is found only in RNA, and is replaced by thymine in DNA. A derivative of cytosine, 5-methyl cytosine, is found less commonly in DNA only.

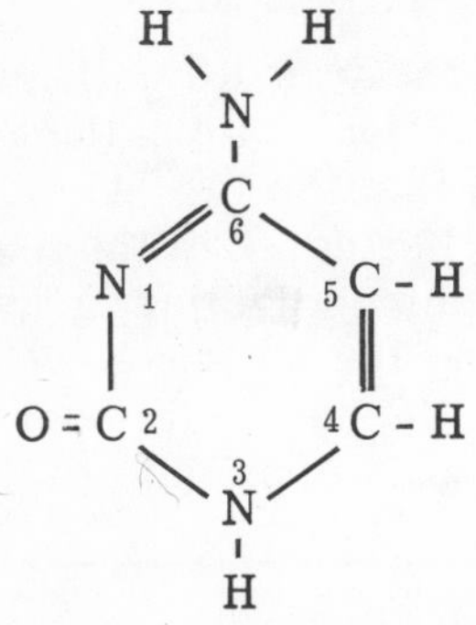

Cytosine
(2-oxy-6 aminopyrimidine)

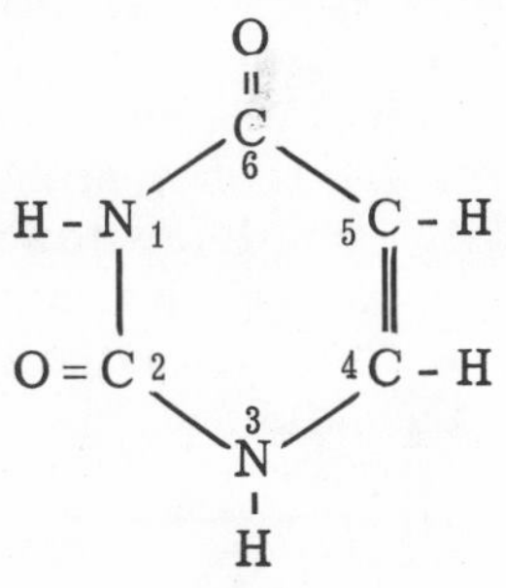

Uracil
(2, 6 dioxypyrimidine)

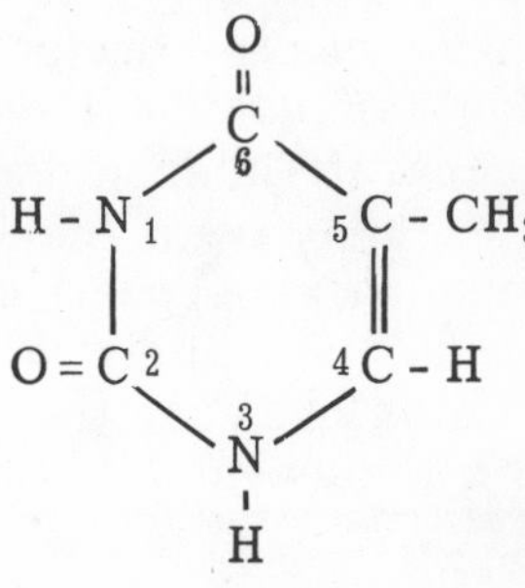

Thymine
(2, 6 dioxy-5-methylpyrimidine)

STRUCTURE OF NUCLEIC ACIDS. Figure 45 shows a section of a nucleic acid chain. It can be seen that the "backbone" of the chain is made up of sugar molecules linked by phosphate groups. Each sugar unit carries a side chain which is one of the bases whose

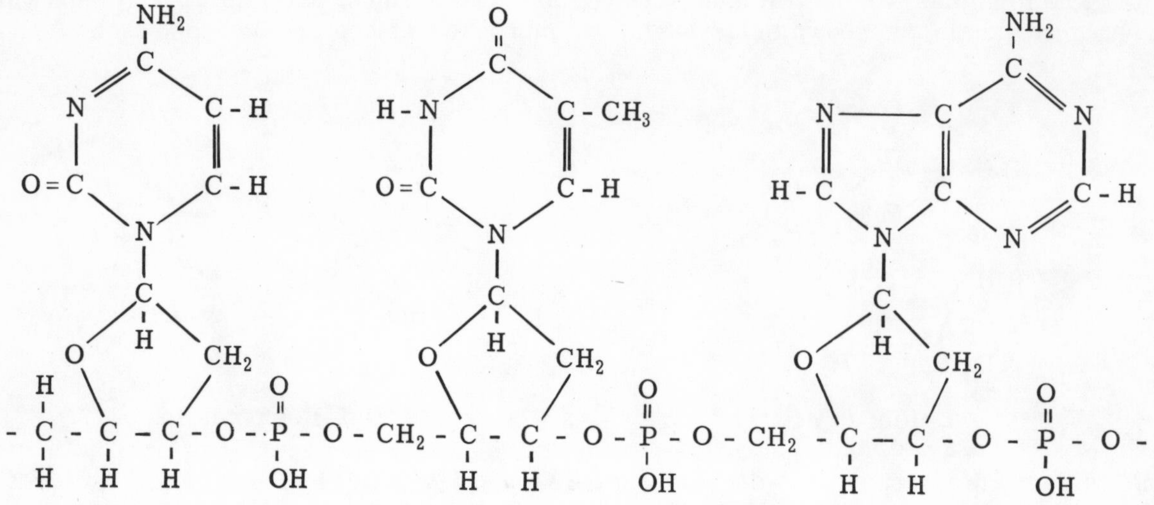

Figure 45. Section of nucleic acid chain. Bases shown: Cytosine, thymine and adenine. Sugar: D-2-deoxyribose.

formulas are shown above. Since this chain contains D-2-deoxyribose units, it is part of a DNA molecule.

The bases along the backbone of the nucleic acid do not follow a repeating pattern, but it is probable that the sequence of bases in each nucleic acid molecule is unique for that molecule, and determines its function in the living cell. In this respect the bases resemble the "R" groups in polypeptide chains, giving specificity to the nucleic acid molecule just as "R" groups give specificity to the protein molecule.

By x-ray analysis it has been found that DNA is a double molecule, a two-strand helix (compare alpha-helix of proteins, p. 60). The bases of one strand fit neatly onto the bases of the other. However, in order to fit, a given base on one chain must be opposite a particular one on the other. Thus, *guanine* pairs only with *cytosine,* and *adenine* only with *thymine.* Because of this required pairing, the sequence of bases on one strand determines the sequence on the other.

Less is known about the structure of RNA, but x-ray studies suggest that it also is a two-strand helix. RNA is much more difficult to separate from cells, and the rather poor x-ray pictures obtained may be due to changes during extraction.

Genetic role of DNA. All evidence to date suggests that DNA is genetic material, and is capable of reproducing itself. The exact mechanism of reproduction is a challenging problem for biological scientists. Crick of England has proposed that the two strands of DNA separate in some way; monomers are then supplied by the cell, and align themselves along each separate "mold" strand with complementary bases (adenine-thymine, guanine-cytosine) pairing up. A new single strand is then synthesized along the mold. If we call one of the original strands the hand, and the other the glove, then the hand acts as a mold for a new glove, and the glove acts as a mold for a new hand. This is depicted graphically in Figure 46.

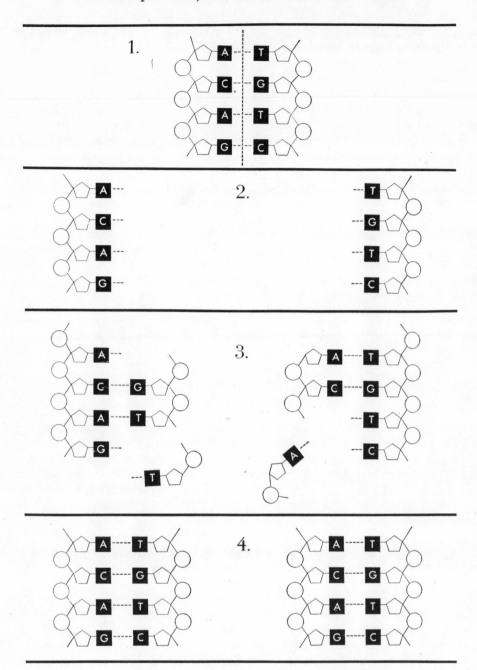

Figure 46. Suggested replication mechanism of DNA. In diagram 1, two linked
chains come apart to give diagram 2. Monomers (A = adenine,
G = guanine, C = cytosine, T = thymine) then assemble along each
chain as shown in diagram 3. The end result (diagram 4) is two pairs
of chains whose bases have the same sequence as the linked chains in
diagram 1. (From F. H. C. Crick, Scientific American 197, p. 196
(1957)).

At present, most evidence suggests that DNA is the reproducing unit of the gene. In
this capacity DNA holds the master plans, transmitting them from generation to generation. DNA directs these activities from the nucleus, to which it is confined. Present theory gives to RNA the position of production supervisor. It is assumed that RNA is a working copy (blue print) of the master plan DNA molecule, and is released (after production by
DNA in the nucleus) to the cytoplasm. Here RNA directs the synthesis of a specific protein, assembling the amino acids in a particular sequence in the polypeptide chain, which
is dictated by the sequence of bases in RNA. Thus, a single DNA can duplicate itself and

make a specific RNA, which in turn can make a specific protein which is unique and different from other proteins in structure and function.

Evidence that RNA is responsible for construction of specific proteins comes from the work of Fraenkel-Conrat in this country and Schramm in Germany. They separated RNA from its specific protein in tobacco mosaic virus grown on one species of tobacco plant. They then inoculated the protein-free RNA into a different species of tobacco plant. The RNA infected the second plant and produced RNA nucleoprotein (virus). Examination of this new virus showed that the protein was the same as that produced by the *first* species of infected tobacco plant, although the second plant had never seen this protein before! This is convincing evidence that the infected plant manufactures a protein dictated by the *RNA* of the virus, and *not* the RNA of the infected plant.

NUCLEOTIDES AND NUCLEOSIDES. RNA and DNA can be hydrolyzed with acids or enzymes to yield the basic building stones. If the breakdown is stopped before it is complete, nucleotides and nucleosides are obtained. The points of hydrolysis can be seen by examination of the nucleic acid structure in Figure 45 (p. 110).

$$\text{Nucleic acid} \xrightarrow[\text{enzyme}]{\text{acid or}} \text{Nucleotides (base-sugar-}H_3PO_4)(-P \overset{B}{|} S- P|)$$

$$\xrightarrow[\text{enzyme}]{\text{acid or}} \text{Nucleosides (base-sugar)}(-S \overset{B}{|} P) \quad +H_3PO_4$$

Nucleotides and nucleosides are named after the base which they contain. The prefix "deoxy" is added if they contain deoxyribose instead of ribose. The mononucleotides containing ribose are adenylic acid, guanylic acid, cytidylic acid, uridylic acid and thymidylic acid. The mononucleosides containing ribose are adenosine, guanosine, cytidine and uridine. An exception to the above naming occurs with thymidine, which at present is used to denote the deoxyriboside nucleoside of thymine. Todd in England has synthesized adenylic acid and adenosine.

Nucleotides Having Special Functions. A number of nucleotides not found as components of nucleic acids exist in tissues and have special functions. These are briefly described below.

Adenosine Phosphates. A nucleotide with the phosphoric acid attached to carbon 5 of the ribose, instead of carbon 3, is the widely distributed *muscle adenylic acid*. It is also called adenosine monophosphate (AMP). Adenosine also forms a diphosphate (ADP) and a triphosphate (ATP) (p. 166). These three derivatives play an important role in enzyme chemistry and intermediate metabolism (see p. 154).

Pyridine Nucleotides. Nicotinamide-adenine dinucleotide (NAD) and nicotinamide-adenine dinucleotide phosphate (NADP) are important coenzymes in biological oxidation reactions

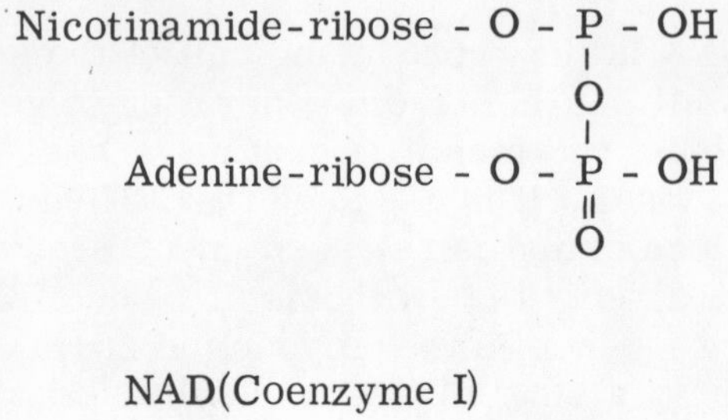

NAD(Coenzyme I) 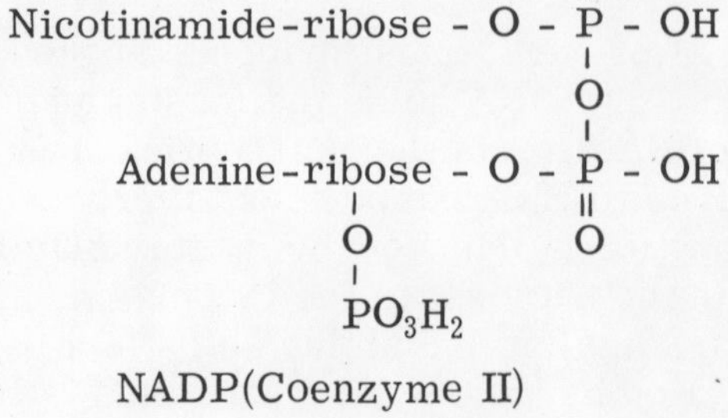   NADP(Coenzyme II)

(p. 162). The formula for nicotinamide, a vitamin constituent, is shown on p. 236. In NAD, the nicotinamide is attached to carbon 1 of ribose by the splitting out of a molecule of water between this carbon and the ring nitrogen of the amide. The two ribose molecules are hooked by ester linkage at carbon 5 to the two phosphoric acid units. Nitrogen 9 of adenine (see p. 109) and carbon 1 of ribose are attached by imide linkage. In NADP, the extra phosphoric acid molecule is attached by ester linkage to carbon 2 of ribose.

Flavin Nucleotides. These also act as coenzymes (see p. 162) in biological oxidations. They derive their name from the presence of a vitamin, riboflavin, which is the key constituent. Riboflavin is a combination of isoalloxazine and ribose (see formula, p. 238). Flavin mononucleotide (FMN) contains riboflavin with a phosphoric acid molecule attached to carbon 5 of ribose. Another important flavin nucleotide is flavin adenine dinucleotide (FAD). In FAD a ribose molecule is attached to phosphoric acid at carbon 5, and to adenine at carbon 1. Adenine is attached through nitrogen 9 to ribose. A ring nitrogen of flavin is attached to ribitol, the alcohol analog of ribose, at a terminal carbon.

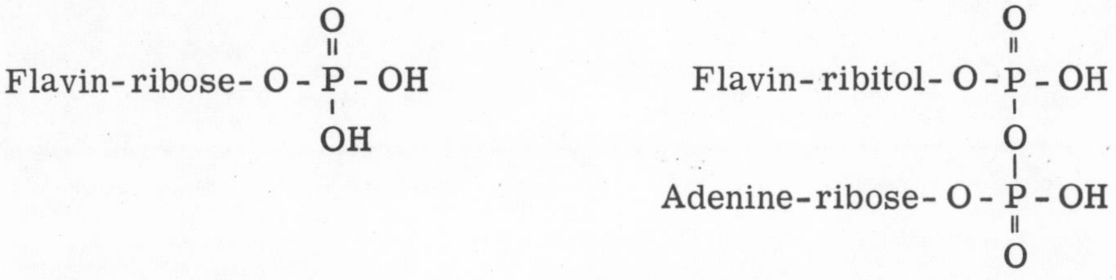

$$
\begin{array}{cc}
\text{Flavin-ribose-O-}\overset{\overset{O}{\|}}{\underset{\underset{OH}{|}}{P}}\text{-OH} & \text{Flavin-ribitol-O-}\overset{\overset{O}{\|}}{\underset{\underset{O}{|}}{P}}\text{-OH} \\
 & \text{Adenine-ribose-O-}\overset{}{\underset{\underset{O}{\|}}{P}}\text{-OH} \\
\text{(FMN)} & \text{(FAD)}
\end{array}
$$

Coenzyme A. This important coenzyme (see p. 159) contains adenine, ribose, phosphoric acid, pantothenic acid (a vitamin) and mercaptoethanolamine.

$$\overset{\overset{OPO_3H}{/}}{\text{Adenine-ribose}}\text{——O-}\overset{\overset{O}{\|}}{\underset{\underset{OH}{|}}{P}}\text{-O-}\overset{\overset{O}{\|}}{\underset{\underset{OH}{|}}{P}}\text{-O-pantothenic acid-mercaptoethanolamine.}$$

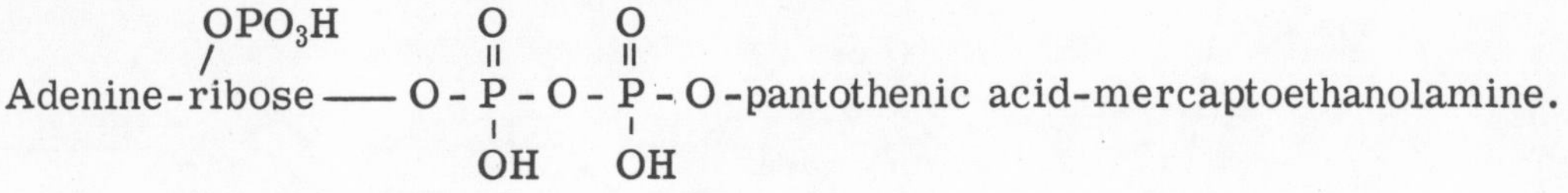

(Coenzyme A)

Uridine Diphosphate Glucose (UDPG). This is a coenzyme which functions in the conversion of galactose-1-phosphate to glucose-1-phosphate (see p. 155). It contains the pyrimidine, uracil, and ribose, phosphoric acid and glucose.

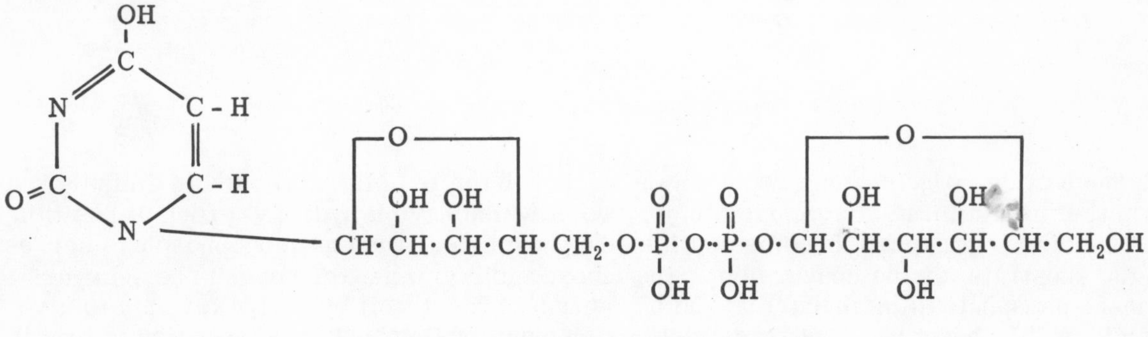

Uridine diphosphate glucose (UDPG)

Nucleotide Component of Vitamin B_{12}. Examination of the formula for vitamin B_{12} (p. 241) shows the presence of a nucleotide containing a base, 5,6-dimethylbenzimidazole, and ribose and phosphoric acid. The nucleotide and its corresponding nucleoside have been obtained by degradation of vitamin B_{12}.

Biosynthesis and degradation of nucleic acids, purines and pyrimidines. Pyrimidines.
Figure 47 shows the steps in the synthesis of uracil starting with carbamyl phosphate and
aspartic acid. Carbamyl phosphate is an energy-rich compound which drives the enzyme-
catalyzed reaction to completion. Ring closure with formation of a "ring" peptide bond
gives dihydroorotic acid. This is dehydrogenated to give *orotic acid*. Orotic acid is converted to the nucleotide, orotidine-5'-phosphate, (orotidylic acid), the orotic acid decar-
boxylates to give uracil, and the end-product is the nucleotide, uridine-5'-phosphate
(uridylic acid, uridine monophosphate (UMP)). The other pyrimidines are formed from

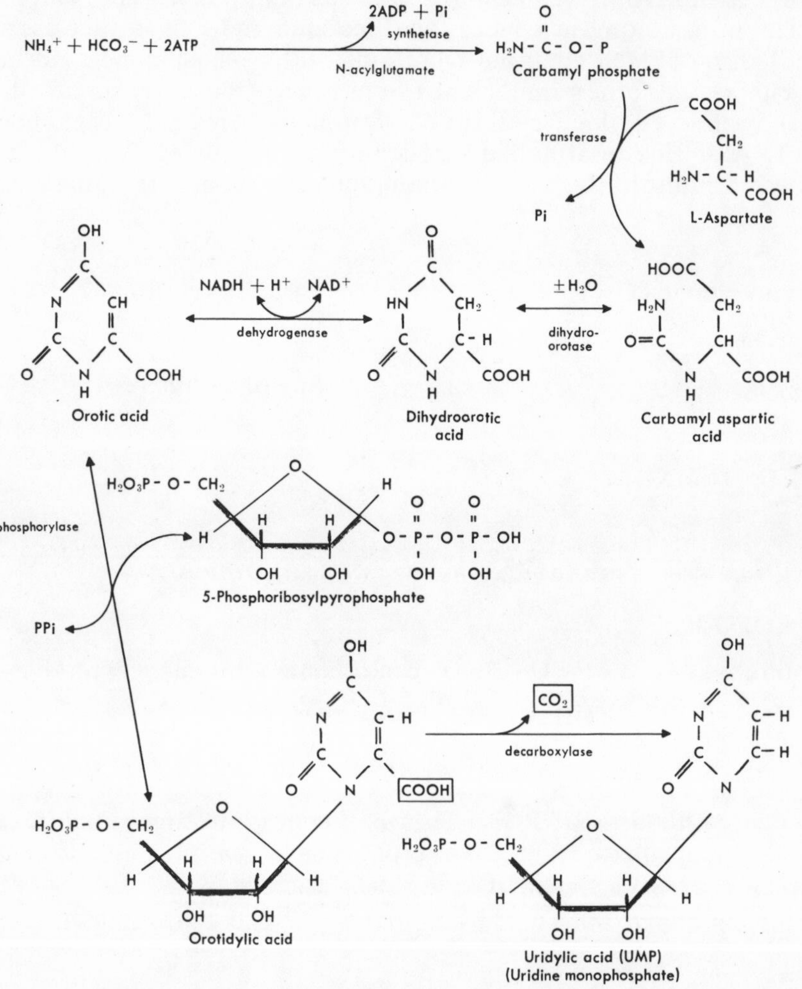

Figure 47. Biosynthesis of uracil and uridine monophosphate (UMP).

this nucleotide. One enzyme replaces the carbon-6 oxygen of uracil with an amino group
(uracil exists in three tautomeric forms, two of which have a hydroxyl group at position
6). Uridine triphosphate becomes cytidine triphosphate. Uridine monophosphate serves
as the substrate for the conversion of the ribose moiety to deoxyribose. The deoxyuri-
dine-5'-phosphate is methylated at the 5-position of the uracil by active formate to give
thymidine-5'-phosphate, a characteristic component of DNA. The degradation of uracil
is apparently the reverse of its synthesis, but since carbon dioxide was split off in the
conversion of orotic acid to uracil, the final degradation product is beta-alanine instead
of aspartic acid.

Purines. Figure 48 shows the origin of the atoms of the purine ring. This information
was obtained mainly by Buchanan, Greenberg, Kornberg, and their associates. The ring

is synthesized in a step-wise fashion on carbon-1 of ribose-5-phosphate, leading directly to the formation of purine ribonucleotides. Neither free purines of nucleosides serve or appear as intermediates in the synthesis.

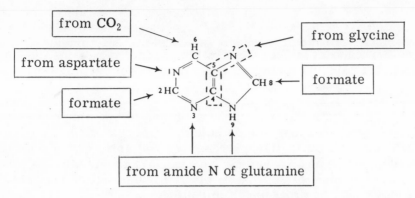

Figure 48.   Origin of the atoms of the purine ring.

5-Phosphoribosyl-1-pyrophosphate a key substance. This substance, a high energy derivative of the nucleoside ribose-1-phosphate, is a key compound in the synthesis of both pyrimidines (see Fig. 47) and purines. In the synthesis of the purine ring (Fig. 48), it is converted to the 5-phosphoribosylamine by reaction with glutamine, and the amine condenses with glycine to form the amide (endergonic reaction requiring ATP). This establishes the central part of the ring (carbons 4 and 5, nitrogens 7 and 9). Carbon 8 is then added by transfer from formyl-coenzyme f (see p. 101). Nitrogen atom 3 is then added from glutamine, and the imidazole ring is closed. This requires energy from ATP. Carbon dioxide (as bicarbonate) next enters the molecule as carbon 6 in a freely reversible reaction. The carboxyl group (carbon 6) then reacts with aspartic acid, nitrogen 1 adding to the carbon as the amide, and the aspartic acid forming fumaric acid as in urea synthesis (see p. 199). The pyrimidine part of the molecule is then completed by addition of another carbon (carbon 2) from formyl-coenzyme F. The first purine derivative which emerges is inosinic acid, which occurs free in muscle.

Degradation of purines. Most purines are degraded to uric acid (2, 6, 8-trioxy purine), which is excreted as such, or in certain animals (see p. 207) degraded further to allantoin (formed by oxidative cleavage of the pyrimidine ring, with loss of carbon 6). In guanosine, ribose is first split off, then the guanine is deaminated to xanthine. Xanthine (2, 6 dioxy purine) is converted by xanthine oxidase, a flavoprotein with low substrate specificity, to uric acid. Adenosine is deaminated as a nucleoside, converting the adenine to hypoxanthine (6-oxy purine). The nucleoside is then cleaved, and the hypoxanthine is oxidized to xanthine.

Biosynthesis of the deoxyribonucleic acids (DNA). Kornberg, in studies with the bacterium, *Escherichia coli*, was the first to define the factors required for synthesis of the DNA strand. These are (1) DNA polymerase, (2) the triphosphates of the four nucleosides, i.e., deoxy adenosine triphosphate, deoxyguanosine triphosphate, deoxycytidine triphosphate, and thymidine triphosphate, (3) primer DNA, and (4) Mg^{++}. The primer DNA controls the nature of the nucleic acid synthesized. Base composition, base sequence, and the physical dimensions of the polymer correspond to the compound used as primer. The polymerase enzyme is not species specific, and will multiply primer nucleic acids of different origins. The addition of nucleotides occurs at the free 3' hydroxyl of deoxyribose, with the loss of pyrophosphate. In the following equation, P equals phosphate, N equals nitrogen base, S equals sugar.

$$\text{Strand - P -}\overset{\overset{\text{N}}{|}}{\text{S}}\text{ + P - P - P -}\overset{\overset{\text{N}}{|}}{\text{S}} \longrightarrow \text{Strand - P -}\overset{\overset{\text{N}}{|}}{\text{S}}$$

$$\overset{|}{\underset{\text{P - S}}{\overset{\text{N}}{|}}} \text{ N + P - P}_i$$

The Watson-Crick model in Figure 46, p. 111, readily explains the influence of the primer DNA. Each individual strand of the primer helix acts as a template for the proper arrangement of bases as the new strand of DNA is formed.

What *initiates* DNA synthesis is not known. It can only begin after the strands of the primer DNA separate. The magnitude of the task of separation is appreciated when one considers the DNA of *E. coli*. Here, as in other bacteria, the "chromosome" is apparently a single molecule of DNA in a closed circular structure. The total length of the structure is about 0.5 mm. or approximately 200,000 complete helical turns. This must all be unwound during the process of replication.

Degradation of nucleic acids. This is accomplished by a group of enzymes called phospho-esterases (mainly diesterases) of the class of hydrolases (see p. 91). The most important ones in the living cell are the *deoxyribonucleases* and the *ribonucleases*. Pancreatic deoxyribonuclease has been prepared in crystalline form. It has a molecular weight of 60,000, and a pH optimum in the range of 6 to 7. It splits the 3'-phosphoester bond, freeing small (di, tri, etc.) nucleotides (oligonucleotides) with some non-dialyzable large fragments. Other tissues (spleen, etc.) contain a similar enzyme which completes the job by splitting the other bond, the 5'-phosphate bond, in the oligonucleotides released by the pancreatic enzyme.

Pancreatic ribonuclease has already been discussed (see p. 107). Its molecular weight is rather low (13,000), and its amino acid sequence has been determined. This enzyme has remarkable specificity. It splits only those phosphodiester bonds that will leave as one fragment a pyrimidine 3'-phosphate. The final cleavage products are uridine 3'-phosphate, cytidine 3'-phosphate, and various oligonucleotides with one pyrimidine nucleoside-3'-phosphate end group.

Phosphatases. These phosphomonoesterases are widely distributed. Acid phosphatases have a pH optimum of about 5, and alkaline phosphatases a pH optimum in the range of 7 to 8. They split monoesters exclusively, both the 3' and the 5'-monophosphates, nucleosides and phosphoric acid. An acid phosphatase is present in high concentration in the human prostate gland. Alkaline phosphatases are found in the small intestine, and in bones where they are active in the formation of bone tissue.

Nucleosidases. These enzymes cleave the bond between the sugar residue and the base. The cleavage of the nucleoside bond is accomplished through phosphorolysis, giving sugar phosphate and free base.

Biochemistry of viruses. The viruses are the smallest biological units containing all the information needed for their own replication. Viruses show many differences morphologically and in internal complexity, but also share many properties. The diameter of viruses varies from about 10 millimicrons to 200 millimicrons. Because of their small size most observations have been made with the electron microscope. A common characteristic is their totally parasitic nature. All viruses studied to date have an extremely close relationship with the living cell, outside of which they cannot reproduce. Their chemical nature is rather simple when compared with bacteria or cells of higher organisms. The very small viruses usually contain only nucleic acid and protein, which in some cases are only single molecular species. The nucleic acid may be either DNA or RNA, but not both, as one finds in higher organisms. For example, herpes, polyoma, T-even bacteriophage and vaccinia viruses contain DNA, whereas tobacco mosaic and influenza viruses contain RNA.

Viruses are important pathogenic agents, and are responsible for a host of diseases affecting plants, animals and humans. Even bacteria are susceptible to a group of viruses called bacteriophages. Most viruses contain a core of nucleic acid and external shell of protein. In some of the larger viruses, the entire particle is enclosed in a membrane, or envelope. The protein serves as a protective coating, and in some instances appears to assist in the penetration of the cell walls of the host. In all cases, the viral nucleic acid enters the cell and diverts the synthetic apparatus of the cell to the production of new complete virus. A large amount of information as to the nature of the genetic code and the mechanism of protein synthesis has been obtained from a study of viruses.

Tobacco mosaic virus. More information is available on this virus than on any other, and its properties will therefore be discussed in some detail. The virus molecule is a rod-shaped particle, 3,000 angstroms long and 170 angstroms wide (see Fig. 49). The center of the molecule contains a helical core which is a single chain of ribonucleic acid (see Fig. 50). The core is surrounded by 2,200 protein subunits each with a molecular weight of 18,000. The protein subunit is a single peptide chain. Its amino end is blocked by an acetyl group on the nitrogen of a serine, which is followed by a tyrosine residue. The carboxyl end (C-terminal end) consists of the amino acid sequence, prolyl-alanyl-threonine. As pointed out in a previous chapter (see p. 66), the amino acid sequence of the subunit has been determined by workers in California and Germany. The molecule contains 158 amino acid residues.

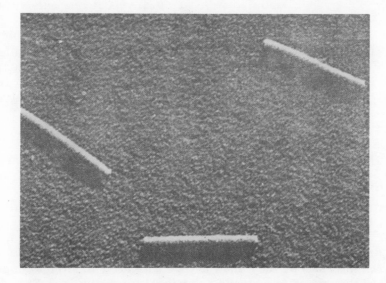

Figure 49.   Tobacco mosaic virus. Electron micrograph at 120,000 magnifications taken by
Dr. Robley C. Williams, University of California (Berkeley). (From H. Fraenkel-
Conrat and W. M. Stanley, Chemical and Engineering News, p. 139, May 15, 1961).

The single chain of ribonucleic acid that serves as the core in the tobacco mosaic virus molecule contains about 6,500 nucleotides. If stretched out, this would give a molecule nearly 30,000 angstroms long. The pitch of the helix is such that the effective length of the RNA is reduced to 3,000 angstroms, the length of the TMV particle.

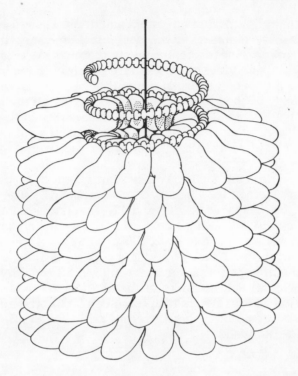

Figure 50.   Tobacco mosaic structure. In this drawing, the internal chain helix
is RNA and the external bodies are the protein subunits or individual
peptide chains. (From p. 141 of the same article cited in Figure 49).

The protein subunits can aggregate at about pH 5, to form the typical helical structure and rods of indeterminate length. The aggregates are quite unstable to pH, heat, enzymes, etc. The incorporation of RNA, however, produces the typical rod of 3,000 angstrom length which is stable over the pH range of 3 to 9 and is very resistant to heat and enzymes. The RNA in turn is now quite inaccessible and resists attack by ribonuclease.

TMV mutants. Schramm and coworkers have obtained a large number of mutants by treatment of TMV with nitrous acid. This transforms the three amino bases cytosine, adenine and guanine (see p. 109) into uracil, hypoxanthine and xanthine, respectively. When 99 per cent of the RNA molecules are inactivated, almost all of the survivors appear to differ from the parent type TMV in the nature of the disease symptoms they produce.

Animal viruses. The animal viruses such as vaccinia, mumps, herpes, adenovirus, polyoma, influenza and poliomyelitis, vary from 90 to 3,000 angstroms in diameter. Under the electron microscope they show a regular and symmetrical appearance. At low magnification, they seem to possess spherical symmetry (see Fig. 23, p. 83). At high magnification, they are found to consist of subunits, called *capsomeres*, arranged in a regular structure. The pattern is that of an icosahedral crystal (20 faces), which is found with herpes, adenovirus, and polyoma. Influenza virus (Fig. 23, p. 83) possesses helical symmetry. The helix is wound up in a compact spiral resembling the core of a golf ball, which is surrounded by an external membrane. Numerous projections extend from the membrane surface, which are believed to participate in the attachment of the virus to the membrane of attacked cells.

Bacteriophage. The bacteriophages consist of numerous species of different size, composition, and properties. Most of the research on phage action has been derived from studies with a series of seven phages which attack a common host, strain B of *Escherica coli*. These seven are known as the T phages and fall into related classes. The ones named T2, T4 and T6 have been particularly useful. They are often called the "T-even" phages. The electron microscope shows the phages to be shaped somewhat like tadpoles, with a bipyrimidal hexagonal head and an elongated tail (see Fig. 51). The tail consists of a helical contractile sheath surrounding a central hollow core. At the end of the core there is a plate to which six tail fibers are attached.

The particle weight of the T-even phages is from 200 to 500 million. Approximately 25-50 per cent of the total mass consists of DNA. Several proteins are also found in the phage. These include the head protein, which encloses the DNA, the protein of the tail fibers, an enzyme in the tail which can attack the bacterial cell wall, and other proteins in the tail. Tightly bound ATP is also present in the tail.

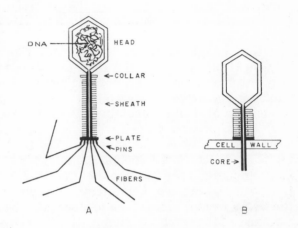

Figure 51.   Diagram of T-even phage. A shows the parts of the phage with the sheath in the uncontracted position. B shows the sheath in the contracted position.

Mechanism of infection. T-even phages are completely inert and show no signs of reproduction or metabolism in the absence of host cells. When introduced into a culture of *E. coli*, the T-even phage particles become attached to the bacterial cells by their tails. Initial contact is probably made by the fibers and plate of the tail. After contact has been made, the helical sheath contracts, both shortening and thickening. Next, the bacterial wall is attacked by the tail enzyme, after which the DNA contents of the head are injected into the bacterium. Essentially all of the viral protein remains outside of the bacterial cell. After introduction of viral DNA into the bacterial cell, the synthesis of bacterial DNA and RNA stops. Nevertheless, synthesis of certain proteins essential for phage replication occurs. These are not found in the mature phage and probably include enzymes needed to make specific viral components. RNA is also made at this stage, but is not found in mature phage. After about 6 minutes, synthesis of new viral DNA begins, and after about 8 minutes, synthesis of phage protein can be detected. After about 10 minutes following the injection of DNA into the bacterial cell, the first mature phage appears within the cell. The accumulation of intact phage continues until the cell wall ruptures after about 21 minutes. This releases phage into the solution. As many as 100 phage particles may be released from one cell.

The T-even bacteriophages, especially T-4, have been valuable tools in studying the genetic aspects of phage replication, since each phage particle contains only a single copy of its genetic information, i.e., it is said to be *haploid*. This together with the rapidity of phage replication, has simplified the problem of genetic analysis. By studying mutant phages and mutant crosses, Benzer and coworkers have been able to prepare a "genetic map" of the T4 phage. In this map, more than 80 distinguishable mutations are arranged on a continuous molecular strand in the "r II" region of the chromosome. These presumably represent either "breaks" in the nucleic acid chain or changes in the sequence of nucleotides in a particular spot on the chain. The coding problem and theory of gene action will be discussed in detail in the next chapter.

Chapter 8 | BIOSYNTHESIS OF PROTEINS AND ITS CONTROL BY GENES

Factors involved in protein synthesis. The synthesis of the polypeptide chain of proteins involves not only the building stones themselves, but also the intervention of nucleic acids, enzymes and high energy bonds. First, the complete details regarding the primary structure (amino acid sequence) of the protein is stored in coded form (a specific nucleotide sequence) in a segment of a DNA molecule in the nucleus of the cell. The DNA molecule is in turn, a segment of a chromosome. Specific chemicals, such as the various hormones in the animal body, initiate a *transcription* process which ultimately leads to the production of the new protein in the cytoplasm of the cell.

Transcription from DNA to RNA. The DNA molecule first undergoes a "puffing" or swelling stage in which the double helix unwinds, then a section of *one* strand of the helix serves as a template for the synthesis of an RNA molecule. The method of transcription is identical with the method of replication proposed by Watson and Crick (see Fig. 46, p. 111) for DNA, except uracil (see p. 109) replaces thymine as a building stone in the base pairing, and in the newly formed RNA. The biosynthesis is analogous to that discussed for DNA (see p. 115), involving an RNA-polymerase primarily localized in the nucleus. Except for RNA destined to become "soluble RNA" or a part of the ribosomes (ribosomal RNA), the RNA thus produced is metabolically unstable *messenger RNA,* produced by transcription from DNA in order to eventually synthesize a specific cytoplasmic protein. The messenger RNA is released from the nucleus and enters the cell cytoplasm where it attaches itself to a *ribosome.*

The ribosome: site of protein synthesis. Ribosomes are morphologically well-defined elements which occur in the cytoplasm of the cells (see Fig. 1, p. 2). They contain about equal amounts of RNA and protein, with a high concentration of bound magnesium ion. Ribosomes can be isolated by fractional centrifugation of tissue homogenates. The usual range of sedimentation coefficient is from 20 to 100 Svedberg units, with the most common value 70-80S. It is believed that the latter is an aggregate of one 30S and one 50S particle. The actual assembly of amino acids into a peptide chain takes place on the surface of the ribosome.

Formation of amino acid-"soluble" RNA compounds. Soluble RNA (s-RNA; also called "transfer" or "adapter" RNA) may be defined as that RNA remaining in a broken cell suspension after centrifuging at 100,000 x gravity for several hours. It is composed of relatively small molecules with a molecular weight of approximately 30,000. The DNA of the nucleus directs the synthesis of at least 20 different soluble RNA molecules, each specific for a single amino acid. The manner in which each amino acid becomes attached to its specific RNA is as follows:

(1) An enzyme, *amino acyl synthetase*, specific for each amino acid, catalyzes the formation of amino acyl adenylate with ATP. Pyrophosphate is split out in the reaction, an anhydride bond forms between the carboxyl group of the amino acid and the phosphoric acid of the AMP, and the compound remains attached to the enzyme (reaction (1)).

$$\text{Amino acid + ATP + enzyme} \rightleftharpoons \text{amino acyl-AMP-enzyme} + PP_i \qquad (1)$$

In reaction (2), the same enzyme catalyzes the transfer of the amino acid acyl moiety to its specific soluble RNA.

$$\text{Amino acyl-AMP-enzyme} + \text{sRNA} \longrightarrow \text{amino acyl-sRNA} + \text{AMP} + \text{enzyme} \quad (2)$$

The net result of these two reactions is that the carboxyl group of the amino acid is linked by an ester bond to a hydroxyl group of the ribose of a terminal adenylic residue of the sRNA. Either the 2' or the 3'-hydroxyl group of ribose is involved, but the exact one of these two is not known. Analysis of the terminal nucleotides in soluble RNA molecules shows that they all end in the sequence -pCpCpA, where p is phosphate, C is cytidine (nucleoside of cytosine and ribose), and A is adenosine (nucleoside of adenine and ribose). To visualize this structure, the reader is referred to Fig. 45, p.110.

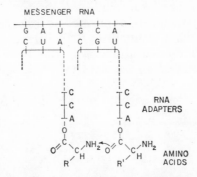

Figure 52.   The function of adapter RNA in protein synthesis. (From G. Zubay, Science, 140, 1092 (1963)).

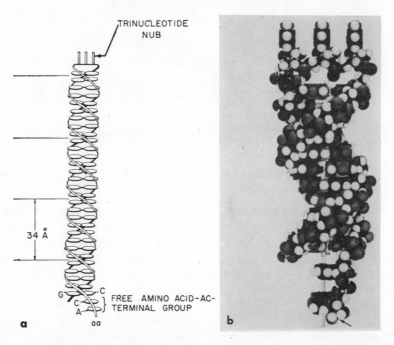

Figure 53.   (a) Proposed structure for adapter RNA. A single polynucleotide chain interacts with itself by forming a bend near the middle. Hydrogen bonding takes place between the nucleotides from the two halves of the chain and results in the formation of a double-helix structure. In the bend, three bases are of necessity unpaired. The guanine from one end of the chain forms a base pair of the Watson-Crick type with the cytosine third from the other end. This leaves two nucleotides on the end bearing the amino acid in the flexible state. The molecule is about 100 angstroms long and 20 angstroms wide. (b) A space-filling molecular model. Only one of the three turns of a double helix are shown. Position for attachment of amino acid is indicated by arrow. (From p. 1093 of article cited in Figure 52).

Assembly of amino acids into peptide chains. The theory of how the amino acids are put
in the proper juxtaposition for peptide synthesis on the surface of the ribosome is credited
to Crick, and is explained in Figure 52. Since there are 20 amino acids, and only 4 nucleotides containing the coded information in the messenger RNA, a sequence of three
nucleotides would be the minimum to code for 20 amino acids ($4^2 = 16$; $4^3 = 64$. If we
assume that each soluble (adapter) RNA contains a sequence of three nucleotides coding
for one of the 20 amino acids, then this portion of the adapter molecule could hydrogen
bond (see Fig. 52) with the three complementary nucleotides on the messenger RNA, placing the attached amino acid in the proper juxtaposition for peptide synthesis. Since the
three nucleotides in the messenger RNA are also complementary to the sequence in the
DNA from which the RNA sequence was transcribed, it is apparent that the sequence on
the adapter RNA and the nuclear DNA are identical, and an exact reading of the coded information on the DNA molecule has been made. Zubay recently proposed a molecular
model for the above synthesis, which is explained in Figures 53 and 54. He suggests
that the single polynucleotide chain of adapter RNA forms a bend in the middle which ex-
poses a trinucleotide "nub". This nub attaches to the appropriate trinucleotide on messenger RNA and places the attached amino acid in the proper position.

In Figure 54, Zubay has constructed a model of a 70S ribosome to demonstrate the
role of the ribosome in protein synthesis. The ribosome is made up of a 50S and a 30S

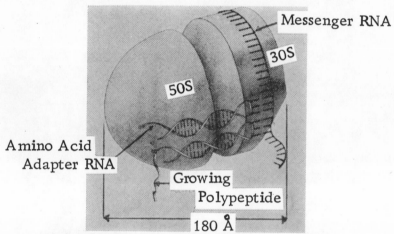

Figure 54.   Model showing role of the ribosome in protein synthesis.
(From p. 1095 of article cited in Figure 52).

particle. The ribosome provides a stabilizing surface for (1) maintaining the messenger
RNA in a configuration that would be thermodynamically unstable in solution, and (2)
maintaining the reacting adapter molecules in parallel register. Peptide synthesis begins from the N-terminal (free alpha-amino) end of the chain. Only part of the messenger
is bound at one time. The growing polypeptide chain can be seen dropping away from the
ribosome.

Use of synthetic polynucleotides to decipher the genetic code. Nirenberg and Matthaei,
and Ochoa, have shown that the ribosome will accept synthetic polynucleotides as well as
natural messenger RNA, extending the molecules sufficiently to make the nucleotide bases
accessible to coupling with adapter RNA molecules carrying the individual amino acids.
When Nirenberg and coworkers used a cell-free system from *E. coli,* which contained
whole ribosomes, amino acyl synthetases, amino acids, soluble RNA, ATP and GTP
(guanosine triphosphate), they were able to produce a new polypeptide on addition of
synthetic polyribouridylic acid.   The polypeptide contained only phenylalanine, which
proved that the triplet nucleotide, *UUU,* codes for phenylalanine. This result provided

an excellent confirmation of the template function of messenger RNA. Other experiments by the above workers showed that the addition of polyribonucleotide copolymers of variable composition could stimulate the incorporation of a variety of amino acids. Assuming that the genetic code is of the triplet type, they have worked out a tentative set of RNA code words (see Table 20).

Table 20. Tentative genetic code

Amino acid	RNA Code Triplet*			
Alanine	CCG	UCG'	ACG'	
Arginine	CGC	AGA	UGC'	CGA'
Asparagine	ACA	AUA	ACU'	
Aspartic acid	GUA	GCA'	GAA'	
Cysteine	UUG			
Glutamic acid	GAA	GAU'	GAC'	
Glutamine	AAC	AGA	AGU'	
Glycine	UGG	AGG	CGG	
Histidine	ACC	ACU'		
Isoleucine	UAU	UAA		
Leucine	UUG	UUC	UCC	UUA
Lysine	AAA	AAU		
Methionine	UGA			
Phenylalanine	UUU	CUU		
Proline	CCC	CCU	CCA	CCG'
Serine	UGU	UCC	UCG'	ACG
Threonine	CAC	CAA		
Tryptophan	CGU			
Tyrosine	AUU			
Valine	UGU	UGA'		

* Arbitrary nucleotide sequence (may be reversed, but this is not known at present).
' Probable nucleotide.

As can be seen from the table, two or more coding units can direct the incorporation of a single amino acid in most cases. The code is therefore considered to be "degenerate". The degeneracy of the code may be due to the occasional occurrence of two different transfer (adapter) RNA's which correspond to the same amino acid. It is probable that several revisions of the table will be made in the next few years.

Control of protein synthesis. Efficient control mechanisms exist in the cell to turn on and shut off production of proteins. Also, some type of regulatory system must be present to permit cells to specialize in the production of certain proteins. For example, the genes responsible for the synthesis of hemoglobin must be present in every cell, yet the manufacture of hemoglobin is confined to the red blood cell.

Enzyme induction. Excellent evidence for a control mechanism is provided by the phenomenom of enzyme induction. When E. coli is grown in the absence of a beta-galactoside such as the disaccharide, lactose, only traces of the enzyme, beta-galactosidase are formed by this organism. The addition of a galactoside to the culture medium results in a marked increase in galactosidase production. The synthesis of this enzyme can be traced to a specific gene, which has been definitely located on chromosomal maps of E. coli. However, the action of this gene becomes apparent only in the *presence* of a galactoside.

Enzyme repression.   Studies with *E. coli* have also revealed the phenomenon of enzyme repression.   The enzyme, tryptophan synthetase, is formed by the bacterium only when it is grown on a tryptophan-free medium.   The addition of tryptophan to the medium completely suppresses the formation of the enzyme.   Here again, the gene responsible for the synthesis of this enzyme has been identified and located on the chromosomal map.

Structural and regulatory genes.   To explain enzyme induction and repression, Monod and coworkers have proposed an ingenious mechanism.   This is shown in diagram form in Figure 55.   In this model, it is assumed that there are two types of genes: structural

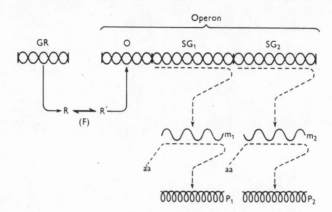

Figure 55.   Model for the regulation of protein synthesis.   GR is the regulator gene, O the operator gene, SG$_1$ and SG$_2$ are structural genes, m$_1$ and m$_2$ are messenger RNA's made by SG$_1$ and SG$_2$, respectively, and P$_1$ and P$_2$ are proteins made by m$_1$ and m$_2$, respectively.   R and R' are forms of the repressor, and F is the effector.   (From J. Monod, F. Jacob, and F. Gros in Structure and Biosynthesis of Macromolecules, Biochemical Society Symposia, no. 21, p. 104, Cambridge University Press, London (1962)).

and regulatory.   The molecular structure of each protein is completely specified by structural genes, one of which accounts for each type of polypeptide chain produced, if more than one is present in the protein synthesized.   According to Monod, the formation of the messenger RNA is an oriented and sequential process which can be initiated only at certain points on the DNA strand.   These points (segments?), of initiation are called *operators*.   In some instances, the transcription of several adjacent genes may depend upon a single operator.   The genes whose action is controlled by the same operator are collectively called the *operon* (see Fig. 55).

In addition to structural genes, the chromosome is assumed to contain genes with a different function, named *regulator genes*.   The nucleotide sequence of a regulator gene (GR in Fig. 55) is assumed to be identical with all, or part, of that of an operator gene (O in Fig. 55).   The regulator acts by producing a *repressor* molecule (R), which is able to combine reversibly with the operator.   This association blocks the initiation of messenger RNA synthesis on the operon, and thus inhibits the formation of the proteins controlled by the structural genes of the operon.   The repressor (R) is also assumed to react specifically with certain small molecules, called *effectors* (F).

$$R + F \rightleftharpoons R' + F'$$

Inducible enzyme systems.   Here only the intact repressor (R) is supposed to be capable of interaction with the operator.   The reaction with an effector, such as a galactoside, blocks the action of the repressor, and permits enzyme synthesis to take place.

Enzyme repression. Here the modified repressor (R') is active, and the presence of effector (for example, tryptophan in the case of tryptophan synthetase) inhibits the transcription from the DNA.

Studies with *E. coli*, mainly with mutations, are consistent with the Monod hypothesis. Thus, numerous regulatory mutations have been identified which affect the synthesis of several enzymes, including betagalactosidase, to the same degree. They all are located outside the structural gene areas of these same enzymes on the genetic map. Mutations have also been identified which block the synthesis of several enzymes, and which are located outside the regulator gene area. This would imply a mutation in the *operator*.

Mutant genes: Their importance in medicine and agriculture. The somatic cells of the human contain 46 chromosomes. Human white blood cells can be grown in tissue culture and arrested in the dividing stage with colchicine. The nuclei of cells with the full complement of dividing chromosomes still attached at the centromere are photographed using a special light microscope and camera. The photographs are enlarged, and the individual chromosomes arranged as shown in Figure 56. The male and female chromosome patterns (karyotypes) each contain 22 pairs of chromosomes varying in length and shape.

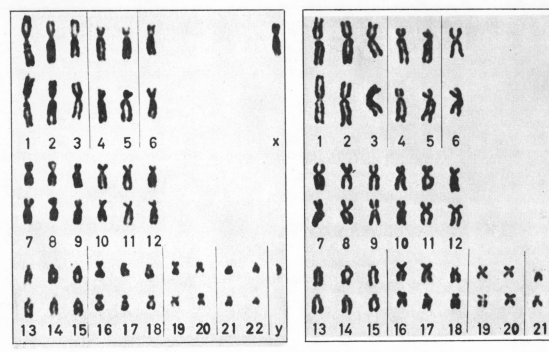

Figure 56. The human male (left) and female (right) karyotypes. (From J. H. Tjio, Am. J. Human Genet., 12, 384 (1960).

In addition, the female has two large X chromosomes, and the male one large X chromosome and one small y chromosome. The finding of Tjio and Levan in 1956, that the human has 46 rather than 48 chromosomes renewed interest in this field, and several chromosome abnormalities have been discovered during the past decade.

Mongolism. Lejeune showed in 1959 that the human with Down's syndrome (mongolism) has one extra, small, acrocentric chromosome at position 21 (Fig. 56). This is thought to arise as a result of nondisjunction during oogenesis in the female. This abnormality is much more prevalent in women after forty years of age, and may be due to aging of the ova, which are all present in the female at birth. The extra chromosome is completely responsible for the severe mental retardation and other stigmata associated with this condition. The author and coworkers have found that the serum uric acid and the serum urea and creatinine levels are elevated in mongolism. In some as yet unknown manner the extra genes in the extra chromosome at position 21 affect the metabolism of these three nitrogenous end-products.

Pernicious anemia. There is some evidence that this type of anemia may be associated with *monosomy* of chromosome 21, i.e., only one chromosome at position 21 in the karyotype.

<u>Sex abnormalities.</u> Changes in the number of sex chromosomes can have a profound effect on the normal development of the human. In many cases these are associated with moderate to severe mental retardation, as well as improper development of the gonads. In Turner's syndrome, one of the two X chromosomes is missing. Such patients, who are phenotypically female, have no testes, the "gonads" consist of slender streaks of connective tissue, and most secondary sex characteristics fail to develop at puberty. Males with Klinefelter's syndrome are sterile, have small testes and certain female traits. They have 47 chromosomes, with an XXY pattern of sex chromosomes. Females with an XXX complement of sex chromosomes associated with severe abnormalities have also been reported. The list of these abnormalities continues to grow.

Table 21. Hereditary metabolic disorders caused by gene mutations

Disorder	Enzyme or Protein Affected	Symptoms
Afibrinogenemia	Fibrinogen	Bleeding.
Agammaglobulinemia	Gamma-globulin	Susceptible to infection.
Albinism	Tyrosinase	Lack of melanin in skin.
Alkaptonuria	Homogentisic acid oxidase	Urine turns black in air.
Galactosemia	Galactose 1-phosphate uridyl transferase	Milk intolerance; mental retardation.
Glycogen storage diseases:		
Type I (von Gierke's)	Glucose 6-phosphatase	Abnormal deposition of glycogen in liver.
Type III	Amylo-1, 6-glucosidase	"
Type IV	Amylo-(1, 4 ⟷ 1, 6)-trans-glycosylase	"
Type V (McArdle's)	Muscle phosphorylase	"
Type VI (Her's)	Liver phosphorylase	"
Goiter (familial)	Iodotyrosine dehalogenase	Cretinism, hypothyroidism.
Hartnup's disease	Tryptophan pyrrolase	Abnormal tryptophan metabolism; mental retardation.
Hemoglobinopathies	Hemoglobins	Sickle cell anemia; anemia.
Hemophilia A	Antihemophilic factor A	Bleeding.
Hemophilia B	" " B	"
Maple syrup urine disease	Amino acid decarboxylase	Mental retardation. High levels of branched chain amino acids in blood.
Methemoglobinemia	Methemoglobin reductase	Cynanosis.
Para hemophilia	Accelerator globulin	Bleeding.
Phenylketonuria	Phenylalanine hydroxylase	Mental retardation. Phenylpyruvic acid in urine.
Wilson's disease	Ceruloplasmin	Mental retardation. Increased copper in tissues.

Hereditary disorders due to mutation of a single gene. In man, mutations associated with a single gene usually cause a disorder of metabolism. The lack of an essential enzyme or functional non-enzymatic protein disturbs the normal pathways of synthesis and degradation. On page 67 it was pointed out that a mutation in the gene controlling the synthesis of one of the chains of hemoglobin resulted in sickle cell anemia. On page 193, pheylketonuria was described as an inherited disease in which the gene responsible for the production of phenylalanine hydroxylase in the liver had mutated, thus upsetting the normal pathway of phenylalanine conversion to tyrosine. In Table 21 are listed some hereditary disorders in man which are due to gene mutations.

Importance of mutant genes in agriculture. The improvement of the quality or quantity of plants and seeds produced for animal and human consumption is an important goal of modern agriculture, especially with the population explosion now in progress. Since gene mutations can change the composition of the storage tissues of plants, a search is in progress for plants of improved quality.

The author and a plant geneticist, Prof. O. E. Nelson, and the author's graduate student, L. S. Bates, recently found that the *opaque-2* mutant gene in corn *(Zea mays)* (Fig. 57) markedly changed the amino acid composition of the endosperm. Table 23 shows that in the whole defatted corn, the mutant corn contains nearly 2 per cent more lysine* along with higher levels of arginine, aspartic acid, threonine and glycine, and lower levels of glutamic acid, proline, alanine, and leucine.

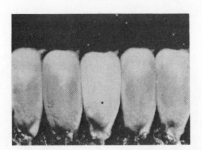

Figure 57.   A row of kernels on an ear of maize showing opaque-2 mutant (center) and normal kernels. (From E. T. Mertz, L. S. Bates, and O. E. Nelson, Science, 145, 279 (1964)).

Table 22. Amino acids in opaque-2 and normal defatted corn (expressed as grams per 100 g. of protein). Values for tryptophan were not available.

Amino Acid	Opaque-2	Normal corn
Lysine	4.7	2.8
Histidine	3.0	3.0
Ammonia	2.7	3.4
Arginine	6.5	4.8
Aspartic acid	10.6	6.7
Glutamic acid	17.9	20.8
Threonine	3.9	3.6
Serine	4.9	4.8
Proline	8.1	10.0
Glycine	4.8	3.8
Alanine	6.9	7.9
Valine	5.5	5.0
Cystine	1.4	1.2
Methionine	1.9	2.0
Isoleucine	3.8	4.0
Leucine	9.8	13.9
Tyrosine	3.6	4.0
Phenylalanine	4.8	5.2

* Lysine is the first limiting amino acid in corn and other cereal grains.

When *opaque-2* corn and normal corn were both fed at a level of 90 per cent in the diets of weanling albino rats, the rats on the mutant corn gained at 3.5 times the rate of the animals on normal corn (see Fig. 58).

In Figure 59 it can be seen that the animals on the mutant corn were much larger and had better hair coats than the animals on ordinary corn after 28 days on the diet.

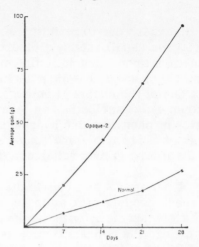

Figure 58.   Curves showing average weekly gains of rats fed on opaque-2 maize and Indiana hybrid 453. (From E. T. Mertz, O. A. Veron, L. S. Bates and O. E. Nelson, Science, 148, 1741 (1965).

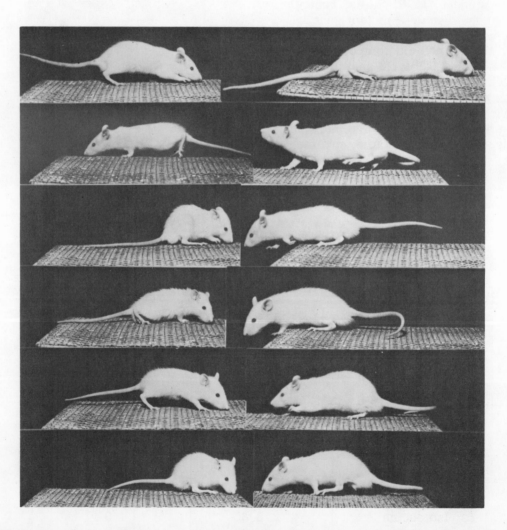

Figure 59.   Weanling albino rats after 28 days on diets containing 90 per cent whole ground corn, 5 per cent corn oil, 4 per cent mineral mixture, and 1 per cent of vitamin supplementation mixture. The rats in the left column received Indiana hybrid 257, those on the right received opaque-2 maize. Arranged in order of decreasing weight. The smallest animal in the right column gained more than twice as much as the largest animal in the left column.

These studies show the great possibilities of improving the protein quality of corn by introducing the *opaque-2* mutant gene into our present stocks. Similar mutations probably exist at the same locus on the chromosome in other cereal grains like wheat, rice, etc. Another mutant gene, *floury-2,* has an effect similar to that of *opaque-2* in corn, and is being studied by Prof. Nelson and the author.

It may be concluded that mutant genes are, in general, harmful when found in the human chromosome. However, they can prove extremely valuable to man when they provide useful changes in the nutrient composition of plants.

Chapter 9

MINERALS, SOILS, AND PLANT NUTRITION

Certain mineral elements are an essential part of the diet of animals, plants, and microorganisms. Those required in relatively large amounts are used in most cases in the synthesis of structural tissues, whereas those required in trace amounts usually function as activators, or as component parts of enzyme systems. In the majority of cases, the same essential mineral elements are required by all living organisms; however, a few elements do have unique functions in only one class of organism.

With the exception of the four elements furnished to a greater or lesser degree by the atmosphere (O_2, C (as CO_2), N_2, and S (as SO_2)), all of the elements required by living organisms must be furnished initially by the soil. The plant kingdom makes the direct withdrawals of minerals from the soil, with relatively minor withdrawals by microorganisms, man, and animals. The latter groups depend primarily on the plants for their supply of mineral elements.

In order to gain an understanding of the mechanism of uptake of minerals from soils, and the prevention of mineral deficiencies in plants, the following section on the chemistry and microbiology of soils is included.

Chemistry of Soils

COMPOSITION. Soils vary widely in composition because of the variety of physical and chemical agents which brought them into existence from the original rock crust of the earth. Soil formation and erosion goes on constantly (see "Soils and Men", U.S.D.A., Washington (1938)). The average composition of a good silt loam soil in the fertile "corn belt" states is approximately 45% minerals, 30% water, 20% air, and 5% organic matter. The mineral matter of the soil, as well as the relative content of organic matter, determine to a large degree the nature or type of soil. The nature of the mineral phase is de-

Table 23. Classification of soils

Soil Type	Name	Region	Nature
Acid	podsol (forest soil)	cold, moist climate	high in silica, organic matter
Slightly acid	black soil	humid climate	balance of all four groups*
Neutral	black silt loam	prairies	high in organic, calcium
Alkaline	arid soil	desert	high in alkali and alkaline earth carbonates, low in organic

* Silica, alkali and alkaline earth metals, iron and aluminum, organic matter.

termined by the presence of three groups of inorganic compounds: (1) compounds of silicon (silica, etc.), (2) alkali and alkaline-earth metal compounds (Na, K, Mg, and Cu most important), and (3) compounds of iron and aluminum, usually as the oxides (for example, Al_2O_3, Fe_2O_3, etc.). Soil types vary, depending on the relative proportions of the above groups of compounds. A brief summary is given in Table 23.

Composition of the mineral fraction of an "average" soil. Wide variations, especially in silica and aluminum oxide content, are found in soils from different areas. An "average" value for individual mineral constituents is therefore not too helpful. However, it does arrange the mineral elements in the order of their relative abundance in tillable soils. Table 24 shows the "average" elemental composition of the A horizon* of an "average" fertile soil. The elements are calculated as their oxides, although they actually occur as complex silicates and similar compounds.

Table 24.   Elemental Composition of the A horizon of an
average fertile soil

Element (as oxide)	Per cent of total mineral oxides
SiO_2	76. 5
Al_2O_3	10. 0
Fe_2O_3	3. 6
K_2O	1. 7
CaO	1. 0
TiO_2	0. 9
Na_2O	0. 8
MgO	0. 6
P_2O_5	0. 1
MnO	0. 1
SO_2	0. 1

It can be seen from Table 24 that the oxides of silicon, aluminum and iron predominate, accounting (in this example) for 90% of the total major elements expressed as oxides. They actually form the "framework" of the soil, for they exist primarily as complex silicates, which form a lattice work to which many important inorganic ions are attached, and from which the ions can be exchanged for hydrogen by the root hairs of the plant. Other properties of soil, such as porosity and capillarity, are determined to a large extent by the combinations of these three elements. In addition to the elements listed in Table 24, there are many other elements occurring at levels of less than 0.1%, some of which are required for plant growth.

Composition of the organic fraction. The soil organic matter consists of living microorganisms, and of the organic residues of dead microorganisms, plants, and animals. The living microorganisms are responsible for the gradual decomposition of the organic residues of dead organisms. As the organic residues are used as food by the microorganisms, products of metabolism such as water, CO_2, NH_3, and CH_4 (methane) are released. Finally, a mixture of organic compounds resistant to further decomposition is left. This mixture is called *humus*. It is an amorphous, dark-colored material with little odor, containing about 60% carbon and 3-6% nitrogen. Members of all of the major classes of nutrients are present in humus, but the two most abundant constituents are protein and lignin (see page 314, Appendix). It is probable that these are combined mainly as lignoproteinate. Many soil chemists divide humus substances into two groups (1) *temporary humus*, having the physical characteristics of humus, but still serving as a source of carbon to microorganisms, and (2) *permanent humus*, humus that is attacked

* The A horizon is the surface soil - about 7 inches in depth.

only slowly by microorganisms, and serves as an important organic colloidal material in the soil.

SOIL COLLOIDS. Permanent humus is a negatively charged, highly hydrated colloid. In soil, it exists as a gel which is closely associated with, and coats, the inorganic particles. This coating can absorb positively charged ions, and take part in ion exchange reactions. Permanent humus is an *organic soil colloid*. Soil also contains *inorganic colloids*.

Composition of inorganic colloid fraction. In the discussion of the elemental composition of the inorganic phase of soil, it was pointed out that the oxides of Si, Al and Fe accounted for about 90 per cent of the mineral matter of an average soil. Soil particles can be separated into four major physical fractions (1) coarse sand (0.2-2 mm.), (2) fine sand (0.02-0.2 mm.), (3) silt (0.002-0.02 mm.) and (4) clay (less than 0.002 mm.). From the standpoint of plant *nutrition*, the most important fraction is the clay fraction. This fraction contains *colloidal clay particles* (100 mμ or less in diameter - see page 5) which, together with the organic soil colloids, are mainly responsible for the ion-exchange properties, water-holding capacity, and the buffering action of the soils.

Clay colloids are composed of laminated plates of crystalline minerals and organic colloids. Each colloidal particle contains in its lattice work a large amount of internal and external surface. The external surface carries a negative electrical charge, balanced by an outer layer of positive ions. Because of this double layer of ions (Helmholz double layer), the surface of the particle shows a definite electrical potential (called the Zeta potential). In an electrical field, clay colloid particles move to the positive pole inasmuch as they carry a negative charge. Cation or base exchange occurs readily on the colloidal clay particles. When arranged in the order of replacing ability, $H > Sr > Ba > Ca > Mg < Rb < K > NH_4 > Na > Si$. However, replacement of ions follows the Law of Mass Action, so that an excess of any one ion can reverse the process. Thus, one method of determining the base-exchange capacity of soil is to flood the soil with ammonium acetate, and measure the amount of ammonium ion retained on the colloids. The same principle is used to regenerate a zeolite water softener, except in this case, sodium ion in the form of sodium chloride is used to flood the complex silicate (zeolite), and displace the calcium and magnesium ions previously picked up by the zeolite from the hard water (see page 299, Chapter 15).

THE SOIL SOLUTION. The ions on the colloidal particles of soil are in equilibrium with the same ions in the *soil solution*, or water solution present in the soil. As indicated previously, a good silt loam soil will contain about 30 per cent (by volume) of water. As the plant removes ions from the soil, or they are leached by rain fall or irrigation, the ions of the soil solution are replenished from the ion supply bound to the soil colloids. Eventually, if the loss of ions by leaching or overcropping is excessive, the equilibrium must be established at a lower level of ions, and poor plant growth results. At this point, inorganic nutrient ions must be restored to the soil colloids by fertilization.

Fertilization of the soil. A replenishment of the inorganic nutrient elements of the soil can be accomplished by (a) plowing under succeeding plant crops, especially leguminous crops such as clover, which increase the nitrogen content of soil by nitrogen fixation, (b) plowing under farm manure, which is a combination of plant residues and animal excretory products rich in nitrogen, potassium and phosphorus, and (c) adding a scientifically balanced commercial fertilizer containing the nutrient elements which are at suboptimal levels in the soil. This is in accordance with the principle first set forth by Liebig in his famous "Law of the Minimum".

Methods (a) and (b) are valuable, but they have their limitations. In combination with method (c), they provide the best farming practice available today. Thus, in raising corn on a selected field, it is a good practice to break the repetition every three or four years by planting the field to clover, and plowing this under at the end of the season. The efficient use of farm manure is also very beneficial, for the manure increases the per cent organic matter and the microorganism count of the soil, and in addition supplies, per ton, about 10 lb. of nitrogen, 5 lb. of P_2O_5, and 10 lb. of K_2O.

Supplying essential elements with commercial fertilizer. The methods used to determine the mineral requirements of plants will be discussed later. The mineral elements which have been found essential for plant growth are: phosphorus (P), potassium (K), nitrogen (N), sulfur (S), calcium (Ca), magnesium (Mg), iron (Fe), manganese (Mn), copper (Cu), boron (B), zinc (Zn), and molybdenum (Mo). The last six elements are required in such small quantities by plants that they are called "micronutrients".

It is possible to supply any one or all of these elements in a utilizable form as commercial fertilizer. Most state agricultural experiment stations have a service whereby a farmer or gardener can send in a sample of his soil for ion-exchange, pH, and elemental analysis. On the basis of this analysis, the soil chemist will recommend the proper combination of elements to add as fertilizer to the soil to give it maximum fertility. The sale of commercial fertilizers is controlled in most states in a manner similar to that exercised over the sale of feeds (see page 294, Chapter 15). Minimum guarantees for the major inorganic nutrients supplied must be printed on the label of the fertilizer container.

The elements most commonly deficient in soils are the three which are used in largest amounts by the plant, namely, nitrogen, phosphorus, and potassium. The majority of commercial fertilizers are composed of salts providing stated quantities of these three elements. The elements are expressed as per cent nitrogen, P_2O_5, and K_2O, and the fertilizer is identified by its "NPK" ratio. For example, a popular fertilizer for lawns is a "10:10:10" fertilizer; it contains 10% total nitrogen, 10% P_2O_5, and 10% K_2O. Fertilizers with more than about 25% total NPK nutrients do not contain inert bulking material, but only the compounds carrying the N, P and K.

Other elements can be applied to soils that need them. Thus, manganese and iron solutions are sprayed on the leaves of pineapple plants in Hawaii, because of a deficiency

Table 25. Commercial fertilizer ingredients

Name	Elements supplied
Anhydrous ammonia ("liquid nitrogen")	N(as NH_3)
$\quad$ $NaNO_3$	N
$\quad$ NH_4NO_3	N
$\quad$ KNO_3	N, K
$\quad$ $(NH_4)_2SO_4$	N, S
$\quad$ Urea	N
$\quad$ $CaCN_2$ (calcium cyanamide)	N, Ca
Packing house protein wastes	N
Oil seed wastes (castor bean meal, etc.)	N
Dried activated sewage sludge	N, P, K
Superphosphate ($CaH_4(PO_4)$ and $CaSO_4 \cdot H_2O$)	P, Ca
Ammoniated super phosphate	P, N
Basic slag (phosphate)	P, Ca
Bone meal	P, N, Ca
$\quad$ KCl	K
$\quad$ K_2SO_4	K, S
$\quad$ $K_2SO_4 \cdot MgSO_4$	K, S, Mg

of available manganese and iron in the soil. The leaves absorb these ions almost as efficiently as the roots. Calcium (as limestone) is applied in large quantities to many soils, not to relieve a calcium deficiency, but to neutralize soil acidity, which makes many mineral elements unavailable for ion exchange. Boron deficiency is the most widespread of the micronutrient deficiencies, and copper deficiency the least.

Common ingredients of commercial fertilizers. Table 25 lists some of the common ingredients of commercial fertilizers, and the nutrient elements that they supply in greatest amount.

SOIL CONDITIONERS. The use of special organic polymeric compounds to increase the moisture-retaining properties and to improve the texture of soils has attracted considerable interest. Two products of this nature manufactured commercially are "Krillium" and "Loamium". They are recommended by the manufacturers for improving the texture of heavy clay soils, but their cost limits their use to special greenhouse and garden applications.

Soil Microbiology

According to S. A. Waksman* "The soil is by no means an inert mass of organic and inorganic debris. On the contrary, it fairly teems with life. ------ Many thousands of species, capable of a great variety of activities, are represented in the soil. ----- One gram of soil contains hundreds, even thousands, of millions of bacteria, fungi, actinomycetes, protozoa, and other groups of microorganisms".

As we have mentioned previously, the soil particles are surrounded by films of a colloidal mixture which is both organic and inorganic in nature. The microorganisms inhabiting the soil tend to adhere to these films, although some also move freely in the water which surrounds the soil particles. The nature of the soil microbial population is controlled to a large extent by the water and air content of the soil, and by the nature of the soil fractions. Well-aerated soils, such as the sandy type, favor growth of aerobic bacteria and fungi. On the other hand, water-logged peat bogs are an example of a soil in a perpetual anaerobic state. Here the fungi and actinomycetes tend to decrease, and bacteria of the anaerobic type predominate.

Seasonal and temperature changes affect the soil population. Microorganisms vary in their temperature optima, and an increase in the species having the best growth characteristics at a fixed temperature is often observed. The pH of the soil also affects the population. Thus, in acid soils, fungi predominate because they can tolerate acid conditions. Conversely, actinomycetes predominate in dry and alkaline soils. The soil population is also markedly influenced by the nature and abundance of higher plant and animal life in and on the surface of the soil. Thus, root systems harbor certain symbiotic organisms (*rhizobia* on legumes, etc.), and also bring about better aeration of the soil. The plants favor the growth of certain plant pathogens, and plants and animals leave residues from metabolism, as well as from their dead bodies, which favor the growth of selected microorganisms.

The soil population can be divided into eight major groups: bacteria, actinomycetes, fungi, algae, protozoa, worms, insects and other near-microscopic animals, and the ultramicroscopic forms. The ultramicroscopic group covers the range from the living systems to the products of the latter, and include reproducing units such as the phages and the viruses. The soil microbiologist uses several methods to determine the nature and relative abundance of these groups in a specific soil. The methods most commonly employed are: plate culture, selective culture, contact slide, direct micro-

* S. A. Waksman, Microbial Antagonisms and Antibiotic Substances, p. 1, The Commonwealth Fund, N.Y. (1945).

scopy, and mechanical separation. Students interested in the details of these methods are referred to the literature. The influence of soil treatment and of growing plants on the number of microorganisms in the soil is shown in Table 26 below. Table 26 is based on data compiled by Waksman.

Of the various organisms present in the soil, fungi are found in the form of mycelial filaments and spores, algae are usually found only in the surface layers of the soil, and protozoa are present either in an active vegetative state or in the form of cysts. Nematodes, earthworms, rotifers and larvae of insects are often found in abundance.

Table 26. Effect of soil treatment and influence of plant cultivation on microbial population of soil

Soil treatment	pH of soil	Microorganisms found (x 1,000/gm. soil)		
		Bacteria	Actinomycetes	Fungi
Unfertilized, unlimed	4.6	3,000	1,100	60
K salts, phosphates	5.5	5,360	1,520	38
Stable manure, salts	5.4	8,800	2,920	73
Plant cultivated				
Corn				
Soil near roots	--	41,000	13,400	178
Soil away from roots	--	24,300	8,800	134
Alfalfa				
Soil near roots	--	93,800	9,000	268
Soil away from roots	--	17,800	3,300	254

SURVIVAL OF PATHOGENIC BACTERIA; ANTIBIOTICS IN SOILS. The continuous addition of human and animal wastes to the soil and water basins of the earth raises the question of the survival of organisms pathogenic to living animals and humans. Improper methods of disposing of human and animal wastes were undoubtedly responsible for many of the epidemics of typhoid, cholera, plague, and other diseases which have decimated mankind. Medical bacteriologists since the time of Koch (1880) have studied the survival of pathogens in human and animal excreta, and in the soil and water used to dispose of them. Although many pathogens persist for relatively long periods of time in isolated undecomposed excreta, bacteriologists have demonstrated that, with the exception of about a dozen hardy species, most of the disease-producing organisms die out rapidly in the soil. The hardy species are the organisms causing anthrax, tetanus, gas gangrene, actinomycosis in cattle, hookworm infections, coccidiosis in poultry, trichinosis, blackleg in cattle, enteric disorders in man, Texas fever, and botulism. Most of these agents appear to survive by going into a dormant, resistant, spore form.

The fairly rapid disappearance of most disease-producing bacteria may be attributed to a variety of causes: environment, food supply, destruction by protozoa and other microscopic animals, and destruction by antagonistic bacteria and fungi.

Antibiotics from antagonistic organisms. As early as 1879, De Bary designated the antagonistic action of one organism toward another as "antibiosis". Many reasons for this antagonism have been proposed, but the most logical and demonstrable reason is the production of specific *toxic* substances which inhibit or even kill the competing organisms. These toxic substances have been named *antibiotics*, and were not studied systematically and intensively until their potentialities were uncovered by the pioneer work of Dubos working with antibiotics from the soil, and by the pioneer work of Fleming on antibiotics from penicillium molds. The commercial production and widespread use of various anti-biotics to control disease organisms (see page 291) stems from the pioneer studies of these two investigators.

Microbiologists are making a continual search for new antibiotics. Most petroleum exploration companies are cooperating by sending in soil samples from drillings all over the world. These samples are being screened for new antagonistic microorganims which may produce a superior antibiotic for one or more diseases of man or animals. Several methods are used for screening new microorganisms, all based on the principle of bring-ing a living culture of a known bacterium or fungus in close contact with the mixed natu-ral population of the new soil sample, and observing which members of the natural popu-lation grow at the expense of the added known microorganism. For details of these meth-ods, the reader is referred to the literature.

Mineral Nutrition in Plants

ESSENTIAL ELEMENTS. Hoagland has set up the following criteria for the essentiality of an element for plant growth: (1) the plant will not complete its life cycle in the absence of the element in question, even if all other known essential elements are present and all other factors of the environment are favorable for growth, (2) no other element can be substituted for the element under investigation, (3) the element is directly necessary for the nutrition of the plant and is not merely required under special conditions, to neutral-ize some external toxic substance, or to protect the plant against an invading microor-ganism.

In addition to the criteria above, it may be necessary to show that growth failure under the above conditions may be overcome by direct application of the element to the plant (by spraying the leaves or injecting the element into the plant).

The following ten elements were accepted as essential for plants on the basis of early water culture experiments, or experiments in which nutrient salts were added to pure sand: Water culture: carbon, hydrogen, oxygen - (Liebig and others); sand culture: N, S, P, K, Ca, Mg and Fe.

Sand culture* experiments, using highly purified chemicals under rigorously con-trolled conditions, were needed to add an additional five elements to the list: B, Mn, Cu, Zn and Mo. These elements are needed in only trace amounts, and are often refer-red to as "micronutrient" or "minor" elements. The former term is preferred by plant physiologists. It should be pointed out that many micronutrient elements become toxic to the plant when present in the nutrient medium at a concentration in great excess of physiological needs.

ABSORPTION OF IONS BY ROOTS. The plant roots selectively absorb cations, giving hydrogen ions in exchange. In contrast, anions, such as SO_4^{--}, are absorbed directly without ion exchange. The living and uninjured root cells may be considered the active agents in the adsorption and absorption processes. They have the ability to absorb ions from extremely dilute solutions, and store them in the cell sap, or in other liquid phases of the cell, in concentrations often much higher than those found in the external solution.

The uptake and storage of ions under such conditions is contrary to the osmotic pressure tendencies of the soil and sap solutions; ion exchange ordinarily would operate in a reverse direction. To accomplish the transfer of ions, metabolic energy is required.

---

* This is the basis for the modern science of hydroponics - "soilless gardening". Sand supports the roots; the plants are fed a nutrient solution containing all needed elements.

This is apparently supplied through energy obtained in the oxidative processes of aerobic respiration (see p. 159). The transfer of ions from the root hair to the aerial parts of the plant also requires metabolic energy. Transpiration (movement of water to leaves due to evaporation from leaves) does not account for translocation of ions. Here again *aerobic respiration* plays the key role. It can be seen from this that any toxic substances interfering with root respiration will reduce the ability of the root to absorb and translocate ions. It is also apparent that a well-aerated soil is essential for good ion absorption by the plant's roots. In such a soil, oxygen is readily available to the root hair, and the carbon dioxide produced quickly diffuses out.

FUNCTION OF ESSENTIAL ELEMENTS. The function of some mineral elements is at once apparent, but certain elements have yet to be classified with certainty. The obvious (or probable) functions of the elements are listed below.

Nitrogen. Part of many structural and protoplasmic components (proteins, phospholipids, vitamins, etc.)

Sulfur. Part of the structure of proteins (cystine, cysteine, methionine), sulfhydryl compounds (glutathione, etc.) and vitamins (thiamine, biotin, thioctic acid, etc.)

Phosphorus. Part of the structure of nucleoproteins, phospholipids, phosphorylated carbohydrates, dinucleotides, etc.

Potassium. Not found as a structural component. May function as a co-enzyme in carbohydrate metabolism. Also a part of the buffering system in the plant sap.

Calcium. Part of the buffering system in the plant sap. Calcium pectate is a cementing substance in the middle lamella of plants, and is a component of root hairs.

Magnesium. Component of chlorophyll. Also functions as a metallic activator of coenzymes in carbohydrate metabolism.

Iron, Boron, Manganese, Copper, Zinc, Molybdenum. All are probably components of specific enzyme systems in plants.

EFFECT OF MINERAL DEFICIENCIES. The lack of any essential mineral element causes a marked stunting of growth of plants, with corresponding decreases in yield of crop dry matter. In addition to this general deficiency symptom, certain elements when present at suboptimal levels produce characteristic symptoms in plants which help to identify the deficient element. Excellent black and white, and color plates, showing the effects of mineral deficiencies in various plants of economic importance, are published in the book entitled "Hunger Signs in Crops" (see p. 308, Appendix).

In Figure 60 are shown the effects of nitrogen, phosphorus, and potassium deficiencies on oats plants. The earthenware pots were filled with a Crosby silt loam soil which had been cropped excessively and had low fertility. Treatment of Pot 16 with a complete fertilizer (N + P + K) gave healthy, vigorous plants. Omission of nitrogen (Pot 13) gave spindly, yellowish green plants with slightly purplish stems. Omission of phosphorus (Pot 14) gave dark green plants with weak stems with slight purple tinge. Omission of potassium (Pot 15) gave dark green plants with weak stems and with oldest leaves brown and tip ends deadened. In addition, the dry matter yields of forage from Pots 13, 14 and 15 were much lower than that from Pot 16.

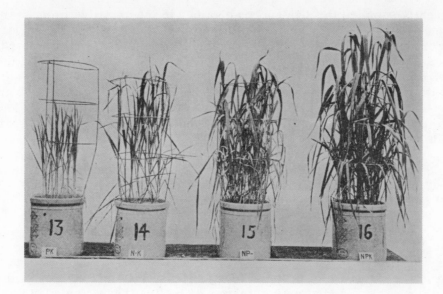

Figure 60.   The effect of nitrogen, phosphorus, and potassium deficiency on oats.   (From Purdue
Agricultural Experiment Station.   Reproduced from Hunger Signs in Crops).

The lack of one of the "trace" minerals required by plants can be equally disastrous as shown by the effect of a zinc deficiency on the development of the grapefuit (Fig. 61).

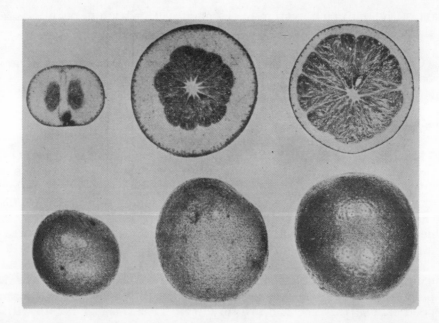

Figure 61.   Effect of zinc deficiency on fruit production of grapefruit tree.   (Left).   Grapefruit showing
effects of an acute zinc deficiency.   (Center).   Grapefruit from zinc-deficient tree two
months after treatment with zinc, showing some improvement.   (Right).   Grapefruit from
zinc-deficient tree treated 15 months previously with zinc, showing normal development
of fruit.   (From California Agricultural Experiment Station.   Reproduced from Hunger
Signs in Crops.)

MINERAL NUTRITION IN MICROORGANISMS. The determination of the mineral requirements of microorganisms is more difficult than for plants. It is almost impossible to prepare culture media free of certain elements, and there is also the problem of transference of elements to succeeding generations of bacteria through the process of cell division. In spite of these difficulties, the following ten elements have been proved essential for most of the microorganisms tested to date: C, H, O, N, Mg, K, P, S, Fe, and Mn. In addition, the following five elements have been reported to be essential for at least one species of microorganism: Ca, Cu, Zn, Mo, and Co. It is probable that the mineral requirements for microorganisms are quite similar to those for plants. With the possible exception of calcium and magnesium, the elements also probably have the same functions in plants and microorganisms.

Chapter 10 | DIGESTION AND ABSORPTION

Digestion may be defined as the process of hydrolysis of complex food substances to produce simpler forms which can be assimilated by the organism. Plants and a few micro-organisms do not utilize complex outside sources of food. Thus, the plant is dependent only on a supply of water, minerals, carbon dioxide and sunlight. Only in the germinating seed is digestion of complex food substances required. Here, the digestion of carbohydrates, lipids, and proteins is mainly intra-cellular with the simplified nutrients flowing by diffusion to the embryo.

Many micro-organisms secrete enzymes into the surrounding medium and thus bring about digestion of food substances in their vicinity. In both the germinating seed and the micro-organism, there is no movement of complex food substances to the site of digestion. In animals, however, from insect to man, special anatomical parts are provided for transporting complex food substances from the outside to the organs of digestion. These are discussed below.

Comparative Anatomy of Digestive Tracts and General Physiology of Digestion

The digestive tract of animals, from insects to man, can for purposes of discussion be divided into five regions, namely, the mouth, the esophagus, the stomach (or equivalent), the small intestine (or equivalent) and the large intestine.

THE MOUTH. The mouth of man and four-footed animals contain teeth, for the mastication of food, and salivary glands, which secrete saliva to aid in mastication. Fish and birds do not masticate their food, whereas the chewing type of insects resemble man and the higher animals in this respect, and secrete saliva to aid in mastication.

THE ESOPHAGUS. The esophagus (see Figure 62) is a muscular tube which connects the mouth to the stomach, or its equivalent. In birds and many insects there is an enlargement of the esophagus in which storage of food takes place. This storage organ is called the crop. It is believed that the first three parts of the "stomach" of the ruminant are actually enlargements of the esophagus.

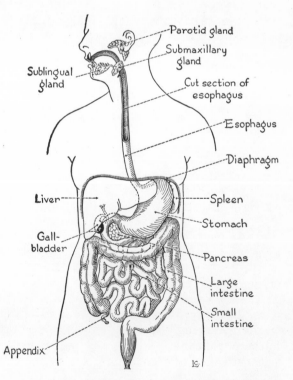

Figure 62. Diagram of digestive tract in man. (Reproduced by permission from Etheredge: Health Facts for College Students. 7th Ed. W. B. Saunders Co., 1958).

THE STOMACH.   The sketches in Figure 63 below, indicate the major differences in the anatomy of the stomach region in different species.   In man and the higher non-ruminant animals, the stomach is a single sac which is relatively thin-walled in the capacious fundus area, and thick-walled in the pylorus area.   The inside wall of the stomach is lined with parietal (HCl-producing) cells and with chief (enzyme-producing) cells.   The mixed secretion of these two types of cells is called *gastric juice*.   In ruminants, the

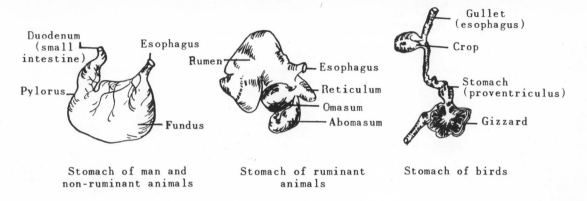

Figure 63.   Comparison of monogastric, ruminant, and avian stomachs.   Not drawn to same scale.

stomach consists of four parts, the rumen (paunch), reticulum, omasum, and abomasum. In cattle, the paunch or rumen has a capacity of about 30 gallons, the reticulum, 2 gallons, the omasum, 3 gallons, and the abomasum, 3 gallons.   Food passes from the esophagus to the rumen, from the rumen to the reticulum, from the reticulum to the omasum, and from the omasum to the abomasum.   Food can be regurgitated from the rumen and the reticulum for further mastication.   When ruminants are used as draft animals, it has been established that they must have at least 8 work-free hours out of every 24 for "chewing the cud", or they will lose weight and become ill.   The *abomasum*, or fourth stomach of ruminants corresponds to the single sac stomach of man and non-ruminant animals. Here gastric juice is secreted, and digestion of proteins proceeds as in the non-ruminant stomach.

In birds, the stomach (proventriculus) secretes gastric juice which aids in the breakdown of proteins, but the stomach is small and has no storage capacity.   As a result, food is moistened with gastric juice in the stomach, and the mixture passes to the gizzard, a large muscular organ.   Here the food material is ground to a fine state of subdivision with the aid of grit (previously swallowed by the bird) and muscular action, and partially digested by the gastric juice added previously.

In fish, (see Figure 64 on the following page) the stomach is a single sac with a fundus and pylorus region.   Attached to the pylorus walls, however, are a large number of blind segments called *pyloric caeca*, which may be considered part of the intestinal structure.

In many insects, the stomach region consists of a muscular gizzard (see Figure 65 on the following page) and gastric caeca, which are blind tubes secreting gastric juice. In the cockroach, the gizzard is provided with rows of massive teeth, which seize and triturate the solid particles of food from the crop.

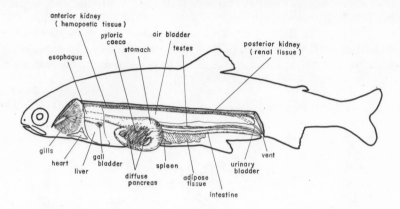

Figure 64.   Digestive tract of the rainbow trout. (Drawn by W. T. Yasutake,
Western Fish Nutrition Laboratory, Cook, Washington).

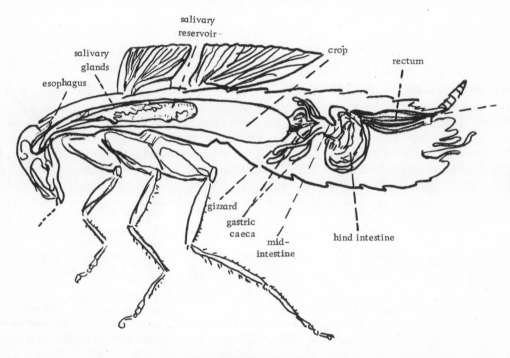

Figure 65.   Digestive tract of cockroach.

THE SMALL INTESTINE. The small intestine of man, all four-footed animals, and
birds, can be divided into three anatomical regions, the duodenum, the jejunum, and the
ileum. Figure 62 shows the position of the small intestine with relation to other parts of
the digestive tract in one of these species, man.

The small intestine is much longer than the sketch in Figure 62 indicates. It is
about 25 feet long in man (duodenum - about 1 ft., jejunum - about 10 ft., ileum - about
15 ft.), 60 feet long in the hog, and 130 feet long in the cow. The small intestine is lined
with glands (Lieberkuhn's and Brunner's) which secrete intestinal juice, a digestive secretion. These glands are especially abundant in the duodenum and the first part of the
jejunum.

In addition to intestinal juice, two other secretions empty into the first part of the small intestine (duodenum) from either separate ducts or a common duct. One of these, bile, is manufactured in the liver, stored in a small organ embedded in the liver, the gall bladder, and passes from the gall bladder into the duodenum. The second secretion is pancreatic juice, which is manufactured by the acinous tissue of the pancreas (Fig. 62).

Villi. The small intestine is lined with tiny finger-like projections called villi. These organs possess ciliary (whip-like) motion, and under the microscope the villi of the small intestine of the living animal look somewhat like a stand of ripe wheat waving in a strong wind. This movement aids the villi in absorbing the end-products of digestion from the food masses passing through the small intestine. Figure 66 below shows a sketch of villus. The blood capillary network in the villus absorbs a higher per cent of the end-products of protein and carbohydrate digestion, whereas the lacteal is an organ which absorbs a higher per cent of the end-products of lipid digestion.

The small intestine of the fish has been modified into a cluster of pyloric caeca, or blind segments of intestine (see Fig. 64). These are lined with villi, and absorption of the end-products of digestion in the stomach and caeca occurs here.

No well-defined small intestine is observed in insects. In the cockroach (Fig. 65) and most other insects, the midintestine probably corresponds to the small intestine of higher animals, for most of the absorption of digested food nutrients takes place here. However, the intestinal wall is not lined with villi as in higher animals. The dissolved nutrients diffuse through a delicate membrane, composed of chitin (see page 23) mixed perhaps with some protein, known as the *peritrophic membrane*, and are absorbed directly by the epithelial cells of the intestinal wall.

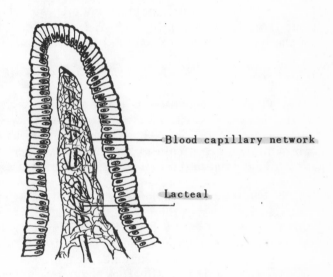

Figure 66.   Structure of a villus.

THE LARGE INTESTINE. In man and all higher animals, the contents of the ileum empty into the first part of the large intestine, the caecum, through the ileo-caecal valve (Fig. 62). The caecum is greatly enlarged in the horse and in the rabbit. In the horse, it has a capacity of 7-8 gallons, and serves (in both rabbits and horses) as a fermentation vat for the utilization of part of the cellulose and hemicelluloses of the diet. In other species, the caecum, colon, and rectum serve mainly as a water-absorbing canal for the conversion of liquid fecal material into a semi-solid mass suitable for excretion. Very little absorption of nutrients occurs in the large intestine region of most animals. This applies also to the cockroach and other similar insects, where the hind intestine and rectum comprise the large intestine (Fig. 65).

Comparative Biochemistry of Digestive Secretions

SALIVA. The salivary glands in the mouth parts (under the tongue, and jawbone, and in the cheek, of man and higher animals) secrete a viscous solution called saliva, which has a pH of about 6-6.6 and is composed of approximately 99.5% water, 0.2% inorganic, and 0.3% organic matter. The inorganic matter consists of calcium, sodium, potassium and magnesium salts of phosphoric, hydrochloric and carbonic acids. The organic matter includes mucin, a glycoprotein, which gives saliva its viscous and ropey consistency. The saliva of humans, pigs, and cockroaches also contains a potent amylase (starch-splitting enzyme).

The primary function of saliva in all species is to moisten the food, dissolve soluble components, and aid in the mastication of the insoluble components. In addition, the saliva lubricates the masticated food so that it can be swallowed more readily. Man secretes about 1-1.5 liters of saliva, the cow about 100 liters, in 24 hours.

GASTRIC JUICE. This secretion, which has the appearance of saliva, is a mixture of the secretions of three main types of cells: mucous, parietal (border) and chief (zymogenic). The mucous cells secrete a liquid high in mucin, the parietal cells one high in hydrochloric acid, and the chief cells supply the proenzymes or zymogens. The parietal cells secrete an HCl solution with an acidity of approximately 0.15N, and a pH of about 1.

The hydrochloric acid is made by selective absorption of hydrogen ions and chloride ions from the blood (pH of 7.3-7.4), which bathes the cells. The reaction is a reversal of the neutralization of sodium bicarbonate with HCl, and thus requires energy.

$$H_2CO_3 \text{ (blood)} + NaCl \text{ (blood)} \dashrightarrow HCl \text{ (gastric juice)} + NaHCO_3 \text{ (blood)}.$$

After the ingestion of a heavy meal, a large amount of HCl is made by the parietal cells. This, in turn, increases the alkalinity of the blood due to the formation of extra quantities of $NaHCO_3$. The kidneys excrete the extra alkalinity in the form of sodium and ammonium salts. This is referred to as the "alkaline tide", and can often be observed as a cloudiness in the urine due to precipitation of the urinary phosphates.

The pH of the parietal cell secretion is raised by dilution with the secretions of the mucous and chief cells, so that the final pH of gastric juice is 1.5-2.0. Gastric juice contains about 99% water, 0.5% HCl, 0.2% inorganic salts, and 0.3% organic matter. The inorganic salts are the same as those found in saliva. The organic matter consists mainly of mucin, and the proenzymes, pepsinogen, prorennin (in calves and other young mammals), and a rather ineffective enzyme, gastric lipase.

The classical studies of Beaumont on a human with a stomach fistula, and later studies, show that the flow of gastric juice in higher animals is regulated by several factors. Among these are taste, odor, or sight of food (increase flow), fear or worry (suppress flow), ethyl alcohol (increases HCl and mucin content), meat extracts (increase flow), histamine (increases HCl, decreases pepsinogen), and the hormone enterogastrone (decreases flow - see p. 270).

BILE. Bile is produced continuously by the liver in higher animals and man, and is collected by a series of ducts which empty via the hepatic duct (see p. 140) into the gall bladder, a storage organ. When the gall bladder is absent (e.g., humans with gall bladder removed), the hepatic duct enlarges and takes over as a storage organ.

Liver bile is more dilute than gall bladder bile, indicating that water is removed on storage. Gall bladder bile contains about 86% water and 14% solids. The solids are made up of about 8% bile salts (sodium glycocholate and sodium taurocholate-related to sterols, p. 50), 2% bile pigments and mucin, 3% cholesterol (p. 51) and other lipids, and about 1% inorganic salts. Bile has an amber color, but on exposure to air, it changes to a green color (the red pigment bilirubin is converted to the green pigment biliverdin).

Glycocholic Acid   Taurocholic Acid   Bilirubin   Biliverdin

Bile is alkaline (pH 7.7 to 8.6) due in large part to the bile salts. It contains no digestive enzymes except a phosphatase, and exerts its beneficial effects on digestion mainly through its dissolving and emulsifying effects on dietary lipids (see p. 148). It is estimated that the adult human secretes about one liter of bile in 24 hours. A large proportion of the bile salts excreted into the intestines via the bile duct is reabsorbed and returned to the bile by the liver. The presence of bile salts in the intestines is the main stimulus to bile secretion by the liver. Contraction of the gall bladder is regulated by relative pressure of the bile in the duct and in the gall bladder, and in some animals by a hormone, cholecystokinin (see p. 270) produced in the duodenum when acid "chyme" enters from the stomach.

PANCREATIC JUICE. This secretion is produced in the acinous tissue of the pancreas, and flows through the pancreatic duct, or the common bile duct in man and certain animals, into the first part of the duodenum (see Fig. 62). Pancreatic juice is a liquid which looks like saliva. It contains about 99% water, 0.5% inorganic matter, and 0.5% organic matter. The inorganic salts are similar to those found in saliva except that $NaHCO_3$ is present in relatively high concentration, giving the pancreatic juice a pH of 7.5-8.0. The major constituents of the organic matter are mucin, the proenzymes trypsinogen, and chymotrypsinogen, and the enzymes carboxypeptidase, pancreatic amylase, and pancreatic lipase. The flow of pancreatic juice is under both nervous and hormonal control. The walls of the duodenum contain a prohormone, prosecretin, which is converted to the hormone secretin (see p. 270), by the acidity of the acid chyme from the stomach. Secretin enters the blood stream and stimulates the acinous tissue of the pancreas to produce pancreatic juice. Another hormone present in the duodenal mucosa, pancreozymin, increases the enzyme content of the juice without affecting the volume of the secretion. In adult man, about 800 ml. of pancreatic juice are secreted in 24 hours.

INTESTINAL JUICE. Intestinal juice is secreted by Brunner's and Lieberkuhn's glands, which are embedded in the intestinal mucosa of the small intestine. It is a liquid which looks like saliva, and contains about 99% water, 0.5% inorganic salts, and 0.5% organic matter. The inorganic salts are similar to those found in saliva, except that $NaHCO_3$ is present in significant amounts, giving the secretion a pH of approximately 8.0. The major constituents of the organic matter are mucin, aminopeptidases, dipeptidases, enterokinase, nucleases, nucleotidases, nucleosidases, phosphatases, lactase, maltase, and sucrase (see Table 47, p. 322, Appendix) for a description of these enzymes. Mechanical pressure on the intestinal wall stimulates the flow of intestinal juice, and it is believed that the presence of food masses provides this stimulus.

Digestion of Carbohydrates in Animals

Digestion of carbohydrates in insects and higher animals is accomplished by extracellular enzymes which are closely related in function to the carbohydrate-splitting enzymes of plants and microorganisms. The cockroach, man, and pig secrete a potent salivary amylase (a mixture of alpha and beta amylases) which resembles plant and bacterial amylases in its ability to split amylose and amylopectin to maltose. Maltase is sometimes, but not always, associated with the salivary amylase. Other species of animals (dog, ox, rat, bird, etc.), do not secrete salivary amylase. The cockroach depends entirely on the salivary secretion to split starches, inasmuch as it does not have a pancreas.

The stomach secretion of higher animals contains no carbohydrate-splitting enzymes. The blind pouches (gastric caeca) of the cockroach (see Fig. 65, page 142), however, do secrete the disaccharidases lactase, maltase, and sucrase. The rumen, or first stomach of the ruminant animals (Fig. 63, page 141), contains microorganisms which secrete a potent mixture of cellulose, hemicellulose, and starch-splitting enzymes.

The acinous tissue of the pancreas of higher animals secretes a potent starch-splitting enzyme, pancreatic amylase, and the intestinal juice of higher animals contains the disaccharidases sucrase, lactase, and maltase*.

END-PRODUCTS OF DIGESTION. The end-products of carbohydrate *digestion* in all animal species, from cockroach to man, are the three monosaccharides, *glucose, galactose,* and *fructose.* In addition, microbial fermentation in the rumen of ruminants breaks down carbohydrates to lactic acid, low molecular weight fatty acids such as acetic, propionic, and butyric acids, and the gases CO_2 and CH_4 (methane). Many insects harbor microorganisms in their intestines that contain cellulases and hemicellulases, and the snail contains a cellulase in its intestinal secretion. In these instances, the end-products of digestion are cellobiose and glucose rather than the fermentative end-products produced in the rumen by a mixed population of bacteria. Table 27 summarizes the digestive changes that take place in animals.

Table 27. Digestion of carbohydrates in animals

Food Carbohydrates	Species	Secretion	Enzymes	End-products
Cellulose	Ruminants, (certain insects)	Bacterial	Cellulase, mutases	Cellobiose, glucose, CO_2, CH_4, low M.W. fatty acids
Hemicellulose	" " "	"	Hemicellulase, mutases	" "
Starch	All	Saliva, pancreas	Alpha, beta amylases	Maltose
Lactose	All	Intes. juice, (gastric caeca)	Lactase	Glucose, galactose
Maltose	All	" " " "	Maltase	Glucose
Sucrose	All	" " " "	Sucrase	Glucose, fructose

ABSORPTION OF END-PRODUCTS. As the monosaccharides are released by digestion, they pass through the cells lining the wall of the villi or, in insects, peritrophic membrane (see page 143). Enzymes in the cell wall of higher animals convert part of the galactose and fructose to glucose. The mixture of monosaccharides in higher animals then enters the blood capillary system of the villus, and is carried from there by a series of connecting vessels of increasing diameter to the portal vein, a large vein which empties into the liver. In the liver, the monosaccharides are converted to glycogen (see p. 27). A smaller proportion of the monosaccharides enters the lacteal of the villus, then enters the lymph system, whence it travels by a more circuitous route (via thoracic duct, left subclavian vein, superior vena cava, heart, hepatic artery) to the liver.

* Borgstrom and Dahlquist in 1961 published results of disaccharide absorption tests in men. They found that disaccharides were hydrolyzed by the cells of the intestinal mucus membrane and monosaccharides formed within the cell were secreted into the portal blood stream. These cells are rich in disaccharide hydrolases and the hydrolysis apparently occurs within the cell rather than in the gut lumen. The results cast doubt on the importance of the succus entericus (intestinal juice) as a source of disaccharide hydrolases in man. In contrast to the digestion of disaccharides, however, the breakdown of starch seems to occur entirely in the lumen of the intestine, and very rapidly at that.

Ruminants must dispose of the end-products of bacterial fermentation formed in the rumen, as well as the end-products of pancreatic and intestinal digestion discussed above. The fermentation end-products are absorbed by the villi, the fatty acids being carried mainly via the lacteal and lymph, but also by the blood capillaries and portal vein. The higher fatty acids are converted to fats in the liver and fat depots, and the acetic, lactic and propionic acids are converted to glycogen in the liver. Absorbed CH_4 and CO_2 are carried by the blood to the lungs, and exhaled.

Digestion of Lipids in Plants and Microorganisms

Plants do not utilize outside sources of lipids; they synthesize them as they are needed. Only in the germinating seed does digestion of stored food lipid take place. A fat-splitting enzyme was first identified in plants by Green in 1890, when he found significant amounts in the germinating castor bean. Since then, lipases have been found in both the resting and germinating seeds of rape, opium, poppy, hemp, flax, soybean, corn, and other seeds. During germination, the seed lipases split stored triglycerides to di and monoglycerides, free fatty acids, and glycerol, and the carbon of these compounds is converted to carbohydrates, amino acids, new lipids, and other chemical building blocks needed by the developing seedling for vegetative growth.

Microorganisms secrete lipases, and thereby split triglycerides in the surrounding liquid medium, absorbing the simpler glycerides, fatty acids, and glycerol. The activity of microorganisms is a problem in the storage of edible fats, and is mainly responsible for the rancidity that develops in butter on storage.

Digestion and Absorption of Lipids in Insects

Omnivorous forms of insects, such as the cockroach, have a full complement of enzymes capable of digesting all common foodstuffs. Insects which take mainly a protein diet, such as the exclusively blood-sucking species, have little but proteolytic enzymes. In omnivorous insects, the lipase is produced by secreting cells lining the mid-gut (see Fig. 65, page 142). The extent of cleavage of the food triglycerides may be similar to that observed in higher animals (see next section) but this has not been determined. The lack of bile may decrease the amount of emulsification of the lipids. The end-products of lipid digestion diffuse through the peritrophic membrane and are absorbed by the epithelial cells lining the mid-gut.

Digestion and Absorption of Lipids in Higher Animals

According to R. Reiser, "Few subjects in biochemistry have been the object of as much controversy for so long a time as the question of the degree of hydrolysis of fat in the intestine and the mechanism of its passage through the intestinal epithelium." From 1880 to 1935, there were two diametrically opposite theories on fat digestion; the proponents of one theory contended that all fat must be split to fatty acids and glycerol before absorption, whereas the proponents of the other held that fats did not need to be split before absorption. Neither theory was entirely correct, for in 1935, Artom and Reale showed that the digestion of fats yielded mono and diglycerides and free fatty acids, with the release of only small amounts of free glycerol.

The 2-monoglycerides are less stable than the 1-monoglycerides and are converted to the latter in the digestion mixture.

$$\underset{\text{Triglyceride}}{\begin{array}{l} \text{R-C(=O)-O-CH}_2 \\ \text{R-C(=O)-O-CH} \\ \text{R-C(=O)-O-CH}_2 \end{array}} \xrightarrow[\text{H}_2\text{O}]{\text{lipase}} \underset{\text{1,3 Diglyceride}}{\begin{array}{l} \text{R-C(=O)-O-CH}_2 \\ \text{HO-C-H} \\ \text{R-C(=O)-O-CH}_2 \end{array}} + \underset{\text{1,2 Diglyceride}}{\begin{array}{l} \text{HO-CH}_2 \\ \text{R-C(=O)-O-CH} \\ \text{R-C(=O)-O-CH}_2 \end{array}} + \underset{\text{Fatty acid}}{\text{R-C(=O)-OH}}$$

$$\xrightarrow[\text{H}_2\text{O}]{\text{lipase}} \underset{\text{1-Monoglyceride}}{\begin{array}{l} \text{HO-CH}_2 \\ \text{HO-CH} \\ \text{R-C(=O)-O-CH}_2 \end{array}} + \underset{\text{2-Monoglyceride}}{\begin{array}{l} \text{HO-CH}_2 \\ \text{R-C(=O)-O-CH} \\ \text{HO-CH}_2 \end{array}} + \underset{\text{Fatty acid}}{\text{R-C(=O)-OH}}$$

Ten years later, Frazer, without knowledge of the above work, which had been done in Italy, rediscovered this reaction, and in addition, showed that the mono and diglycerides, in conjunction with bile, emulsified undigested triglycerides to a particle size of 0.5 microns or less. These particles, which have been named *chylomicrons*, can be absorbed directly through the intestinal epithelium.

Later workers have confirmed the findings of Artom and Reale, and of Frazer, and it is now accepted that the hydrolysis of triglycerides stops at the di- and monoglyceride stage, and that the digestion mixture consists of free fatty acids, di- and monoglycerides, and unsplit (or resynthesized) triglycerides. In recent tests on humans, *monoglycerides* accounted for as high as 50% of the lipides in the intestinal contents after a fat meal. Calcium ions increase the proportion of monoglycerides during fat digestion by removing fatty acids from the interface between the oil and water phases of the digestion mixture.

DISTRIBUTION OF LIPASES IN DIGESTIVE TRACT. Lipases have been reported to be present in gastric juice, pancreatic juice, and intestinal juice. Contemporary investigators believe that the only lipase that plays a significant role in the digestion of fats is *pancreatic lipase*. This enzyme has its optimum activity in the pH range 7.5-8.0, and is a potent tri and diglyceridase, both in the intestine, and in the test tube.

ABSORPTION OF END-PRODUCTS OF FAT DIGESTION. Free fatty acids, mono- and diglycerides, and chylomicrons (triglyceride globules with diameters of 0.5 microns or less), pass through the epithelium of the villus (page 143). As these hydrolyzed and unhydrolyzed fragments pass through (1) the outer border, (2) the body, and (3) the basal membrane, of the mucosal columnar epithelial cells of the villus, the free fatty acids are converted to triglycerides. In this resynthesis, the free fatty acids combine with either simultaneously absorbed mono- or diglycerides, or with *endogenous glycerol precursor* (probably dihydroxy acetone). Tracer studies show that free dietary glycerol does not participate in this resynthesis. Phospholipids (page 45) are also synthesized here from (1) a phosphorylated base, (2) *triglyceride*, and (3) endogenous glycerol precursor.

The chylomicrons, preformed or synthesized in the wall of the villus, are transferred mainly to the lacteal (page 143), where they enter the lymph and are transported to the thoracic duct and thence to the main blood stream. A small proportion enters the blood capillary system of the villus.

Digestion of Proteins in Plants and Microorganisms

Microorganisms which are unable to synthesize all of the amino acids must obtain them from an outside source. In most cases, this source is plant or animal protein. Since proteins are not diffusible through the cell wall, the microorganisms must break down the proteins to diffusible particles; it does this by secreting *proteases* into the surrounding medium. In this respect, microorganisms resemble the germinating seed of the plant. Here the embryo must depend on an outside source for its amino acids; accordingly, during germination, endosperm proteases mix with the proteins stored in the endosperm, and break them down to simple peptides and amino acids, which diffuse into the embryo. It is probable that the proteases of plants and microorganisms are similar in number and function to those found in animals.

Digestion of Proteins in Insects and Higher Animals

The digestion of proteins to amino acids is a step-wise process in all living organisms, including germinating seeds and microorganisms. The proteases that bring about this break-down have been divided into two major classes by Bergmann: (1) the endopeptidases - proteases that are capable of splitting specific peptide linkages which usually are *inside* the molecule, and (2) the exopeptidases - polypeptidases and dipeptidases that attack only *terminal* peptide linkages. Group 1 attacks native proteins, breaking them down to soluble products (proteoses, peptones, polypeptides) which can be attacked by the aminopeptidases, carboxypeptidases and dipeptidases. Group 2 enzymes are not able to digest native proteins.

Bergman made a study of the specificity characteristics of animal proteases. He found that pepsin (an endopeptidase) splits peptide linkages containing the *alpha-amino* group of phenylalanine and tyrosine*, whereas chymotrypsin (another endopeptidase) splits peptide linkages containing the *alpha-carboxyl* group of phenylalanine, tyrosine, tryptophan, and methionine. On the other hand, trypsin, an endopeptidase, can split only those peptide linkages which contain the alpha-carboxyl group of arginine and lysine.

The exopeptidases were also found to have certain specificities. Thus, amino peptidase attacks the terminal amino acid which has its alpha-amino group free, splitting it from tri- or higher peptides.

Leucyl alanyl histidine   Leucine   Alanyl histidine

---

* Sanger has shown in studies on the structure of insulin that pepsin splits several types of peptide linkages, in addition to those found by Bergmann, and is therefore not as specific as other proteases studied.

In contrast, carboxy peptidases attack the terminal amino acid which has its alpha-carboxyl group free, splitting it from tri- or higher peptides.

Leucyl alanyl histidine   Leucyl alanine   Histidine

The dipeptidases are also specific in that they attack only dipeptides, and require the presence of some particular amino acid (proline, leucine, etc.) in the dipeptide.

A study of comparative protein digestion in different species (insects, fish, amphibians, birds, mammals, etc.) shows that a collection of endo- and exopeptidases convert the native proteins of the food to amino acids. The endo- and exopeptidases of different species vary in pH optima and in relative activity, yet achieve the purpose for which all were developed, namely, to split dietary proteins to amino acids. Inasmuch as more data have been accumulated on the proteases of the mammalian species, a summary of the step-wise break-down of proteins in the mammalian tract is given below.

STOMACH (OR ABOMASUM) OF MAMMALS. The *gastric juice* (page 144) contains the endopeptidase *pepsin* which is released from its zymogen, pepsinogen, by the action of hydrogen ions. Pepsin has the following action on the native proteins in foods (denatured proteins are even more easily digested than native proteins by endopeptidases):

1. Native protein ------------------→ Proteoses, peptones, polypeptides
2. Calcium casein (milk) ----------→ Calcium paracasein (curd) + a proteose
3. Calcium paracasein (curd) ------→ Proteoses, peptones, polypeptides

In addition, the gastric juice of certain young mammals (calf, kid, etc.) contains a protease, rennin, which is released from its zymogen, prorennin, by the action of hydrogen ions. Rennin is specific for only one substrate, casein, splitting the calcium salt (calcium-casein) to a calcium paracasein curd and a proteose. Rennin does not split the products further; however, it splits casein many times more rapidly than pepsin does.

SMALL INTESTINES OF MAMMALS. The pancreatic juice (page 145), which flows into the duodenum through the pancreatic duct (or a common pancreatic-bile duct), contains three proenzymes (zymogens) of proteases: trypsinogen, chymotrypsinogen and procarboxypeptidase. When the pancreatic juice mixes with the intestinal secretions, trypsinogen is converted to trypsin by enterokinase (page 145), and trypsin then converts chymotrypsinogen to chymotrypsin, and procarboxypeptidase to carboxypeptidase.

Trypsin and chymotrypsin attack native proteins and calcium-casein in a manner similar to that displayed by pepsin, but because of different specificities, they produce different proteoses, peptones, and polypeptides, and a different calcium-casein curd. Chymotrypsin is a more active caseinase than either trypsin or pepsin, but is less active than rennin.

Carboxypeptidase attacks the end-products of pepsin, trypsin and chymotrypsin digestion, converting them to amino acids and dipeptides.

                              carboxypeptidases
Proteoses, peptones, polypeptides --------------------→ dipeptides + amino acids

Intestinal juice. The intestinal juice (page 145) contains the active peptide-splitting enzymes, *aminopeptidases*, and various *dipeptidases*, and also a series of nucleic acid-splitting enzymes *(ribonucleases, phosphatase, nucleosidase)*. Aminopeptidase attacks the end-products of endopeptidase digestion, converting them to amino acids and dipeptides.

$$\text{Proteoses, peptones, polypeptides} \xrightarrow{\text{aminopeptidases}} \text{dipeptides + amino acids}$$

The *dipeptidases* split the remaining dipeptides to free amino acids.

$$\text{Dipeptides} \xrightarrow{\text{dipeptidases}} \text{amino acids}$$

Nucleoproteins (see Chapter 7) are broken down to their respective building blocks as follows:

(1) The endo- and exopeptidases in the digestive tract split the protein part of the nucleoproteins to amino acids.

(2) The freed nucleic acid is digested by the enzymes of the intestinal juice (see p. 145):

$$\text{Nucleic acid} \xrightarrow{\text{ribo and deoxyribonucleases}} \text{nucleotides}$$

$$\text{Nucleotides} \xrightarrow{\text{phosphatase}} \text{nucleosides + } H_3PO_4$$

$$\text{Nucleosides} \xrightarrow{\text{nucleosidase}} \text{sugar + purine or pyrimidine}$$

It is apparent that more than seven different enzymes capable of splitting peptide linkages are involved in the step-wise break-down of native proteins to amino acids in the digestive tracts of mammals. It is probable that equally as many are required in other species. This protein break-down takes place primarily in the stomach and small intestine regions of different animal species.

PROTEIN DIGESTION IN THE LARGE INTESTINE REGION. No protein-splitting enzymes are secreted by the cells lining the caecum, colon and rectum or their equivalent (hind gut, rectum) in insects. However, microorganisms (including protozoa) which inhabit this region, secrete enzymes which split proteins to amino acids. These amino acids may actually be used, at least in part, by the animal to satisfy his amino acid requirements. Certain microorganisms in this region also secrete deaminases and decarboxylases. As a result of the action of the latter, putrefactive-type products are produced from the amino acids. For example, the decarboxylation of tryptophan produces such products as indole and skatole (methyl indole), decarboxylation of histidine produces

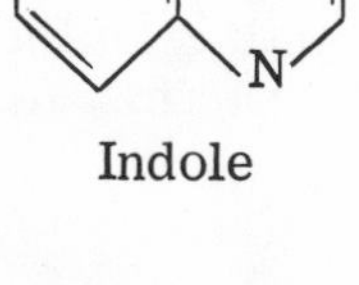

Indole

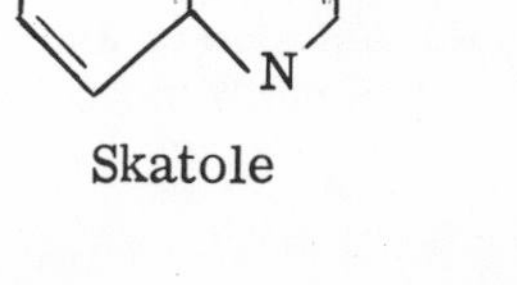

Skatole

histamine, tyrosine yields tyramine, lysine yields cadaverine, and arginine yields putrescine. The last two amines were first isolated from human cadavers, hence the names.

$$H - C - N - H$$
$$C - N = C - H$$
$$CH_2$$
$$CH_2NH_2$$
Histamine

$$HO \langle\rangle - CH_2CH_2NH_2$$
Tyramine

$$H_2N\,CH_2\,CH_2\,CH_2\,CH_2\,CH_2\,NH_2$$
Cadaverine

$$NH$$
$$H_2N - C - NH - CH_2\,CH_2\,CH_2\,CH_2\,NH_2$$
Putrescine

Hydrogen sulfide and mercaptans are produced from cystine and methionine, and methane gas is produced by the action of putrefactive-type microorganisms on the various amino acids.

ABSORPTION OF THE END-PRODUCTS OF DIGESTION. The free amino acids released by digestion in the stomach and small intestine regions of animals, are absorbed by the villi (page 143) in higher animals, and directly through the peritrophic membrane (page 143) in insects. Once they reach the blood stream they become a part of the "amino acid pool" of the animal body.

Digestion and Absorption of Vitamins

Most of the vitamins in plants, animals and microorganisms are components of enzymes, usually in the coenzyme part of the holoenzyme. Here they are attached by bonds of different strengths to protein, nucleotides, or phosphate (see coenzymes, p. 97). Some vitamins (for example, ascorbic acid) are in the free state in foods. The bound vitamins in foods are released by the action of the appropriate digestive enzymes in the stomach and small intestines of insects and higher animals.

The vitamins are *absorbed* in all species mainly in the free state. The water-soluble vitamins are absorbed directly in higher animals, most of them passing into the villi capillaries (p. 143), in insects through the peritrophic membrane; the fat-soluble vitamins follow the pathway of fat absorption, in higher animals passing to a large extent into the lacteal and into the lymph stream (p. 260). In higher animals bile is essential for the absorption of the fat-soluble vitamins. This is dramatically shown in human patients suffering from obstructive jaundice; lack of bile in the intestines prevents the absorption of the fat-soluble vitamins in the food, and the patient develops hemorrhagic tendencies due to a vitamin K deficiency (see p. 231). Ingestion of excessive amounts of mineral oil with the feed or food also interferes with the absorption of the fat-soluble vitamins.

Digestion and Absorption of Minerals

The element oxygen enters the animal body in two forms, (1) as gaseous molecular oxygen absorbed by the lungs and used for oxidative respiration in the cells (p. 159), and (2) reduced oxygen in water, proteins, lipids, carbohydrates, etc. The elements carbon, hydrogen, nitrogen and sulfur enter the body as carbon compounds and water. The remaining 13 elements are taken into the alimentary canal mainly in the form of mineral salts, although some are an integral part of the ingested proteins, lipids and carbohydrates.

In most animal species, the low pH of the gastric juice is quite effective in dissolving insoluble minerals such as calcium carbonate and tertiary calcium phosphate. Mineral elements which are constituents of proteins, lipids or carbohydrates, are released in soluble form upon digestion of the carbon compounds to which they are attached.

The soluble mineral salts in the small intestines pass through the peritrophic membrane in insects, and through the villi in higher animals, and enter the blood and lymph streams. The intestinal mucosa not only absorbs inorganic ions, but also is capable of excreting ions after they have served the body. Any factor (such as pH, precipitating ions like oxalate toward calcium, etc.) that decreases the solubility of an inorganic ion in the tract, decreases its absorption. It is obvious that absorption is also lowered in animals and man during diarrhea.

Chapter 11 | METABOLISM

INTRODUCTION. In the previous chapter, the nutrients eaten as food were followed through the alimentary canal to the point where the hydrolysis products were absorbed and appeared in the blood stream. Once in the blood stream, absorbed nutrients are distributed to the cells of the body, where they undergo many remarkable changes. The sum total of these changes has been named *metabolism*. Metabolism not only includes (1) the energy-requiring synthesis of new complex organic compounds similar to those previously digested, but also includes (2) the energy-releasing *degradation* of absorbed nutrients to such simple end-products as carbon dioxide and water. The first aspect of metabolism is called *anabolism*, whereas the second is called *catabolism*. In plants, all chemical changes occurring within the plant are included under the name *metabolism*.

Metabolism of Carbohydrates

CARBOHYDRATE METABOLISM IN ANIMALS. Probably the most important function of carbohydrates is to provide energy in a form that the animal (or plant) can use. Carbohydrates provide energy by being "burned" to carbon dioxide and water in the living cell. As can be seen from the equation, one gram molecular weight (180 gm.) of hexose yields 686 kilocalories* of heat when burned to CO_2 and water. The biological form of combus-

$$C_6H_{12}O_6 + 6O_2 \text{------} \rightarrow 6CO_2 + 6H_2O + 686 \text{ Cal.}$$

tion is called *respiration*. The same amount of energy is released in the cell as can be released by burning the carbohydrate directly in a flame. However, the cell wants only a small part of the energy as heat energy. Most of the energy released by respiration is stored in the form of high energy bonds, particularly those found in adenosine triphosphate (ATP). This the cell can use for muscle contraction, electrical energy of nerve impulse, synthesis of new compounds, etc.

The oxidation or "burning" of carbohydrates to the final end-products, carbon dioxide and water, is a step-wise process. This permits the cell to convert most of the stored energy into chemical bond energy instead of having it all lost as heat.

I. Glucose to Glycogen. The first step in glucose metabolism is the conversion of absorbed glucose, fructose and galactose to *glycogen* in the liver, and blood glucose to *glycogen* in the muscles. In order to become activated for "biological" burning, all three of the monosaccharides must first combine with phosphate supplied by adenosine triphosphate (ATP). With the transfer of one of the phosphate radicals of ATP to the sugar, some of the energy of the phosphate bond is also transferred.

---

* One kilocalorie = heat required to raise the temperature of 1 kilogram of water from 15°C. to 16°C.

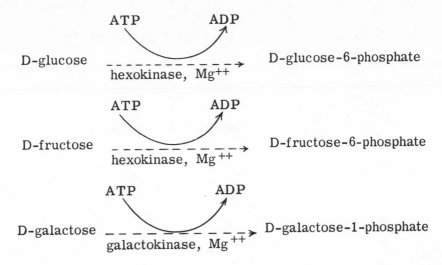

D-glucose $\xrightarrow[\text{hexokinase, Mg}^{++}]{\text{ATP} \quad \text{ADP}}$ D-glucose-6-phosphate

D-fructose $\xrightarrow[\text{hexokinase, Mg}^{++}]{\text{ATP} \quad \text{ADP}}$ D-fructose-6-phosphate

D-galactose $\xrightarrow[\text{galactokinase, Mg}^{++}]{\text{ATP} \quad \text{ADP}}$ D-galactose-1-phosphate

The three phosphated sugars are then converted to D-glucose-1-phosphate by the following reactions:

D-glucose-6-phosphate $\xrightarrow{\text{phosphoglucomutase}}$ D-glucose-1-phosphate

D-fructose-6-phosphate $\xrightarrow{\text{phospho hexose-isomerase}}$ D-glucose-6-phosphate

D-galactose-1-phosphate $\xrightarrow[\text{(coenzyme: UDPG*)}]{\text{uridyl transferase}}$ D-glucose-1-phosphate + UDP-galactose

UDP-galactose $\xrightarrow{\text{galactowaldenase}}$ UDPG

In these reactions, fructose-6-phosphate is first isomerized to glucose-6-phosphate before the phosphate shift from carbon 6 to carbon 1 occurs. Galactose is isomerized to glucose *after* conversion to UDP-galactose, in a two step reaction.

The D-glucose-1-phosphate (Cori ester) formed in these reactions then serves as the building unit for liver or muscle glycogen. In the synthesis, glycogen synthe-

UDPG + (D-glucose-1-phosphate)$_n$ $\xrightarrow[\text{branching enzyme**}]{\text{glycogen synthetase}}$ (glucose)$_{n+1}$ + (PO$_4^{---}$)$_n$ + UDP

tase, with UDPG as coenzyme, adds glucose to the nonreducing end of the chain, thus building straight chains, which, when they reach a length of approximately 8 glucose units, are acted on by the branching enzyme. This enzyme converts a certain number of α-1,4 linkages to α-1,6 linkages (see p. 25), causing branching on a glucose unit which still contains a carbon 4 linkage.

* uridine-diphosphate-glucose (p. 113).
** amylo (1,4 $\to$ 1,6) - transglucosidase.

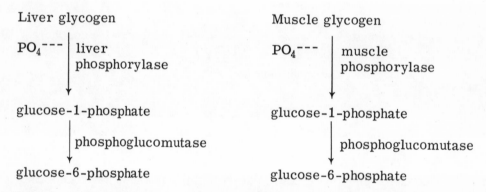

II. <u>Glycogen to glucose</u>. The second step in the metabolism of carbohydrates is the conversion of glycogen to glucose.

Liver glycogen	Muscle glycogen
PO_4^{---} liver phosphorylase	PO_4^{---} muscle phosphorylase
↓	↓
glucose-1-phosphate	glucose-1-phosphate
↓ phosphoglucomutase	↓ phosphoglucomutase
glucose-6-phosphate	glucose-6-phosphate

Synthetase, branching enzyme, and phosphoglucomutase are involved in the synthesis of glycogen. Degradation of glycogen requires phosphorylase a. Whether glucose will be converted to glycogen, or vice versa, depends upon the relative abundance of glucose in the blood, and on the relative influence of the hormones insulin, epinephrine, and glucagon.

<u>Insulin</u> (p. 272) stimulates conversion of *glucose* to liver and muscle *glycogen.* Its exact action is not known. One possibility is that insulin speeds up the transfer of glucose across the cell membrane to the site of glycogen synthesis. Another possibility is that insulin accelerates the hexokinase reaction (p. 157). It is known that the pituitary secretes a hormone (diabetogenic hormone) that *inhibits* the action of hexokinase, and Houssay found that the removal of the pituitary in a diabetic animal *eliminates the need for insulin injections.* This favors the hexokinase acceleration theory.

<u>Epinephrine</u> (see p. 269) stimulates conversion of glycogen to glucose. It is probably an accelerator of phosphorylase enzyme activity. Phosphorylase has been found in liver and muscle in two forms, a and b. The a form is active, whereas the b form is inactive. However, the b form can be activated by the addition of

adenylic acid (p. 112). It is assumed that epinephrine stimulates the conversion of the b form to the a form.

Glucagon (see p. 273) stimulates the conversion of glycogen to glucose. It has no significant effect on muscle glycogen, but apparently accelerates *liver* phosphorylase activity, presumably by conversion of the b form to the a form.

III. Glucose-6-phosphate to pyruvic acid and lactic acid. The first two steps in carbohydrate metabolism (monosaccharides → glycogen → glucose) involve only modest energy changes. The synthesis (or splitting) of the glycosidic bonds of glycogen require (or release) approximately 4 kilocalories of energy per mol. (gram molecular weight) of glucose. This represents less than 1 per cent of the energy released by the complete combustion of one mol. of glucose to carbon dioxide and water.

The third step, which may be called *anaerobic glycolysis* (fermentation), yields about 57 kilocalories of energy per mole of glucose, or about 8 per cent of the total stored energy of the glucose molecule when glucose is converted to lactic acid. About one-fourth of this energy is recovered as chemical bond energy (2ATP molecules synthesized from ADP per mole of glucose).

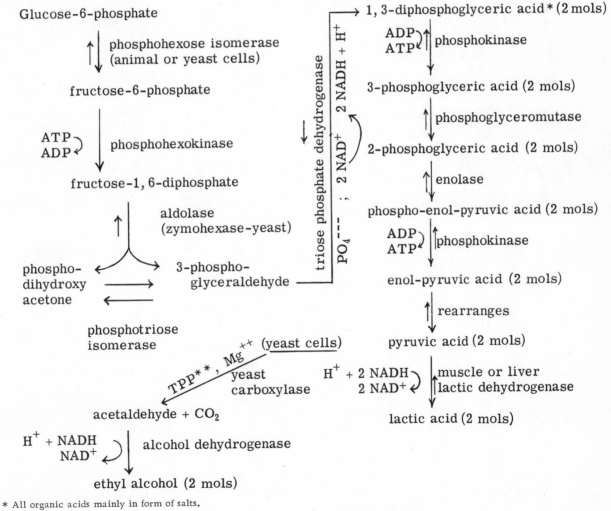

* All organic acids mainly in form of salts.
** TPP: Thiamine pyrophosphate

Figure 67. Glycolysis scheme

The conversion of glucose-6-phosphate to pyruvic acid (Fig. 67) requires 9 enzymatically catalyzed steps. One additional step is required to form lactic acid from pyruvic acid. It is of interest to note that the conversion of glucose-6-phosphate to pyruvic acid follows the *same pathway* in the muscle and liver of animals as it does in the yeast microorganism. The formulas of the compounds named in the glycolysis scheme are shown below.

If muscle contained one more enzyme (yeast carboxylase), alcohol would compete with lactic acid as a product of glycolysis in the animal body.

Examination of the above steps from glucose to alcohol shows that there is a net gain of two ATP molecules per mol of glucose fermented. The yeast cells derive their energy from this modest gain in high energy bonds, which explains why they

FORMULAE OF COMPOUNDS INVOLVED IN GLYCOLYSIS.

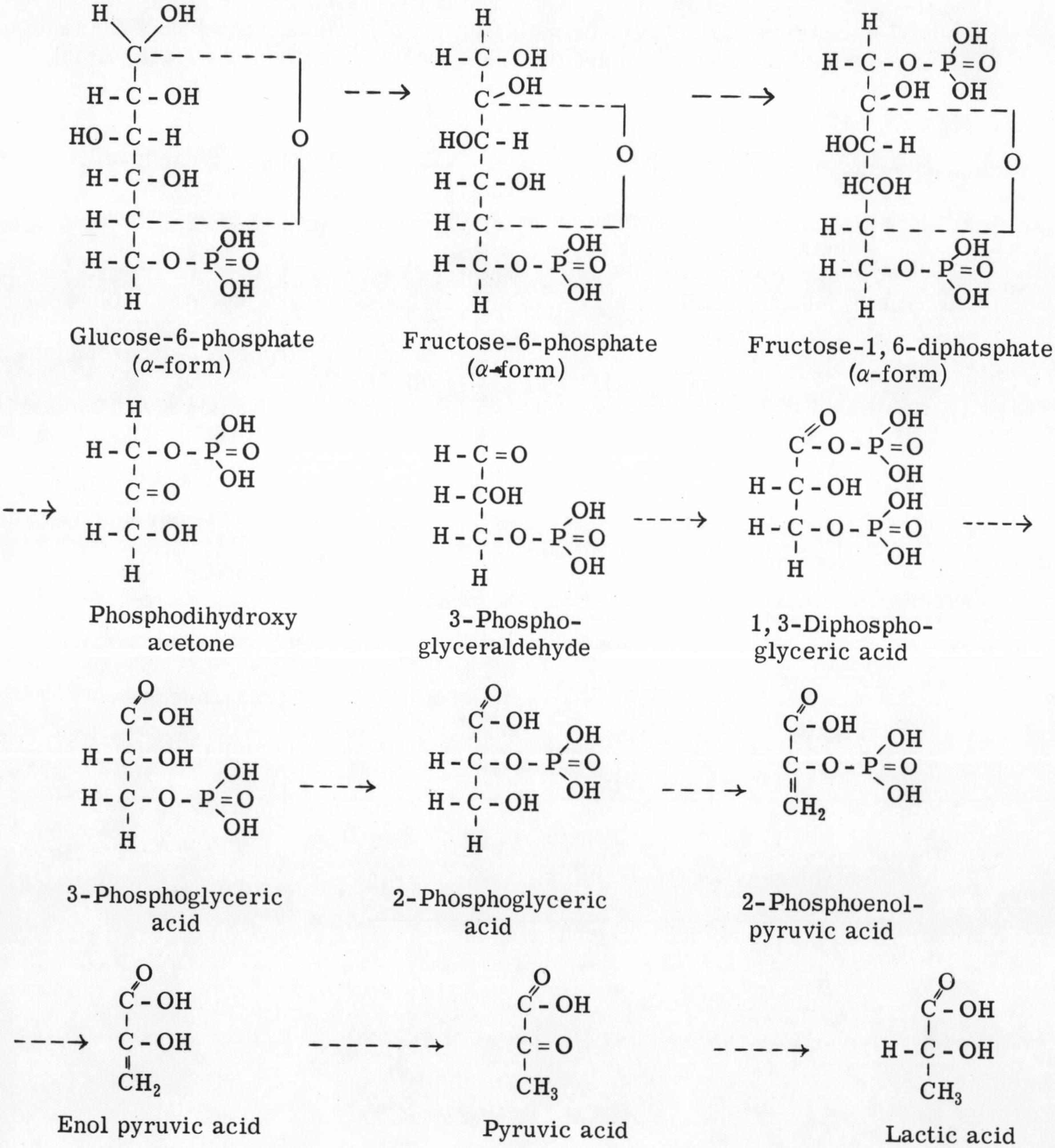

Glucose-6-phosphate
(α-form)

Fructose-6-phosphate
(α-form)

Fructose-1, 6-diphosphate
(α-form)

Phosphodihydroxy
acetone

3-Phospho-
glyceraldehyde

1, 3-Diphospho-
glyceric acid

3-Phosphoglyceric
acid

2-Phosphoglyceric
acid

2-Phosphoenol-
pyruvic acid

Enol pyruvic acid

Pyruvic acid

Lactic acid

must ferment relatively large amounts of glucose in order to grow and multiply. Muscle cells also depend on these high energy bonds to supply the explosive energy for contraction.

The reactions of anaerobic glycolysis (fermentation) outlined in steps II and III are often referred to as the "Embden-Meyerhof Pathway" of glycolysis.

IV.   Pyruvic and lactic acids to CO_2 and water. By far the greatest proportion of the stored energy of the glucose molecule (about 90 per cent) is released by the oxidation (aerobic glycolysis) of pyruvic acid and lactic acid to carbon dioxide and water. Pyruvate (or lactate) is "burned" to carbon dioxide and water in a cycle of enzymatically catalyzed steps about equal in number to those of anaerobic glycolysis. This cycle is called the "Krebs cycle" in honor of the biochemist who made major contributions to its clarification. It is also called the "citric acid cycle" or "tricarboxylic acid cycle". The cycle is outlined below (Fig. 68). The formulas of the compounds named in the Krebs cycle are given on p. 160.

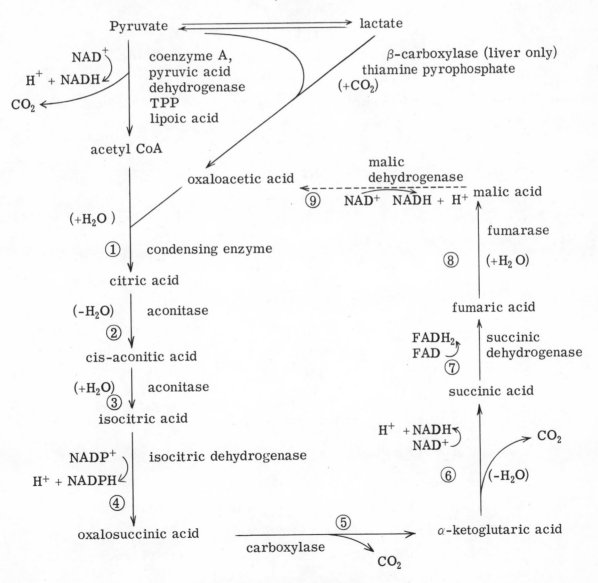

Figure 68. The Krebs Cycle

The student will note that in the Krebs cycle, pyruvate is converted to acetyl CoA, and fed into the cycle in this form. In addition, both pyruvate and lactate are carboxylated directly in the liver to form oxaloacetic acid.

FORMULAE OF COMPOUNDS INVOLVED IN KREB'S CITRIC ACID CYCLE.

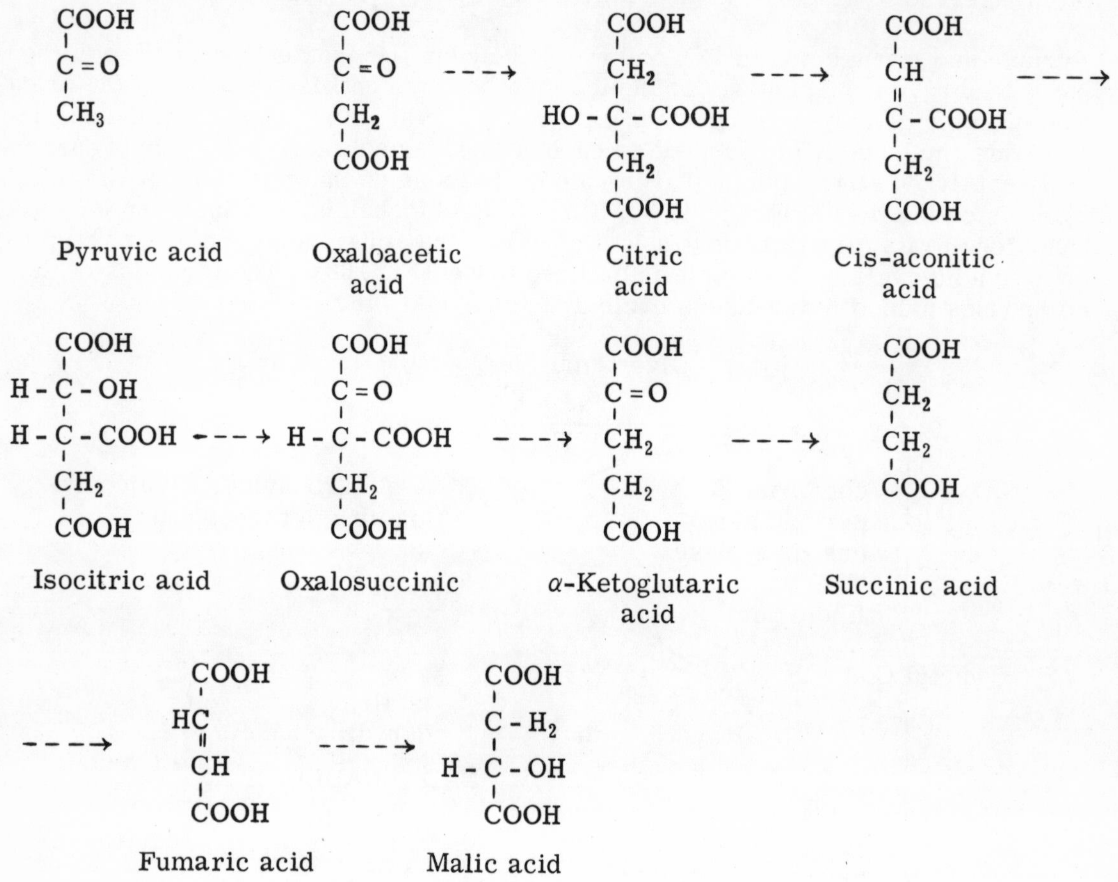

$$
\begin{array}{cccc}
\text{COOH} & \text{COOH} & \text{COOH} & \text{COOH} \\
| & | & | & | \\
\text{C}=\text{O} & \text{C}=\text{O} \;\dashrightarrow & \text{CH}_2 \;\dashrightarrow & \text{CH} \;\dashrightarrow \\
| & | & | & \| \\
\text{CH}_3 & \text{CH}_2 & \text{HO}-\text{C}-\text{COOH} & \text{C}-\text{COOH} \\
 & | & | & | \\
 & \text{COOH} & \text{CH}_2 & \text{CH}_2 \\
 & & | & | \\
 & & \text{COOH} & \text{COOH}
\end{array}
$$

Pyruvic acid   Oxaloacetic   Citric   Cis-aconitic
                 acid   acid   acid

$$
\begin{array}{cccc}
\text{COOH} & \text{COOH} & \text{COOH} & \text{COOH} \\
| & | & | & | \\
\text{H}-\text{C}-\text{OH} & \text{C}=\text{O} & \text{C}=\text{O} & \text{CH}_2 \\
| & | & | & | \\
\text{H}-\text{C}-\text{COOH} \dashrightarrow & \text{H}-\text{C}-\text{COOH} \dashrightarrow & \text{CH}_2 \dashrightarrow & \text{CH}_2 \\
| & | & | & | \\
\text{CH}_2 & \text{CH}_2 & \text{CH}_2 & \text{COOH} \\
| & | & | & \\
\text{COOH} & \text{COOH} & \text{COOH} &
\end{array}
$$

Isocitric acid   Oxalosuccinic   α-Ketoglutaric   Succinic acid
                       acid

$$
\begin{array}{cc}
\text{COOH} & \text{COOH} \\
| & | \\
\text{HC} & \text{C}-\text{H}_2 \\
\dashrightarrow \quad \| & \dashrightarrow \quad | \\
\text{CH} & \text{H}-\text{C}-\text{OH} \\
| & | \\
\text{COOH} & \text{COOH}
\end{array}
$$

Fumaric acid   Malic acid

<u>Conversion of pyruvic acid to acetyl CoA.</u> This is a complicated reaction involving many factors. The pathway is shown below.

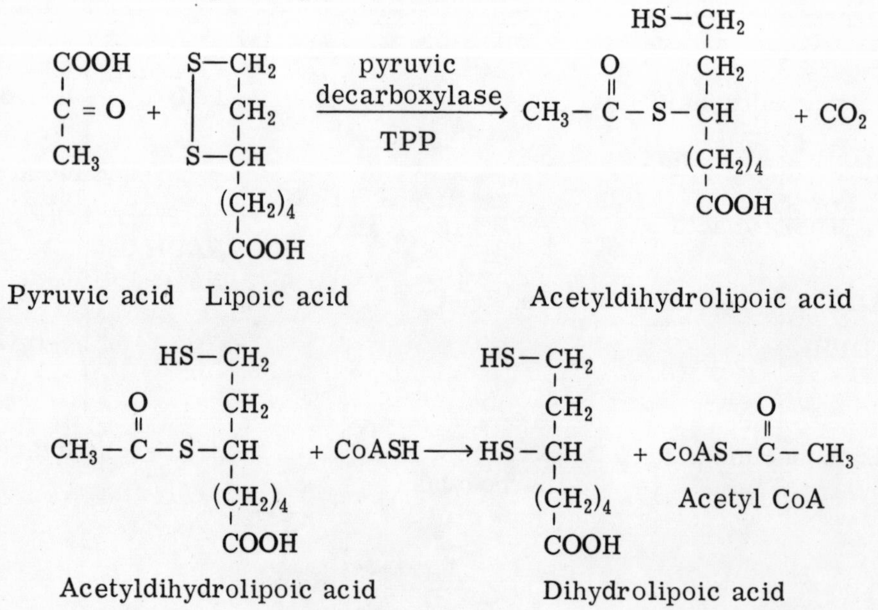

$$
\begin{array}{ccccc}
\text{COOH} & \text{S}-\text{CH}_2 & & & \text{HS}-\text{CH}_2 \\
| & | & \text{pyruvic} & & | \\
\text{C}=\text{O} \;+ & \text{CH}_2 & \xrightarrow[\text{TPP}]{\text{decarboxylase}} & \overset{\text{O}}{\overset{\|}{\text{CH}_3-\text{C}}}-\text{S}-\text{CH} & \text{CH}_2 \;+\; \text{CO}_2 \\
| & | & & & | \\
\text{CH}_3 & \text{S}-\text{CH} & & (\text{CH}_2)_4 & \\
 & | & & | & \\
 & (\text{CH}_2)_4 & & \text{COOH} & \\
 & | & & & \\
 & \text{COOH} & & &
\end{array}
$$

Pyruvic acid   Lipoic acid   Acetyldihydrolipoic acid

$$
\begin{array}{cc}
\text{HS}-\text{CH}_2 & \text{HS}-\text{CH}_2 \\
\overset{\text{O}}{\overset{\|}{}} \quad | & | \\
\text{CH}_3-\text{C}-\text{S}-\text{CH} \;+\; \text{CoASH} \longrightarrow & \text{HS}-\text{CH} \;+\; \text{CoAS}-\overset{\text{O}}{\overset{\|}{\text{C}}}-\text{CH}_3 \\
| & | \qquad\qquad \text{Acetyl CoA} \\
(\text{CH}_2)_4 & (\text{CH}_2)_4 \\
| & | \\
\text{COOH} & \text{COOH}
\end{array}
$$

Acetyldihydrolipoic acid   Dihydrolipoic acid

In the presence of pyruvic acid dehydrogenase, with thiamine pyrophosphate as co-enzyme, pyruvic acid reacts with lipoic acid, an eight carbon straight chain fatty acid with sulfur atoms at positions 6 and 8. Acetyl lipoic acid is formed and CO_2 is released. A transfer of the acetyl group to CoASH gives acetyl CoA and reduced lipoic acid. The latter is then oxidized to the ring form by NAD^+.

Formation of citric acid. (Reaction 1, Fig. 68) Acetyl CoA is a high energy compound which can act either as a biological acetylating agent or in condensation reactions. In the presence of condensing enzyme, the methyl group of acetyl CoA is activated and condenses with the keto group of oxalacetic acid. The reaction is reversible, but the equilibrium mixture contains a high percentage of citric acid.

Conversion of citric acid to cis-aconitic and isocitric acids. (Reactions 2 and 3, Fig. 68) An iron (Fe^{++}) - containing enzyme, aconitase, catalyzes both steps. At equilibrium, the respective amounts of the three acids are 90, 4, and 6 per cent. The reaction proceeds in the direction of isocitric acid in respiring tissues because the latter is removed in the next reaction of the cycle. Aconitase is believed to attach to three of the four groups of citric acid, making its center carbon asymmetric during the dehydration reaction which gives cis-aconitic acid.

Formation of oxalosuccinic acid. (Reaction 4, Fig. 68) This reaction involves removal of hydrogen by the coenzyme $NADP^+$ in the presence of the apoenzyme, isocitric dehydrogenase. The reaction is reversible.

Formation of α-ketoglutaric acid. (Reaction 5, Fig. 68) In the presence of the enzyme, carboxylase, oxalosuccinic acid loses a molecule of CO_2, to give α-ketoglutaric acid. The reaction is reversible.

Oxidative decarboxylation of α-ketoglutaric acid to give succinyl CoA. (Reaction 6, Fig. 68) The conversion of α-ketoglutaric acid to succinic acid is a two-stage reaction involving succinyl CoA as an intermediate. The formation of succinyl CoA is analogous to the oxidative decarboxylation of pyruvic acid.

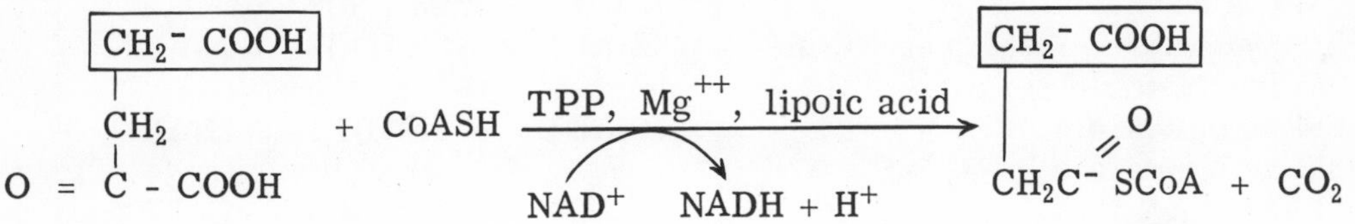

$$\boxed{CH_2^- \ COOH} \quad \quad \quad \quad \boxed{CH_2^- \ COOH}$$
$$\underset{\underset{\alpha\text{-Ketoglutaric acid}}{O = C - COOH}}{\overset{|}{CH_2}} \ + \ CoASH \ \underset{NAD^+ \quad NADH + H^+}{\overset{TPP, \ Mg^{++}, \ lipoic \ acid}{\longrightarrow}} \ \underset{\text{Succinyl CoA}}{CH_2 C^- \ SCoA} \ + \ CO_2$$

Thiamine pyrophosphate (TPP) condenses with α-ketoglutaric acid releasing CO_2 and forming α-hydroxy-γ-carboxypropyl thiamine pyrophosphate. On the surface of the enzyme, a complex which has not been named, the succinyl group is transferred from the thiamine to enzyme-bound lipoic acid. Succinyl lipoic acid then reacts with CoASH to give succinyl CoA and reduced lipoic acid. The latter is then oxidized to the cyclic form by NAD^+. In both this reaction and that with pyruvic acid, the lipoic acid is probably not free, but bound to the enzyme by amide linkage with the ϵ-amino group of lysine.

The thioester energy of succinyl CoA may be utilized to initiate fatty acid oxidation, for acylation reactions, and by condensation with glycine, to initiate porphyrin synthesis (p. 204). However, most of the succinyl CoA formed by the operation of the citric acid cycle is utilized for additional ATP synthesis. Succinyl CoA reacts with guanosine diphosphate and inorganic phosphate to form succinic acid, GTP, and CoASH. The GTP then reacts with ADP to give GDP and ATP. The two reactions are catalyzed by succinic acid thiokinase and nucleoside diphosphokinase, respectively. The formation of succinyl CoA is not reversible. Although other reactions in the cycle can be reversed, the irreversibility of this reaction prevents the cycle from running in the reverse direction.

Dehydrogenation of succinic acid. (Reaction 7, Fig. 68) This reaction is catalyzed by succinic acid dehydrogenase. It is the only dehydrogenation in the citric acid cycle in which pyridine nucleotides (NAD^+ and NADP) do not participate. The enzyme contains four atoms of iron and one mole of flavin per mole of protein, and has a molecular weight of 200,000. The enzyme will produce only the trans form of fumaric acid, and can not produce the cis form, maleic acid. Reaction 7 is reversible. Malonic acid ($HOOC-CH_2-COOH$) is a specific competitive inhibitor of the oxidation of succinic acid. As a result, when present in sufficiently high concentration, malonate can be employed to interrupt the citric acid cycle at this point, with resultant accumulation of succinate.

Formation of malic acid. (Reaction 8, Fig. 68) The enzyme, fumarase, catalyzes the hydration of fumaric acid to malic acid. The reaction is freely reversible, and fumarate is the most abundant member of the citric acid cycle in mammalian tissues.

Regeneration of oxaloacetic acid. (Reaction 9, Fig. 68) Malic acid is oxidized by NAD^+ in the presence of malic dehydrogenase, to yield oxaloacetic acid. With this reaction, the cycle is completed, and the generated oxaloacetic acid is made available for condensation with another mole of acetyl CoA. Reaction 9 is reversible.

Total yield of ATP from glucose. Table 28 summarizes the energy yield in the form of ATP moles formed per mole of glucose converted to CO_2 and water in the glycolytic scheme and in the Krebs cycle.

Table 28.   Production of adenosine triphosphate (ATP) from glucose

Reaction	Nature of Transfer	ATP/mole glucose
2M triose phosphate ---→	$2NAD^+$---- 2NADH---- $2NAD^+$	6
2M 3-phosphoglyceric	substrate high energy bond	2
2M phosphoenol pyruvate ---→		
2M pyruvate	substrate high energy bond	2
2M pyruvate---→2M acetyl CoA	$2NAD^+$---- 2NADH---- $2NAD^+$	6
2M isocitrate ---→		
2M ketoglutarate	$2NADP^+$--- 2NADPH---$2NADP^+$	6
2M ketoglutarate ---→		
2M succinyl CoA	$2NAD^+$---- 2NADH---- $2NAD^+$	6
2M succinyl CoA ---→		
2M succinate	substrate high energy bond	2
2M succinate ---→2M fumarate	$2FAD^+$---- 2FADH---- $2FAD^+$	4
2M malate ---→2M oxaloacetate	$2NAD^+$---- 2NADH---- $2NAD^+$	6
	Total produced	40
1M glucose ---→1M fructose 1, 6-diphosphate		-2

Net   38

Step-wise release of energy from glucose. If one follows the pathway from pyruvate via acetyl CoA around the cycle, the three carbon dioxide molecules released when one molecule of pyruvic acid is "burned" with oxygen can be accounted for. However, two molecules of water are also formed per mole of pyruvic acid (see equation) which are not apparent in the cycle. The water molecules are accounted for when the reduced NAD^+, NADP and succinic dehydrogenase formed in the cycle are

$$CH_3\ CO\ COOH + 2.5O_2\ ---→\ 3\ CO_2 + 2\ H_2O$$

reoxidized with molecular oxygen by means of the flavoprotein enzymes and the electron transport system. This also occurs in the anaerobic glycolysis scheme when 3-phosphoglyceraldehyde is oxidized to 1,3-diphosphoglyceric acid (p. 157) in the presence of NAD^+.

NADH + H^+ (from cell buffer medium) + $1/2$ O_2 $---\rightarrow NAD^+$ + H_2O

NADPH + H^+ + $1/2$ O_2 $---\rightarrow NADP^+$ + H_2O

Reduced succinic dehydrogenase (E·H) + H^+ + $1/2$ O_2 $\rightarrow$ oxid. enz. + H_2O

The oxidation of the hydrogen acceptors in the Krebs cycle is not as direct as the above equations suggest. Molecular oxygen will not react directly with NADH, NADPH, etc. If we look at oxidation as a *removal of electrons*, then a total of five *intermediate* electron acceptors are required to "pass along" the electrons from NADH, NADPH, etc. to molecular oxygen. These will be discussed briefly below.

Mechanism of biological oxidation. Oxidation may be defined as the addition of oxygen (2 Mg + O_2 $\rightarrow$ 2Mg O), the loss of hydrogen (CH_3CHO+H_2O $\rightarrow$ CH_3COOH + 2H), or by the most general definition: the *loss of electrons*. Thus, in the first two examples, a magnesium atom loses two electrons to oxygen, and a carbon atom also loses two electrons to oxygen, in the formation of magnesium oxide and acetic acid, respectively. The ability of a substrate to be oxidized (or to be reduced, which is a *gain* of electrons) depends upon its oxidation-reduction potential (redox potential). A clearer understanding of redox potential can be gained by using an electrochemical illustration.

If gaseous hydrogen is circulated over a platinum electrode dipping into a solution of acid which is 1 normal with respect to hydrogen ion (H^+), an equilibrium will be set up. The gaseous hydrogen will have a tendency to *lose electrons* and go into solution as H^+. If one lead of an amneter is connected to the platinum electrode and another dipped into the solution, this electron-losing tendency of hydrogen will be observed as a flow of current. The electrode-hydrogen gas-1N solution is referred to as a *half cell*, and under the conditions outlined it is called a standard hydrogen half cell. If another half cell is constructed containing a platinum electrode in a solution containing a mixture of ferrous (Fe^{++}) and ferric (Fe^{+++}) salts, the electron-losing tendency of this cell ($Fe^{++} \rightarrow Fe^{+++}$ + e) will be different from that of the hydrogen half-cell. The two half cells can be converted into a simple battery by placing the ends of a salt bridge into each solution. One electrode will then become the positive pole, the other the negative pole of the battery. If we arbitrarily assign a potential of zero to the hydrogen half cell (making it the standard reference cell), then the observed voltage (potential) across the two electrodes will represent the voltage of the ferrous-ferric ion half cell (with respect to hydrogen). The observed potential is +0.75 volts. Therefore, the potential of the ferrous-ferric ion half cell is higher than that of the hydrogen half cell. If it had been equal to the potential of the latter, the observed potential would be 0.0.

The observed potential varies with the ratio of ferrous to ferric ion. The lower the ratio, the higher the potential. This is expressed mathematically by the following equation:

$$E_h = E_o - \frac{RT}{nF} \log \frac{\text{reduced form } (Fe^{++})}{\text{oxidized form } (Fe^{+++})}$$

In this equation E_h = observed potential in volts

E_o = potential in volts under standard conditions (30°C, pH = 7)

R = gas constant

T = absolute temperature

F = Faraday (96,500 coulombs of electricity)

n = number of electrons transferred in the reaction (one in the case of $Fe^{++} \dashrightarrow Fe^{+++} + e$)

In order to determine the standard electrode potential E_o for any oxidation-reduction system, it is only necessary to measure the observed potential of the system against the hydrogen half cell when *equal amounts* of reduced and oxidized form of the redox agent are present. Under these conditions the fraction: reduced form/ oxidized form equals 1, and since log 1=0, the equation becomes $E_h = E_o$.

Since the pH of the solution affects the potential of a redox system, E_o will vary with pH. If the E_o value is determined at some pH other than 7, the term E_o should be changed to E_o' to indicate the introduction of a new constant ($E_o \times K_{pH} = E_o'$).

The ability of a redox agent to react readily with atmospheric oxygen will depend upon its E_o value. This must be 0.2-0.3 volt below that of oxygen, which is +0.8 volt. The respiratory pigment, cytochrome a_3 (cytochrome oxidase) fulfills this requirement. Like the other cytochromes (see p. 98) it contains ferrous ion which can be oxidized to ferric ion, and its E_o value is high enough so that it can react directly with atmospheric oxygen.

Cytochrome a_3 (Fe^{++}) + $O_2 \dashrightarrow$ Cytochrome a_3 (Fe^{++}). O_2
(activated complex)

Cytochrome a_3 (Fe^{++}). $O_2 + 2H^+ \dashrightarrow$ Cytochrome a_3 (Fe^{+++}) + H_2O(or H_2O_2)

Cytochrome c (formula on p. 99) and cytochrome a have an E_o of 0.27 and 0.29 volts respectively, which is about 0.3 volt below that of cytochrome a_3. Both readily give up electrons (are oxidized) by cytochrome a_3.

Cytochrome c (or a) (Fe^{++}) + Cytochrome a_3 (Fe^{+++})

$\dashrightarrow$ Cytochrome c (or a) (Fe^{+++}) + Cytochrome a_3 (Fe^{++})

Cytochrome b, the fourth member of the cytochromes has an E_o (-0.04 volt) which is again about 0.3 volt below cytochromes, c and a. It readily gives up electrons (is oxidized) by cytochromes c and a.

Cytochrome b (Fe^{++}) + Cytochrome c (or a) (Fe^{+++})

$\dashrightarrow$ Cytochrome b (Fe^{+++}) + Cytochrome c (or a) (Fe^{++})

Not only does cytochrome c oxidize cytochrome b readily, but it also oxidizes the two flavoprotein coenzymes, FAD and FMN (see p. 113 for formulas). Their E_o (-0.09 volt) is approximately the same as that of cytochrome b.

Cytochrome c (Fe^{+++}) + enzyme $\cdot$ FADH(or FMNH)

------$\rightarrow$ Cytochrome c (Fe^{++}) + enzyme $\cdot$ FAD (or FMN) + H$^+$

Finally, cytochrome b and the flavoproteins have redox potentials approximately 0.2 volt higher than the pyridine nucleotides (E$_O$ = -0.28). They therefore readily oxidize them:

Cytochrome b (Fe^{+++}) + Enzyme $\cdot$ NADH (or NADPH)

------$\rightarrow$ Cytochrome b (Fe^{++}) + Enzyme $\cdot$ NAD (or NADP) + H$^+$

Enzyme $\cdot$ FAD (or FMN) + Enzyme $\cdot$ NADH (or NADPH)

------$\rightarrow$Enzyme $\cdot$ FADH (or FMNH) + Enzyme $\cdot$ NAD (or NADP)

In summary, oxidation of the Krebs cycle intermediates and pyruvic acid is a step-wise process which involves a transfer of electrons. Each intermediate has a redox potential that is 0.2-0.3 volts larger than the preceding electron transfer agent. In a sense, the electron transport agents are a part of a cycle (Fig. 69) in which Krebs substrate electrons flow to acceptors with the lowest E$_O$, then the electrons travel around the cycle, each agent being oxidized, then reduced, until the electrons flow out of the cycle to molecular oxygen, which, thus activated, in the presence of hydrogen ions is converted to water molecules.

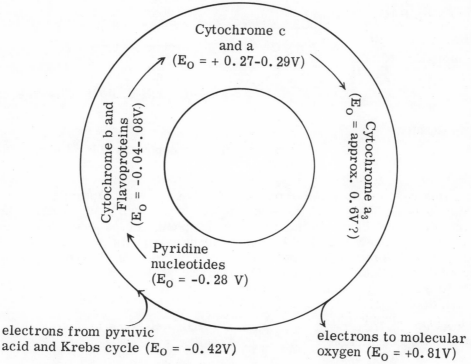

Figure 69. Electron Transfer Cycle

<u>Fate of energy released by glucose oxidation.</u> In the step-wise oxidation of glucose to carbon dioxide and water, parcels of energy are released as the electrons are transferred from a redox transfer agent to one with a higher E$_O$ value. These parcels of energy in some unknown manner convert ADP to ATP. The energy transfer

is, however, not 100 per cent efficient. It is estimated that approximately 38 moles of ATP are produced when 1 mole of glucose passes through the glycolysis and Krebs cycles to the end-products, carbon dioxide and water (see Table 28, p. 162). This would mean that 38 x 7* X 100/686 or about 40%, of the energy released is trapped by the cell in the form of chemical bond energy; thus, 60% is lost in the form of heat.

Not all of the "high energy phosphate" bonds are stored as ATP. Other compounds containing a high energy phosphate bond (written as "~P") are acetyl phosphate, pyruvic acid enol phosphate, creatine phosphate, and arginine phosphate. The formulas for these compounds are shown below. The standard free energy of hydrolysis of the energy-rich bond is shown in parentheses after three of the compounds.**

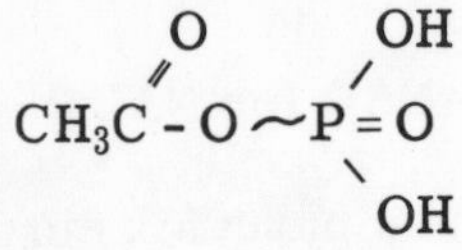

acetyl phosphate

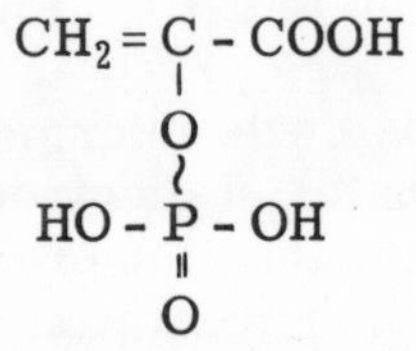

pyruvic acid enol phosphate (12 kcal/mole)

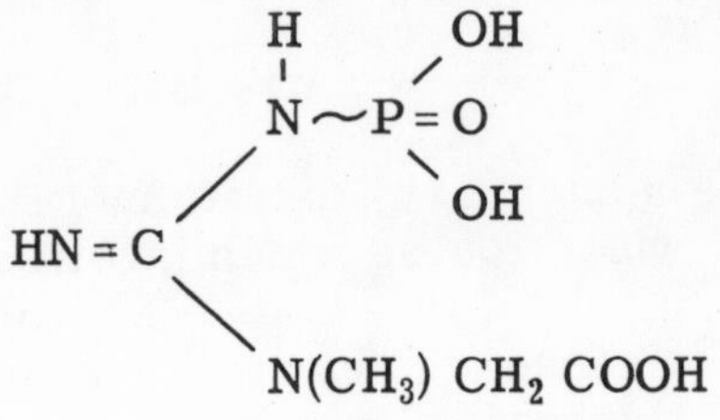

creatine phosphate (8 kcal/mole)

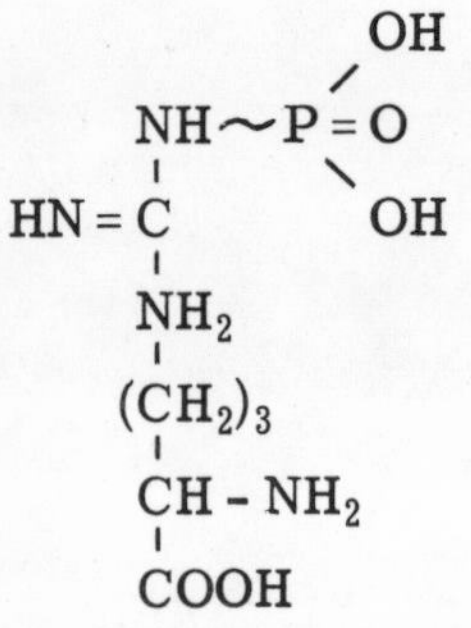

Arginine phosphate

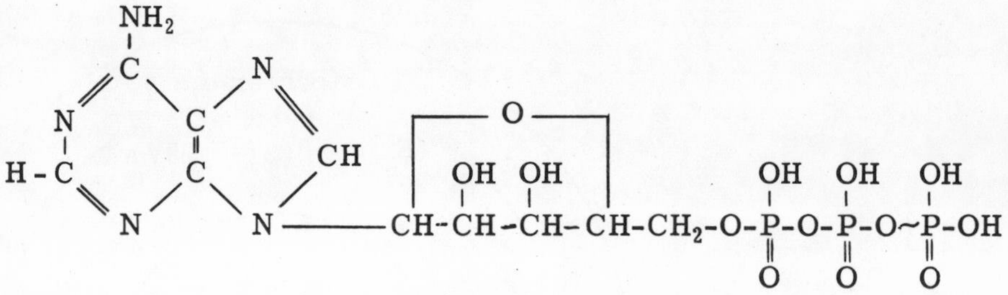

adenosine triphosphate (ATP) (7 kcal/mole)

More information is available on the function of these compounds in muscle than in other tissues. The resting muscle contains four times more creatine phosphate than ATP. This indicates that creatine phosphate serves as the high energy phosphate storehouse in muscle. Present evidence suggests that ATP is used, probably exclusively, as the *immediate* source of energy for muscle contraction. The supply would be quickly exhausted if creatine phosphate were not available for conversion to ATP by the Lohmann reaction:

$$\text{ATP} \xrightarrow[\substack{\text{contraction}\\ \text{(ATP-ase)}}]{\text{muscle}} \text{ADP} + H_3PO_4 + 11.5 \text{ kilocal.}$$

Creatine phosphate + ADP $\rightleftharpoons$ ATP + creatine (Lohmann reaction)

* Kilocalories of energy stored in the high energy phosphate bond of ATP per mole of ATP.
** Other energy-rich compounds are: pyrophosphate (6 kcal/mole), phosphoglyceryl phosphate (11 kcal/mole), acetyl Coenzyme A(8 kcal/mole) and amino acyl-AMP(7 kcal/mole).

During severe exercise, creatine phosphate stored in the muscle is converted to ATP*. This continues until about one-half of the creatine phosphate is used up, and the muscle becomes exhausted. When muscular exercise ceases, glycogen break-down continues to produce ATP, causing the Lohmann reaction to go into reverse; the reverse reaction is then maintained until the level of creatine phosphate in the muscle is restored to normal.

$$Glycogen + O_2 \dashrightarrow CO_2 + H_2O + ATP$$

$$ATP + creatine \rightleftharpoons ADP + creatine\ phosphate$$

The presence of creatine phosphate in muscle gives muscle a much greater supply of readily available energy than the ATP alone could furnish. Compounds, such as creatine phosphate, which act as storehouses for high energy phosphate bonds are called *phosphagens*. Creatine phosphate is the phosphagen in vertebrate animals. In most invertebrate animals, creatine phosphate is replaced by another phosphagen, *arginine phosphate*. The role of acetyl phosphate and pyruvic enol phosphate in en-ergy metabolism is not clearly understood at present, nor is the exact manner in which ATP is converted into the mechanical energy of contraction. The enzyme, ATP-ase, which causes ATP to break down to ADP, is a long, thread-like protein which is present in muscle in large amounts. It might be arranged along the mus-cle fiber in such a manner that it releases energy from ATP to break hydrogen bonds and rearrange the fiber in a shorter configuration (see Chapter V, p. 62).

The Hexose Monophosphate Shunt-Alternate Pathway. Although the main pathway of glucose metabolism is via glycolysis (Embden Meyerhof pathway) and the Krebs cycle, plants, bacteria and mammals do have another series of enzymes which per-mit direct oxidation without the anaerobic breakdown of glucose. This has been called the hexose monophosphate shunt, the Warburg-Lipmann-Dickens pathway, alternate pathway, and direct oxidative pathway.

In the Embden-Meyerhof glycolysis pathway, no molecular oxygen is required from glucose to lactic acid (see p. 157). In the hexose monophosphate shunt (Fig. 70), molecular oxygen is introduced in the first step, and NADP acts as the first elec-tron acceptor. Electrons are then transferred in the usual fashion via flavoproteins and cytochromes to molecular oxygen.

---

* During moderate exercise, the rate of metabolism of glycogen (glycolysis and Krebs cycle) increases sufficiently to produce ATP as fast as it is needed.

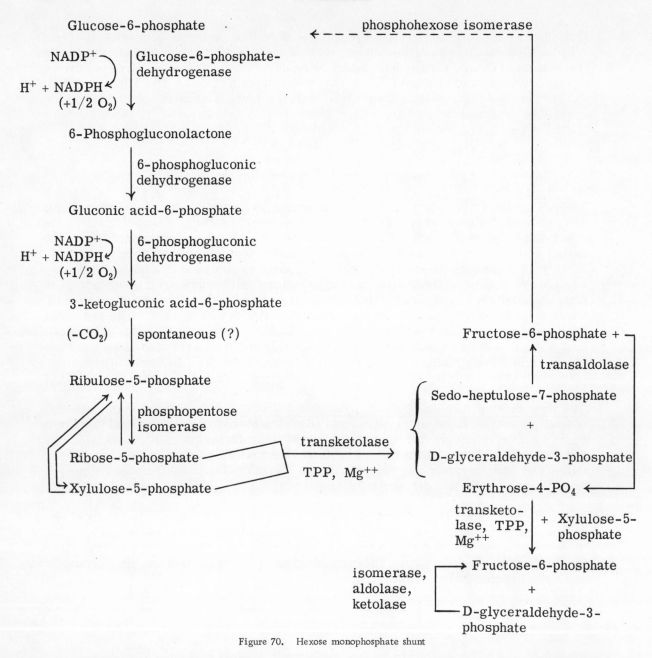

Figure 70. Hexose monophosphate shunt

FORMULAE OF COMPOUNDS INVOLVED IN THE HEXOSE MONOPHOSPHATE
SHUNT.

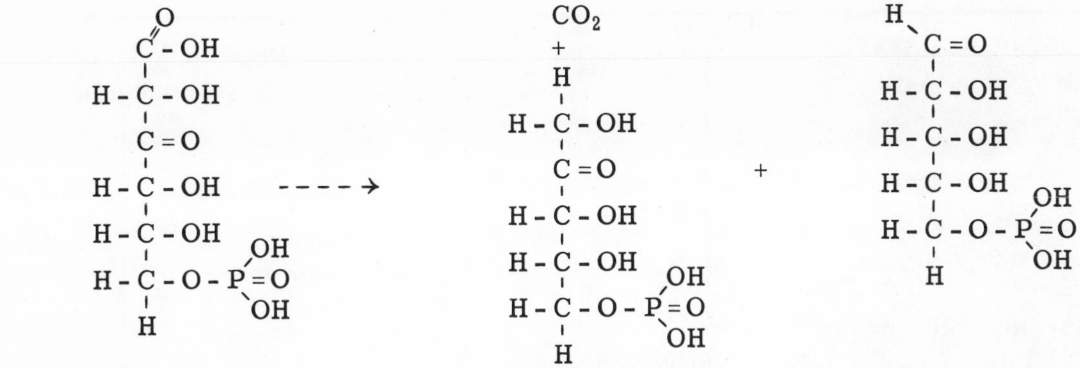

$$
\begin{array}{c}
\overset{O}{\overset{\|}{C}}-OH \\
| \\
H-C-OH \\
| \\
C=O \\
| \\
H-C-OH \\
| \\
H-C-OH \\
| \\
H-C-O-\overset{OH}{\underset{OH}{\overset{|}{P}=O}} \\
| \\
H
\end{array}
$$

3-Ketogluconic acid-
6-phosphate

$- - - \rightarrow$

$$
\begin{array}{c}
CO_2 \\
+ \\
H \\
| \\
H-C-OH \\
| \\
C=O \\
| \\
H-C-OH \\
| \\
H-C-OH \\
| \\
H-C-O-\overset{OH}{\underset{OH}{\overset{|}{P}=O}} \\
| \\
H
\end{array}
$$

Ribulose-5-
phosphate

$+$

$$
\begin{array}{c}
H \\
| \\
C=O \\
| \\
H-C-OH \\
| \\
H-C-OH \\
| \\
H-C-OH \\
| \\
H-C-O-\overset{OH}{\underset{OH}{\overset{|}{P}=O}} \\
| \\
H
\end{array}
$$

Ribose-5-
phosphate

$\xrightarrow[\text{(C, }C_2\text{ of}]{\text{2-carbon}}$
transfer
ribulose)

$$
\begin{array}{c}
H \\
| \\
H-C-OH \\
| \\
C=O \\
| \\
HO-C-H \\
| \\
H-C-OH \\
| \\
H-C-OH \\
| \\
H-C-OH \\
| \\
H-C-O-\overset{OH}{\underset{OH}{\overset{|}{P}=O}} \\
| \\
H
\end{array}
$$

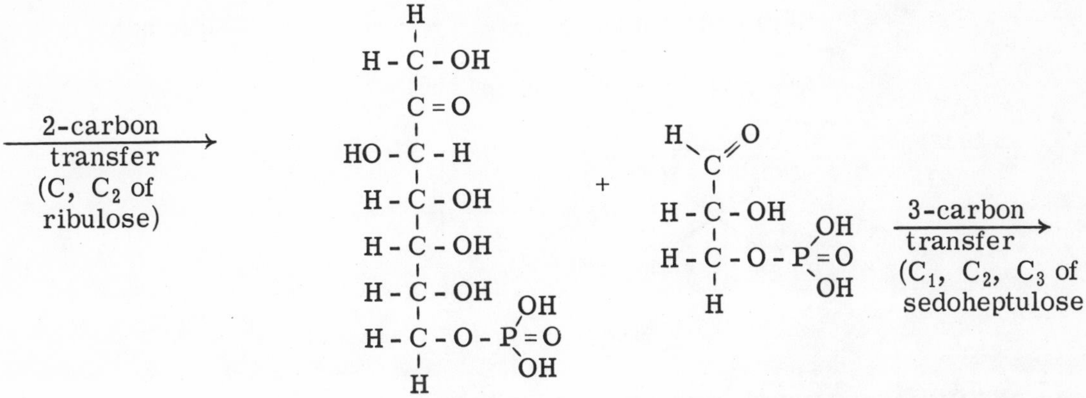

Sedo heptulose-
7-phosphate

$+$

$$
\begin{array}{c}
H \\
\overset{}{\underset{}{C}}\!\!=\!\!O \\
| \\
H-C-OH \\
| \\
H-C-O-\overset{OH}{\underset{OH}{\overset{|}{P}=O}} \\
| \\
H
\end{array}
$$

D-glyceraldehyde-3-phosphate

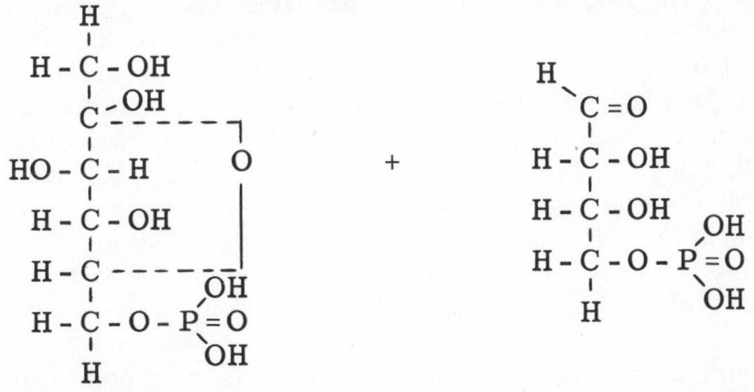

$\xrightarrow[\text{(C}_1\text{, }C_2\text{, }C_3\text{ of}]{\text{3-carbon}}$
transfer
sedoheptulose

$$
\begin{array}{c}
H \\
| \\
H-C-OH \\
| \\
C-OH \\
| \\
HO-C-H \quad O \\
| \\
H-C-OH \\
| \\
H-C - - - OH \\
| \\
H-C-O-\overset{}{\underset{OH}{\overset{|}{P}=O}} \\
| \\
H
\end{array}
$$

Fructose-6-phosphate
(α-form)

$+$

$$
\begin{array}{c}
H \\
\overset{}{\underset{}{C}}\!\!=\!\!O \\
| \\
H-C-OH \\
| \\
H-C-OH \\
| \\
H-C-O-\overset{OH}{\underset{OH}{\overset{|}{P}=O}} \\
| \\
H
\end{array}
$$

Erythrose-4-phosphate

Summary. The major metabolic transformations of glucose in animals are summarized in Figure 71. The details of the intermediate steps in the conversion of glucose to pyruvic acid, and pyruvic acid to carbon dioxide, are not shown.

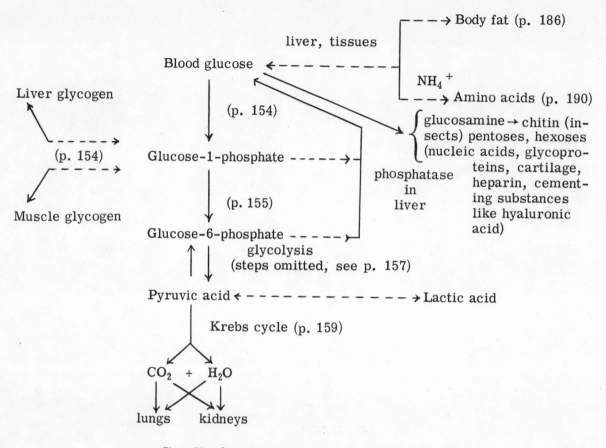

Figure 71.   Summary of glucose metabolism in animals

CARBOHYDRATE METABOLISM IN PLANTS.

<u>Photosynthesis</u>.   Photosynthesis is a process by which green plants convert the energy of sunlight into the potential energy of reduced carbon compounds, simultaneously evolving molecular oxygen.   This process is undoubtedly the most important process on earth, for it directly or indirectly supplies the essential nutrients for most forms of life.   In addition to currently supplying carbon compounds for plants, animals, and most microorganisms, it created in prehistoric times the vast stores of potential energy (coal, oil, gas, etc.) which man is now using as a major source of heat, locomotion, and many other forms of power.   Industry is beginning to use atomic energy derived from uranium for heat and power.   Many people are unaware of the fact that the sun itself is a huge atomic reactor, which operates on the principle of the hydrogen bomb.   If we could trap the light energy striking the earth with the efficiency of the green plant, we would not need to burn up the stores of potential energy still remaining in the ground.

<u>Mechanism</u>.   The ability to carry on photosynthesis is confined mainly to green plants and algae, although there are certain other lower forms of life (for example, the protozoon *Haematococcus pluvialis*) which are in this group.   In all cases, photosynthesis is associated with discrete green bodies, called chloroplasts, which are suspended in the cytoplasm of the cell.   It is possible to break leaf cells into several fractions by grinding them with a buffer solution in a colloid mill.   This treatment breaks the chloroplasts into smaller fragments called *grana*.   Three major fractions are recovered: (a) cytoplasm, a red-brown transparent solution, (b) solid grana (green), and (c) cell walls mixed with unbroken cells.

The grana, which are still capable of carrying on photosynthesis, contain, on a dry basis, about 40% protein, 35% lipids, 7% minerals, and 5% of a green pigment called *chlorophyll*. Chlorophyll is essential for photosynthesis. In most plants it exists as two closely related compounds, chlorophyll a and chlorophyll b, which serve as the prosthetic groups in an unidentified conjugated protein. The formulas for the a and b forms as proposed by Hans Fischer are shown below. Chlorophyll contains the tetrapyrrole or porphyrin nucleus which is found in the cytochromes and certain enzymes (see page 98), and in the blood constituent, hemoglobin (see page 262). In chlorophyll, the coordinating metallic ion is magnesium, whereas in most other porphyrins it is iron.

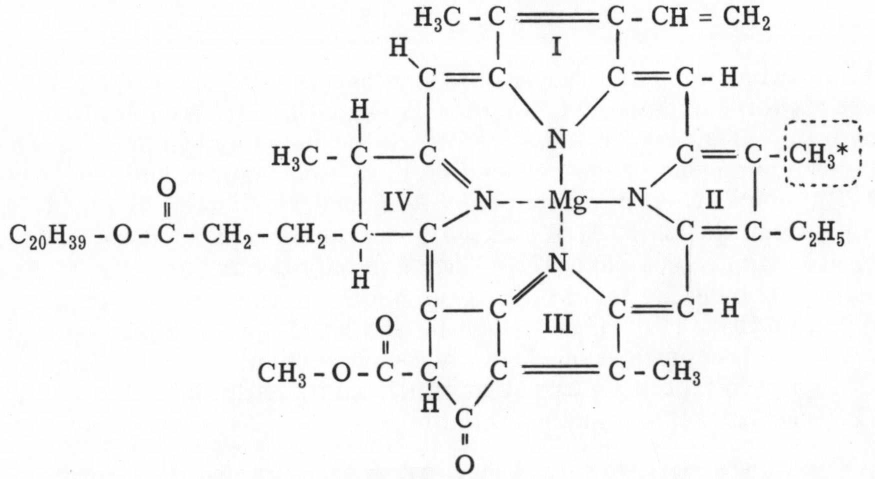

Chlorophyll a (* - $C = O$ replaces CH_3 in Chlorophyll b)

Chlorophylls a and b.

The simplest general equation for the photosynthetic reaction may be expressed as follows:

$$CO_2 \quad + \quad 2\,H_2O \quad \xrightarrow[\text{(2) enzymes}]{\text{(1) light, chlorophyll}} \quad 1/6(C_6H_{12}O_6) \; + \; H_2O \; + \; O_2$$

In this equation, which is essentially the reverse of respiration, the water molecule shown on the right hand side of the equation contains oxygen which was originally present in the CO_2, and is therefore not identical with the H_2O shown on the left hand side of the equation. This important discovery was made by Ruben and coworkers, who allowed *Chlorella*, a water plant, to photosynthesize in water containing heavy oxygen (O^{18}) and ordinary CO_2 (as carbonate) in one experiment, and in another, used ordinary water and CO_2 (as carbonate) containing heavy oxygen. They then analyzed the oxygen (see the equation) which is released during photosynthesis, and found that it contained O^{18} when marked water was used, but did not contain O^{18} when marked CO_2 was used. This proved that the oxygen released during photosynthesis comes *only* from water consumed in the photosynthetic reaction, and does not come from the CO_2 consumed. The oxygen of the CO_2 consumed appears in the *carbohydrate* and in the *water formed* during photosynthesis.

It has been established that the overall reaction shown in the above equation occurs in two steps: (1) the *light* reaction which requires the two agents above the arrow, namely, light and chlorophyll, and (2) the *dark* reaction, which is a series of enzyme-catalyzed reactions.

The light reaction. For all practical purposes, the energy used in photosynthesis is supplied by visible light, i.e., wave lengths from 390-760 mμ. This is absorbed almost exclusively by chlorophylls a and b, although other pigments (beta-carotene and luteol, see page 311) are always associated with the chlorophylls in the chloroplasts, and can contribute some absorbed energy for transfer to the chlorophylls. The energy absorbed by chlorophyll is used in the photolysis of water.

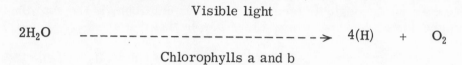

$$2H_2O \xrightarrow{\quad\text{Visible light}\quad} 4(H) \quad + \quad O_2$$
$$\text{Chlorophylls a and b}$$

In the light reaction, or primary phase of photosynthesis, the radiant energy trapped in chlorophyll serves to synthesize two compounds essential for the actual incorporation of CO_2 into carbohydrate. The first of these, ATP, is produced by the *photophosphorylation* of ADP. The second compound is the reduced form of nicotinamide adenine dinucleotide phosphate (NADPH), which arises by a photochemical reduction of the oxidized ($NADP^+$) form. Both the phosphorylation of ADP and the reduction of $NADP^+$ consume energy, and are strongly endergonic (see page 92). They can only occur naturally if this energy loss is compensated for by some form of energy supply, in this case, the energy of light. It is interesting to note that the dark reaction, in which CO_2 is incorporated into carbohydrate, is only indirectly dependent on the primary photochemical event, and can proceed in the absence of light. In fact, CO_2 can be assimilated by cells devoid of chlorophyll provided that ATP and NADPH are made available.

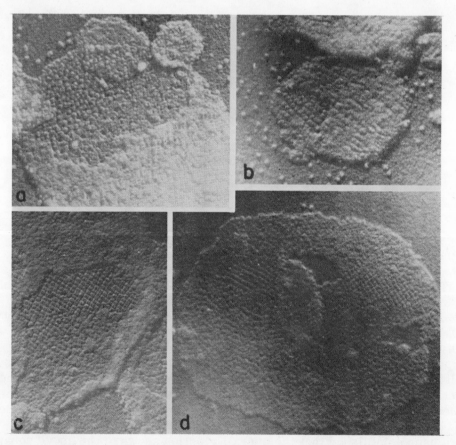

Figure 72. Chromium-shadowed spinach chloroplast lamellae, all X 71,000. (a) random quantasome array, (b) linear quantasome array, (c) crystalline quantasome array, and (d) random, linear and crystalline quantasome arrays within one lamella. (From R. B. Park and J. Biggins, Science, 144, 1010 (1964).

The chloroplasts, and their subunits, the quantasomes. The photosynthetic apparatus of higher plants is located in a discrete structure called the *chloroplast* (Fig. 2). Examination of the chloroplast with the electron microscope reveals a large number of closely spaced layers or lamellae which are set in a finely granular matrix. In certain regions there is a pairing of lamellae giving a more dense and closely packed region. This is known as the *grana*. With higher resolution, the lamellae are found to consist of subunits called *quantosomes* (Fig. 72). The quantosome is 185 Å long, 155 Å wide, and 100 Å thick. It has a molecular weight of 2×10^6. Park and Biggins have compiled an interesting balance sheet on the total number of moles of lipid, protein, and metal atoms contained in one quantasome. The name of the compound is followed by the number of moles in parentheses: chlorophyll a (160), chlorophyll b (70), β-carotene (14), lutein (22), violaxanthin (6), neoxanthin (6), plastoquinone A (16), plastoquinone B (8), plastoquinone C (4), α-tocopherol (8-10), α-tocopherylquinone (4), vitamin K_1 (4), glycerophosphoryl glycerol (52), glycerophosphoryl inositol (14), glycerophosphoryl ethanolamine (6), glycerophosphoryl choline (42), glycerophosphate (2), digalactosyldiglyceride (144), monogalactosyldiglyceride (346), sulfolipid (48), protein (9,380 atoms of nitrogen), manganese (2 atoms), iron including two cytochromes (12 atoms) and copper (6 atoms). It is believed that the quantosome, which is 100 angstroms thick, is like a sandwich, with a center protein layer about 33 angstroms thick, and the two outer lipid layers each 33 angstroms thick. The quantosome is assumed to be the basic photosynthetic unit, containing everything needed for the photolytic cleavage of water and the photophosphorylation of ADP.

Mechanism of the light reaction. This reaction is concerned with the formation of two compounds, ATP and NADPH. Neither formation requires the reduction or incorporation of CO_2. These two compounds represent the first stable, chemically well-defined products of the energy conversion occurring in the quantasomes.

Cyclic photophosphorylation. At least two distinct photochemical pathways are postulated to occur in the quantosomes, according to Arnon. The first is the mechanism for the phosphorylation of ATP. Figure 73 sketches Arnon's model for this mechanism.

The steps are as follows:

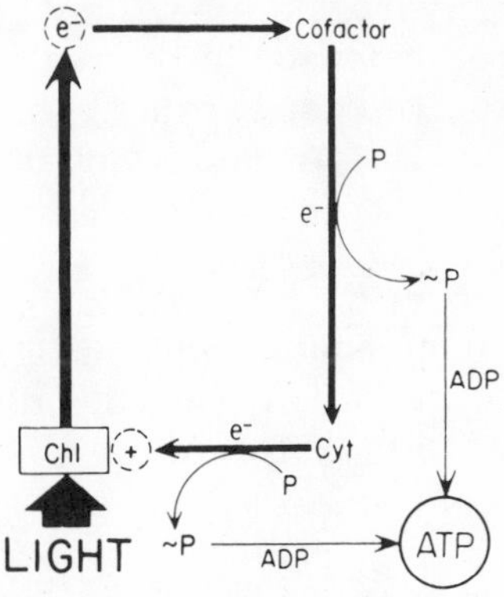

(1) Chlorophyll is raised from its normal, *ground* state to a higher energy level by the absorption of a quantum of light energy. (Chl + h ---➤ Chl*)

(2) The "excited" chlorophyll molecule loses an electron to become oxidized, thereby forming a "hole" or "odd ion", which will avidly accept another electron in order to return to its ground state. (Chl* ----➤ Chl$^+$ + e$^-$)

(3) The expelled electron is captured by, and reduces a cofactor which has not been identified. (X + e$^-$ --➤ X$^-$)

(4) The cofactor is in turn reoxidized by passing on its electron to the series of cytochromes in the quantasome. (X$^-$ + Cyt-Fe ---➤ Cyt-Fe + X)

(5) The "terminal" cytochrome is reoxidized by transfer of its electron to Chl$^+$, thereby completing the cycle.

Figure 73. Model for cyclic photophosphorylation (Arnon).

The most important feature of Arnon's model is the indirect mechanism for the recapture of its electron by Chl$^+$. The return to the ground state, of course, results in an important release of energy.

The actual phosphorylation of ADP occurs in coupled reactions which are powered by the processes occurring in stages (4) and (5). These are enzyme-catalyzed, but the nature of the enzymes is not known.

The overall reaction may be written as follows:

$$2 \ Chl^+ + 2 \ Fe^{++}\text{-}Cyt + ADP + P \ \text{-------} \rightarrow \ ATP + 2 \ Chl + 2 \ Fe^{+++}\text{-}Cyt$$

This equation shows that the terminal cytochrome is left in the oxidized state, to be reduced and then reoxidized in another turn of the cycle.

Noncyclic photophosphorylation. Arnon's model for this mechanism is shown in Figure 74. The TPN and TPNH₂ in Figure 74 are the older names for $NADP^+$ and NADPH. In this mechanism, the initial steps are believed to be the same as those shown for cyclic phosphorylation. The electron expelled from chlorophyll is captured by $NADP^+$, together with a proton from water, to form NADPH. This reaction is catalyzed by NAD reductase. The electron returned to Chl^+ is derived from the hydroxyl ion of water left after the acceptance of a proton by NAD. Arnon has isolated an iron-containing protein from spinach chloroplasts which is similar to ferrodoxin first isolated from *Clostridium pasteuranium.* This is the most electronegative electron carrier in cellular physiology, with a redox potential value (see p. 96) of -432 mv at

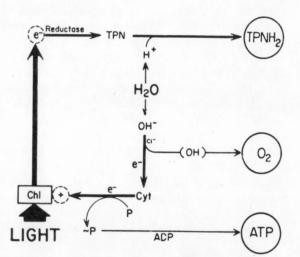

Figure 74. Model for noncyclic photophosphorylation (Arnon).

pH 7.55. Hydrogen is -420 mv at pH 7. Ferrodoxin may be the first carrier to accept the electron released in the reaction: $2 \ OH^- \ \text{------} \rightarrow \ O_2 + 2 \ H^+ + 4 \ e^-$. The transit of the electron released from hydroxyl ion through the ferrodoxin and cytochromes is coupled to an enzymatic process which phosphorylates ADP to ATP. The complete equation is as follows: $2 \ NADP^+ + 2 \ ADP + 2P + 2 \ H_2O \ \text{-----} \rightarrow \ 2 \ NADPH + O_2 + 2 \ ATP$.

The dark reaction. The dark reaction has a name that is misleading, since the reaction will take place equally well in light or darkness. It is an enzyme-controlled reaction involving the reduction of carbon dioxide to carbohydrate. The general equation for the dark reaction is as follows:

$$CO_2 \quad + \quad 4(H) \ \text{------} \xrightarrow{\text{Enzymes}} \text{------} \rightarrow 1/6(C_6H_{12}O_6) \quad + \quad H_2O$$

Many steps, each catalyzed by a specific enzyme, are involved in the conversion of carbon dioxide to carbohydrates such as fructose, glucose and sucrose. The pathway of carbon in the dark reaction is discussed on the following pages.

The pathway of carbon in the dark reaction. Radioactive carbon and other isotopic tracer elements have made it possible for the biochemist to successfully follow the pathway of carbon in photosynthesis. Calvin and his associates have made important contributions to this phase of carbohydrate metabolism in plants. They have used the green alga, *chlorella,* in an apparatus designed so that a suspension of this single-celled plant can be exposed to radioactive carbon dioxide ($C^{14}O_2$) and then illuminated with measured amounts of light for various time intervals. The glass apparatus has the shape of a lollipop.

After exposure to light, samples of the plant are quickly removed, the enzymes inactivated with alcohol, and the new compounds formed are identified by filter paper chromatography (see p. 81), including identification by exposure of radioactive spots to x-ray film.

Using these methods, Calvin has found that the *first* product of photosynthesis is *3-phosphoglyceric acid*, which is produced by the reaction of carbon dioxide with ribulose-1,5-diphosphate. Radioactive carbon appears in this compound when the period of exposure to light has been as short as *5 seconds*.

The complete cycle, as proposed by Calvin, is shown below (Fig. 75). It should be noted that ATP supplies the energy, and that TPNH(NADPH) is an electron donor in the dark reaction.

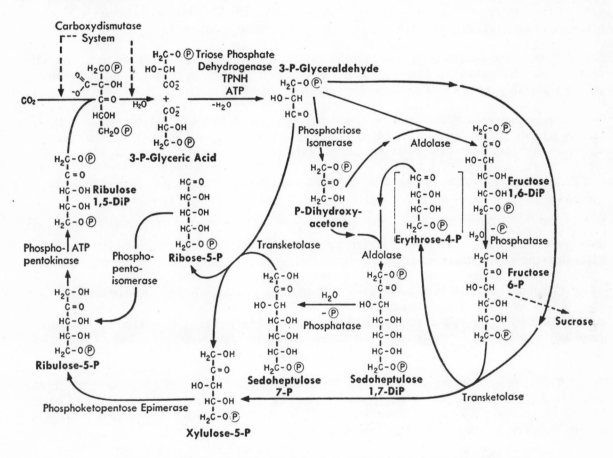

Figure 75.   The photosynthetic carbon cycle (M. Calvin, Science, <u>135</u>, 886 (1962)).

In the carbon fixation cycle, carbon dioxide is fed in, and excess fructose and other intermediates of the glycolytic scheme (see p. 157) are drained off to serve as starting materials for the synthesis of carbon compounds needed by the plant cell.

The three sugars which appear to accumulate in photosynthesizing leaves are fructose, glucose, and sucrose. Fructose diphosphate is the first hexose to appear, being converted via the monophosphate to glucose and sucrose (page 18). As these first products of photosynthesis accumulate, they are converted to other carbohydrates (pentoses, hexoses, mono-, di-, tri-, polysaccharides, etc. (page 180)) and to amino acids (page 54), lipids (page 35), and vitamins (page 226). The speed with which the plant can convert CO_2 into some of the more complex compounds is amazing. Workers in the National

Research Council of Canada found radioactive cellulose in the leaves of beets after they had absorbed radioactive carbon dioxide ($C^{14}O_2$) for only *ten seconds*.

Factors limiting the rate of photosynthesis. Several factors may limit the rate of photosynthesis. These will be discussed separately.

   Light. Under low light intensity, light becomes a limiting factor (for example, at daybreak on a hot summer day).

   Temperature. Temperature does not affect the light reaction, but affects the dark reaction, which involves the action of many enzymes. Orchids in the tropics are large in size, whereas arctic orchids are so tiny that they must be examined under a hand lens to observe details of structure. Temperature is believed to be the limiting factor in the case of the arctic orchid. It is also a limiting factor for all plant growth in the early spring and late fall in most parts of the North American continent.

   Water. No decrease is noted in the rate of photosynthesis in leaves until the wilting stage is reached; then the rate declines abruptly. It is obvious from the equation for the photosynthetic process that water is an essential reactant.

   Carbon dioxide. The atmosphere contains about 0.03% CO_2. Reduction of the level of CO_2 will decrease the rate of photosynthesis. Reduced levels of CO_2 have actually been observed in the center of a closely planted stand of corn on a hot sunny day.

   Chlorophyll. This is essential for photosynthesis. Variegated leaves do not carry on photosynthesis in those areas which are devoid of this green pigment.

   Enzymes. These are essential for the many steps in the photosynthetic reaction. However, no studies have been carried out on the effect of destroying or blocking a specific enzyme in the dark reaction.

   Carotenoids. Closely associated with the chlorophylls in the chloroplast are several yellow and colorless compounds known as carotenoids (see p. 311). The most abundant of these are the two carotenoids, beta-carotene (precursor of Vitamin A in animals, page 226) and luteol. The formulas for these two compounds are shown on the following page.

   The carotenoids are not essential for the light reaction of photosynthesis, for carbohydrate formation occurs when green leaves are exposed to red light, which is not absorbed by these compounds. However, the light energy absorbed by the carotenoids can be transferred at least in part to chlorophyll.

Organisms possessing photosynthetic ability. The ability to carry on photosynthesis is confined mainly to the green plants and algae. An unusual case is the protozoon *Haematococcus pluvialis*, which contains chlorophyll, carotenoids, etc., and is capable of deriving energy directly from the sun.

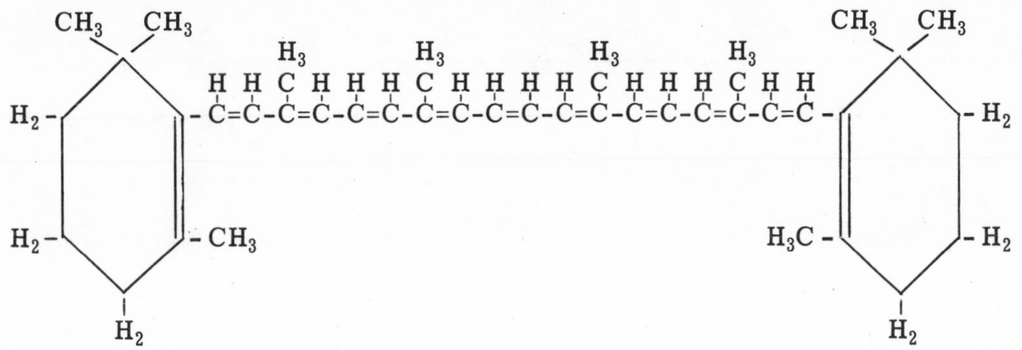

$$
\begin{array}{c}
\text{CH}_3 \quad \text{CH}_3 \\
\end{array}
$$

beta-carotene

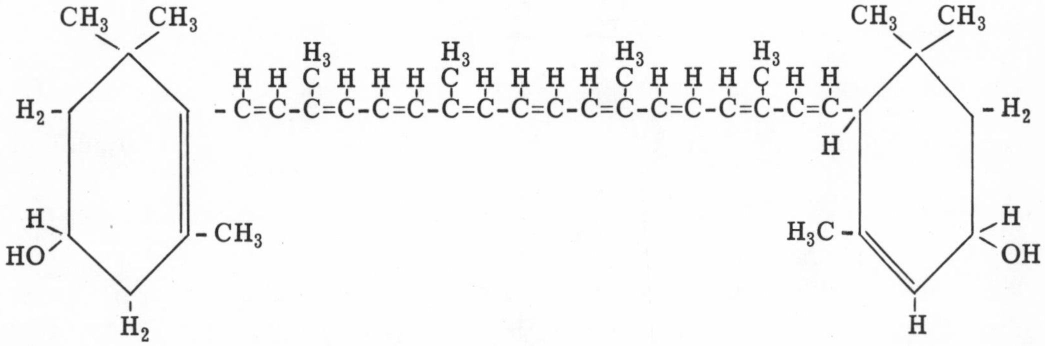

luteol

Intracellular digestion of carbohydrates in plants.   Plants do not obtain food carbohydrates by a process of extracellular digestion such as that occurring in microorganisms and animals. Carbohydrates are supplied in a directly utilizable form(glucose, fructose, sucrose) by photosynthesis in the leaf, followed by translocation to the plant parts requiring these nutrients. Excess carbohydrates formed by photosynthesis, and not needed to build structural materials like cellulose, or protoplasmic materials like proteins and lipids, are stored as food polysaccharide, which is usually starch. If the plant does not form starch in the cells of a particular tissue, then the excess is stored there as sucrose.

Digestion in plant tissues is therefore concerned with *intracellular* digestion of stored food carbohydrate. The most important sites of storage of starch are in seeds, especially cereal grains, tubers (e.g., potatoes) and in the leaves (during photosynthesis). The digestion of stored starch is most rapid during the germination of seeds and the sprouting of tubers, and is most rapid in photosynthesizing leaves, when they are placed in the dark.   In all cases, there are apparently two main pathways for the breakdown of starch to its building unit, glucose. These two pathways are shown in Figure 76 on the following page.

Pathway (1) was demonstrated by Hanes in pea seeds and potato tubers. The enzyme phosphorylase splits the starch molecule by introducing phosphate groups at the glycosidic linkages. The reaction is reversible, and under appropriate conditions, the phosphorylase enzyme can synthesize an amylose type of starch. Another enzyme, the Q enzyme, is present to form the amylopectin type from the amylose type (compare with glycogen synthesis, page 154). Recent research suggests that the main pathway of synthesis of most polysaccharides is by *transglycosylation*, with UDP-monosaccharide units as the transfer agent (see p. 155). Some agents are: UDP-glucose (starch, cellulose), UDP-N-acetyl-D-glucosamine and UDP-galacturonic acid (hyaluronic acid).

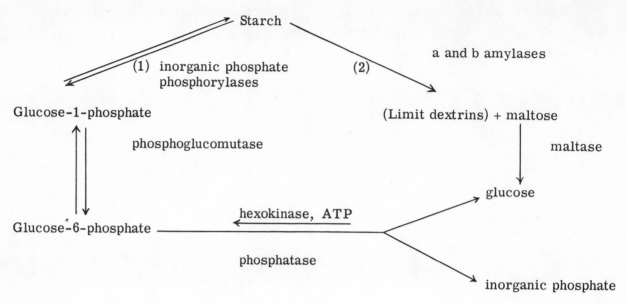

Figure 76.   Digestion of starch

Pathway (2) has been studied more extensively than pathway (1). The enzyme, beta-amylase, attacks the non-reducing ends of the starch molecules (see p. 24), splitting off successive units of maltose until a point is reached at which amylose is completely split to maltose, and, in amylopectin, until a branching of the chain occurs (Fig. 77).

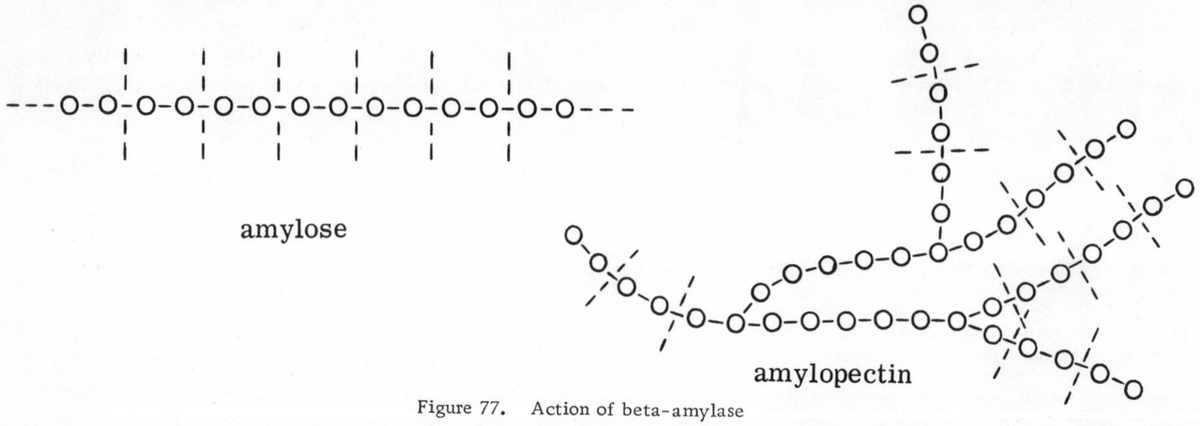

amylose

amylopectin

Figure 77.   Action of beta-amylase

The enzyme, alpha-amylase, produces dextrins (polymers of lower molecular weight than starch) by rupturing the linear molecules of amylose as well as the free branches and between-branch portions of branched amylopectin (Fig. 78).

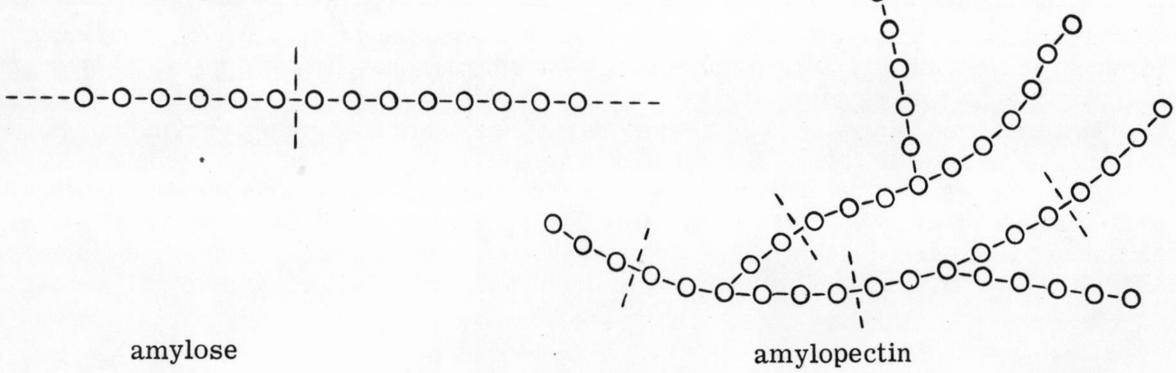

amylose   amylopectin

Figure 78.   Action of alpha-amylase

Through its dextrinizing action, alpha-amylase provides an increased number of non-reducing end-groups for attack by beta-amylase.

In the above combined digestive action of alpha and beta amylase, there remains (at least in the laboratory) a certain number of "limit dextrins", with 1,6-glycosidic linkages, which are highly, if not completely, resistant to rupture. Whether these "limit dextrins" are present in the plant cell during starch digestion is not known.

Either pathway of intracellular digestion discussed above leads to glucose-6-phosphate, which can be utilized at the site of digestion for metabolic purposes, or converted to free glucose for translocation to some other part of the plant or seed where it is needed as a nutrient.

In those plant parts where sucrose serves as the storage form of carbohydrates, the enzyme sucrase (invertase) is probably involved in the cleavage of sucrose to glucose and fructose. This enzyme is widely distributed in plant tissues. Sucrose is readily used for growth in intact plants, excised roots, various plant tissues and young embryos, and is phosphorylated with ease. It is possible that some pathway other than digestion with sucrase is also followed in the metabolism of this carbohydrate.

General metabolism of carbohydrates. Plants. The evidence which has been accumulated to date indicates that the breakdown of carbohydrate in the higher plants follows a course which is similar, if not identical, to that found in microorganisms and animals. A discussion of this breakdown was given at the beginning of the chapter. Higher plants also contain a complement of enzymes, similar to those in yeast, which are able to convert glucose to ethyl alcohol and carbon dioxide. This conversion takes place when the plants are deprived of oxygen. Higher plants do not immediately succumb when placed in an oxygen-free environment. They will remain alive for varying periods of time, depending on the particular plant, the stage of growth, etc. Under these conditions, they invariably produce CO_2 and form ethyl alcohol in their tissues.

A large number of intermediates, or carbohydrate fragments, are produced in the main pathway of oxidation (aerobic respiration) of glucose to carbon dioxide and water, and in the alternate pathway, alcoholic fermentation (anaerobic respiration). Many of these intermediates must be used as building blocks for the formation of the variety of organic compounds present in the plant. Some of the steps in the two types of respiration are energy-yielding steps and undoubtedly furnish, through transfer, the energy required for synthesis of new compounds. With the exception of starch, glucose, fructose and sucrose, little is known regarding the mechanism of synthesis of the various carbohydrates found in plants. A list of the principal carbohydrates found in plants (and therefore synthesized from hexose or its fragments) is given in Table 29 on the following page.

All of the carbon compounds of the plant can be synthesized, starting with either glucose, fructose, or sucrose; this is shown by the ease with which excised plant tissues can be cultured in a nutrient solution in which one of these sugars serves as the sole source of carbon. The synthesis of complex carbohydrates is not limited to the plant kingdom; many are found in microorganisms and animals.

Table 29.   The principal carbohydrates in plants*

Sugars		Non-sugars	
Monosaccharides	Oligosaccharides	Polysaccharides	Compound Carbohydrates
Trioses	Disaccharides	Pentosans	Uronides
Glyceraldehyde	Sucrose	Arabans	Hemicelluloses
Pentoses	Maltose	Xylans	Pectins
Arabinose	Trehalose	Hexosans	Mucilages
Xylose	Cellobiose	Dextrins	Gums
Ribose	Melibiose	Starch	Glycosides
Hexoses	Trisaccharides	Inulin	Anthocyanidin-**
Glucose	Raffinose	Galactans	Anthracene-
Fructose	Melizitose	Fructosans	Flavon-**
Galactose	Gentianose	Mannans	Phenol-
Mannose	Rhamnose	Cellulose	Sterol-
Methyl-pentose	Tetrasaccharides		Sulfur-
Rhamnose	Stachyose		Nitrogen-
			Saponins

* From J. F. Stauffer in Frear, Agricultural Chemistry, I, Principles, p. 362, D. Van Nostrand Co., New York, 1950.
** For formulas of these pigments see p. 312, Appendix.

CARBOHYDRATE METABOLISM IN MICROORGANISMS.   The pathways of metabolism of carbohydrates in microorganisms are, in general, the same as those found in plants and higher animals. The hexose sugars, glucose and fructose, are the pivotal compounds, excess quantities being stored as starch or glycogen in the bacterial or other microbial cell, or converted to a variety of carbon compounds needed by the cell, or broken down to CO_2 and water (or to other end-products such as alcohol, acetone, etc., by fermentative microorganisms) to yield energy for synthetic processes.

Metabolism of Lipids

METABOLISM OF LIPIDS IN PLANTS AND MICROORGANISMS. Recent work using radioactive carbon has shown that in both the developing and the germinating cotyledon of the peanut plant, acetic acid (as acetate), glucose, and fructose, are important precursors of fatty acids. Of these three, acetate is at least four times more active as a precursor than the two monosaccharides. It thus appears that fatty acids are synthesized mainly via the Krebs cycle (see p. 159) from a 2-carbon precursor. This pathway of synthesis is also found in the cells of microorganisms and in animals, again showing the remarkable similarity in life processes of different types of living organisms.

Oleic acid is probably the first C_{18} fatty acid to be synthesized from carbohydrate precursors in the developing soybean. Quackenbush and Simmons found that after excised soybean stems had been in contact for six hours with a solution containing sucrose labeled with radioactive carbon, radioactivity was detected in the fatty acids of the developing soybeans in the following order of appearance: (1) oleic acid, (2) saturated fatty acids (C_{16} and C_{18}), (3) linoleic acid, and (4) linolenic acid.

In the final synthesis of triglycerides, glycerol (made by enzymatic reduction of a 3-carbon intermediate - see p. 186) is condensed with appropriate fatty acids in the presence of lipase to form mainly mixed triglycerides. This pattern of synthesis is probably followed in both plants and microorganisms.

The mechanism of digestion of lipids in germinating seeds and in microorganisms has been discussed (page 147). No information is available on the actual pathway of metabolism of the glycerol and fatty acids released. However, it is probable that glycerol enters the carbohydrate metabolism scheme (see p. 186), and that fatty acids are converted by beta oxidation (p. 182) to two-carbon fragments which serve as precursors for carbohydrates, amino acids, and other constituents of the developing seedling. In the germination of high oil seeds (rape, castor, hemp, soybean, etc.), the carbohydrate content of the germinating seed and seedling increases as the fat content decreases, showing a synthesis of the former from the latter.

Lipid Content of Various Plant Tissues. Lipids are widely distributed in both plants and microorganisms, occurring in variable amounts in all living cells and in their secretions. Table 30 shows the per cent crude fat (ether-soluble lipid) in various plant parts.

Table 30. Total lipids in plant parts

Plant Part	Crude Fat (%)	Plant Part	Crude Fat (%)
Alfalfa, stem, leaves	1.5	Cocoa bean	45
Navy beans	1.5	Peanut	45
Peas	1.4	Almond	50
Soybeans, stem, leaves	2.5	Olive pulp	50
Bluegrass, blades	2.8	Castor bean	60
Corn seed	3.8	Coconut	65
Soybeans	20	Walnut	65
Cottonseed	20	Brazil nut	65
Sunflower seed	25		
Flaxseed	32		
Rapeseed	40		

In general, seeds contain more crude fat than other plant parts. Most of this fat is true fat (triglyceride). The true fat serves as a reserve food supply in oil seeds such as the soybean, peanut, etc., in the same manner that starch serves as a reserve food in starchy seeds such as the cereal seeds, peas, and navy beans. In general, a seed will store large amounts of either true fat or starch, but not both. This is shown by the data in Table 30. In starchy seeds, the true fat (oil) is confined primarily to the embryo, whereas in the oily seeds it is found in both embryo and endosperm. The plant parts which make up forage (i.e., leaves and stems), have a relatively low crude fat content, most of which is present as waxes, compound lipids and derived lipids, rather than as true fat (triglycerides).

METABOLISM OF LIPIDS IN ANIMALS. The liver is a key organ in both the transportation and utilization of triglycerides. If the blood from the portal vein is shunted around the liver and into the inferior vena cava, by means of an Eck fistula, the animal rapidly loses its fat stores in both the liver and the adipose tissues. It is believed that the liver "conditions" triglycerides before they go to the fat depots; the "conditioning" is conversion to phospholipid.

The fatty acid pool. Fatty acids of the body lipids are continually replaced by dietary fatty acids. They are a part of a pool. By feeding deuterostearic and deuteropalmitic acids to mice on a low fat diet, Schoenheimer was the first to show a constant turnover

$$\overset{\displaystyle D \quad\ D}{\underset{}{CH_3(CH_2)_7\,CH - CH - (CH_2)_7\,COOH}}$$

Deuterostearic acid

$$\overset{\displaystyle D \quad\ D}{\underset{}{CH_3(CH_2)_5\,CH - CH - (CH_2)_7\,COOH}}$$

Deuteropalmitic acid

of fatty acids in depot fats. Analysis of the body fats of normal mice for the labeled fatty acids showed that about one-half of the fatty acids in the liver is replaced by new fatty acids every 24 hours, and one-half of the fatty acids in adipose tissue (p. 280) is replaced every 5-7 days. The replaced fatty acids enter the blood plasma (mainly in the form of phospholipids), where they (1) merge with dietary fatty acids, are carried to various tissues, and are deposited, (2) converted into other saturated and unsaturated fatty acids (except linoleic and arachidonic acids), or (3) are oxidized to carbon dioxide and water. In the tissues, new fatty acids can also be synthesized by condensation of small molecules derived from other nutrients (carbohydrates and proteins). All of these reactions involving fatty acids, glycerides, and phospholipids, are so well balanced in the mature animal of constant weight, that the total amount and structure of the free plus combined fatty acids in the fatty acid pool (blood plus adipose tissues plus organs) is a *constant*.

Mechanism of fatty acid oxidation. The oxidation of fatty acids is a step-wise process, involving the cleavage of 2-carbon fragments, starting from the carboxyl end of the chain. This mechanism was first discovered by Franz Knoop, who named it *beta-oxidation*. A minor amount of oxidation of the terminal methyl groups (omega-oxidation) also takes place.

$$CH_3 \ \ CH_2 \,|\, CH_2 \ \ CH_2 \,|\, CH_2 \ \ CH_2 \,|\, CH_2 \ \ CH_2 \,|\, CH_2 \ \ CH_2 \,|\, CH_2 \ \ CH_2 \,|\, CH_2 \ \ CH_2 \,|\, CH_2 \ \ COOH$$

Palmitic acid

$$\xrightarrow{\quad (O) \quad} \quad CO_2 \ + \ H_2O$$

Coenzyme A (p. 100) plays an important role in the step-wise break-down of fatty acids.

The intermediates in fatty acid oxidation are all acyl ($R - \overset{\displaystyle O}{\overset{\|}{C}} - S - CoA$) derivatives of this important coenzyme. It has been possible to demonstrate the sequence of events in the step-wise oxidation (beta oxidation) of fatty acids, using the specific purified enzymes isolated from beef liver mitochondria. Before a fatty acid (for example, palmitic acid) can be oxidized it must be "activated" by conversion to an acyl CoA derivative. This is Step 1 in its oxidation.

1. $CH_3(CH_2)_{12}CH_2CH_2COO^- + ATP^* + CoA - SH$ (p. 100) $\overset{\displaystyle Mg^{++}}{\underset{\text{Fatty Acid Activating Enzyme}}{\longleftrightarrow}}$

    Palmitate ion

$CH_3(CH_2)_{12}CH_2CH_2COSCoA \quad + \quad AMP^* \ + \ PPi^*$

"Active palmitate"

The active palmityl CoA derivative is then dehydrogenated by a yellow enzyme (yellow acyl CoA dehydrogenase, consisting of flavine adenine dinucleotide (FAD p. 98) and specific apoenzyme). This enzyme will be designated as FAD_{enz}.

* ATP: adenosine triphosphate (p. 166)
  AMP: adenosine-5'-phosphate (p. 112)
  PPi: inorganic pyrophosphate

2. $CH_3(CH_2)_1)CH_2CH_2COSCoA \xrightarrow[\text{FAD} \quad \text{FADH}_2]{\text{acyl} \atop \text{dehydrogenase}} CH_3(CH_2)_{12}CH{:}CHCOSCoA$

The unsaturated acyl CoA derivative is converted to a hydroxy derivative by the addition of water in the presence of a specific hydrase.

3. $CH_3(CH_2)_{12}CH{:}CHCOSCoA + H_2O \xrightarrow{\text{crotonase}} CH_3(CH_2)_{12}CHOHCH_2COSCoA$

The beta-hydroxy acyl derivative is then converted to a beta-keto derivative by dehydrogenation in the presence of a specific apoenzyme combined with nicotinamide adenine dinucleotide (NAD - p. 112).

4. $CH_3CH_2)_{12}CHOHCH_2COSCoA + \xrightarrow[\text{NAD}^+ \quad \text{NADH} + \text{H}^+]{} CH_3(CH_2)_{12}COCH_2COSCoA$

The alpha-keto acyl CoA derivative is then cleaved by a specific enzyme (thiolase), in the presence of reduced CoA(CoASH), to give one molecule of *Acetyl-CoA,* and the acyl CoA derivative of *myristic acid.*

5. $CH_3(CH_2)_{12}COCH_2COSCoA + CoASH \xrightarrow{\text{thiolase}} CH_3COSCoA + CH_3(CH_2)_{12}COSCoA$

  Acetyl CoA   myristyl CoA

Steps 1 to 5 are repeated, giving lauryl, capryl, caprylyl, caprooyl, and finally butyryl CoA. *Butyryl CoA* is dehydrogenated in step 2 by a *green* acyl CoA dehydrogenase enzyme instead of the yellow acyl CoA enzyme; otherwise, steps 1-5 are the same for all of these fatty acids. Cleavage of the C_4 acid (step 5) gives *2* mols of Acetyl CoA.

The net result of beta oxidation is the production of acetyl CoA molecules. These enter the Krebs cycle as shown on p. 159 of this chapter, and are oxidized to carbon dioxide and water.

In addition to the enzymes catalyzing the above reactions, the liver also contains a potent deacylase enzyme, which converts acetoacetyl CoA (the product obtained in reaction 4 from beta-hydroxy butyryl CoA) into acetoacetate ion. The reaction is not reversible.

6. $CH_3COCH_2COSCoA + H_2O \xrightarrow{\text{deacylase}} CH_3COCH_2COO^- + CoASH + H^+$

  acetoacetate ion

Anything interfering with utilization of acetyl CoA in the Krebs cycle will increase the proportion of acetoacetyl CoA irreversibly degraded to free acetoacetate ion in reaction 6. When acetoacetate accumulates in the liver, it is converted to beta-hydroxy butyrate ion and acetone. These three compounds are called *acetone bodies.*

7. $CH_3COCH_2COO^- \dashrightarrow CH_3CHOHCH_2COO^- + CH_3COCH_3$

  acetoacetate ion   beta-hydroxy butyrate   acetone
                                 ion

In *diabetes mellitus*, the lack of the hormone, insulin, interferes with glycogen storage in the liver and the normal metabolism of glucose. This forces the organism to burn excessive amounts of fatty acids for energy, with a diminished amount of Krebs cycle intermediates to oxidize extra acetyl fragments to CO_2 and water.

Reactions 6 and 7 then become dominant, and acetone bodies accumulate in the blood, and spill into the urine. Injection of the hormone, insulin, corrects this defect.

Acetone bodies are also produced during the first few days of a fast. Here the combination of excessive fatty acid metabolism, combined with a decrease in Krebs cycle intermediates, tends to favor reactions 6 and 7. As the fast proceeds, the body becomes more efficient in producing the necessary intermediates, and the acetonemia and acetonuria disappear.

<u>Synthesis of fatty acids</u>. It was thought at first that synthesis of fatty acids would be simply a reversal of their step-wise oxidation. This apparently happens to a small extent in the mitochondria. However, most of the synthesis of fatty acids takes place in the cytoplasm by a mechanism which is similar but not identical to that of degradation. The fatty acid molecule is actually built from acetyl CoA, but acetyl CoA, except for the acetyl CoA unit at the tail end of the chain, is converted to *malonyl CoA* before condensation. In palmitic acid, the origin of the carbons is as follows:

Acetyl CoA   Malonyl CoA

$$CH_2 \quad CH_2 \quad CH_2 \quad CH_2 \quad CH_2 \quad CH_2 \quad CH_2 \quad CH_2 \quad CH_2 \quad CH_2 \quad CH_2 \quad CH_2 \quad CH_2 \quad CH_2 \quad CH_2 \quad COOH$$

Malonyl CoA is formed from acetyl CoA and bicarbonate with biotin as coenzyme and ATP to supply the energy. Biotin is first converted to carboxy-biotin by reaction with bicarbonate and ATP($ATP \rightarrow ADP + P_i$). The carboxy-biotin then reacts with acetyl CoA to give biotin and malonyl CoA.

(1) $CH_3COSCoA$ - - - - - - - - - - - $\rightarrow$ $HOOC-CH_2-CO-S-CoA$
         biotin, HCO_3^-, Mn^{++}

The malonyl-CoA then reacts with an enzyme "fatty acid synthetase" which binds the malonyl group and coenzyme A at separate sites. The malonyl enzyme then reacts with another acetyl CoA with loss of CO_2 and formation of acetoacetyl-enzyme:

(2) $HOOC-CH_2COS-enzyme + CH_3COSCoA$ - - $\rightarrow$ $CoASH + CO_2 + CH_3COCH_2COS-enzyme$

The acetoacetyl-enzyme is reduced by NADPH:

(3) $CH_3COCH_2COS-enzyme$ - - - - - - - - - - - - - - $\rightarrow$ $CH_3CHOH \, CH_2 \, CO-S-enzyme$

         $NADPH + H^+$ $NADP^+$

A water molecule is then lost.

(4) $CH_3CHOHCH_2COS-enzyme$ $\xrightarrow{(-H_2O)}$ $CH_3CH=CHCOS-enzyme$

NADPH then reduces the unsaturated compound to butyryl-enzyme

(5) $CH_3CH=CHCOS-enzyme$ - - - - - - - - - - - - $\rightarrow$ $CH_3CH_2CH_2COS-enzyme$

         $NADPH + H^+$ $NADP^+$

The final step is conversion of the butyryl enzyme to butyryl-CoA.

(6) $CH_3CH_2CH_2CO$-enzyme + CoASH $----\rightarrow$ $CH_3CH_2CH_2COSCoA$ + enzyme

Butyryl CoA then reacts with malonyl enzyme in step (2), and the cycle is repeated. When the chain length reaches 16 or 18 carbons, the fatty acid is released from the enzyme-CoASH complex, or converted to fats.

<u>Synthesis of fats from fatty acids.</u>   The fatty acids in the form of their acyl-CoA derivatives react with glycerol phosphate, which is formed by reduction of dihydroxyacetone phosphate (see p. 186) or direct phosphorylation of glycerol with ATP in the presence of glycerokinase.

$$2\ RCH_2COSCoA\ +\ \begin{array}{c} HO\text{-}CH_2 \\ | \\ HO\text{-}CH \\ | \\ P\text{-}O\text{-}CH_2 \end{array} \xrightarrow{\text{enzyme}} \begin{array}{c} RCH_2CO\text{-}O\text{-}CH_2 \\ | \\ RCH_2CO\text{-}O\text{-}CH \\ | \\ P\text{-}O\text{-}CH_2 \end{array}\ +\ 2\ CoASH$$

Glycerol phosphate   Phosphatidic acid

$$\xrightarrow{\text{phosphatase}} \begin{array}{c} RCH_2CO\text{-}O\text{-}CH_2 \\ | \\ RCH_2CO\text{-}O\text{-}CH \\ | \\ HO\text{-}CH_2 \end{array} \xrightarrow{RCH_2COSCoA} \begin{array}{c} RCH_2CO\text{-}O\text{-}CH_2 \\ | \\ RCH_2CO\text{-}O\text{-}CH \\ | \\ RCH_2CO\text{-}O\text{-}CH_2 \end{array}\ +\ CoASH$$

Diglyceride   Triglyceride

(+ P)

<u>Synthesis of phosphatides.</u>   Lecithin (phosphatidyl choline) is synthesized from phosphatidic acid by the transfer of a choline group from cytidine diphosphate choline (CDP choline), a nucleotide (see p. 112), in the presence of a transferase enzyme and magnesium ion. Other phosphatides are synthesized by similar reactions.

<u>Synthesis of sterols.</u>   Sterols are synthesized from acetyl CoA.   Porter and coworkers have shown that malonyl CoA and acetyl CoA are precursors of both fatty acids and sterols, that these two types of lipids share certain common pathways in their synthesis. The pathway for sterol synthesis is as follows (several intermediates omitted):

(1)   Acetoacetyl-enzyme + acetyl CoA $-----\rightarrow$ β-hydroxy-β-methylglutaryl-coenzyme A
                                                                                          (HMG-E)

(2)   HMG-E + NADPH $-----\rightarrow$ mevalonic acid

$$\text{(3)   mevalonic acid} \xrightarrow[\text{ATP,}]{\quad 2NADP^+ \quad 2NADPH + 2H^+ \quad} \text{squalene}$$

(4)   squalene $--------\rightarrow$ cholesterol $----\rightarrow$ other sterols

The formulas for HMG-E, mevalonic acid, and squalene are shown below.   The formulas for cholesterol and other sterols are shown on pages 51 and 52.

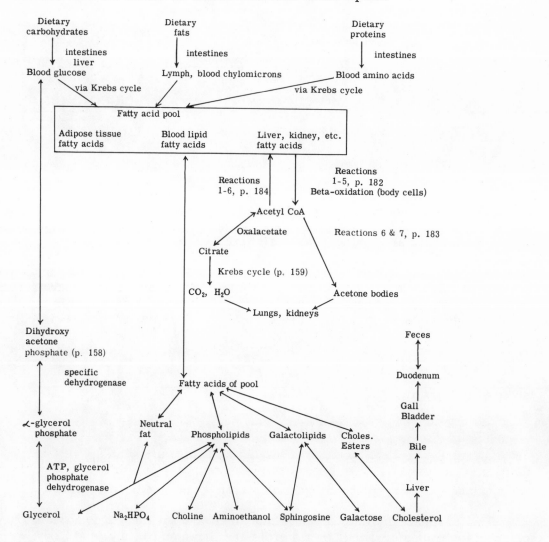

Hydroxymethylglutaryl
coenzyme A (HMG-E)

Mevalonic acid

Squalene

Figure 79 summarizes the metabolic transformations of the lipids.

Figure 79.   Metabolic transformations of lipids in animals

Metabolism of Proteins

PROTEIN METABOLISM IN PLANTS. The major functions of proteins in single and multicelled plants are (1) as nucleoproteins in the genes and (2) as enzymes in the various units of the cell (nucleus, cytoplasm, mitochondria, ribosomes, etc.). In higher plants, proteins serve also as an important reserve of amino acids in the seed.

Formation of Amino Acids and Proteins. Plants are able to synthesize all of the amino acids they need, from carbohydrates and a simple nitrogen source such as ammonium ion, nitrate ion, etc. The legumes are even less dependent, for they are supplied with fixed nitrogen by symbiotic bacteria living in root nodules. These bacteria are able to fix atmospheric nitrogen.

It is highly probable that all forms of fixed nitrogen are converted to ammonium ion, either free or combined, before incorporation into amino acids. The reduction of nitrate to ammonia may follow this pattern:

$$NO_3 ------- \rightarrow NO_2 ------- \rightarrow NH_2OH ------ \rightarrow NH_3$$

The mechanism of fixation of nitrogen by symbiotic bacteria associated with legumes (several species of *Rhizobium*) and by independent microorganisms (several species of *Azotobacter*) has not been explained to the satisfaction of all workers. Vertainen has obtained evidence for the following steps:

$$N_2(atmosphere) --- \rightarrow NH_2OH --- \rightarrow oxime\ of\ oxalacetic\ acid \longrightarrow aspartic\ acid$$

If this scheme is correct, then aspartic acid and/or its oxime furnish fixed nitrogen to the legume, the nitrogen-containing compound diffusing into the roots from the root nodules.

If the legume obtains most of its nitrogen from the root nodule bacteria, in the form of aspartic acid, how is this nitrogen transferred to other amino acids? Workers have found that plant tissues contain enzymes, called transaminases, which catalyze this reaction for aspartic and other acids. The reaction for the transfer of an amino group from aspartic acid to pyruvic acid to form alanine is shown below.

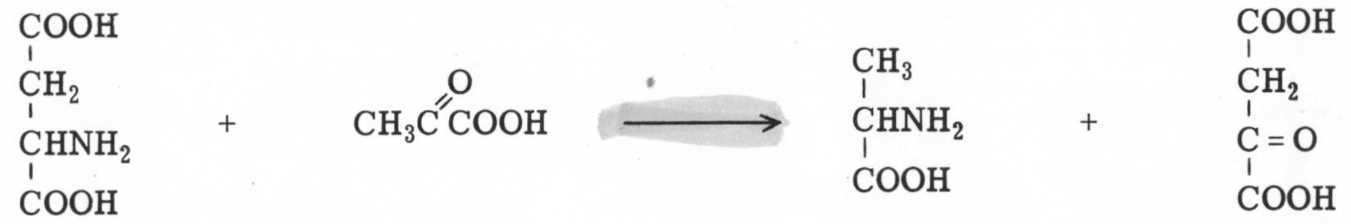

$$
\begin{array}{ccccccc}
COOH & & & & CH_3 & & COOH \\
| & & O & & | & & | \\
CH_2 & + & \| & \longrightarrow & CHNH_2 & + & CH_2 \\
| & & CH_3C\ COOH & & | & & | \\
CHNH_2 & & & & COOH & & C=O \\
| & & & & & & | \\
COOH & & & & & & COOH
\end{array}
$$

Aspartic acid   Pyruvic acid   Alanine   Oxalacetic acid

The transamination reaction does not take place with all of the amino acids. It is probable that arginine and tryptophan are synthesized by reactions involving direct amination. Tyrosine, phenylalanine, and histidine are probably also synthesized without benefit of transamination. Some of these mechanisms have been clarified for mold microorganisms and will be discussed later.

Summary of protein metabolism in plants. In Figure 80 on the following page is presented a summary of protein metabolism in plants.

In this scheme nitrogen is supplied to the plant from three sources: NH_4^+, NO_3^-, and N_2 (legumes). Regardless of the source, however, all forms of nitrogen are converted to

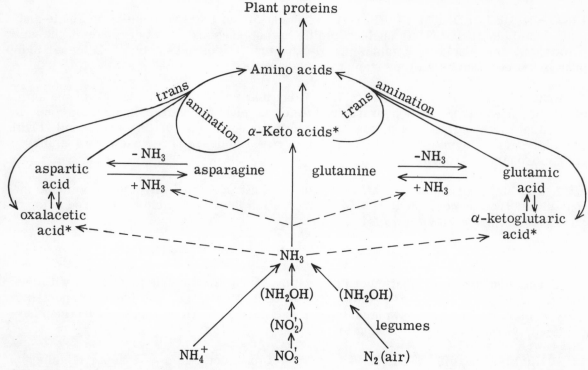

* Synthesized from Krebs cycle intermediates.

Figure 80.   Summary of protein metabolism in plants.

NH_3, before reaction with the appropriate alpha-keto acid to form an amino acid. In this cycle, both direct amination, and transamination via aspartic and glutamic acids, take place. The scheme also indicates that plants do not excrete nitrogen (compare with animals, page 207), but store excess nitrogen as asparagine or glutamine.

$$
\begin{array}{c}
C\overset{\displaystyle O}{\underset{|}{\diagup}}NH_2 \\
CH_2 \\
| \\
CHNH_2 \\
| \\
COOH
\end{array}
\qquad\qquad
\begin{array}{c}
C\overset{\displaystyle O}{\underset{|}{\diagup}}NH_2 \\
CH_2 \\
| \\
CH_2 \\
| \\
CHNH_2 \\
| \\
COOH
\end{array}
$$

Asparagine   Glutamine

Legumes store mainly asparagine, cereal grains store mainly glutamine; in contrast, cucumber plants store the two in about equal amounts. In alfalfa plants unable to use the nitrogen available because of a severe sulfur deficiency, the writer found that the asparagine content of the leaves increased as much as threefold, and the asparagine content of the stems as much as tenfold. Correction of the sulfur deficiency caused the asparagine level to return to normal in five days.

In plants, the alpha-keto acids which serve as precursors of the amino acids are primarily products of carbohydrate metabolism, but could also come from the deamination of other amino acids, or from fatty acids, especially in germinating seeds.

Once the amino acids are synthesized, they are linked together to form the many proteins needed by the growing plant. Protein formation requires energy, and proceeds via a series of phosphorylation reactions. See p. 120.

PROTEIN METABOLISM IN MICROORGANISMS. Microorganisms bridge the gap between the independent plant and the dependent animal as far as synthetic abilities are concerned. For example, molds such as *Neurospora* can grow in a nutrient solution which contains only inorganic elements, including fixed nitrogen (nitrate or ammonium ion), and glucose. These microorganisms can synthesize all of the amino acids required, and resemble plants in this respect. In contrast, the lactic acid-producing bacterium, *Leuconostoc mesenteroides*, requires 18 of the common amino acids in the nutrient solution in order to grow.

It is probable that nitrogen follows the same pathways of metabolism in microorganisms as in plants. Exceptions to be noted are (1) variations in storage of ammonia as amides (plant-like microorganisms store amides, animal-like microorganisms do not), and (2) the differences in the ability of various microorganisms to synthesize amino acids from carbohydrates and ammonia.

Some light has been thrown on the synthesis of the more complex amino acids from studies of mutants of the mold *Neurospora*. Beadle and Tatum were pioneers in these studies. The bread mold *Neurospora Crassa* was exposed to ultraviolet light, and mutant strains were produced which were lacking in one or more enzymes needed for synthesis of certain amino acids. Thus, seven different strains were produced which could not synthesize arginine. This indicated that at least seven different enzymes are needed for its synthesis. By a careful study of the requirements of these mutants, it was found that one would grow only on a medium containing arginine, another on a medium containing either ornithine, citrulline, or arginine. Since arginine will serve as a growth factor for all three mutants, it must be the last step in the reaction. By similar reasoning, citrulline must be the next to last step, etc. On the basis of these data, the last three steps in the synthesis of arginine in *Neurospora* are as follows:

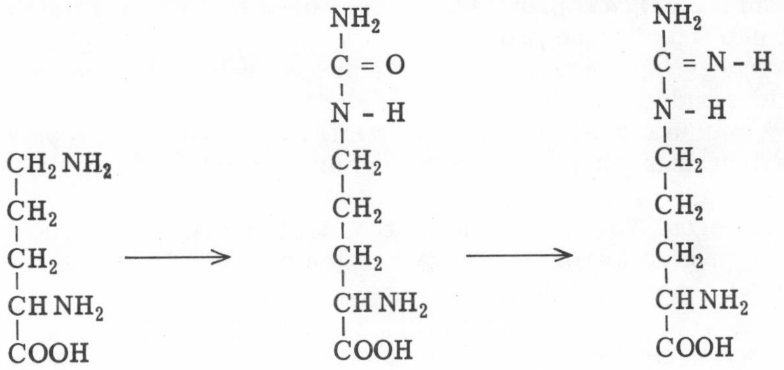

$$
\begin{array}{ccc}
& NH_2 & NH_2 \\
& | & | \\
& C = O & C = N-H \\
& | & | \\
& N-H & N-H \\
& | & | \\
CH_2NH_2 & CH_2 & CH_2 \\
| & | & | \\
CH_2 & CH_2 & CH_2 \\
| & | & | \\
CH_2 \longrightarrow & CH_2 \longrightarrow & CH_2 \\
| & | & | \\
CHNH_2 & CHNH_2 & CHNH_2 \\
| & | & | \\
COOH & COOH & COOH
\end{array}
$$

Ornithine   Citrulline   Arginine

Mutants which were incapable of synthesizing tryptophan were also produced. Studies analogous to those discussed above showed that the last three steps in the synthesis of tryptophan are as follows:

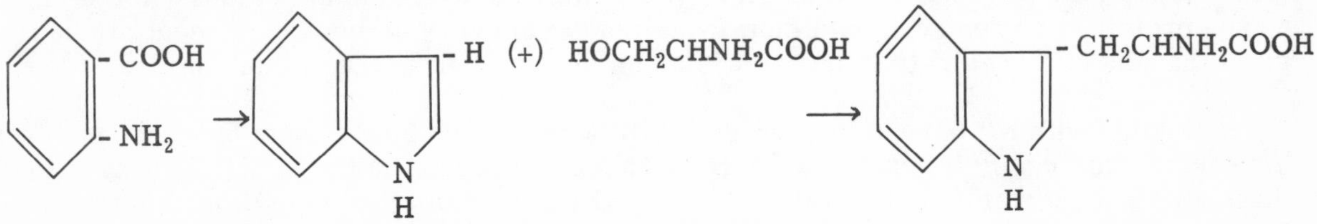

Anthranilic acid   Indole   Serine   Tryptophan

USE OF ISOTOPES IN METABOLISM STUDIES. Most of our earlier knowledge of the pathways of nitrogen in plants and microorganisms was gained by indirect methods. A new approach which has appeared in recent years is the use of isotopes as tracers of metabolic reactions. Both stable isotopes such as N^{15} and H^2 (deuterium), and radioactive isotopes such as C^{14} have been used.

An excellent example of the use of isotopes is the experiment of Vickery in which he supplied ammonium salts containing N^{15} to tobacco and buckwheat plants grown in nutrient solution. On analysis of the amino acids of these plants, he found that the highest concentrations of N^{15} were in the glutamic and aspartic acids of the plant proteins. This is excellent support for assigning key roles to these two amino acids in the nitrogen metabolism scheme (Fig. 80, p. 188).

In another experiment with N^{15}, Burris supplied *Azotobacter* with gaseous nitrogen containing N^{15}. He found the N^{15} distributed among all of the amino acids of the bacterial proteins, with the highest concentrations again in the dicarboxylic acids, *aspartic* and *glutamic* acids.

The radioactive isotope of carbon, C^{14}, has been invaluable in determining the pathway of carbon in photosynthesis (see p. 174).

METABOLISM OF AMINO ACIDS IN ANIMALS. The bulk of our knowledge regarding the metabolism of the various amino acids in animals has been gained from the use of isotopes. The pioneer in this field was Rudolph Schoenheimer. Schoenheimer's classical studies with heavy nitrogen (N^{15}) in mice and rats proved that a dynamic state of equilibrium exists in the animal body between dietary amino acids, blood amino acids, and amino acids fixed as residues in tissue proteins. In his first studies, when L-leucine (or glycine) containing N^{15} was fed at a level of 25 mg. of amino acid nitrogen per day for 3 days in the stock diet of rats, approximately 50% of the added marked amino acid was recovered from the *carcass* proteins. This proved that dietary amino acids are *rapidly incorporated* into fixed tissue proteins. Even under conditions of protein starvation, a *continuous exchange* of amino acids takes place between the amino acids of the blood, and the amino acid residues in the proteins of the fixed tissues. Schonheimer showed this by feeding N^{15}, in the form of diammonium citrate, to young rats on an almost protein-free, high carbohydrate diet. Although the animals lost weight rapidly on this diet, analysis of their carcass proteins at the end of the five-day feeding period showed that 94% of the amide nitrogen, 70% of the glutamic acid nitrogen, 55% of the aspartic acid nitrogen, 30% of the proline nitrogen, and 57% of the guanidine nitrogen of arginine, had been replaced with N^{15}. Other amino acids were not examined.

These studies showed that the animal body has an "amino acid pool". The blood amino acids in this pool are in *dynamic equilibrium* (constantly exchanged) with the tissue amino acids, which are in turn constantly incorporated into, and released from, the fixed proteins of the carcass tissues. Later studies with isotopes have shown that tissues vary in their exchange rates. The most active tissues are the intestinal wall, and the liver. Here approximately one-half of the amino acid residues in the tissue proteins are replaced with dietary amino acids every 4 to 5 days. The least active tissue is the epithelial tissue (skin, hair, nails). Here approximately one-half of the amino acid residues in the "live" tissue proteins are replaced with dietary amino acids every 100 days. Recent studies show that the exchange rate in humans is much slower than in the rat (about 1/5).

Studies with N^{15} have also shown that all of the amino acids (page 55), except *lysine*, *threonine*, and *arginine*, exchange their alpha-amino groups in the pool. This exchange is mediated by glutamic acid, which is especially active in *transamination* reactions.

Although the majority of the amino acids exchange alpha-amino groups, differences are apparent in their individual syntheses and metabolic fate. It is possible to divide amino acids into two main groups, (1) those whose carbon skeletons cannot be synthesized by the animal from materials ordinarily available in the diet, and (2) those whose carbon skeletons can be synthesized. Group (1) amino acids are called "essential" or "indispensable" amino acids, and group (2) amino acids are called "non-essential" or "dispensable". These two groups will be discussed separately.

METABOLISM OF INDISPENSABLE AMINO ACIDS. There are nine amino acids which are *completely* indispensable for growth in all animal species tested to date (see page 55-57). They are *histidine, isoleucine, lysine, leucine, methionine, phenylalanine, threonine, tryptophan* and *valine.* In addition, arginine is indispensable for growth of the avian and fish species. Arginine is not completely indispensable in mammals, however, for it can be synthesized at about two-thirds of the rate needed for maximum growth. Glycine can be placed in the same category for the bird, where it can be synthesized, but not at a sufficiently rapid rate to permit optimum growth *and* feathering (see page 220).

As stated previously, all of the amino acids, except lysine, threonine, and arginine, exchange alpha-amino groups in the amino acid pool. Recent studies have shown that in the case of lysine, the epsilon-amino group is lost first, with the formation of alpha-amino adipic acid. The reaction is apparently irreversible. In the case of arginine, its metabolism involves the reversible formation of ornithine (an analog of lysine) and urea. Ornithine does not form the alpha-keto analogue (see below).

The metabolism of each of the *completely* indispensable amino acids is discussed below.

Histidine. The liver contains an enzyme, histidase, which converts histidine into the dispensable amino acid, glutamic acid. The reaction is not reversible.

$$CH = C - CH_2 - CH(NH_2)COOH$$
$$N = CH - NH$$

L-histidine

$$\xrightarrow[\text{deaminase (liver)}]{(-NH_3)}$$

$$CH = C - CH = CHCOOH$$
$$N = CH - NH$$

urocanic acid

$$\xrightarrow[\text{enol, keto intermediates}]{2\ H_2O}$$

$$CH = NH$$
$$NH$$
$$HOOC - CH - CH_2 CH_2 COOH$$

N-formamino-L-glutamic acid

$$\xrightarrow[\substack{\text{transferase,}\\ \text{folic acid}}]{2\ H_2O}$$

$$NH_2$$
$$HOOC - CH - CH_2 CH_2 - COOH$$

L-glutamic acid

$$+ \quad HCOONH_4$$

ammonium formate

D-histidine *can* be converted (via the alpha-keto form) to L-histidine in the amino acid pool. Histidine is also decarboxylated in the pool to form small amounts of histamine.

Isoleucine. The catabolic pathways of the three branched chain amino acids are similar, but not identical. In animals, isoleucine has the following pathway to the two Krebs cycle intermediates, acetyl CoA, and succinyl CoA:

L-isoleucine $\xleftrightarrow{\text{transaminase}}$ α-keto-β-methylvalerate $\xrightarrow[-CO_2]{CoASH}$ α-methylbutyrl CoA

$\xrightarrow[-2H]{\text{dehydrogenase}}$ α-methyl crotonyl CoA $\xrightarrow{+ H_2O}$ α-methyl-β-hydroxy-butyryl CoA

$\xrightarrow[(-2H)]{\text{-oxidation}}$ α-methyl acetoacetyl CoA $\xrightarrow[\substack{\alpha,\ \beta\text{-carbon} \\ \text{cleavage}}]{CoASH}$ acetyl CoA + propionyl CoA.

Propionyl CoA $----\rightarrow$ succinyl CoA.

<u>Leucine</u>. Leucine is catabolized to acetyl CoA and acetoacetic acid:

L-leucine $\xleftrightarrow{\text{transaminase}}$ α-ketoisocaproate $\xrightarrow[(-CO_2)]{CoASH}$ isovaleryl CoA $\xrightarrow{(-2H)}$

β-methylcrotonylCoA $((CH_3)_2\text{-}C\raisebox{0.3ex}{$=$}CH\text{-}COSCoA)$ $\xrightarrow[(+ CO_2)]{ATP}$ β-methylglutaconyl CoA

$\underset{\text{(HOOC-CH}_2\text{-C}=\text{CH-COSCoA)}}{\overset{CH_3}{}}$ $\xrightarrow[(\alpha,\ \beta\text{-addition})]{(+ H_2O)}$ β-hydroxy-β-methyl-glutaryl CoA

$\xrightarrow{\text{scission of C}_2\text{-C}_3 \text{ bond}}$ acetoacetic acid + acetyl CoA.

<u>Valine</u>. Valine is catabolized to succinyl CoA:

L valine $\xleftrightarrow{\text{transaminase}}$ α-ketoisovalerate $\xrightarrow{CoASH}$ isobutyryl CoA $\xrightarrow{(-2H)}$ methylacrylyl CoA

$\xrightarrow[\alpha\text{-}\beta\text{-addition}]{(+ H_2O)}$ β-hydroxyisobutyryl CoA $\xrightarrow{(+ H_2O)}$ β-hydroxyisobutyric acid + CoASH $\xrightarrow{(-2H)}$

methylmalonic semialdehyde $\xrightarrow[(-2H)]{CoASH (+H_2O)}$ methylmalonyl CoA $\xrightarrow{\text{isomerase}}$ succinyl CoA.

The D-analogs of isoleucine, leucine, and valine cannot be converted to the L-amino acids in the amino acid pool.

<u>Lysine</u>. L-lysine is irreversibly deaminated in the amino acid pool, and therefore does not exchange its amino group with other amino acids. In the liver, lysine is converted via a ring compound, pipecolic acid, to α-amino adipic acid, and finally to acetyl CoA.

L-lysine $\xrightarrow{(-NH_3)}$ α-keto-ϵ-aminocaproic acid $\xrightarrow{(-H_2O)}$ Δ^1-piperidine-2-carboxylic acid

$\xrightarrow{+ 2H}$ pipecolic acid $\xrightarrow{(-2H)}$ Δ^6-piperidine-2-carboxylic acid $\xrightarrow{(-H_2O)}$ α-aminodipic-ϵ-

semialdehyde $(CHO\text{-}CH_2\text{-}CH_2\text{-}CH_2\text{-}CHNH_2\text{-}COOH)$ $\xrightarrow{\text{oxidase}}$ L-α-aminoadipic acid

$\xrightarrow{(-NH_3)}$ α-ketoadipic acid $\xrightarrow{(-CO_2)}$ glutaric acid $\xrightarrow{R\text{-}SCoA}$ glutaryl CoA $\xrightarrow{\hspace{2cm}}$

Acetyl CoA. The D-analog of lysine cannot be converted to the L-amino acid in the amino acid pool.

<u>Phenylalanine.</u> This amino acid undergoes transamination, and can exchange amino groups with other amino acids. D-phenylalanine can be converted to L-phenylalanine in the amino acid pool. The normal pathway for degradation of phenylalanine is conversion to tyrosine:

(1) L-phenylalanine + O_2 + tetrahydropteridine (folic acid) $\xrightarrow[\text{hydroxylase (liver enzyme I)}]{\text{phenylalanine}}$

L-tyrosine + H_2O.

(2) Oxidized pteridine $\xrightarrow{\text{liver enzyme II}}$ tetrahydropteridine

$$NADPH + H^+ \quad NADP^+$$

Only phenylalanine hydroxylase and tetrahydropteridine are needed to convert phenylalanine to tyrosine. The second enzyme, together with NADPH, serves to keep the cofactor, tetrahydropteridine, in the reduced, active form.

In the hereditary disease, phenylketonuria, phenylalanine hydroxylase is absent, or modified and ineffective. This block in the normal pathway causes an accumulation of other metabolites usually found in only trace amounts in the liver, blood and urine.

<u>Phenylketonuria metabolites:</u> phenylpyruvic acid, phenyllactic acid, phenylacetic acid, phenylacetylglutamine, ortho-tyrosine (ortho-hydroxy phenylalanine), ortho-hydroxyphenylpyruvic acid, ortho-hydroxyphenylacetic acid.

<u>Threonine.</u> Threonine does not undergo transamination, and therefore does not exchange amino groups in the amino acid pool. D-threonine cannot be converted to L- threonine, and neither the D- form nor the D- or L-allo forms substitute for the L- form in the diet of animals.

Two pathways are known for its catabolism in the liver: deamination to ketobutyrate and cleavage to glycine and acetaldehyde.

(1) L-threonine $\xrightarrow[\text{(-}H_2O)]{\text{threonine dehydrase}}$ α-aminocrotonic acid $\xrightarrow{\text{rearranges}}$ α-iminobutyric

acid $\xrightarrow[\text{(-}NH_3)]{\text{(+}H_2O)}$ α-ketobutyric acid $\xrightarrow[\text{(+}H_2O;\text{-2H)}]{\text{(-}CO_2)}$ propionic acid $\xrightarrow{\text{(+}CO_2)}$ succinyl CoA.

(2) L-threonine $\xrightarrow[\text{aldolase}]{\text{hydroxamino-}}$ glycine + acetaldehyde

<u>Tryptophan.</u> Tryptophan undergoes transamination and exchanges amino groups in the amino acid pool. The D-isomer will replace the L-form in the diet of animals. Tryptophan gives many degradation products, one of the most important of which is nicotinic acid. It has been estimated that in the human, 60 mg. of dietary tryptophan is equivalent to 1 mg of nicotinic acid.

The many pathways are given below.   Each is coded and assumed to originate from L-tryptophan:

(1)   tryptophan $\xrightarrow{\text{(-CO}_2\text{)}}$ tryptamine $\xrightarrow{\text{(O)}}$ indoleacetic acid

(2)   tryptophan $\dashrightarrow$ 5-hydroxytryptophan $\xrightarrow{\text{(-CO}_2\text{)}}$ 5-hydro-

xytryptamine (serotonin) $\xrightarrow{\text{(O)}}$ 5-hydroxyindoleacetic acid

(3)   tryptophan $\dashrightarrow$ indolepyruvic acid $\xrightarrow{\text{(CO}_2\text{)}}$ indoleacetic acid

(3.1)   indolepyruvic acid $\dashrightarrow$ indoleactic acid

(4)   tryptophan $\dashrightarrow$ N-formyl kynurenine $\dashrightarrow$ kynurenine

(4.1)   kynurenine $\dashrightarrow$ anthranilic acid + alanine

(4.2)   kynurenine $\dashrightarrow$ kynurenic acid

(4.3)   kynurenine $\dashrightarrow$ 3-hydroxykynurenine $\dashrightarrow$ xanthurenic acid

(4.31)   3-hydroxykynurenine $\dashrightarrow$ alanine + 3-hydroxyanthranilic acid

(4.311)   3-hydroxyanthranilic acid $\dashrightarrow$ 2-acroleyl-3-amino-fumaric acid(AAFA) $\dashrightarrow$ quinolinic acid

(4.312)   3-hydroxyanthranilic acid $\xrightarrow{\text{(VIA AAFA)}}$ glutaryl CoA $\dashrightarrow$ Acetyl CoA

(4.313)   3-hydroxyanthranilic acid $\xrightarrow{\text{(VIA AAFA)}}$ picolonic acid (pyridine-1-carboxylic acid)

(4.314)   3-hydroxyanthranilic acid $\xrightarrow{\text{(VIA AAFA)}}$ nicotinic acid (pyridine-2-carboxylic acid)

The formulas for several of these metabolites are shown below.

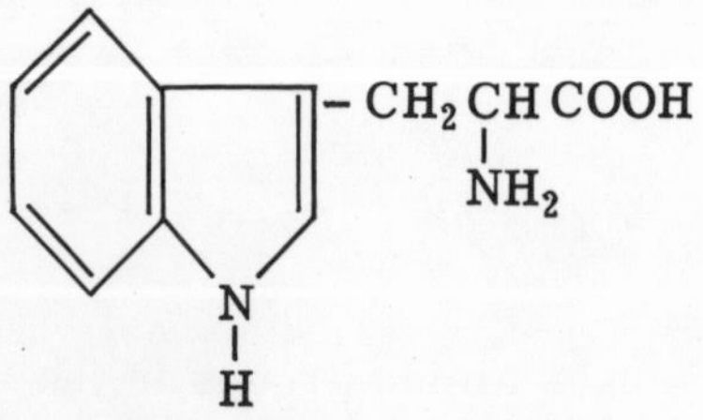

Tryptophan 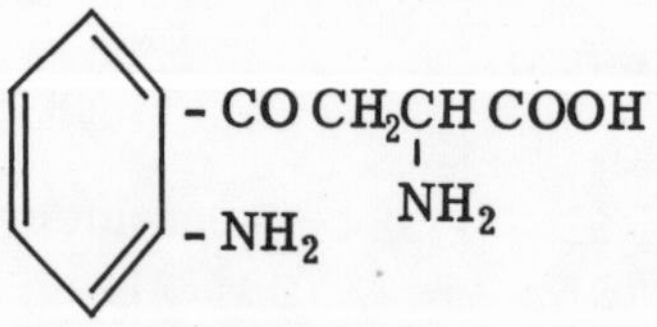   Kynurenine 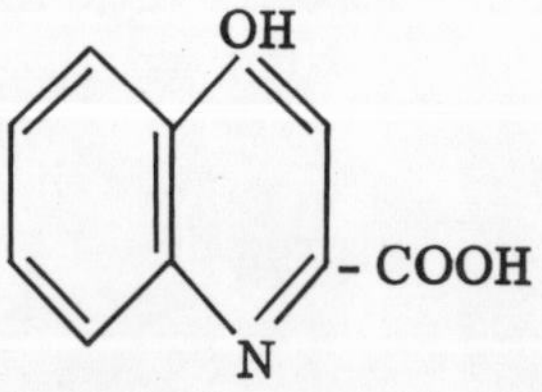   Kynurenic acid

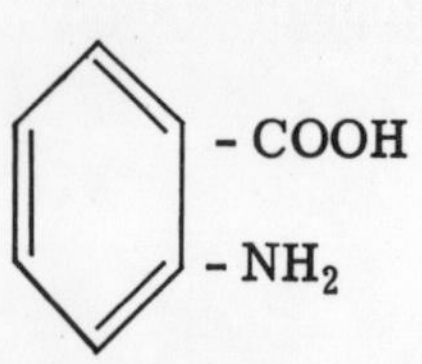

Anthranilic acid 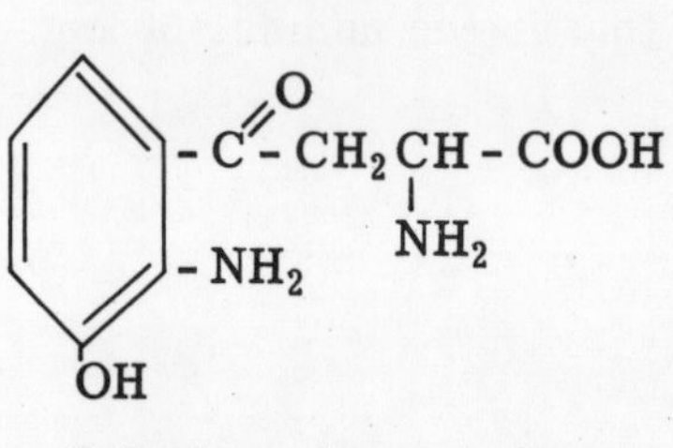   3-hydroxykynurenine 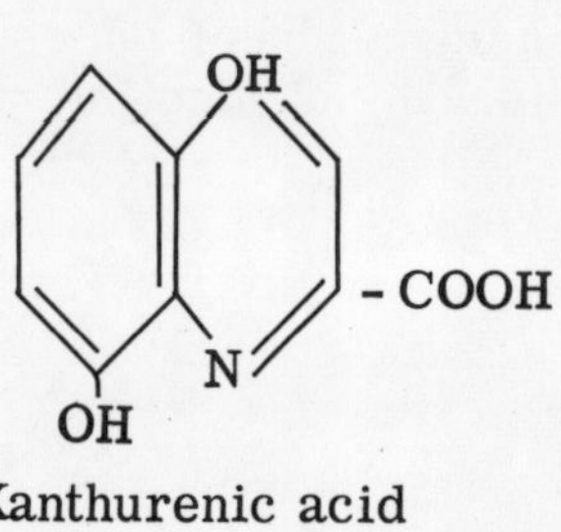   Xanthurenic acid

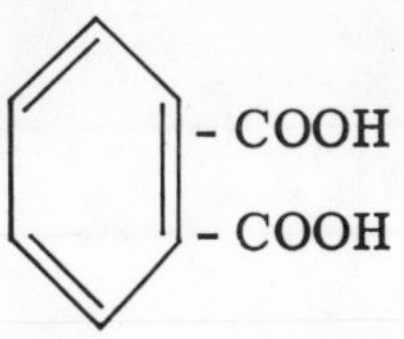

Quinolinic acid 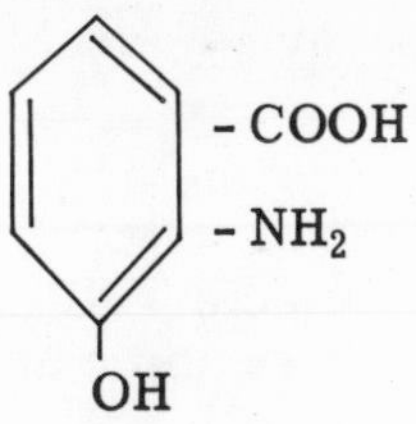   3-hydroxy anthranilic acid 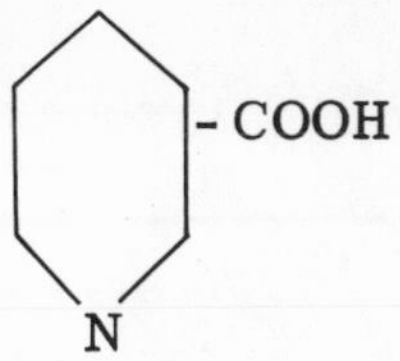   Nicotinic acid

<u>Methionine</u>. Methionine undergoes transamination and therefore exchanges its amino group in the amino acid pool. D-methionine can replace dietary L-methionine. The α-hydroxy analog is easily oxidized to the keto derivative and from there by transamination to L-methionine. The hydroxy analog is used as a substitute for synthetic DL-methionine in animal feeds.

In addition to being an essential amino acid, methionine is important as a methyl donor and precursor of cysteine. Pathways of metabolism are shown below.

(1)   L-methionine + ATP $\xrightarrow{\text{activating enzyme}}$ S-adenosylmethionine

In this reaction, the 5'-carbon of ribose adds to the sulfur atom of methionine:

$$CH_3-S-CH_2-CH_2-CHNH_2COOH + P-O-P-O-P-O-\text{ribose-adenine} \longrightarrow$$

$$CH_3-\overset{+}{S}-\ CH_2(\text{from ribose})---\ \text{adenine}$$
$$\begin{array}{l} CH_2 \\ CH_2 \\ CHNH_2 \\ COOH \end{array} \qquad + PP_i(\text{pyrophosphate}) + P(\text{phosphate})$$

$$(\text{S-adenosylmethionine (SAM)} \xrightarrow{\text{(methyl acceptor)}} \text{S-adenosylhomocysteine(SAH)})$$

(1.1)   SAM + phosphatidyl-ethanolamine $\dashrightarrow$ SAH + phosphatidyl-methyl ethanolamine

(1.2)   SAM + phosphatidyl-diethanolamine $\dashrightarrow$ SAH + phosphatidyl choline

(1.3)   SAM + norepinephrine $\dashrightarrow$ SAH + epinephrine

(1.4)   SAM + nicotinamide $\dashrightarrow$ SAH + N-methyl nicotinamide

(1.5)   SAM + guanidoacetic acid $\dashrightarrow$ SAH + creatine

(2.0)   SAM $\xrightarrow{\text{enzyme}}$ adenosine + homocysteine

(2.1)   homocysteine + serine $\xrightarrow[\text{pyridoxal phosphate, ATP; (-H}_2\text{O)}]{\text{cystathionine synthetase}}$

$$\dashrightarrow \text{cystathionine(HOOCCHNH}_2\text{CH}_2\text{-S-CH}_2\text{CH}_2\text{CHNH}_2\text{COOH)}$$

$$\text{(2.2)} \quad \text{cystathionine} \xrightarrow{\text{pyridoxal phosphate}} \text{L-cysteine} + (\alpha\text{-amino 3,4 butenoic}$$

acid $\dashrightarrow$ α-amino 2,3 butenoic acid $\longrightarrow$ α-imino butyric acid)

$$\xrightarrow[+H_2O]{} \alpha\text{-ketobutyric acid} + NH_3$$

α-ketobutyric acid $\dashrightarrow$ succinic acid

METABOLISM OF DISPENSABLE AMINO ACIDS. Mammals are able to synthesize the following amino acids: alanine, arginine, aspartic acid, cystine, glutamic acid, glycine, hydroxyproline, proline, and serine. Birds and fish are able to synthesize all of these except arginine; birds (and fish?) have all of the enzymes of the urea cycle (see below) except the one(s) required to convert ornithine to citrulline. This break in the urea cycle is responsible for the high arginine requirement in chicks (see Table 33, page 222), and also helps to explain why uric acid instead of urea is the main end-product of nitrogen metabolism in birds (p. 208).

Since many of the dispensable amino acids can be synthesized from Krebs cycle intermediates by a process known as transamination, this reaction will be described first.

Transamination. The general equation for transamination shows exchange of amino and keto groups between two compounds.

$$R\text{-}CHNH_2\text{-}COOH + R'\text{-}CO\text{-}COOH \longleftrightarrow R\text{-}CO\text{-}COOH + R'\text{-}CHNH_2COOH$$

This reaction is catalyzed by a widely distributed group of enzymes, called *transaminases*.

In animal tissues, one couple of the reactants is nearly always the pair, glutamic acid/α-ketoglutaric acid. The most abundant of the transaminases catalyze transamination from glutamic to pyruvic and oxalacetic acids, respectively.

L-glutamic acid + oxaloacetic acid $\longleftrightarrow$ α-ketoglutaric acid + L-aspartic acid
L-glutamic acid + pyruvic acid $\longleftrightarrow$ α-ketoglutaric acid + L-alanine

The liver contains transaminases specific for the transamination from glutamic acid to the α-keto acids corresponding to each of the naturally occurring α-amino acids, with the possible exception of lysine, threonine and glycine, and similar enzymes are found in plant and microbial tissues. Thus, once ammonia has been fixed into glutamic acid, transamination provides the cell with a mechanism for synthesis of the α-amino acids whose corresponding α-keto acids can be manufactured. Transamination also provides a means of redistributing nitrogen. For example, if an animal consumes a diet high in leucine and low in aspartic acid, the following pair of reactions would furnish the nitrogen needed to produce more aspartic acid:

(1)   L-leucine + α-ketoglutaric acid $\dashrightarrow$ α-ketoisocaproic acid + L-glutamic acid

(2)   L-glutamic acid + oxaloacetic acid $\dashrightarrow$ α-ketoglutaric acid + L-aspartic acid

Combining (1) and (2): L-leucine + oxaloacetic acid $\dashrightarrow$ α-ketoisocaproic acid + L-aspartic acid

This type of reaction explains why labeled ammonia fed to rats appears in all of the amino acids except lysine and threonine, with greatest abundance in glutamic and aspartic acids (see page 190).

Mechanism of transamination. Pyridoxal phosphate is a component of each of the transaminases studied. It is believed to catalyze the reaction (in the presence of an apoenzyme)
as follows:

$$
\text{(1)}\quad R_1CHNH_2\text{-}COOH + P\text{-}CH{=}O\ \text{-}\text{-}\text{-}\!\!\rightarrow\ \underset{\overset{|}{COOH}}{\overset{\overset{R_1}{|}\ \overset{P}{|}}{HCN{=}CH}}\ \text{-}\text{-}\text{-}\!\!\rightarrow\ \underset{\overset{|}{COOH}}{\overset{\overset{R_1}{|}\ \overset{P}{|}}{C{=}N\text{-}CH}}\ \text{-}\text{-}\text{-}\!\!\rightarrow RCOCOOH + \underset{\overset{|}{H}}{\overset{\overset{P}{|}}{H_2NCH}}
$$

α-amino acid-1	pyridoxal phosphate enzyme	Schiff base I	Schiff base II	α-keto acid 1	Pyridox-amine phosphate enzyme

$$
\text{(2)}\quad R_2COCOOH + \underset{\overset{|}{H}}{\overset{|}{H_2N\text{-}C\text{-}H}}\ \text{-}\text{-}\text{-}\text{-}\!\!\rightarrow\ \underset{\overset{|}{COOH}}{\overset{\overset{R_2}{|}\ \overset{P}{|}}{C{=}N\text{-}C\text{-}H_2}}\ \text{-}\text{-}\text{-}\text{-}\!\!\rightarrow\ \underset{\overset{|}{COOH}}{\overset{\overset{R_2}{|}\ \overset{P}{|}}{HC\text{-}N{=}CH}}\ \text{-}\text{-}\text{-}\text{-}\!\!\rightarrow R_2CHNH_2COOH +
$$

α-keto acid-2 pyridoxamine phosphate enzyme Schiff base III Schiff base IV

α-amino acid-2

$$\underset{\overset{|}{O{=}C\text{-}H}}{\overset{P}{|}}$$

pyridoxal phosphate enzyme

Transamination with glutamine and asparagine. Both of these widely distributed amides
undergo transamination, the transaminase systems having broad specificity and reacting
with more than 30 α-keto acids. A two step reaction occurs, and the amides lose both of
their nitrogen atoms:

(1) glutamine (or asparagine) + α-keto acid —→ α-keto derivative of the amide + α-amino
acid

(2) α-keto derivative of amide $\underset{\text{amidase}}{\overset{\text{transaminase}}{\text{-}\text{-}\text{-}\text{-}\text{-}\text{-}\text{-}\text{-}\!\!\rightarrow}}$ α-keto acid + NH_3

Synthesis of glutamic acid, aspartic acid, and alanine. Glutamic acid is synthesized directly from ammonia and ketoglutaric acid as follows:

NADH (or NADPH) + α-ketoglutaric acid + H^+ + NH_3 ←-→ L-glutamate + NAD^+ (or $NADP^+$)
+ H_2O

Aspartic acid and alanine are formed by transamination from glutamic acid.

Glutamine and asparagine. Glutamine synthesis is catalyzed by *glutamine synthetase:*

$$
HOOC\text{-}CH_2\text{-}CH_2\text{-}CHNH_2\text{-}COOH + ATP + NH_3 \overset{Mg}{\text{-}\text{-}\text{-}\!\!\rightarrow} H_2N\text{-}CO\text{-}CH_2\text{-}CH_2\text{-}CHNH_2\text{-}COOH + ADP + Pi
$$

The mechanism of synthesis of asparagine is not known, but is thought to be similar
to that for glutamine.

Proline, hydroxyproline, and ornithine. Glutamic acid serves directly as the precursor
for the biosynthesis of these three amino acids. Ornithine is not found in proteins, but
is a precursor for the synthesis of arginine, and therefore participates in the urea cycle,
which is described in a following section.

The initial step in the synthesis of these three amino acids is the formation of glutamic semialdehyde. Transamination of glutamic semialdehyde yields ornithine. Ring closure of the semialdehyde gives Δ^1-pyrroline 5-carboxylic acid, which, upon reduction by NADH yields proline.

$$(1) \quad HOOC-CH_2-CH_2-CHNH_2-COOH \underset{NAD^+}{\overset{NADH}{\rightleftarrows}} O\overset{H}{=}\overset{|}{C}-CH_2-CH_2-CHNH_2-COOH \overset{transamination}{\longleftrightarrow}$$

glutamic acid   glutamic semialdehyde

$$\dashrightarrow H_2N-CH_2-CH_2-CHNH_2-COOH$$

ornithine

(1.1)   glutamic semialdehyde $\underset{(+H_2O)}{\overset{(-H_2O)}{\rightleftarrows}}$

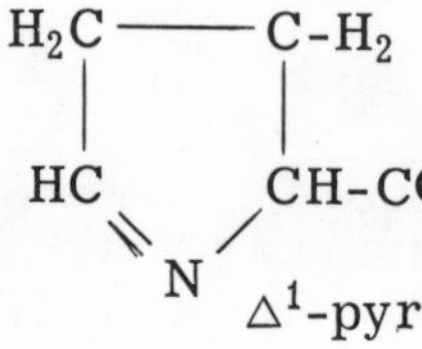

Δ^1-pyrroline-5-carboxylic acid

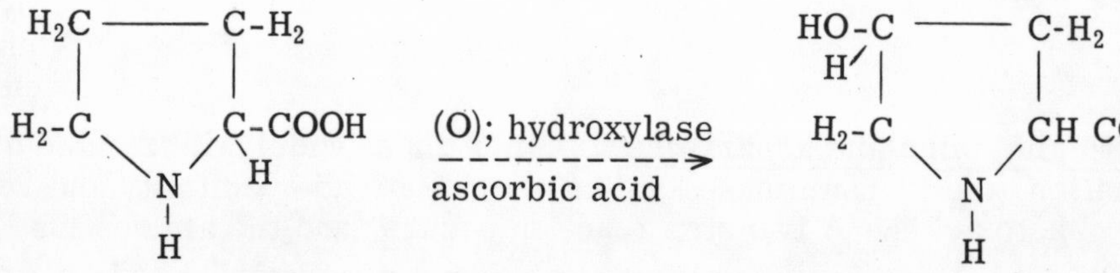

proline   hydroxyproline

Hydroxyproline is metabolized as follows:

$$L\text{-hydroxyproline} \underset{(O_2)}{\overset{oxidase}{\dashrightarrow}} \Delta^1\text{-3-hydroxypyrroline-5-carboxylic acid}$$

$$\overset{NADH + H^+ \quad NAD^+}{\dashrightarrow} \gamma\text{-hydroxy glutamic acid} \overset{transaminase}{\longleftrightarrow} \gamma\text{-hydroxy-}\alpha\text{-keto-}$$

glutaric acid $\dashrightarrow$ pyruvic acid + glyoxylic acid

The oxidation of proline to hydroxyproline apparently occurs *after* the proline is bound in peptide linkage; presumably on the ribosome.

Arginine and the urea cycle. Arginine occupies a key position in the formation of urea in mammals, and the demands for this amino acid as an intermediate in rapidly growing young mammals may explain why it can be synthesized at only two-thirds of the rate needed for optimum growth. About 20 grams of urea are formed each day by a 70-kilogram human on an ordinary diet.

Carbamyl phosphate. The formation of this compound may be considered the first step towards arginine and urea synthesis.

$$(1) \quad NH_4^+ + HCO_3^- + 2ATP \overset{carbamyl\ phosphate\ synthetase}{\underset{Mg^{++},\ N\text{-acetyl glutamic acid}}{\dashrightarrow}} H_2N-CO-OPO_3H_2 + 2ADP + Pi$$

In contrast to bacterial systems, carbamyl phosphate synthetase permits the utilization of two moles of ATP instead of one mole per mole of carbamyl phosphate formed. This allows the utilization of ammonia at a lower concentration than is possible in bacteria.

(2)   carbamyl phosphate + ornithine ---→ citrulline (H_2N-C-N-CH_2-CH_2-CH_2-$CHNH_2$-COOH) + Pi

(with H above N, O below C)

Reaction (2) is catalyzed by *ornithine transcarbamylase*, and the equilibrium is far to the right, thus maintaining a unidirectional flow of the urea cycle in the liver.

Reaction (3) is catalyzed by *arginosuccinic acid synthetase*, and requires as cofactors ATP and magnesium ion.

(3) H_2N-C-N-CH_2-CH_2-CH_2-$CHNH_2$-COOH + HOOC-CH_2-$CHNH_2$-COOH $\xrightarrow[\text{synthetase}]{\text{ATP, }Mg^{++}}$

(with H above N, O below C)

        citrulline   aspartic acid

HOOC-CH_2-C-NH-C-NH-CH_2-CH_2-CH_2-$CHNH_2$-COOH + AMP + PP_i + H_2O

(with H below first C as C=O, O, H; H above second C and N above it)

        arginosuccinic acid

Formation of arginine.   In Reaction (4), argininosuccinase cleaves arginosuccinic acid to *arginine* and the Krebs cycle intermediate, fumaric acid.

(4)   arginosuccinic acid $\xrightarrow{\text{arginosuccinase}}$ arginine + fumaric acid

Examination of these reactions shows that arginine derives two of its three nitrogens from glutamic acid (via ornithine) and the third from carbamyl phosphate.   The fumaric acid can be readily converted via the Krebs cycle to oxaloacetic acid and then by transamination to aspartic acid.

Formation of urea.   In the final step of the urea cycle, L-arginine is split hydrolytically by liver arginase to yield urea and regenerate L-ornithine.

(5)   arginine $\xrightarrow[(+H_2O)]{\text{arginase}}$ urea + ornithine

When one cancels out the intermediates that are regenerated in the cycle, the overall enzymic synthesis of urea may be written:

NH_4^+ + HCO_3^- + H_2O + 3ATP + L-aspartate ---→ urea + fumarate + AMP + 2ADP + 2Pi + PPi

Metabolism of tyrosine.   Tyrosine is formed by the hydroxylation of phenylalanine as described on page 193.   The main pathway of degradation is by transamination with ketoglutaric acid to yield para-hydroxyphenylpyruvic acid (reaction 1).

(1)   L-tyrosine $\xleftarrow{\text{liver transaminase}}$ p-hydroxyphenylpyruvic acid

The keto analog is then oxidized by a liver oxidase system to *homogentisic acid*.

(2)   para-hydroxyphenylpyruvic acid ◄ — — — — — ►

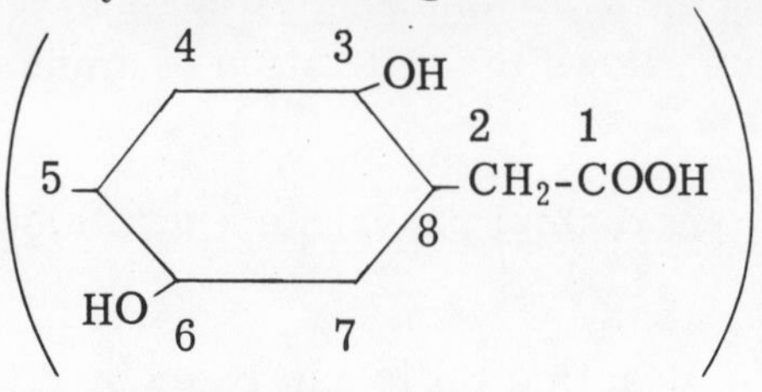

homogentisic acid

Homogentisic acid oxidase then catalyzes the oxidation of homogentisic acid to 4-maleylacetoacetic acid by splitting the ring between positions 3 and 8.

(3)   homogentisic acid   — — — — — — ► $HOOC-CH=CH-CO-CH_2-CO-CH_2-COOH$
                     liver oxidase
             (O_2)   4-maleylacetoacetic acid

In the hereditary disease, alkaptonuria, homogentisic oxidase is defective, and reaction (3) is blocked. Homogentisic acid is excreted quantitatively in the urine. On standing, the urine turns brown or black due to oxidation of the homogentisic acid. In later life, severe arthritis may develop in the alkaptonuric due to gradual deposition of pigment in bones and fibrous tissues.

In the final metabolic step in normal metabolism, 4-maleyl acetoacetic acid is isomerized to the trans isomer, 4-fumaryl acetoacetic acid, and this is then split to fumaric and acetoacetic acids.

(4)   4-maleylacetoacetic acid — — — — — — — ► 4-fumarylacetoacetic acid — — — — — — — ►
                         liver isomerase   liver hydrolase
                         glutathione   ($+H_2O$)

fumaric acid + acetoacetic acid

Formation of thyroxine, epinephrines and melanins. Tyrosine also serves as the precursor of these important metabolites. The pathways are outlined below.

Thyroxine and triiodothyronine. The trapping of iodine by the thyroid gland is inhibited by respiratory inhibitors, so is assumed to be oxygen-dependent. It is believed that at least five enzyme systems are involved in the synthesis and liberation of the thyroid hormones. Enzyme 1 converts plasma iodide to thyroid iodide, enzyme 2 converts thyroid iodide to "active I" which may be the iodonium ion (I^+), enzyme 3 condenses "active I" with tyrosine giving 3-iodotyrosine and 3, 5 diodotyrosine, enzyme 4 couples the mono- and di- derivatives to give thyroxine and triiodothyronine peptide, bound in thyroglobulin, and enzyme 5 releases the two hormones by proteolysis so that they can combine with an α-globulin fraction of blood for transport.

Epinephrines. The pathway to norepinephrine and epinephrine is as follows:

                tyrosinase   ($-CO_2$)
L-tyrosine — — — — — — ► 3, 4-dihydroxyphenylalanine — — — — — ► 3, 4 dihydroxy-
             (O_2)   phenylethyl amine

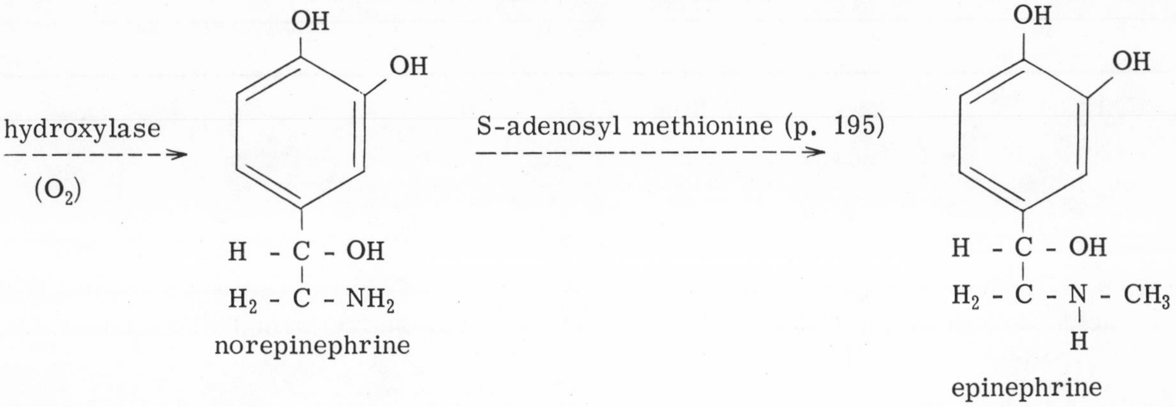

norepinephrine → epinephrine (via hydroxylase (O₂) and S-adenosyl methionine (p. 195))

Melanin formation. This pathway also goes through the intermediate, 3,4-dihydroxyphenylalanine (DOPA):

Tyrosine --tyrosinase--> 3,4-dihydroxyphenylalanine(DOPA)   dopa quinone

leuco dopachrome   dopachrome (red)   (-CO₂)

5,6-dihydroxyindole   indole-5,6-quinone   polymerization → melanin

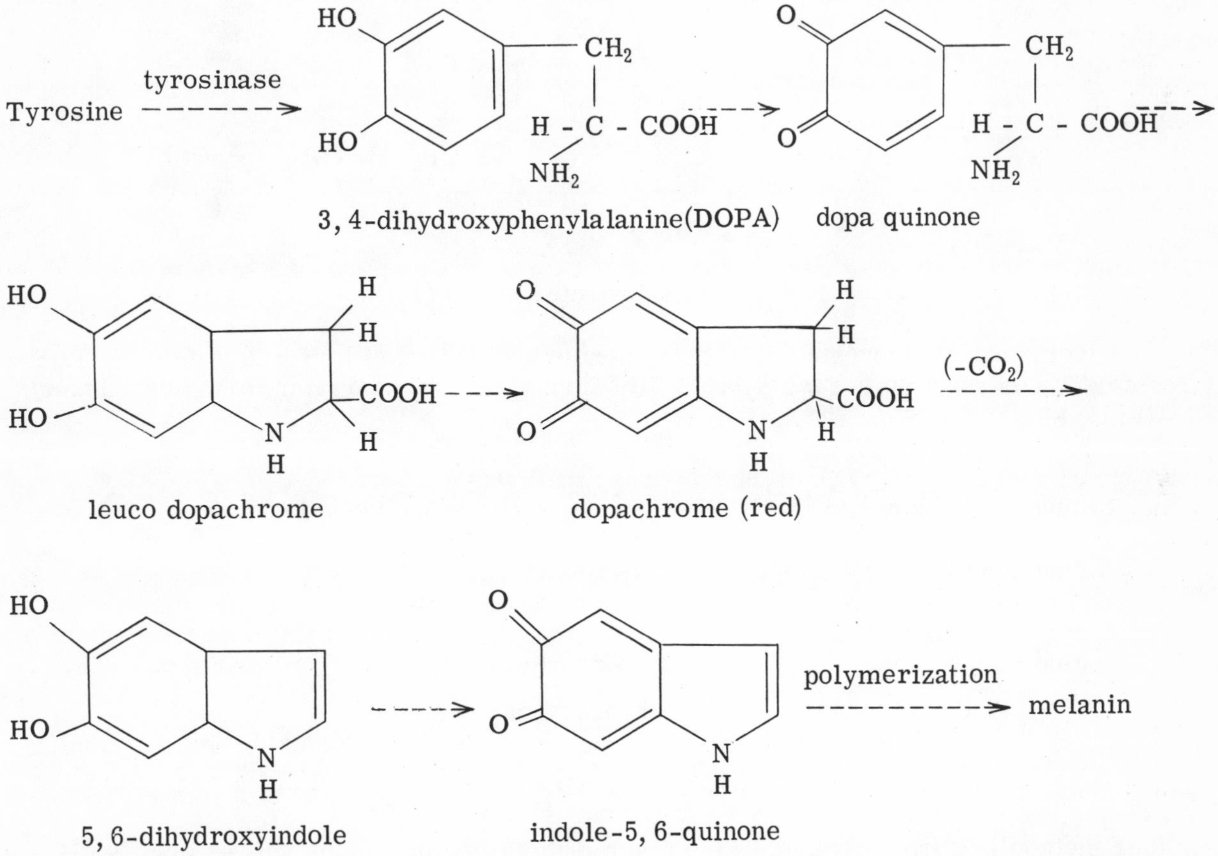

Metabolism of glycine. The major pathway of catabolism of glycine is its conversion to serine. This can be accomplished in two ways, both of which involve the vitamin, tetra-hydrofolic acid. There are eight or more functional forms of this vitamin, and the two that are believed to be the active formate and formaldehyde donors are shown below.

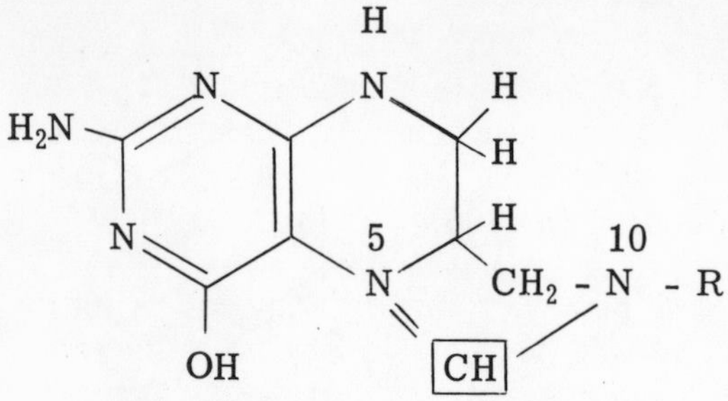

5, 10-methenyltetrahydrofolic
acid (active formate donor)
(THF-formic)

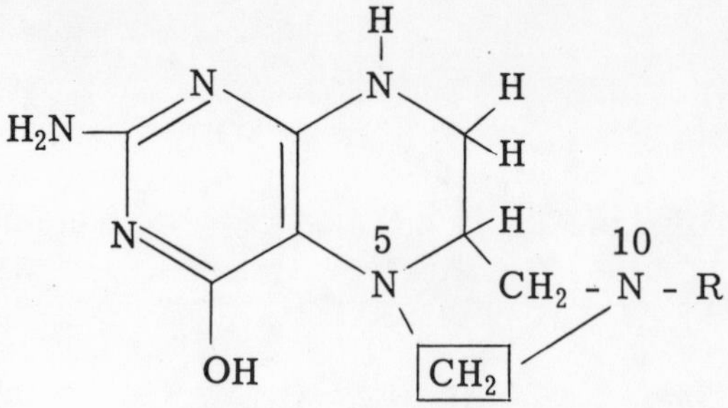

5, 10-methylenetetrahydrofolic
acid (active formaldehyde donor)
(THF-formald.)

These derivatives of folic acid are formed from 5, 6, 7 8-tetrahydrofolic acid (THF), and are interconvertible in the presence of tetrahydrofolate dehydrogenase and NADP.

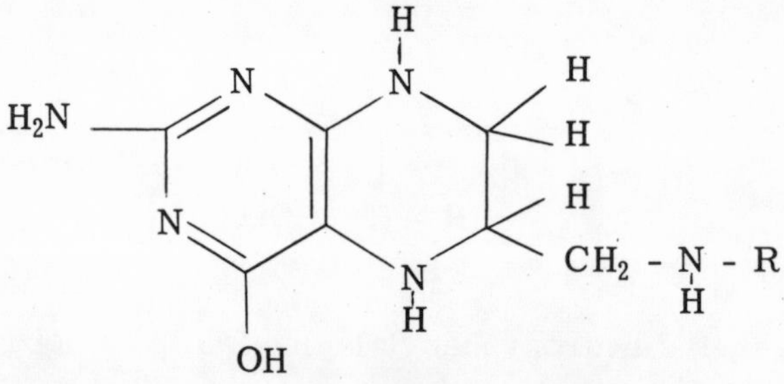

5, 6, 7, 8-tetrahydrofolic acid (THF)

Glycine can be converted directly to serine by addition of formaldehyde from THF-formald. The reaction is reversible. THF formald. is formed from formaldehyde and THF.

(1) glycine + THF-formald. $\xrightarrow{\text{serine hydroxy methylase}}$ serine + THF

A longer pathway involves oxidative deamination:

(2) glycine $\xrightarrow[\text{(O}_2)\ \ (\text{-NH}_3)]{\text{glycine oxidase}}$ glyoxylic acid $\xrightarrow{(O_2)}$ oxalic acid $\xrightarrow{(-CO_2)}$ formic acid

$\xrightarrow{\text{ATP, THF}}$ THF-formic $\xrightarrow[\text{NADP}^+ \quad \text{NADPH + H}^+]{\text{THF dehydrogenase}}$ THF-formald. $\longrightarrow$ reaction (1)

Other metabolites from glycine. Five other metabolites of glycine will be briefly discussed below.

Creatine. This is formed in two steps:

(1)   L-arginine + glycine $\xrightarrow[\text{transamidinase}]{\text{kidney}}$ ornithine + N-guanidoacetic acid

(2)   N-guanidoacetic acid + S-adenosylmethionine $\xrightarrow{\hspace{2cm}}$ creatine (N-methyl guanidoacetic acid)

<u>Heme</u>. The red pigment, heme, or iron protoporphryin, and the green pigment, chloro-phyll, a magnesium tetrapyrrole, are probably the two most important pigments in living organisms. Both compounds have the same basic tetrapyrrole structure, but differ in the metal atom and in the side chains attached to the pyrrole units. The formula for chlorophylls a and b are given on page 171.

The porphyrins are substituted derivatives of a cyclic ring system containing four pyrrole units linked by methene carbons. Since uroporphyrin has the largest number of carbon atoms in the side chains, it is used as the parent compound. The pyrrole rings are lettered as A, B, C, and D, the methene carbons as α, β, γ, and δ. Ring carbons are numbered starting from the nitrogen atom counterclockwise in rings A and B, and clockwise in rings C and D in the formula shown. The heme molecule (iron protoporphy-rin formula on page 263) has methyl groups instead of acetic acid groups at position 6 on rings A, B, C, and D, and a vinyl ($CH_2 = CH-$) group in place of a propionic acid radical at positions 8 and 9 on rings A and B. There are four possible isomers of uroporphyrin, but only two types are found in nature. The most abundant is type III, shown below. The other, type I, has a symmetrical arrangement of the side chains.

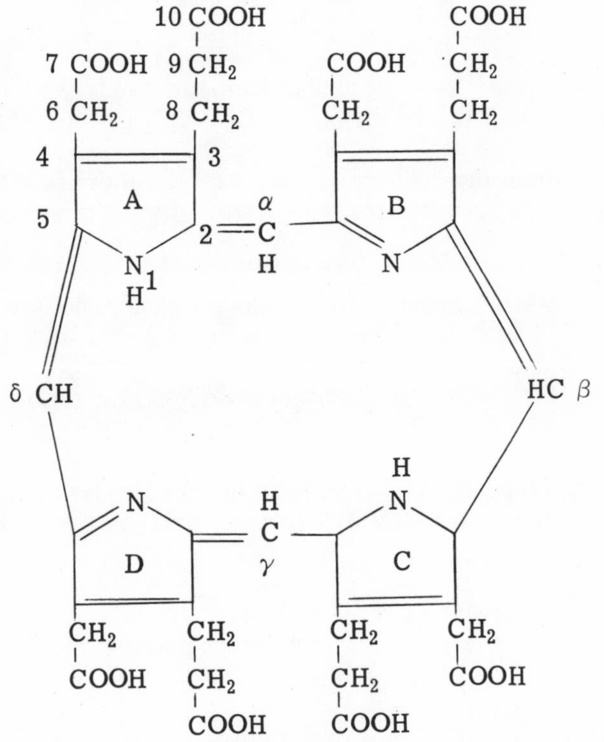

Uroporphyrin III

<u>Synthesis of protoporphyrin 9</u>. The incorporation of Fe^{++} into protoporphyrin is accom-plished by an enzymatic process in the reticulocyte. Iron protoporphyrin (heme) is the prosthetic group in hemoglobin, myoglobin, catalase, peroxidase, and the cytochromes. A protoporphyrin with different side chains and cobalt as the metal ion is found in vita-

min B_{12} (see page 241 for formula).   The pathway of synthesis of protoporphyring starts with succinyl CoA and glycine.

(1)   succinyl CoA + glycine $\xrightarrow[\substack{\text{pyridoxal phosphate} \\ (-CO_2(\text{glycine}))}]{\text{synthetase}}$ $HOOC\text{-}CH_2\text{-}CH_2\text{-}CO\text{-}CH_2\text{-}NH_2$

δ-aminolevulinic acid

In the second step, 2 molecules of δ-aminolevulinic acid condense to form porphobilinogen:

(2)   2 δ-aminolevulinic acid $\xrightarrow[(-H_2O)]{\text{dehydrase}}$

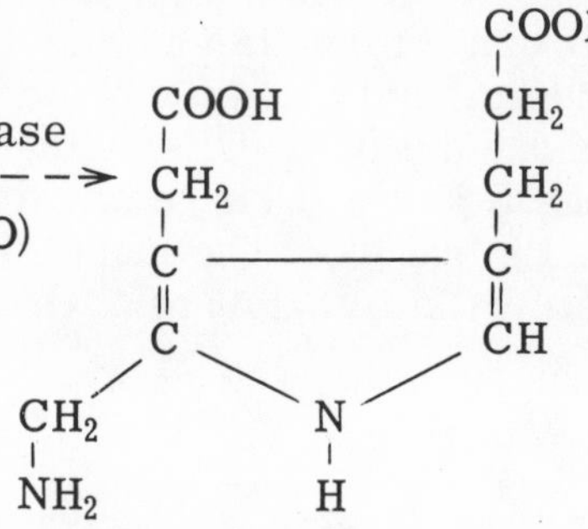

porphobilinogen

In the third step, 4 molecules of porphobilinogen condense to form uroporphyrinogen III, which is the reduced form of uroporphyrin III (-CH_2 groups at positions α, β, γ, and δ).

(3)   4 porphobilinogen $\xrightarrow[(-NH_3)]{\text{deaminase}}$ (intermediate) $\xrightarrow{\text{isomerase}}$ uroporphyrinogen III

In the fourth step, methyl groups are produced at positions 6 by decarboxylation.

(4)   uroporphyrinogen III $\xrightarrow[(-CO_2)]{\text{decarboxylase}}$ coproporphyrinogen

In the fifth and last step, the two propionic acid side chains on rings A and B of coproporphyrinogen are converted to vinyl groups, and six hydrogens are removed from the molecule.

(5)   coproporphyrinogen $\xrightarrow[(O_2)]{\text{decarboxylase, oxidase}}$ protoporphyrin 9

Using radioactive carbon (C^{14}) and N^{15}, incorporation studies with nucleated red cells of the duck, and with mammalian reticulocytes show that the four nitrogen atoms in porphyrins come from glycine, the four methene bridge carbon atoms and the four atoms numbered 2 are derived from the α-carbon of glycine; the carboxyl carbon of glycine is not used. All remaining carbon atoms of the porphyrin structure come from succinyl CoA.

Purines. The synthesis of purines from glycine has been discussed in a previous chapter (see page 115).

Glutathione. Glutathione (γ-glutamylcysteinylglycine) is widely distributed in animal cells, mainly in the reduced form. It serves as a coenzyme in certain enzyme reactions, and is needed for the maintenance of the structural integrity of the erythrocyte. It is synthesized as follows:

(1) L-glutamic acid + L-cysteine + ATP $----\rightarrow$ L-γ-glutamylcysteine + ADP + P_i

(2) L-γ-glutamylcysteine + glycine + ATP $----\rightarrow$ glutathione + ADP + P_i

<u>Hippuric acid.</u> This compound (benzoyl glycine) is a detoxication product synthesized in the liver, and excreted in the urine. The average person excretes 0.1 to 1.0 grams daily, depending on the level of benzoic acid in the diet. It is synthesized as follows:

(1) benzoic acid + ATP $\xrightarrow{\text{activating enzyme}}$ adenylbenzoate + PP_i

(2) adenylbenzoate + CoASH $\xleftarrow{---}\rightarrow$ benzoyl-S-CoA + AMP

(3) benzoyl-S-CoA + glycine $\xrightarrow[\text{enzyme}]{\text{condensing}}$ N-benzoyl glycine + CoASH

<u>Metabolism of serine.</u> The interconversion of serine and glycine has been discussed previously. The major source of serine is from glucose as shown below.

(1) glucose $---\rightarrow$ 3-phosphoglyceric acid $\xrightarrow[\text{NAD}^+ \quad \text{NADH} + \text{H}^+]{\text{phosphoglycerate dehydrogenase}}$

$--\rightarrow$ HOOC-CO-CH$_2$-O-PO$_3$H$_2$

   3-phospho-hydroxypyruvic acid

The product formed in reaction (1) is transaminated to 3-phosphoserine:

(2) 3-phospho-hydroxypyruvic acid $\xrightarrow[\text{glutamate} \quad \alpha\text{-ketoglutarate}]{\text{transaminase}}$ 3-phosphoserine

A phosphatase enzyme then splits the phosphoserine.

(3) 3-phosphoserine $\xrightarrow[\text{(+H}_2\text{O)}]{\text{phosphoserine phosphatase}}$ L-serine + Pi

<u>Formation of ethanolamine and choline from serine.</u> Serine is decarboxylated to ethanolamine in a reversible reaction with phosphatidylethanolamine:

(1) phosphatidylethanolamine + L-serine $\xleftarrow[]{\text{enzyme}}\rightarrow$ phosphatidyl serine + ethanolamine

(2) phosphatidyl serine $\xrightarrow{\text{enzyme}}$ phosphatidyl ethanolamine + CO_2

This is a cycle in which phosphatidylethanolamine acts as a coenzyme and is continuously regenerated, the serine being decarboxylated to ethanolamine.

Serine also serves as a precursor of choline via ethanolamine:

$$\text{(1)} \quad \text{phosphatidylethanolamine} \xrightarrow{\text{S-adenosylmethionine (page 195)}} \text{N-methyl derivative}$$

$$\text{(2)} \quad \text{N-methyl derivative} \xrightarrow{\text{S-adenosylmethionine}} \text{N, N-dimethyl derivative}$$

$$\text{(3)} \quad \text{N, N-dimethyl derivative} \xrightarrow{\text{S-adenosylmethionine}} \text{phosphatidyl choline}$$

Formation of cysteine from serine. This was discussed in a previous section (see page 195).

Metabolism of cysteine and cystine. Most of the peptide-bound portion of this sulfur amino acid occurs as the disulfide, cystine. Free cystine is reduced to cysteine before being catabolized.

$$\text{(1)} \quad \text{L-cystine} \underset{\text{NADH} + \text{H}^+ \qquad \text{NAD}^+}{\overset{\text{reductase}}{\rightleftharpoons}} \text{2 L-cysteine}$$

The synthesis of L-cysteine from serine and methionine has been discussed previously (see p. 195). Pathways for the catabolism of cysteine are shown below. The sulfur atom of cysteine is excreted in various forms in the urine: ethereal sulfate, 5 per cent, organic sulfide sulfur, 15 per cent, and inorganic sulfide sulfur, 80 per cent.

$$\text{(1)} \quad \text{cysteine} \xrightarrow{\text{transaminase}} \beta\text{-mercaptopyruvate} \dashrightarrow \text{pyruvate} + \text{H}_2\text{S}$$

$$\text{(2)} \quad \text{cysteine} \xrightarrow[\text{ATP, NADP}^+]{\text{liver enzyme}} \underset{\text{cysteine sulfinic acid}}{\text{HO}_2\text{S-CH}_2\text{-CHNH}_2\text{-COOH}}$$

$$\text{(2.1)} \quad \text{cysteine sulfinic acid} \xrightarrow{(-\text{CO}_2)} \text{hypotaurine} \xrightarrow[(+\text{O}_2)]{\text{oxidase}} \text{taurine (H}_2\text{NCH}_2\text{CH}_2\text{SO}_3\text{H})$$

$$\text{(2.2)} \quad \text{cysteine sulfinic acid} \xrightarrow[(\text{O}_2)]{\text{oxidase}} \underset{\text{cysteic acid}}{\text{HO}_3\text{S-CH}_2\text{CHNH}_2\text{COOH}} \xrightarrow{(-\text{CO}_2)} \text{taurine}$$

$$\text{(2.3)} \quad \text{cysteine sulfinic acid} \xrightarrow{\text{transaminase}} \underset{\beta\text{-sulfinylpyruvate}}{\text{HO}_2\text{S-CH}_2\text{-CO-COOH}} \dashrightarrow \text{pyruvic acid}$$

$$+ \text{ sulfur dioxide (SO}_3^{--}) \xrightarrow{\text{oxidase}} \text{sulfate (SO}_4^{--})$$

Summary of metabolism of major nitrogen compounds. In Figure 81 the author has attempted to summarize the major changes which take place in the nitrogen-containing nutrients once they leave the gut in all species (from insects to man) and appear *in the blood stream*.

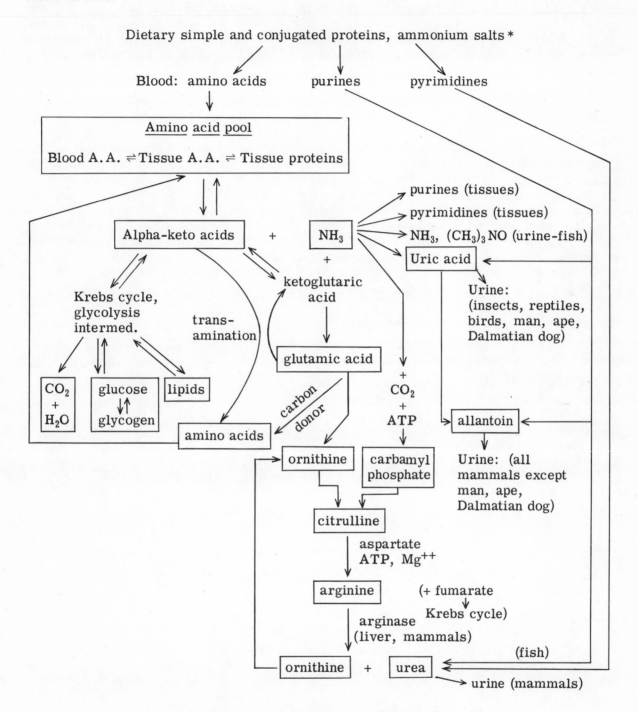

Figure 81.   General metabolism of nitrogen in animals

* Dietary ammonium salts are probably converted nearly completely to L-glutamic acid in the intestinal wall, so do not appear in significant amounts in the blood stream.   Ammonium ion is actually toxic when present in moderate amounts in the blood stream.   Thus, injection of the enzyme, urease, can cause death in mammals (but not birds - no urea in blood stream), because it splits the urea to ammonium carbonate.

It can be seen from Figure 81 that the carbon skeletons of the excess dietary amino acids are converted to glucose, glycogen or fat, or are burned via the carbohydrate or fat metabolism pathways to carbon dioxide and water. The ammonia from the alpha-amino, epsilon-amino, delta-guanidine, beta-imidazole, and to some extent, the beta-indole groups is transferred to ketoglutaric acid, and eventually appears as urea in mammals, and in some insects. In most insects, in birds and in reptiles, the nitrogen is excreted as uric acid, probably going via glutamic acid to glycine, to intermediate purine(s), to uric acid. In fish, excess amino acids are deaminated (by deaminases) and the ammonia is excreted as such* or as the trimethyl amine oxide in the urine. Thus, *urea* is the main end-product of nitrogen metabolism in mammals, *uric acid* the main end-product in insects, reptiles, and birds, and *ammonia* (or an amine complex) the main end-product in fish.

Both purines and pyrimidines (which together with pentose and phosphoric acid make up the nucleic acids found in nucleoproteins) are readily synthesized from ammonia in all animals studied. The pathway for purine synthesis apparently is through glycine as an intermediate. Purines are excreted mainly as uric acid by man, the great apes, the Dalmation dog, insects, reptiles, and birds. Most mammals, however, form uric acid as an end-product of purine metabolism, then cleave it to another compound, allantoin, before excreting it in the urine. In the metabolism of pyrimidines, the nitrogen is released as ammonia, which is then excreted as such, or converted to urea or uric acid, depending on the species.

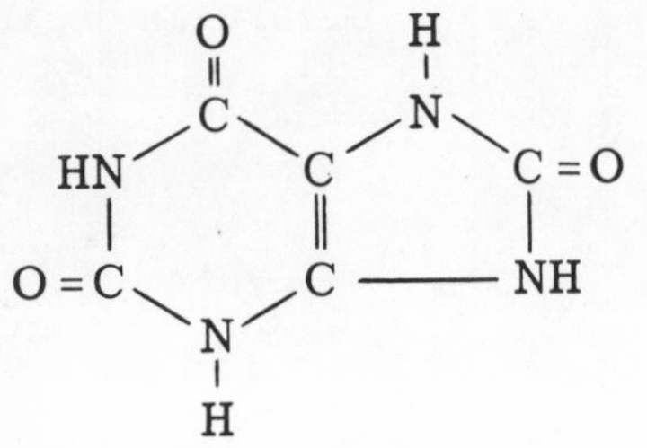

Uric acid 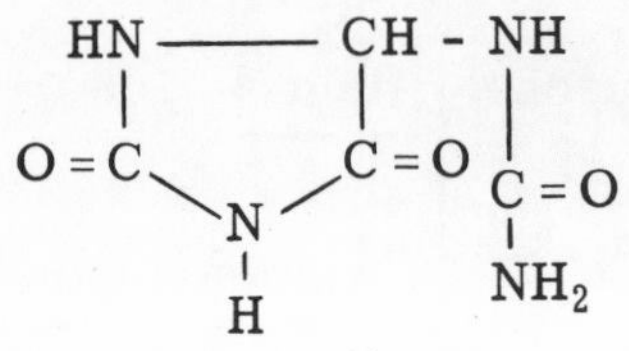   Allantoin

---

* Recent studies in fish show that a considerable amount of nitrogen is converted to glutamine, and this compound is split in the gill membrane by the enzyme glutaminase to glutamic acid and ammonia. The ammonia diffuses across the gill membrane into the surrounding water. Ammonia is formed in a similar manner in the mammalian kidney. The kidney is a small rudimentary structure in fish, and it appears that most of the nitrogen in this species diffuses out of the gills as ammonia.

Chapter 12 | ANIMAL NUTRITION

Animal nutrition may be defined as an important subdivision of biochemistry which deals with the caloric and nutrient requirements of animals. The nutritionist is keenly interested in determining what physiological and chemical effects are produced in the animal by modifications in the composition of its diet. To be adequate, a diet must provide all of the needs of the animal, particularly for maintenance, growth, and reproduction. Not only must the diet provide all necessary nutrients, but in recent years evidence has been obtained to show that the individual nutrients must be in *proper balance* one with another. The complexity of this science is evident when one considers that in addition to the factors of calories and water, the animal requires in its diet a proper balance of one or more fatty acids, 8 to 11 amino acids, 13 minerals, and 17 or more vitamins.

CALORIC REQUIREMENTS AND ENERGY METABOLISM. The normal adult animal requires just sufficient calories to balance the total loss from his body. It is obvious that caloric needs are increased by muscular activity. The caloric demands are also influenced by the external temperature. When more calories are given off by an animal than are consumed in the form of food, the animal is no longer in caloric equilibrium. Calories are produced under such circumstances at the expense of the tissues, and there is a loss of weight. In the normal growing animal, more food must be provided than the amount sufficient for maintenance of energy balance. Here potential calories are being laid down in the form of new cells, and there is a condition of positive caloric balance. The caloric needs under different conditions have been determined by a study of energy metabolism, which is discussed below.

Energy Metabolism in Animals

Voris* states that "The economic return from feed consumed is the primary concern of animal husbandry. The profitable end-products of animal feeding, such as milk, meat, eggs, wool, or work represent only a fraction of the feed provided for the purpose. The largest portion of the feed has rather literally gone up in smoke with concomitant production of heat. This constant combustion of feed within the animal body, with the resulting production of heat, has been designated as energy metabolism".

Energy metabolism is a field of great interest to the human as well as the animal nutritionist. Determination of the nutrient needs of different age groups, from infants to the aged, must take into account the energy needs at different levels of activity. Energy metabolism is also of interest to the physician, for certain diseases produce alterations in the basic energy metabolism pattern.

Definition of terms. The energy involved in the energy exchanges between most animals and their environment are of two types: *chemical* energy and *heat* energy. All chemical energy can be ultimately expressed as heat energy. The unit of heat energy most commonly used is the large calorie (Calorie), or kilogram calorie. This is defined as the quantity of heat required to raise the temperature of one kilogram of water from 15° to 16° C.

*L. Voris, Agricultural Chemistry. I. Principles, Edited by D. E. H. Frear, p. 498, D. VanNostrand Co., N. Y. (1950).

The term *metabolism* (see p. 154) refers to the sum total of all chemical processes which occur within the body and include all of the transformations of matter and energy involved in growth, muscular activity, heat production, and the maintenance of vital functions. Metabolism by this definition does not include the processes of digestion, which are actually taking place outside the body tissues (in the intestinal tract). It is not until the digested feed or food has been transported through the intestinal wall that the nutrients enter the "metabolic pool" of the body.

When food is eaten, a large part of it is digested and absorbed. The unabsorbed residue, which contains a fraction of the food energy, passes on through the alimentary canal and may be recovered in the feces. By subtracting the energy of the fecal output representing a given quota of food, from the original total energy of the food, one obtains a value for that part of the food energy which entered the body tissues. This part of the feed or food energy which is actually absorbed is called the *digestible energy* of the food. After the absorbed nutrients have run their course in the metabolic pool, a portion of their energy may be recovered in the urine, and, in ruminants, a significant amount of energy may be lost as combustible gases, such as methane. This residual energy, which represents the non-metabolized fraction of the digestible energy, can be subtracted from the digestible energy to obtain a value for that part of the original feed or food energy which is both digestible and metabolizable. The digestible, metabolizable energy of a feed or foodstuff is called its *metabolizable energy*.

The metabolizable energy of carbonaceous nutrients is utilized by the body for maintenance of body functions (pumping of the heart, breathing, etc.), tissue regeneration, growth, reproduction, lactation, muscular activity, etc. However, this is not accomplished without energy expense. Thus, the net energy utilized for the above purposes is less than the metabolizable energy by the energy cost of metabolism. This cost of metabolism is extracted as heat. The heat thus released is eliminated from the body by delicate thermostatic mechanisms whereby the over-all internal temperature is maintained within narrow limits.

It is obvious, then, that the transformation of the *gross energy* of feeds and foods into *net metabolizable energy* involves three energy losses: (1) loss in digestion, (2) loss of non-metabolized energy of the urine and combustible gases and (3) loss of energy expended in utilizing the metabolizable energy.

METHODS USED FOR MEASURING ENERGY VALUE OF FEEDS AND FOODS. The *gross chemical energy* of a feed or food can be measured as the heat derived from burning the substance in the presence of oxygen. The "heat of combustion" value is usually determined by burning a weighed sample of the feed or food under highly compressed oxygen in a steel bomb (bomb calorimeter). The heat released is absorbed by a weighed quantity of water in which the bomb is submerged, and the calories of heat are calculated from the rise in temperature of the water.

The energy loss of the undigested food residues in the feces can also be determined by bomb calorimetry of the dry feces, after making the necessary correction for the energy of the excretions normally in the tract, and the energy of bacterial residues. The latter two can be determined by feeding a control diet which is completely digestible, or made up of known amounts of digestible and completely indigestible foodstuffs.

The loss of gross energy in the form of combustible gases can be determined accurately by confinement of the animal in a respiration chamber (see below) with analysis of the gases released.

In Table 31, values for the gross energy and digestible energy of representative feeds and foods are presented. These are based on their heats of combustion determined in a bomb calorimeter.

Table 31. Gross and digestible energy of selected nutrients

Nutrient	Kilocalories per Gram of Dry Matter		
	Heat of Combustion	Loss in Feces (%)	Digestible Energy
Glucose	3.75	0	3.75
Starch	4.18	2	4.10
Sucrose	3.96	0	3.96
Butterfat	9.25	5	8.80
Casein	5.94	*	5.70
Corn	4.63	10	4.17
* See page 213.			

The gross energy value (heat of combustion) is a constant for a specific feed or food. However, the digestible and metabolizable portions of the gross energy value will vary with the species, environment, quantity and nature of food consumed, previous nutrional status of the subject, and any other factors affecting food utilization. For example, the gross energy value for dry alfalfa hay is 4.65 kilocalories per gram. A pig will derive 2.14 kilocalories per gram, or 46% of the gross energy in the hay, whereas a cow (ruminant) will derive 3.56 kilocalories per gram, or 77% of the gross energy. This serves to illustrate the more complete digestion of high fiber plants in the ruminant, and its effect on the digestible energy value.

In precise studies on energy metabolism, it is always necessary to determine with accuracy the gross energy value (heat of combustion) of the feed. In actual feeding practice in animal husbandry, the gross energy value of feedstuffs is roughly estimated as total digestible nutrients (TDN), which equals the sum of the percent digestible carbohydrates, per cent digestible proteins, and 2.25 x per cent digestible fat. Some examples of the TDN values for feeds are shown in Table 32.

Table 32. TDN values

Feedstuff	Total Dry Matter (%)	Digestible Crude Protein (%)	Digestible Carbohydrate (%)	Digestible Fat (%)	TDN* (%)
Dent corn	89.4	7.6	67.5	4.6	85.4
Peanut (no hull)	92.5	23.4	14.5	34.9	116.4
Cow's milk, whole	12.8	3.6	4.9	3.7	16.8
Alfalfa leaves	93.2	15.8	35.1	1.3	53.8
* Digestible crude protein plus digestible crude carbohydrate plus 2.25 x % digestible crude fat.					

As can be seen from Table 32, the TDN value is based on weight units rather than calories, and the superior energy value of fat is compensated for by multiplying it by the factor 2.25. TDN thus represents, according to Voris**"-------a confusion of units giving respect to the greater energy value of fat." The value is a measure of the gross energy content of the diet, and for this reason has had practical application in comparative feeding tests with farm animals.

** See Footnote p. 209.

THE MEASUREMENT OF HEAT PRODUCTION. In the body, carbohydrates and fats are oxidized to the same products as in the bomb calorimeter, and therefore yield corresponding amounts of heat. Protein, however, which burns to CO_2, H_2O, and nitrogen (see p. 211) in the calorimeter, yields in the body no free nitrogen; urea and other organic nitrogenous compounds are formed which are excreted in the urine. Urinary nitrogen is thus a measure of protein metabolism.

Heat production due to the combustion of nutrients in the animal body can be measured by two general methods: (a) indirect and (b) direct calorimetry.

INDIRECT CALORIMETRY. As shown in Table 31, the heats of combustion of glucose, starch and sucrose vary from 3.75 to 4.18 kilocalories per gram of dry matter. Since the volume of CO_2 produced equals the volume of oxygen consumed (see equation below), carbohydrates have a respiratory quotient (CO_2/O_2) which equals 1.

$$C_nH_{(2n-2)}O_{(n-1)} \quad + \quad nO_2 \quad ----\rightarrow \quad nCO_2 \quad + \quad (n-1) H_2O$$

$$\frac{nCO_2}{nO_2} = 1$$

If the animal organism is burning only carbohydrates, the oxygen consumed will be equal in volume to the CO_2 released, and for each gram molecular weight of carbohydrate burned, a gram molecular weight (22.4 liters at standard temperature and pressure) of oxygen will be consumed. It is possible, by the use of a suitable face mask, to measure the volume of oxygen consumed and CO_2 released by an animal, or human, in a fixed period of time. From this can be calculated the respiratory quotient, and also the total calories of heat energy released. For this latter calculation, in practical work, 4.1 kilocalories per gram of carbohydrate (equivalent to 5.047 kilocalories per liter of O_2 consumed) is used to calculate heat production. The liters of O_2 consumed in a prescribed time when multiplied by the factor 5.047 will equal the heat production in kilocalories *if* the respiratory quotient (R.Q.) equals unity, i.e., only carbohydrate is being burned.

RESPIRATORY QUOTIENT FOR FAT. The heat of combustion for butterfat, as shown in Table 31, is 9.25 kilocalories per gram. This is about 2.25 times that of carbohydrates, and is due to the lower oxygen content of the triglyceride molecule. The equation below shows the oxidation of a typical triglyceride in the bomb calorimeter and in the animal body.

$$C_{57}H_{104}O_6 \quad + \quad 78.5\ O_2 \quad \longrightarrow \quad 57CO_2 \quad + \quad 52H_2O \quad + \quad \text{heat}$$

triolein

The R.Q. for triolein ($\frac{CO_2}{O_2}$) is 0.69, and 4.59 kilocalories are produced for each liter of oxygen absorbed.

Since the heats of combustion of individual triglycerides differ somewhat, the average values of 0.707 (R.Q.) and of 4.686 kilocalories per liter of oxygen are used in animal calorimetry studies on fat. For the same reason, the average caloric value of one gram of fat is taken as 9.5 kilocalories (compare Table 31).

RESPIRATORY QUOTIENT FOR PROTEIN. Proteins are more complex and of more variable composition than carbohydrates and fats. It is therefore difficult to calculate an exact R.Q. for proteins (it lies between 0.7 and 1.0). One gram of protein, when burned in the bomb calorimeter (see Table 31), yields about 5.9 kilocalories of heat.

In the animal, losses of undigested protein in the feces reduce the theoretical yield of kilocalories to 5.7 per gram of dietary protein. Of this, the body loses 1.3 kilocalories in the form of potential energy by excreting the ammonia from proteins as urea plus small amounts of other nitrogenous compounds, instead of burning it to free nitrogen. The actual yield of energy from one gram of food protein therefore equals 5.7 - 1.3 = 4.4 kilocalories.

By indirect calorimetry, i.e., measuring the R.Q. and the excretion of nitrogen, the nutritionist can determine whether the body is burning mainly carbohydrates, fats, or proteins. In actual practice, the measurement of oxygen consumption is more accurate than the measurement of carbon dioxide output; the latter is affected by the rate of breathing. Slow breathing causes a temporary storage of CO_2 with a low apparent quotient, whereas fast breathing causes the reverse effect. Oxygen consumption alone is therefore used, and related to heat production and nitrogen losses in the urine by using standard tables.

BASAL METABOLISM. This term refers to the metabolism of animals, and humans, in the resting and fasted state. For most animals, and humans, a period of 12 to 18 hours should elapse after the last meal; for ruminating animals, a longer time must elapse because of the longer digestion times encountered in the first three parts of the stomach.

The *basal metabolism* test is used by physicians in the diagnosis of certain diseases, such as hypo-and hyperthyroidism, etc. The patient wears a mask while fasting and at complete rest. The oxygen consumption is measured. This is compared with that of normal subjects (average "norm") and the per cent difference from the norm is calculated. Values within 100 ± 10% of the "norm" are considered to be within the normal range of variation. In hyperthyroidism, values of 120 - 140% are obtained, whereas in hypothyroidism, the values drop to 60 - 80% of the "norm".

Basal metabolic rate is affected by the height, build, body surface, etc., of the human or animal, and it is necessary to express the rate in standard units of time and body build. Since the metabolic rate is related directly to body surface area, it is usually expressed as kilocalories per hour per square meter of body surface area. For humans, body surface area can be calculated from the height-weight formula of DuBois. The body surface area $A = W^{0.425} \times H^{0.725} \times 71.84$, where W = weight in kilograms, and H = the height in centimeters. Tall, thin individuals have more surface area per unit of weight than fat, stocky individuals, and hence have a higher BMR (basal metabolic rate).

Several formulas have been developed for finding the surface area of various animals, from white rats to cattle. They involve the use of the exponential power of the weight and in most cases another measurement such as length or height. Armsby proposed the formula $S = KW^{5/9}$, where S = body surface area, W = the weight of the animal in grams, and K is a constant for all animals of the same shape. K can vary with the thinness or fatness of the animals. For beef cattle, for example, Moulton proposes a value of 10.34 for K.

Brody has concluded that the fasting catabolism (basal metabolic rate) of domestic animals is proportional to the body weight of the animal raised to the 0.73 power. He has prepared a chart showing the basal metabolic rates of different species. This is reproduced in Figure 82. In the chart, the rising curve relates body weight in kilograms (or pounds) to the basal metabolic rate in Calories (or B.T.U. - British Thermal Units) consumed in 24 hours. This curve is represented very well by the equation: Calories/24 hours = 70 x (body weight in kilograms)$^{0.73}$. In order to compare the basal metabolic rates of different species per unit of weight, Brody has also plotted body weight against Calories/24 hours/kilogram of body weight. This is shown on the chart by the curve

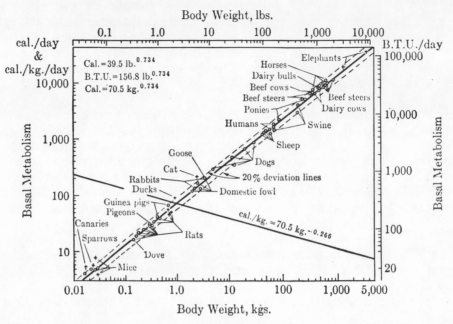

Figure 82. Relationship between basal metabolism and body weight in mature animals of various species. (From Brody, Bioenergetics and Growth, Reinhold Publishing Corp., N. Y.)

with the negative slope. This curve is represented by the equation Calories per Kg. body wt./24 hours = 70.5 x (Body weight in kilograms)$^{-0.266}$. The curve shows that the smallest animals (mice, birds, etc.) have the highest basal metabolic rates per kilogram of body weight. This is shown more clearly in Figure 83, where oxygen consumption (cc. per gram body weight per hour) is plotted against the weight of mature animals. Mature warm-blooded animals weighing less than 5 grams probably cannot exist, for, according to this curve, they simply couldn't eat fast enough to avoid starvation. The Allen and

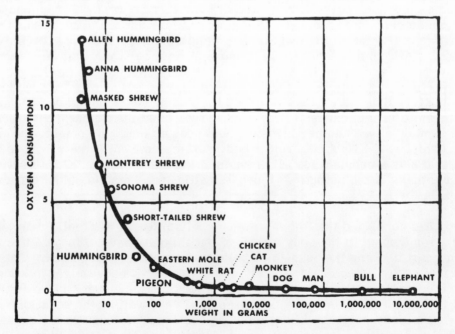

Figure 83. Oxygen consumption of small and large warm-blooded animals. (Reproduced by permission from O. P. Pearson, Scientific American, 188 69 (1953)).

Anna (Fig. 84) hummingbirds cannot feed at night, so they avoid overnight starvation by going into a state of *hibernation*. The rate of oxygen consumption drops to 1/15 of the daytime rate, and they become completely torpid, practically insensible, and scarcely able to move, with a body temperature near that of the surrounding air. Just before daybreak, the hummingbird's body spontaneously returns to its normal temperature and high consumption of oxygen. In contrast, the shrew has no hibernation mechanism, and must hunt for food both day and night to meet his energy requirements. At the other end of the scale is the ponderous elephant. Each gram of tissue in the resting elephant consumes less than 1/100 of the oxygen consumed by each gram of tissue in the resting hummingbird or shrew. It is obvious that the daily food requirement of the elephant per gram of body weight is also less than 1/100 of that of the hummingbird or the shrew.

Figure 84. Anna's Hummingbird. Hovering with wing beat of 55 times per second. (Stroboscopic flash camera picture taken by H. E. Edgerton, R. J. Niedrach and W. Van Riper. Reproduced from photo in National Geographic Magazine, Vol. C, No. 2, p. 246 (1951)).

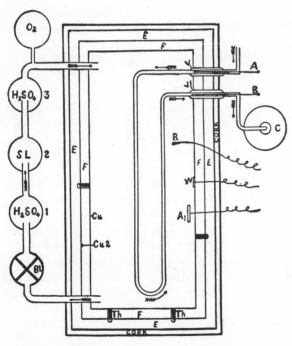

Figure 85. Diagram of Atwater-Rosa-Benedict direct and indirect respiration calorimeter. (From Lusk: Science of Nutrition).

APPARATUS USED TO MEASURE ENERGY METABOLISM. *The animal calorimeter.* *Indirect* calorimetry may be defined as the measurement of water evaporated, CO_2 exhaled, nitrogen excreted, and O_2 consumed, from which heat produced can be calculated for an animal or human. *Direct* calorimetry may be defined as the *direct* measurement of the heat evolved by an animal or human. The apparatus developed by Atwater, Rosa, and Benedict (Fig. 85) is a chamber which can measure heat production both by the *direct* and the *indirect* methods.

In the ventilating system (Fig. 85), Oxygen (O_2) is introduced as consumed by the animal (or human). To remove exhaled and perspired moisture, H_2SO_4 (trap 1) is used. Soda lime (trap 2) removes exhaled CO_2, and H_2SO_4 (trap 3) catches any moisture given off by the soda lime. The blower (BL) keeps the air in circulation. This part of the system supplies data for *indirect* calculation of heat loss: Increase in weight of trap 1 = H_2O lost by subject; increase in weight of traps 2 + 3 = CO_2 eliminated; decrease in weight of O_2 tank = oxygen consumed. Urine voided = nitrogen excreted.

In the heat-absorbing system (Fig. 85), A = thermometer at water inlet, B = thermometer at water outlet, C = tank for weighing water which has passed through coil each hour; V = vacuum jacket; E and F = dead air spaces; R = rectal thermometer; W = thermometer measuring wall temperature; A_1 = thermometer measuring temperature of air; Th = thermocouple; Cu and Cu_2 = copper walls. This part of the system supplies data for *direct* calculation of heat produced. Total calories produced = Average difference of readings on A and B x H_2O flow (liters) $\pm$ (temp. change of wall x specific heat of box) $\pm$ (temp. change of subject x specific heat of subject).

In recent years, the heat-absorbing and measuring system of the Atwater-Rosa-Benedict type calorimeter has been modified by Steward at the University of Missouri. He has eliminated the water-exchange system and replaced the chamber with one whose walls consist of banks of thermocouples. The original thermocouple bank system was developed by Bensinger, Office of Naval Research.

Recently, Guest has devised a simple indirect method of estimating heat production by measuring *insensible weight loss* (IWL) under fasting conditions, using an ordinary scale.

$$IWL = (CO_2 + \text{water lost}) - O_2 \text{ consumed}$$

The equation shows that insensible weight loss is the sum of the carbon dioxide lost by respiration, the water lost by respiration, and the water lost by evaporation from the body surface, corrected for the amount of oxygen consumed. The basal metabolic rate and the IWL measured under identical conditions are related to each other in linear fashion, the higher the BMR, the higher the IWL, and vice versa.

Two sizes of Toledo scales are employed, one of 25 kg. capacity for infants and small animals, the other of 135 kg. capacity for adult human subjects or large animals, Weight is recorded electrically on paper pulled past the indicator needle of the scale, and other needles adjusted to trace calibration lines. The indicator needle, swinging with movements of the subject, makes a tracing that gradually drifts across the paper with loss of weight of the subject. A line drawn through the tracing, crossing the calibration lines, permits close estimation of IWL in grams per hour. The IWL per unit of body surface has been calculated for normal and pathological conditions, and correlates well with the oxygen consumption (face mask) method. The subject is not restrained in any manner, except, of course, by the dimensions of the bed or pen on the platform of the scales.

CALORIC REQUIREMENTS OF MAN AND ANIMALS. Work is accomplished by the body at the expense of increased metabolism. It is of interest to compare the efficiency of muscular work with the thermal efficiency of internal combustion engines. The latter have a thermal efficiency of 20 (gasoline) to 40 (Diesel); i.e. of every 100 gallons of gasoline and Diesel fuel, 20 and 40 respectively are converted into mechanical energy. Brody found that the energy efficiency of muscular work, such as pulling a heavy load is about 25 per cent; it is essentially the same for a 1500-pound Percheron gelding, a 600-pound Shetland pony, or a 150-pound human. Thus, of 100 calories of total energy expended during hard work, a maximum of 25 calories may be received as work accomplished, while the remaining 75 calories is dissipated in various ways (basal metabolism, heat increment associated with digestion of food, energy of standing, walking without load above standing, overcoming internal resistance of body, useless incidental movements associated with pulling load, "recovery" process - removing lactic acid resulting from work, etc.).

Muscular exercise does not influence materially the amount of protein metabolism, provided an adequate amount of fat and (or) carbohydrate is available. In the well-nourished individual, violent exertion produces a high R.Q. without significant alteration in nitrogen excretion, showing that carbohydrate is the chief fuel under these circumstances.

Heat produced in doing muscular work can take the place of heat produced by regular metabolism. Thus, an individual performing muscular exercise in a cold environment will not require as much heat by regular metabolism to maintain his body temperature.

Benedict, using the calorimeter shown in Fig. 85, found that intense mental effort such as that required to solve mathematical problems by mental arithmetic was accompanied by a relatively small increase in oxygen consumption and heat production. He concluded that mental effort itself is without significant influence on energy metabolism.

Occupation and energy requirement. The relation of occupation to energy requirement has been studied extensively. "White collar" workers in sedentary occupations have a total daily metabolism of 2500-2800 calories. About 500-900 calories of this amount are consumed for mechanical work (walking to and from work, etc.). The average American farmer using horses as draft animals had a total daily metabolism of 3500-4000 calories, but this figure is probably too high for today's mechanized farms. With sustained heavy physical work such as that encountered with harvesting crops by hand, or cutting timber using the two-handled saw, energy requirements rise to the range of 6,000-8,000 calories per day.

Energy expenditures. Table 48 (p. 326 appendix) lists energy expenditures (per hour) under different conditions of muscular activity. This table shows that the lowest energy expenditure activity for a 70 kg. man is sleeping (65 calories per hour), and one of the highest is walking upstairs (1,100 calories per hour).

Recommended calorie allowances. Table 49 (p. 327 appendix) shows the calorie allowances recommended by the Food and Nutrition Board of the National Research Council. The allowances have been adjusted to compensate for differences in the average weight of men and women, and for degree of muscular activity, pregnancy and lactation. Children are divided on the basis of age and weight. Because of growth and activity, their caloric requirement per kilogram of body weight is much higher than that of adults.

In dietary experiments carried out at Purdue University, college men required about 50 calories per kilogram of body weight, and college women about 35 calories per kilogram of body weight to maintain caloric equilibrium. It is probable that the human adult male and female differ in their efficiency of utilization of the calories in their diets.

Water in nutrition. Water may be considered as one of the most important nutrients required by animals. A discussion of water requirements in various species was given in Chapter 2.

Carbohydrates in nutrition. Plant carbohydrates make up about 70 per cent of the total weight of nutrients in the diet of man and omniverous animals. The percentage is even higher in the diets of herbivorous animals. Carbohydrates are the least expensive source of calories in the diets of these groups. In spite of their importance as a source of energy, carbohydrates cannot be classed as an essential nutrient, for animals (and man) can live on diets essentially free of carbohydrates with no apparent ill effects. In such diets, calories are supplied by proteins and fats.

Lipids in Nutrition

The crude fat content of the animal carcass varies with the species and with the individual. Lean animals may contain as low as 25% total lipids, and very fat animals as high as 75% total lipids, on a dry weight basis. Most of the fat in the animal carcass is derived from the carbohydrates of the diet, for lipids constitute only about 5% of the total dry weight of the diet. Edible fats are prized for their value in cooking and for their flavor-imparting qualities as a spread, in salads, etc., and are reserved almost entirely for the human diet, which contains (in the United States) about 15-20% of this nutrient.

ESSENTIAL FATTY ACIDS. The first demonstration that fatty acids could not be dropped completely from the diet of rats was that of Burr. He found that a small amount of *linoleic acid* is required (about 0.2%). In the animal, part of the linoleic acid is converted to *arachidonic acid* (p. 36). Arachidonic acid is found only in animal tissues, and is not found in plants. If arachidonic acid is fed to rats on a fatty acid-free diet, part of it is converted to linoleic acid; thus, either of these unsaturated fatty acids can satisfy the requirement for essential fatty acids. Absence of both of them from the diet of the rat causes loss of weight, dermatitis, and finally death. Beeson has demonstrated a similar requirement for these fatty acids in swine. A level of 0.2% linoleic acid cured symptoms of weight loss and dermatitis in this species.

OTHER ESSENTIAL LIPIDS. It should be pointed out that all animals must have choline (p. 46) and phosphate (p. 45) in the diet in order to synthesize phospholipids.

DISTRIBUTION OF BODY FAT; RELATION TO DIET FAT. Neutral or true fat is stored mainly in the adipose tissues (p. 280) of the body. Most of this tissue is just under the skin of animals and humans (subcutaneous adipose tissue). About 50% of the fat is stored here, 45% in the peritoneal cavity (kidney surface, uterine surface, mesentery, omentum), and about 5% in the muscles. The presence of stored fat in the muscle tissues of prime beef gives it a "marbled" appearance.

EFFECT OF DIET FAT ON THE COMPOSITION OF BODY FAT. Animals on a low-fat diet deposit body fat that is characteristic for the species (compare lard (pig) and sardine oil (fish), Table 7, p. 37). Excess carbohydrates, and to a lesser extent, excess proteins, yield Kreb's cycle intermediates (see Fig. 68, p. 159) which are converted to fatty acids characteristic for the species in question. On a high fat diet, however, the depot fat will be modified in the direction of the type of diet fats fed. For example, when swine are fed on diets high in whole ground soybeans or peanuts, the lard contains a higher proportion of linoleic, and lower amounts of palmitic and stearic acids, than is normal (see Table 7, p. 37). The melting point of the lard is lower than normal, and a "soft pork" carcass is obtained. The body fat of these hogs can be "hardened" by placing them on a grain diet for about one month. Turnover of the fatty acids in the fatty acid pool (see p. 181) is rapid enough to cause replacement of the excess unsaturated fatty acids with saturated fatty acids.

The consumption of fat in human diets varies markedly. In the United States, 30-40 per cent of the calories are consumed as fat by the average person. In the Orient this figure drops to 10 per cent or less. The greater tendency to obesity observed in the United States and other countries with food surpluses cannot be blamed on increased fat consumption, however. It should be blamed more on an excessive intake of not only fat calories, but of carbohydrate calories as well. Any human or animal that consumes in excess of immediate needs will produce a state of positive caloric balance. Unless this is accompanied by a compensating increase in total body structure (growth), obesity results.

If total caloric intake is maintained at a level to balance caloric needs, one could assume that a high fat intake is compatible with good nutrition. Recent work has shown, however, that with a high fat diet there is a greater tendency to develop serum hypercholesterolemia and eventually atherosclerosis (fatty plaques lining arterial blood vessels). Although the exact cause of this condition has not been determined, current research suggests that the unsaturated fatty acids, especially linoleic acid, help to clear cholesterol from the blood by forming esters, whereas saturated fatty acids delay the disposal mechanism for cholesterol.

The continuous ingestion of large amounts of fats containing a relatively high per cent of saturated fatty acids (meat-type fats, hydrogenated vegetable oils, dairy fats) has been suspected to be one of the reasons for the high incidence of atherosclerosis in the United States. The peoples of the Orient, who subsist mainly on a cereal type diet supplemented with fish, show a very low incidence of this disease. Not only is the fat content of such a diet low, but the fats contributed by cereals and by fish are oils high in unsaturated fatty acids.

Since the ingestion of unsaturated fatty acids helps to lower serum cholesterol levels, patients with abnormally high serum cholesterol levels are being advised to reduce total fat intake, and to use fats rich in unsaturated fatty acids. One novel method is to use as the table spread and in cooking and baking a margarine (now sold by drug stores) which contains 40 per cent linoleic acid.

Amino Acid and Proteins in Nutrition

Qualitative requirements for growth. Plants and some microorganisms are able to synthesize all of the amino acids from a simple nitrogen source (atmospheric nitrogen, ammonia, nitrate, nitrite, urea, etc.), sulfate (for sulfur), and carbohydrates. Other microorganisms, and animals, can synthesize some, but not all of the amino acids required. It is therefore necessary for them to obtain from the diet those amino acids (i.e., "indispensable" or "essential" amino acids) which they cannot synthesize at all (completely indispensable), or which they can synthesize, but not at an adequate rate for maximum growth.

Supplying sufficient amounts of the indispensable amino acids (and, in addition, preformed dispensable amino acids, or carbohydrate and ammonium salts to make them), is therefore an important problem in the adequate nutrition of a particular animal or microorganism. This problem is complicated by the fact that dietary proteins vary markedly in their relative content of the indispensable amino acids (see Table 46, p. 317, Appendix). In certain proteins, one or more indispensable amino acids may be almost completely absent (for example, zein of corn contains only 0.1% lysine and tryptophan).

Proteins vary in their degree of *digestibility;* this must be also taken into account in determining their value as suppliers of indispensable amino acids.

Little was known regarding the actual qualitative and quantitative amino acid requirements of any animal or microbial species prior to 1935. The isolation and identification of L-threonine in that year by W. C. Rose and coworkers made it possible for the first time to feed mixtures of purified amino acids devoid of the amino acid to be studied, and to determine whether or not the animal or microorganism could synthesize the absent amino acid from other nutrients supplied in the diet. The test diet ordinarily used for amino acid nutrition studies contains adequate amounts of digestible carbohydrates, fats, vitamins and minerals, plus a small amount of roughage (cellulose, agar, etc.). A mixture of purified amino acids replaces proteins in the diet. After it has been found that an amino acid is indispensable, it is often possible, as has been shown by the writer, to use inadequate levels of natural food proteins, and to build up the level of all indispensable amino acids, except the one under study, with purified amino acids. This type of diet (as well as the original diet of Dr. Rose) can be used to determine the *quantitative* requirements for each of the indispensable amino acids.

Using the test diets described above, the qualitative and quantitative requirements for growth, and in mature animals for maintenance, have been determined in several species. An animal has a *qualitative* requirement for a certain amino acid if the amino acid cannot be synthesized from materials ordinarily available in the diet at a rate which is sufficiently rapid to permit optimum growth in the young, or nitrogen equilibrium (see below), in the mature animal. On the basis of this definition, arginine is indispensable in the diet of the young, growing rat, but it is dispensable in the diet of the mature rat. On the same basis, glycine is indispensable in the diet of young, growing birds, but it is probably dispensable in the diet of the mature male, or non-laying female. The major symptom of an amino acid deficiency is *reduced growth rate*, as can be seen for various species in Figures 86, 87, and 88.

Figure 86.   Effect of tryptophan deficiency on chicks. Five-week old female Barred Plymouth Rock chicks. The chick at the left was fed a diet adequate in tryptophan. The chick at the right was fed a diet deficient in tryptophan. Both chicks were of average weight for their respective experimental pens, the difference being 210 grams. (From J. W. West, Ph. D. Thesis, Purdue University, 1951).

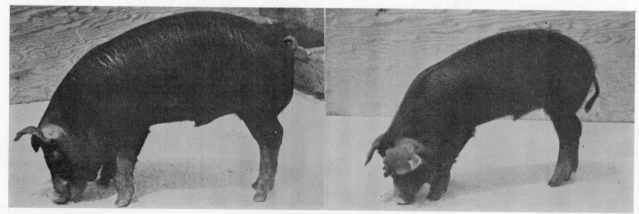

Figure 87.   Effect of lysine deficiency on pigs. Weanling Duroc Jersey pig on left received basal diet plus 2.0% DL-lysine-HCl, and gained 25.0 pounds in 28 days. His litter mate received the basal diet only, which contained 0.02% lysine, and lost 2.0 pounds in 28 days. (From E. T. Mertz, D. C. Shelton, and W. M. Beeson, J. Animal Sci., 8, 528 (1949)).

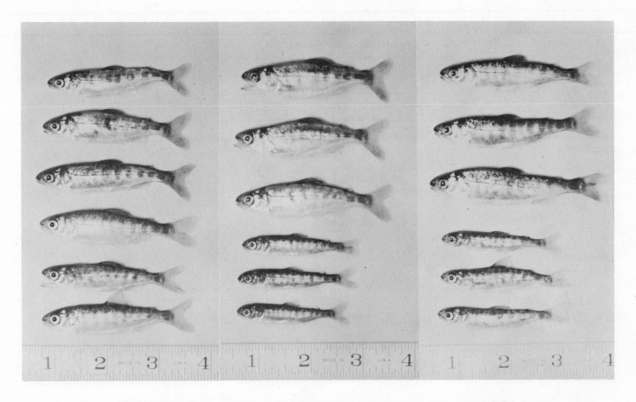

Figure 88. Amino acid deficient and control chinook salmon. Left plate: glutamic acid deficient (bottom three) and control fish (top three). Center plate: arginine deficient (bottom three) and control fish. Right plate: leucine deficient (bottom three) and control fish. (From J. E. Halver, D. C. DeLong, and E. T. Mertz, J. Nutrition, 63 100 (1957)).

The *quantitative* requirement for an indispensable amino acid may be defined as the minimum per cent of the amino acid in the total dietary protein, or in the total diet, which must be fed to an animal (that is receiving all other nutrients in adequate amounts) in order to obtain optimum growth (young animals) or nitrogen equilibrium (mature animals). For example, the writer and coworkers found that the weanling pig requires 0.4% of L-valine in the diet for optimum growth. The daily gain of weanling pigs receiving 0.3% L-valine was only two-thirds of that of pigs receiving 0.4% (or more).

Table 33, on page 222, is a compilation of data available on the qualitative (and where known, tentative quantitative) requirements of various species of animals. Data on a typical lactic-acid producing microorganism is also shown for comparison. The quantitative data are expressed as minimum per cent of the amino acid required in the diet for optimum growth. Insects present a special problem because of extracellular synthesis in the mycetomes (see p. 225).

If certain dispensable amino acids are absent from the diet of young animals, the minimum requirement for indispensable amino acids which serve as precursors is increased. Thus, when *cystine* is dropped from the diet, the minimum per cent of methionine required is approximately twice the value given for the rat, chick, salmon and pig; when *tyrosine* is dropped from the diet, the minimum per cent of *phenylalanine* required is approximately twice the value given for the rat, chick, salmon and pig.

Table 33. Amino acids indispensable for growth

Amino acid	L. Mesen-teroides	Drosophila Melanogaster Larva	Mouse	Rat (%)	Chick (%)	Salmon* (%)	Pig (%)	Dog	Child
Arginine	+	+	−	0.2	1.2	+	0.2	+	−
Glycine	+	+	−	−	1.0	−	−	−	−
Histidine	+	+	−	0.4	0.2	+	0.2	+	+
Isoleucine	+	+	+	0.5	0.6	1.0	0.5	+	+
Leucine	+	+	+	0.8	1.4	1.6	0.6	+	+
Lysine	+	+	+	0.9	0.9	2.0	0.6	+	+
Methionine	+	+	+	0.5	0.5	1.5	0.3	+	+
Phenylalanine	+	+	+	0.7	0.9	2.1	0.3	+	+
Threonine	+	+	+	0.5	0.6	0.9	0.4	+	+
Tryptophan	+	+	+	0.2	0.2	+	0.2	+	+
Valine	+	+	+	0.7	0.8	+	0.4	+	+
Alanine	+	+	−	−	−	−	−	−	−
Aspartic acid	+	+	−	−	−	−	−	−	−
Cystine	+	+	−	−	−	−	−	−	−
Glutamic acid	+	+	−	−	−	−	−	−	−
Proline	+	+	−	−	−	−	−	−	−
Serine	+	+	−	−	−	−	−	−	−
Tyrosine	+	+	−	−	−	−	−	−	−
Hydroxy proline	−	−	−	−	−	−	−	−	−

* Diets contained 40 per cent protein. Other animal diets contained 15-20 per cent protein.

The level of certain vitamins may also affect amino acid requirements. Thus, experiments with chicks and rats have shown that insufficient amounts of choline and niacin in the diet increase the minimum requirements for methionine and tryptophan, respectively. Insufficient amounts of pyridoxine or vitamin B_{12} also increase amino acid requirements, for these vitamins are required for the proper metabolism of amino acids (see p. 237 and p. 240).

TYROSINE ESSENTIAL IN RARE METABOLIC DISEASE. Children and adults suffering from the rare metabolic disease *phenylpyruvic oligophrenia* (phenylketonuria) are unable to convert phenylalanine to tyrosine (see p. 193). In these patients, tyrosine is an *indispensable* amino acid. Failure to metabolize phenylalanine by the normal oxidative pathway results in production of phenylpyruvic acid, phenylacetic acid, orthohydroxy phenyl acetic acid, etc., which are excreted in the urine. It is believed that these products poison the nervous system during the first postnatal year, and are responsible for the fact that most phenylketonurics are imbeciles or idiots. Feeding a low phenylalanine diet during the first postnatal year reduces the load of abnormal metabolites and permits normal mentation to proceed. Early diagnosis is essential, for starting the diet at one year of age is too late.

AMINO ACID IMBALANCE. During the past decade, nutritionists have shown that the *excess* of one or more amino acids in the diet reduces growth rate, and if the level of protein in the diet is 10 per cent or less, also produces fatty livers. In some cases this is believed to be due to *competitive inhibition* (p. 102) by the amino acid which is in excess. For example, zein, the major protein of corn, contains 7.3% isoleucine and 22.3% leucine, or a ratio of 0.3/1. The excess leucine (which is structurally similar to isoleucine) acts as a competitive inhibitor of isoleucine when zein (supplemented with lysine and tryptophan) is fed as the only source of protein in the diet. Rats show very poor gains on this diet, but show rapid gains if *extra isoleucine* is added to the diet to overcome the inhibitory effects of the natural excess of leucine. In poultry and swine feeding, corn is always fed with a protein supplement such as soybean oilmeal or skim milk, in order to both increase and *balance* total protein.

RUMINANT AMINO ACID REQUIREMENTS. Ruminant animals have been omitted from Table 33 because they present a special problem to the amino acid nutritionist. Studies by Maynard have shown that the bacteria in the rumen can readily synthesize all of the amino acids, if the ruminant animal is provided with urea, diammonium citrate, or a similar source of ammonia nitrogen, with sulfate, and with an easily fermentable carbohydrate like glucose. It is thus impossible to determine the amino acid requirements of ruminants using the test diets described above. However, workers using radioactive isotopes have shown that the mammary gland of the cow cannot synthesize the amino acids which are indispensable in other mature animals studied (see Table 34), but can synthesize the dispensable amino acids. This indicates a similar pattern of metabolism in the amino acid pool of the ruminant and the non-ruminant animal.

QUALITATIVE AND QUANTITATIVE REQUIREMENTS FOR MAINTENANCE. Growth puts much larger demands on animals than a state of maintenance, or nitrogen equilibrium or balance. When an animal is growing, it is increasing in total cell numbers, and this means that amino acids must be retained in the form of tissue proteins in the new cells. Under conditions of growth, the dietary requirement for an indispensable amino acid is roughly 10 times that required for maintaining a condition of nitrogen equilibrium.

It is obvious from the above discussion, that quantitative requirements for indispensable amino acids should be less in animals which are in nitrogen equilibrium. This condition exists in the *mature* animal. Here, in a 24 hour period, the total amount of nitrogen excreted in the urine, feces, and dermal outgrowths and perspiration, is exactly equal to the total amount of nitrogen ingested in the form of food and drink. *Healthy mature* animals are in a state of nitrogen equilibrium, or nitrogen balance as defined above. In contrast, healthy *growing* animals are in a state of *positive nitrogen balance* (or positive nitrogen retention), because more nitrogen is ingested per 24 hour period than is excreted in the same period. If a growing or mature animal receives a diet which does not contain one of the indispensable amino acids, there will be an uncompensated break-down of tissue proteins in the amino acid pool, the 24 hour outgo of total nitrogen will be more than the 24 hour dietary intake, and the animal will be in negative nitrogen balance (have a negative retention of nitrogen).

Maintenance requirements of animals for the amino acids can be determined by feeding the purified amino acid test diets described above, omitting one amino acid, and determining nitrogen intake and outgo for fixed periods (usually 24 hours). If omission of the amino acid in question results in negative nitrogen balance, then the amino acid is indispensable for maintenance in the animal species studied. This method is effective for both growing and mature animals. With it, one could determine requirements for both maintenance and growth in the young animal. Unfortunately, the nitrogen balance method is quite time-consuming (one must determine total nitrogen of the excretory products - feces and urine - daily). Because of this, the growth rate method is usually employed in studies on growing animals, and the nitrogen balance method is used on mature animals.

As one would expect, less data are available on the quantitative amino acid requirements of mature animals. These are summarized in Table 34 on the following page.

Table 34. Amino acids indispensible for maintenance
in mature animals

Amino acid	Rat and Dog[a]	Humans [b]
Arginine	0.0	0.0
Histidine	0.0[c]	0.0[c]
Isoleucine	4.2	0.70
Leucine	5.6	1.10
Lysine	5.0	0.90
Methionine	5.0[d]	1.10[d]
Phenylalanine	4.2	1.10[e]
Threonine	3.0	0.50
Tryptophan	1.1	0.25
Valine	4.7	0.80

a Expressed as per cent of total dietary protein. Daily protein requirement not over
0.5 gm. per kg. body weight.
b Expressed as grams required per 24 hours.
c Gradual drop in hemoglobin occurs on diet devoid of histidine. Therefore required,
but requirement very low.
d Cystine can replace 80-90% of the methionine required in humans. Replacement
value not determined for rats and dogs.
e 70-75% can be replaced by tyrosine.

TOTAL PROTEIN REQUIREMENTS OF ANIMALS. The minimum protein requirement
(using a high quality protein with good amino acid balance, such as egg protein) is estimated to be approximately 0.5 gm. per kilo. of body weight in an adult human. In a growing child, the minimum requirement for optimum growth may be more than 3 gm. per
kilo. of body weight. The level of 0.5 gm. per kilo. probably represents the minimum
level for maintenance of nitrogen equilibrium in animals and man, both young and adult.
Poor quality proteins (for example, most vegetable proteins) would have to be fed at twice
this level to maintain nitrogen balance (without growth). Pregnancy and lactation, fever,
etc., would increase the minimum protein required for nitrogen balance.

The protein requirements of animals are usually expressed as a per cent of the diet.
The National Research Council has published recommended levels of protein for animals
of different species and weights (see Table 49, p. 327, Appendix). This table shows that
as an animal matures, the per cent protein in the diet may be reduced without impairing
growth rate. Thus, a weanling pig weighing 50 pounds requires a diet containing 16 per
cent protein, to make maximum weight gains. When this pig reaches a weight of 200
pounds, a level of 12 per cent protein is sufficient.

Studies conducted recently at the Western Fish Nutrition Laboratory, Cook, Washington, show that the minimum protein requirement of young salmon is 40 per cent of the
diet at a water temperature of 47° F., and 55 per cent at a water temperature of 58° F.
The protein requirement of fish is therefore much higher than that of warm-blooded animals and varies directly with environmental temperature. This may apply also to other
coldblooded animals.

Protein fed to animals (or humans) in excess of body needs is converted to carbohydrate (or carbohydrate or fat intermediates) and burned for energy, or converted to fat
and stored. Since protein is one of the most expensive nutrients in animal feeds, efforts
are made to keep the protein level just at or above that required for optimum growth (or
reproduction). In the case of humans, protein is consumed in excess by about one-third
of the world population, and in inadequate amounts by two-thirds of the population. A

level of protein in excess of 0.5 gram per kilo. of body weight (by a factor of 2 to 3) is desirable for adults because it corrects for any amino acid imbalances existing in the mixed diet consumed by humans. Children consuming adequate levels of good quality protein (3 gm. or more per kilogram body weight) grow to larger size and are more resistant to infectious diseases. Adequate protein consumption probably accounts for the greater weight and stature of children in the United States as compared to their counterparts in under-developed areas such as India, China, Central, and South America.

Vitamins in Nutrition

VITAMINS DEFINED FOR ANIMALS. Vitamins were first recognized in nature because they are essential nutrients for animals. In this class of living organisms they may be defined as carbon compounds of diverse structure which are not used for energy, or fixed into the tissue framework, but which are required in minute amounts *in the diet* for the maintenance of animal health.

VITAMIN REQUIREMENTS OF INSECTS. Our knowledge of the vitamin requirements of insects is quite limited. One difficulty is that many insects contain within their bodies special groups of cells (mycetomes) stuffed with symbiotic microorganisms capable of synthesizing the water-soluble (and fat-soluble?) vitamins (as well as many amino acids) required by the host. Deprived of its mycetomes, the insect would probably show a vitamin requirement pattern similar to that of higher animals. One insect, *tenebrio molitor* (the mealy worm), requires the compound *carnitine* as a vitamin. Carnitine is apparently not required in the diet of higher animals, perhaps because of an adequate supply of "labile" methyl groups in the choline and methionine of the diet.

$$(CH_3)_3N\ CH_2CH_2\underset{\underset{OH}{|}}{\overset{\overset{COOH}{|}}{CH}}$$
$$\underset{OH}{}$$

Carnitine (α-OH-γ-butyro betaine).

Discovery of vitamins. The first clear statement of a recognition of the need of vitamins in the diet was made by Hopkins of England in 1906: "No animal can live on a mixture of pure protein, fat and carbohydrate, and even when the necessary inorganic materials are carefully supplied, the animal still cannot flourish. The animal body is adjusted to live either on plant tissues or other animals, and these contain countless substances other than protein, carbohydrates and fats." He named these additional needed substances "accessory food factors". In 1911, Funk, a Polish chemist working in London, named an accessory food factor extracted from rice polishings, and which cured the disease, beriberi, "vitamine", because it contained an amine group and was vital for life. Since many of the vitamins do not contain nitrogen (see pp. 226-241), the "e" was later dropped from Funk's word, and the term "vitamin" is generally used instead of "accessory food factor" to denote these nutrients.

The crystalline vitamins whose structures are shown on pp. 226-241 were gradually recognized as dietary essentials, separated, purified, and identified over a period of about forty years. Most of them are components of the first crude vitamin fractions separated by the pioneer workers in this field. Thus, "fat-soluble A" of McCollum and Davis, and of Osborne and Mendel (1913) was mainly vitamin A, but may have had traces of other fat-soluble vitamins in it; "water-soluble B" of McCollum and Davis (1913) carried almost all of the now recognized water-soluble vitamins except ascorbic acid; "water-soluble C" or the "antiscorbutic factor" of Holst and Frölich (1907) contained ascorbic acid, and "fat-soluble D" of McCollum (1922) contained vitamin D.

Formulas, Functions, Deficiency Symptoms, and Requirements for Vitamins

BETA-CAROTENE AND VITAMIN A. In addition to beta-carotene, whose formula is shown below, alpha- and gamma- carotene, and cryptoxanthin also serve as provitamins A in animals. These compounds belong to a special class of compounds found in plants called carotenoids (see p. 311). The carotenoids are hydrocarbons containing several (alternate) double bonds in the aliphatic carbon chain, and two-thirds saturation of the end ring structures (see beta-carotene formula). Vitamin A is formed from beta-carotene by symmetrical cleavage of the carotene molecule and conversion of the end carbon to a primary alcohol group. Less than two molecules of vitamin A are obtained from one molecule of beta-carotene, for part of one side of the carotene structure is lost in the conversion. Two forms of vitamin A are recognized, vitamin A_1 found in mammals, and vitamin A_2, found in fresh water fish. Because of the carbon-carbon double bonds, both forms exist

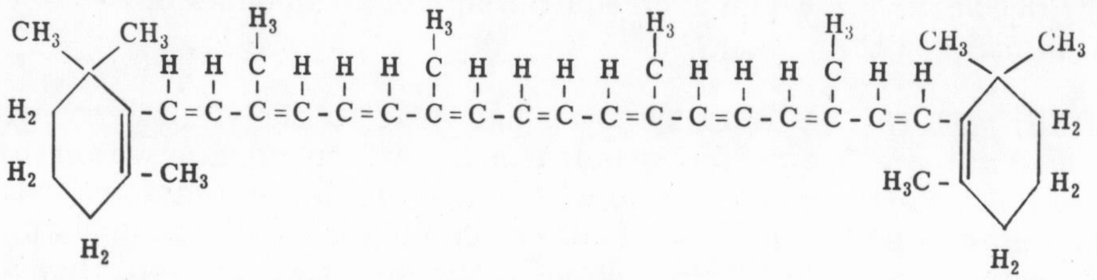

Beta-carotene

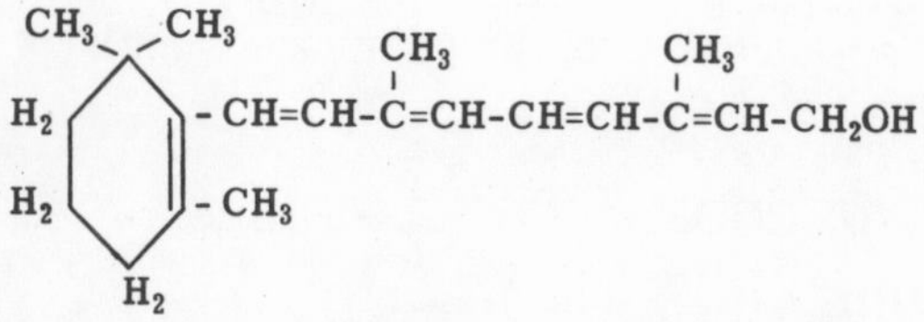

Vitamin A_1 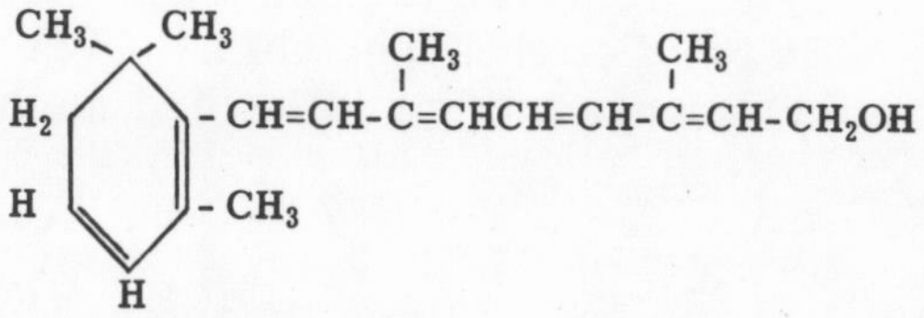   Vitamin A_2

as cis and trans isomers. Conversion of one optical isomer to the other takes place in the visual cycle (see below).

VITAMIN A. This fat-soluble vitamin in higher animals is essential for the health of mucous membranes and other epithelial tissues, and is a precursor of a retinal rod pigment needed for night vision. When inadequate amounts of the vitamin are present in the tissues, the epithelial cells (especially of the mucous membranes) lose their ability to secrete normally, and the cells become dry and hardened. This hardening process is called cornification or keratinization. One of the first tissues to be affected is the eye. Keratinization of the tear ducts and mucous linings leads to infection, corneal ulcers and eventual blindness. The disease is called Xerophthalmia (see Fig. 89), and is observed most often in the young child or animal, deprived of an adequate intake of vitamin A or its precursor, carotene.

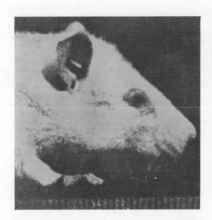

Figure 89.   Xerophthalmia in two stages of severity in the rat. (Right) Eye surrounded by depilated and
hemorrhagic area. (Left) Eye closed completely due to incrustation. (From p. 1112, Hawk,
Oser and Summerson, Practical Physiological Chemistry, McGraw-Hill Book Co., 13th Ed. 1954).
(Reproduced by permission of publishers).

One form of vitamin A (vitamin A_1, p. 226) is converted into a yellow pigment, neo-retinene, in the rods of the retina in the eye. The reaction is catalyzed by NAD (p. 112) and an alcohol dehydrogenase (p. 318). The neo-retinene combines with a specific

$$C_{19}H_{27}CH_2OH \quad + \quad DPN \quad \xrightarrow{\text{alcohol dehydrogenase}} \quad DPN \cdot H_2 \quad + \quad C_{19}H_{27}CHO$$

vitamin A_1 neo-retinene

protein, *scotopsin*, to form a rose-colored pigment, *rhodopsin* (visual purple). When light falls on the retinal rods, rhodopsin splits to scotopsin and *trans*-retinene; this chemical change produces a stimulus which is imparted to the optic nerve and results in vision. The trans-retinene must be isomerized (via vitamin A_1) to neo-retinene before it can be used again to make rhodopsin. This process is not 100% efficient, so vitamin A_1 must be continually supplied to the eyes by the blood stream. Since an adequate level of visual purple (rhodopsin) is the major factor in seeing in dim light, vitamin A_1 deficiency produces night blindness (slow adjustment to dim light).

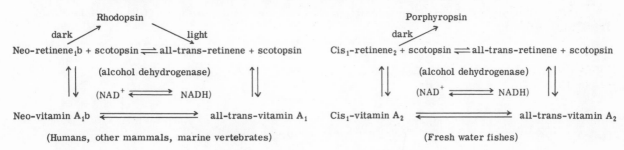

Visual purple cycle in vertebrates*

* The formulas for vitamin A_1 and A_2 are shown on p. 226. The retinenes are vitamin A aldehydes (primary alcohol group replaced by aldehyde group).

Sources of vitamin A. The cis and trans forms of vitamin A$_1$ (see p. 226) are found in the oils and fats from fishes and animals, especially in the oils from glandular tissues such as the liver. Vitamin A$_2$, which is less active than vitamin A$_1$ for humans, is present in the oils and fats from fresh-water fishes. About 35% of the vitamin A potency of the liver oils from halibut, cod, dogfish, and jewfish has been calculated to be cis- vitamin A$_1$ (neo-vitamin A$_1$). Vitamin A$_1$ is now being synthesized in competition with the natural product. All vitamin A in animal products (milk, eggs, meat) came originally from plant carotenes. Plants usually supply adequate amounts of vitamin A in the form of the pro-vitamin, carotene, to meet the requirements of mature animals and humans; babies and very young farm animals often need a supplement of vitamin A which can be supplied by fish liver oil concentrates, or synthetic vitamin A.

Requirements. The international unit (I. U.) is defined as the vitamin A potency of 0.6 micrograms of pure beta-carotene, or 0.25-0.30 micrograms of pure vitamin A$_1$. It can be seen from this that on a weight for weight basis, beta-carotene has only about one-half the potency of vitamin A$_1$.

Table 50 (p. 329, Appendix) shows the recommended allowances for vitamin A in various species. The average adult human needs about 5,000 units daily, with the needs of small children somewhat lower. Pregnancy and lactation increase the needs to about 8,000 units daily. It is interesting to note that the lactating sow needs 27,000 units of vitamin A daily.

ERGOSTEROL, 7-DEHYDROCHOLESTEROL, AND VITAMIN D. Ergosterol, or provitamin D$_2$, is a sterol (see p. 51) found in yeasts and fungi, but not in higher plants. Irradiation with ultrviolet light converts it into vitamin D$_2$ (calciferol), a vitamin for animals.

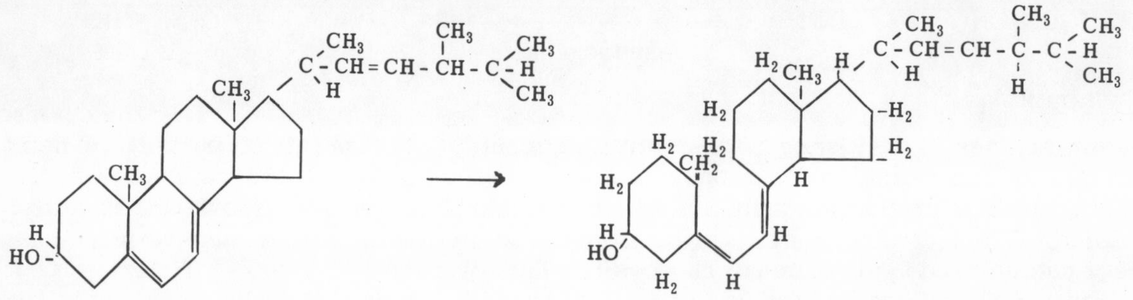

Ergosterol → Vitamin D$_2$ (Calciferol)

In animals, 7-dehydrocholesterol, a lipid in the skin, is converted by ultraviolet light into vitamin D$_3$.

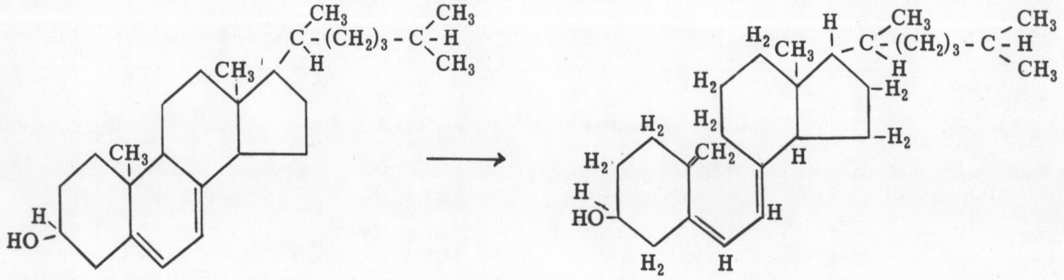

7-Dehydrocholesterol → Vitamin D$_3$

The formulas for vitamin D_2 and D_3 show that these vitamins differ only in the side group attached to carbon 17 of the ring structure (see p. 49 for numbering of rings). Two other modifications having vitamin D activity are vitamin D_4:

$$(- \overset{\text{CH}_3}{\underset{\text{H}}{\text{C}}} - \text{CH}_2 - \text{CH}_2 - \overset{\text{CH}_3}{\underset{\text{H}}{\text{C}}} - \overset{\text{CH}_3}{\underset{\text{CH}_3}{\text{C}}} - \text{H}), \text{ and vitamin } D_5 \ (- \overset{\text{CH}_3}{\underset{\text{H}}{\text{C}}} - \text{CH}_2 - \text{CH}_2 - \overset{\text{CH}_2\text{CH}_3}{\underset{\text{H}}{\text{C}}} - \overset{\text{CH}_3}{\underset{\text{CH}_3}{\text{C}}} - \text{H}).$$

VITAMIN D. The mode of action of this vitamin is still a mystery, inasmuch as it is not associated with any enzyme system. However, it plays an important role in the development of bone and tooth structure in the young growing animal. The specific deficiency disease produced is *rickets* (see p. 244). In this disease there is a deficiency in bone calcification, and an increase in the excretion of minerals, so that a large proportion of the dietary bone-building materials fails to be retained by the body. Because of this, the calcium and phosphorus levels in the blood drop, and the calcium phosphate content of the bones decreases. The lowered mineral content of the bones and teeth leads to bow-legs, knock-knees, beaded ribs and poor teeth.

Sources of vitamin D. Unlike many vitamins, vitamin D is not widely distributed. It is produced in nature by the irradiation of certain sterols. Thus, irradiation of ergosterol from yeast (see p. 228) yields vitamin D_2 (calciferol); irradiation of 7-dehydrocholesterol (see p. 228) yields vitamin D_3. Sterols with antirachitic potency do not exist in the growing plant, but can be formed through irradiation after the plant has wilted, matured, or otherwise lost its powers of photosynthesis. The lipid material in grains, nuts, and also body oils are good sources of vitamin D_3, and serve as a major source, along with commercially irradiated ergosterol (D_2), 7-dehydrocholesterol (D_3), and irradiated foods such as "vitamin D" milk (D_3).

Requirements. Vitamin D_2, obtained by irradiation of ergosterol, can be utilized by four-footed animals and humans, but is relatively inactive in poultry. Vitamin D_3, obtained by irradiation of 7-dehydrocholesterol, can be utilized by all animals, for it is the D vitamin produced by direct irradiation of the skin. The unit of vitamin D activity must be defined with this species difference in mind. One I.U. of vitamin D equals one USP unit of D, or the response in four-footed animals to 0.025 micrograms of pure calciferol (vitamin D_2). In chickens, one I.U. unit equals one AOAC* unit of vitamin D_3.

Adults of any species not subjected to the added needs of pregnancy, lactation or egg production, do not need vitamin D if they are exposed to adequate sunlight. Children need 400 I.U./per day of D_2 (or D_3), and chicks need 90 units of D_3 per pound of feed (see p. 329, Appendix).

VITAMIN E. Four different forms of this vitamin have been isolated from plants. All are phenolic compounds belonging to the class of chroman derivatives called *tocopherols*. They are designated as alpha, beta, gamma, and delta tocopherol. Alpha tocopherol is the most potent form of this vitamin. They are excellent antioxidants (see p. 41).

Alpha tocopherol

---
* Association of Official Agricultural Chemists.

Vitamin E was first recognized as the "antisterility" vitamin, although it was later shown that vitamin A deficiency could also cause sterility. Lack of vitamin E in the diet of the male rat causes irreversible degeneration of the germinal tissue (sperm-forming tissue) of the gonads with attendant sterility. Female rats on vitamin E- free diets can become pregnant, but the foetuses die about the twelfth day of gestation, and are resorbed. The sterility is temporary in the female, for the same rats can later carry on normal reproduction, if supplied with adequate amounts of vitamin E.

Vitamin E deficiency also produces muscular dystrophy (atrophy of muscle fibers) in rats, dogs, rabbits and guinea pigs. If the condition is not allowed to progress too far, the dystrophy can be cured by administering vitamin E. Muscular dystrophy also occurs in humans, but it is not due to a lack of this vitamin, and unfortunately, no cure has been found for it. Vitamin E is an excellent antioxidant (see p. 41), and its function in the body may be associated with this property. The muscles of vitamin E-deficient animals exhibit excessive respiration, or oxygen uptake, which can be reduced by administration of vitamin E.

Sources of vitamin E. Vitamin E is widely distributed in both plant and animal tissues. One of the richest sources is wheat germ oil, but other vegetable oils such as cottonseed, corn and soybean oil have a high content. All four forms of vitamin E, namely, the alpha, beta, gamma, and delta tocopherol forms, are present in vegetable oils.

Requirements. It has been difficult to establish requirements for this vitamin. The amount required in test female rats to insure normal fertility and reproduction is about 3 mg. of dl-alpha-tocopherol acetate during each day of a standard five day feeding period. Under these same conditions, 1 mg. of the acetate per day will prevent resorption in about 50% of the female rats. d1-Alpha-tocopherol acetate is the most active form of vitamin E, and one milligram of the pure crystalline alpha acetate form has been selected as one International and U.S.P. unit of vitamin E potency.

VITAMIN K. Two forms of this vitamin have been isolated, one (vitamin K_1) from alfalfa leaves, the other (vitamin K_2) from putrefied fish meal. It is possible that still another form may be present in corn. The active part of the vitamin K molecule is the 1,4-naphthoquinone nucleus. For this reason, the product first available commercially was the compound 2-methyl, 1,4-naphthoquinone (called "Menadione"); it has activity on a mol. for mol. basis equal to that of the naturally occurring forms of the vitamin, except as an antidote for dicoumarol or Warfarin poisoning (see p. 290).

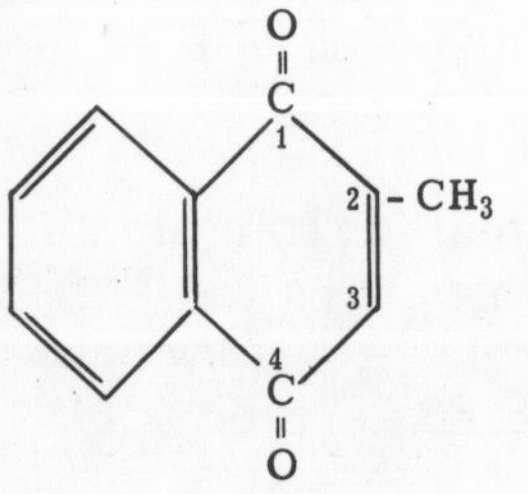

2-Methyl, 1,4-naphthoquinone

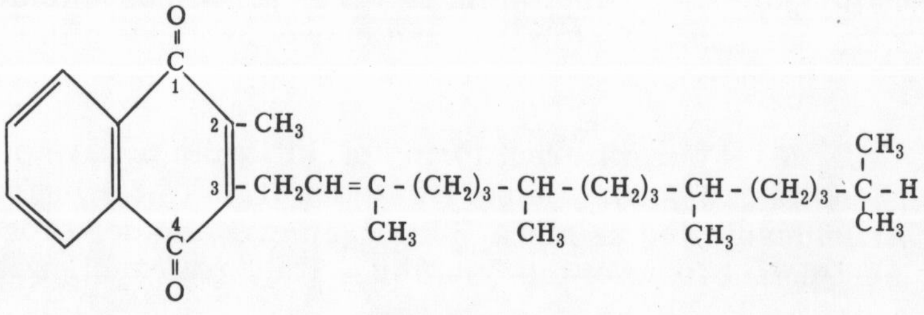

Vitamin K_1

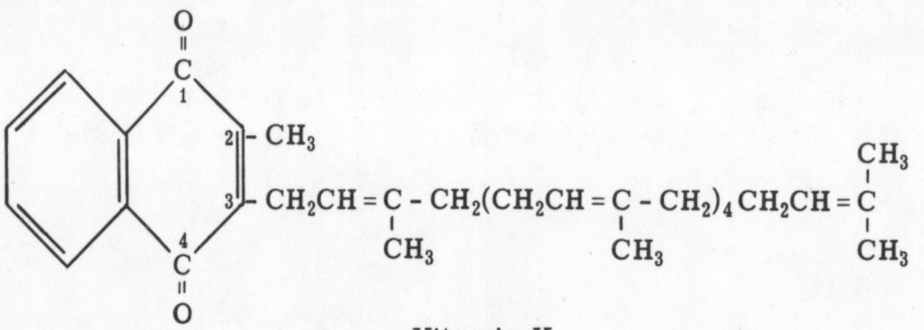

Vitamin K_2

Function. This vitamin has been called the "antihermorrhagic" vitamin, because of the important role it plays in blood coagulation (see p. 258). Vitamin K must be present in the liver of animals and man at normal levels, or the liver cannot synthesize prothrombin. When the prothrombin level of the blood drops below a certain critical value, the animal will bleed to death from minor wounds, or from spontaneous internal or external hemorrhages.

Source of vitamin K. This vitamin is synthesized by green plants, and by certain microorganisms. The vitamin in plants is vitamin K_1 (p. 230), and that synthesized by microorganisms is designated as vitamin K_2 (p. 230). Certain bacteria (for example, the tubercle bacillus) synthesize compounds with vitamin K activity. The compound produced by the latter organism is a yellow pigment called phthiocol (2-methyl 3-hydroxy-1, 4-naphthoquinone). In addition, the simple compound, 2-methyl-1, 4-naphthoquinone, possesses vitamin K activity, and is sold commercially under the trade name, Menadione. This compound is soluble in both water and fat solvents.

Requirements. The requirement for vitamin K in humans has not been determined. In humans and most animal species, sufficient quantities of this vitamin are supplied by the leafy plants in the diet, and by bacterial synthesis in the intestines. Only in the hen has a definite need been established on commercial poultry rations; here the requirement has been placed at 0.8 mg. per pound of feed. This will prevent the development of a K deficiency in the chicks hatched from the eggs she produces, for young chicks are unable to produce enough K in their intestines by bacterial synthesis (the vitamin was discovered by Dam while studying cholesterol metabolism in the chick).

In diseases in which bile is excluded from the intestines (obstructive jaundice due to gallstones, and severe diarrheal diseases) the vitamin K in the intestines is not absorbed (compare p. 152). Vitamin K (usually as Menadione) is administered intravenously and corrects the deficiency, allowing safe surgical intervention without hemorrhage in the case of bile duct obstruction from gallstones.

Another important medical use of vitamin K is in the prevention of hemorrhagic disease of the newborn. The prothrombin level is low in the newborn baby, and head injuries suffered at birth may lead to fatal hemorrhages, or, in case of recovery, to idiocy. It is now standard practice to give the mother a large dose of Menadione just prior to delivery, and to administer Menadione to the newborn shortly after birth; this increases the prothrombin level (see p. 258) in the infant markedly, and has drastically reduced the mortality of infants due to hemorrhage.

Vitamin K_1 and closely related derivatives (the oxide) serve as useful antidotes in case of Warfarin poisoning (see p. 290) or in case of overdosage with dicoumarol in the case of thrombosis therapy (see p. 260). Menadione is not very effective for this purpose.

ASCORBIC ACID (VITAMIN C). This vitamin may be considered as a derivative of L-gulose (p. 13); the reduced form, or L-ascorbic acid, may be considered as a 3-keto-L-gulo-furanolactone. On mild oxidation, L-ascorbic acid loses two hydrogen atoms to form the diketone lactone, *dehydroascorbic acid*. Both forms are biologically active, and the function of this vitamin in cells may be related to its oxidation-reduction properties. Ascorbic acid is a white crystalline solid.

$$
\begin{array}{ccc}
 & \text{O} & \\
 & \parallel & \\
 & \text{C}\!\!-\!\!\!-\!\!\!-\!\!\!-\!\!\!-\!\!\! & \\
 & | & \\
 & \text{C}-\text{OH} & \\
 & \parallel & \quad\text{O} \\
 & \text{C}-\text{OH} & \\
 & | & \\
 & \text{HC}\!\!-\!\!\!-\!\!\!-\!\!\! & \\
 & | & \\
 & \text{HOCH} & \\
 & | & \\
 & \text{CH}_2\text{OH} &
\end{array}
\qquad
\begin{array}{ccc}
 & \text{O} & \\
 & \parallel & \\
 & \text{C}\!\!-\!\!\!-\!\!\!-\!\!\!-\!\!\!-\!\!\! & \\
 & | & \\
 & \text{C}=\text{O} & \\
 & | & \quad\text{O} \\
 & \text{C}=\text{O} & \\
 & | & \\
 & \text{HC}\!\!-\!\!\!-\!\!\!-\!\!\! & \\
 & | & \\
 & \text{HOCH} & \\
 & | & \\
 & \text{CH}_2\text{OH} &
\end{array}
$$

ℓ-Ascorbic acid   Dehydroascorbic acid

<u>Function</u>. This vitamin, which is required only by humans, monkeys and guinea pigs (other species are apparently able to synthesize it), appears to be essential for the proper formation of intercellular cementing substances. In the absence of the vitamin, lack of cementing substance between cells can be seen microscopically in connective tissue, bones, teeth and gums. Similar changes apparently occur in the blood vessels, which consist of fibers (mainly elastin - p. 281) in a cementing matrix. Lack of the vitamin causes a disease called *scurvy*, which is the oldest vitamin deficiency disease recorded in history (authentic accounts of scurvy were recorded in the fifteenth century). Sailors on long voyages in early sailing vessels were particularly susceptible to scurvy because they lacked fresh animal and vegetable foods. Harris tells of a Spanish galleon found adrift at sea, its entire crew dead of scurvy; these ships were undoubtedly the "ghost ships" talked about in those days.

The most prominent symptoms of scurvy in humans are pallor (due often to anemia), weight loss, weakness, heart palpitations, swelling and redness of the gums, loosening of the teeth, hemorrhage into the skin and mucous membranes, bone and joint pains and fragility of bones, edema, and hyperirritability. In mild cases of scurvy, the hemorrhagic tendencies can be demonstrated by applying suction to the skin, whereupon many petechiae (minute hemorrhagic spots) are produced. The presence of a vitamin C deficiency can also be demonstrated by determining the blood level of ascorbic acid, or the absence of excretion in the urine. Correction of the deficiency can be made by adding sufficient amounts to the diet to saturate the tissues and cause excretion of some of the vitamin in the urine.

<u>Source of Ascorbic acid</u>. Ascorbic acid is widely distributed in the vegetable kingdom, especially in acidic fruits, sprouting seeds, leafy vegetables, and certain tubers. It is also present in some animal tissues, especially the adrenal glands. It is also synthesized, and the synthetic product is sold widely for use in vitamin preparations, and as a preservative (inhibits browning reaction) for frozen fruits such as peaches, strawberries, etc.

<u>Requirement</u>. The National Research Council recommends that humans ingest 75-150 mg. daily, depending on physiological demands (pregnancy, lactation, etc.), and that children ingest amounts in proportion to their age (see p. 329, Appendix). The guinea pig needs about 2 milligrams per day, and monkeys require amounts in proportion to their body weight.

<u>BIOTIN</u>. Biotin has an unusual structure, consisting of a fused imidazole and thiophene ring with a fatty acid side chain. Biotin and thiamin (see p. 239) are the only vitamins isolated to date which contain sulfur. There is evidence that more than one form of biotin exists in nature. The formula for biotin isolated from animal liver (presumably deposited there from plant foods) is shown on the following page. Biotin is a white crystalline solid.

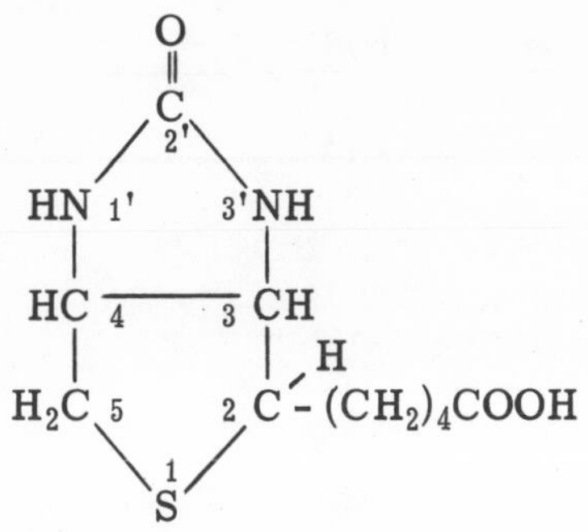

$$
\begin{array}{c}
O \\
\parallel \\
C_{2'} \\
\diagup \quad \diagdown \\
HN_{1'} \qquad _{3'}NH \\
| \qquad\qquad | \\
HC_{\underline{\;4\;}} \;\;\;_{3} CH \\
| \qquad\qquad | \;\; H \\
H_2C_{\;5} \qquad _2 C \!-\! (CH_2)_4COOH \\
\diagdown \quad \diagup \\
_1 \\
S
\end{array}
$$

Biotin

(2'-keto-3, 4-imidazolido-2-tetrahydrothiophene-n-valeric acid)

Function. The various names applied to this vitamin in the course of its isolation suggest some of its functions - "Coenzyme R" because it is a growth factor for the nitrogen-fixing bacterium *Rhizobium*, "anti-egg white injury factor" because it protects animals against the toxic effects of high concentrations of raw egg white in the diet. Raw egg white contains a protein, avidin, which combines specifically with biotin. Excessive amounts of avidin in the diet thus produce a biotin deficiency. In the rat, this disease is characterized by swelling and inflammation of the skin (a dermatitis), and by loss of hair.

Biotin is synthesized by intestinal bacteria, and it is difficult to produce a biotin deficiency in most animals by feeding a biotin-deficient diet. Here again, because of the relatively short intestinal tract and the speed with which food passes through the tract, the chick is an exception (also see vitamin K); a biotin deficiency can be produced in this species without the use of raw egg white.

Biotin appears to function as a catalyst for the addition of carbon dioxide to acetyl CoA in the formation of malonyl CoA in fatty acid synthesis (see p. 184). In bacteria and yeasts, biotin is also required for the deamination of aspartic acid, serine, and threonine.

$$
CO_2 \quad + \quad CH_3COSCoA \quad \xrightarrow[Mu^{++}]{Biotin} \quad
\begin{array}{l}
COOH \\
| \\
CH_2 \\
| \\
C = O \\
| \\
S - CoA
\end{array}
$$

Carbon dioxide   Acetyl CoA   Malonyl CoA

Source of biotin.   Biotin is found in many animal and plant tissues. The best sources are egg yolk, liver, yeast, kidney, pancreas, and milk. Fruits and vegetables contain fair amounts, most of which is in the free form; in animal tissues and in yeast, biotin is bound tightly to protein, and can be liberated only by hydrolysis with acids, enzymatic digestion, or autolysis. Biotin is synthesized commercially, and this is the main source of the vitamin for drug and research purposes.

Requirements. These have been set only for chicks and hens; the former need 45 micrograms, and the latter 70 micrograms, per pound of feed. Humans consume on the average, 25 to 50 micrograms of biotin daily, yet the feces and urine may contain two to five times this amount, indicating synthesis of the vitamin in the intestines by microorganisms.

CHOLINE. Choline may be considered as a derivative of ammonium hydroxide. It is the nitrogenous base in lecithins and sphingomyelins (see p. 45). It is a colorless, viscous alkaline liquid which readily absorbs water and carbon dioxide. It is usually stored and fed as the monohydrochloride, a white, crystalline, hygroscopic salt.

$$HO - \overset{\overset{H}{|}}{\underset{\underset{H}{|}}{C}} - \overset{\overset{H}{|}}{\underset{\underset{H}{|}}{C}} - N \overset{(CH_3)_3}{\underset{OH}{}}$$

Choline

(Trimethyl-hydroxyethyl-ammonium hydroxide)

Function. Choline has several important functions in the animal body. One of these is as a lipotropic factor in the metabolism of lipids in the liver (see p. 181). The liver plays a vital role in fat transport and fat metabolism; dietary triglycerides pass into the liver via the portal vein and are converted to phospholipids. Liver phospholipids can be burned in the liver or transported by the blood to the adipose tissues where they are deposited as triglycerides. A deficiency of choline in the diet reduces the phospholipid content of the liver, causing the piling up of fat in the organ and impairing its function in fat transport.

Another important function of choline is as a supplier of methyl groups for transmethylation reactions. Its methyl groups are available to the body for use in the synthesis of such important compounds as creatine, creatinine (p. 284), adrenaline (p. 269), methionine (p. 195), sarcosine (N-methyl glycine) and trigonelline (betaine of nicotinic acid).

Choline is also important in the transmission of nerve impulses in the form of its ester, acetyl choline. Recent work has also shown that if rats are reared on a choline-deficient diet and at maturity placed on a complete diet, many develop essential hypertension and suffer kidney damage. The reason for this is not known but it is of interest as a clue to the possible etiology of human hypertension.

Source. Choline is widely distributed in animal tissues, usually in proportion to their content of phospholipids (especially lecithin and sphingomyelin, of which it is a component - see p. 45). In plants it is found in proportion to the content of lecithin. Choline is synthesized commercially, and the synthetic product is used extensively in nutrition research, and in commercial poultry feeds.

Requirements. Because of its widespread occurrence in lipid materials, choline deficiency is a problem only in chick production. Here it is recommended that the feed contain at least 0.7 mg. of choline per pound of feed.

FOLIC ACID.* Several forms of this vitamin have been identified, containing one, three and seven molecules of glutamic acid, respectively. All consist of glutamic acid, para-aminobenzoic acid (see p. 237), and a nitrogenous, fused double ring heterocycle called *pterin*. A closely related formyl derivative of the monoglutamate called *folinic acid* is

Pteroylglutamic acid   Folinic acid

* Folacin.

equal, or perhaps superior, in activity to the other forms. The formulas for the monoglutamate (pteroylglutamic acid) and for folinic acid are shown on the previous page. The monoglutamate is synthesized commercially and is a yellow, crystalline solid.

Function. Folic acid supplies the carbon for conversion of glycine to serine (p. 201). Relatively large doses of the pyrimidine, thymine (p. 109), have almost the same therapeutic value as folic acid in human folic acid deficiency diseases. The major deficiency symptoms caused by a lack of folic acid are anemia, leucopenia (reduction in white blood cell count), mouth lesions, and diarrhea. Daily doses of 10 mg. of pteroylmonoglutamate, or of the triglutamate (see p. 234) will cure the disease known as tropical sprue; the vitamin is also helpful in the treatment of Addisonian pernicious anemia (see vitamin B_{12}), and in ordinary macrocytic anemias of nutritional origin.

Source. Green plant tissues are excellent sources of this vitamin. Yeast, liver and kidney tissues are also good sources. The vitamin is sensitive to sunlight, and to high temperatures such as those encountered in the cooking of foods.

Requirements. The folic acid requirement of humans has not been determined. Animals need no more than 0.06 mg. per kg. of body weight per day for good growth.

INOSITOL. Inositol is a derivative of cyclohexane, and can exist in several stereoisomeric forms. The biologically active form is optically inactive, indicating internal compensation of the asymmetric carbon centers. Inositol is a white crystalline solid. In plants it is present mainly in the form of phytin, the calcium-magnesium salt of inositol hexaphosphate (phytic acid).

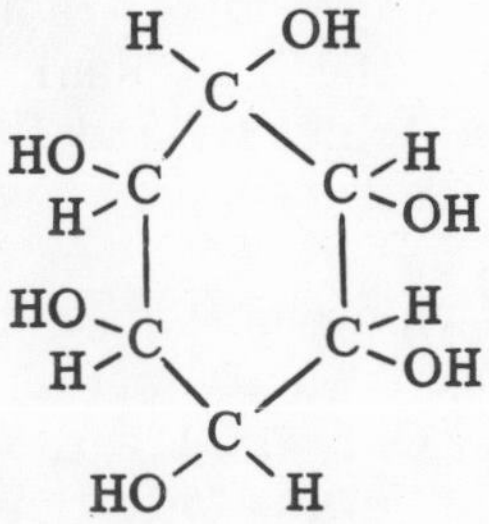

Inositol 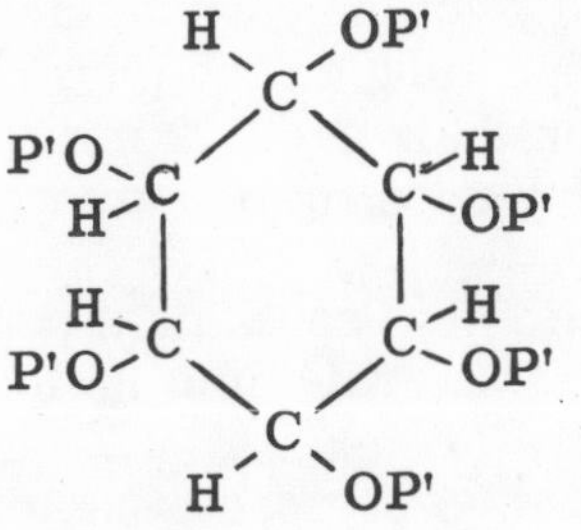   Phytic acid

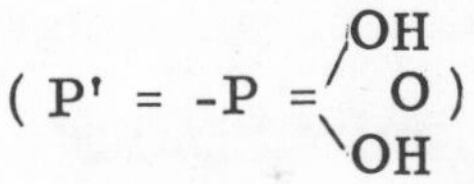

Function. The function of this vitamin is not known. It is required by certain microorganisms (for example, yeast) and by mice and rats. Lack of inositol retards growth in these animals, and causes loss of hair and dermatitis. The need for this vitamin in other species has not been demonstrated.

Source. Inositol is widely distributed in nature. It is present in plant and animal tissues, and in bacteria, molds and yeasts.

Requirements. No quantitative requirements have been determined.

NICOTINIC ACID (NIACIN). This vitamin is a simple carboxyl derivative of pyridine. It is a white crystalline solid. The amide and the sodium salt are as active biologically as the free acid.

$$
\begin{array}{c}
H \\
| \\
C \\
HC \overset{\displaystyle\parallel}{} \quad C - COOH \\
HC \qquad CH \\
\diagdown \; N \; \diagup
\end{array}
$$

Nicotinic acid (Niacin)
(Pyridine-3-carboxylic acid)

$$
\begin{array}{c}
H \\
| \\
C \\
HC \overset{\displaystyle\parallel}{} \quad C - CONH_2 \\
HC \qquad CH \\
\diagdown \; N \; \diagup
\end{array}
$$

Nicotinamide (Niacinamide)

Function. Nicotinic acid is an essential component of two important coenzymes, nicotinamide adenine dinucleotide , and nicotinamide adenine dinucleotide phosphate (see p. 112). These coenzymes, in conjunction with the appropriate apoenzymes, are important in hydrogen transfer metabolism. Lack of nicotinic acid produces black tongue in dogs, and is one of the major vitamin deficiencies in human pellagra. In these diseases, major symptoms are stomatitis (inflammation of the stomach), glossitis (inflammation of the tongue), diarrhea, and hard, crusty skin lesions (patches on the exposed skin).

Source. Nicotinic acid is widely distributed in nature. Animal tissues, and yeast, are the best sources, but leafy plants and vegetables also supply important amounts to the diet. With the exception of corn, cereal grains are fair sources. Nicotinic acid is synthesized commercially, and used in ton quantities for the enrichment of white flour and cornmeal, and in vitamin supplements.

Requirements. The recommended allowances for niacin (see p. 329, Appendix) are 12-16 mg. daily for adult humans, depending on the physiological state of the individual, 6-19 mg. for children depending on their age, 12 mg. per lb. of feed (chicks), and 19-41 mg. daily for young pigs, depending upon their body weight.

PANTOTHENIC ACID. Pantothenic acid contains a peptide linkage which unites a beta-alanine molecule and a dihydroxy isocaproic acid molecule. Pantothenic acid contains one asymmetric carbon atom, and therefore exists in D- and L- forms. Only the D- (dextro-rotatory) form is biologically active. Pure pantothenic acid is a pale yellow, oily liquid. It is usually stored and fed in the form of the white crystalline salt, calcium pantothenate.

$$
\begin{array}{c}
\qquad\quad H \\
\qquad\quad | \\
CH_3 \quad O \\
\quad | \qquad | \\
HOCH_2 - C - C - CONH \\
\quad | \qquad | \\
CH_3 \quad H \qquad\quad | \\
\qquad\qquad\qquad CH_2 - CH_2 - COOH
\end{array}
$$

Pantothenic acid
(α, γ dihydroxy isocaproyl beta alanine)

Function. This vitamin is an important component of Coenzyme A (p. 100), which plays a key role in fatty acid metabolism (p. 182), the citric acid cycle (p. 159), sterol formation (p. 185), and acetyl choline formation (p. 234). A requirement for this vitamin has been shown with chicks, rats, dogs, foxes, and pigs. One of the deficiency symptoms is dermatitis; in pigs, where it is a limiting vitamin in most feeds, a deficiency of pantothenic acid produces "goose-stepping", due to soreness of the hocks.

Source. Excellent sources are egg yolk, liver, and yeast, with green leafy plants and vegetables and whole cereals, muscle meats and dairy products as good sources. About

80% of the pantothenic acid in foods is bound, and must be released by digestion. The vitamin is synthesized, and the calcium salt of the D-form (see p. 236) is manufactured for use in vitamin supplements.

Requirements. The recommended allowances (see p. 329, Appendix) are 4 mg. per lb. of feed in chicks, 2 mg. in hens, and 16-56 mg., depending on weight, in pigs. The requirement for humans has not been determined, but would probably be approximately 10 mg. per day.

PARA-AMINOBENZOIC ACID. This simple benzene derivative is a part of the folic acid molecule (see above). Its biological activity as a pure compound has suggested its function as a separate vitamin. Para-aminobenzoic acid is a white crystalline solid, and is very stable when compared with other vitamins.

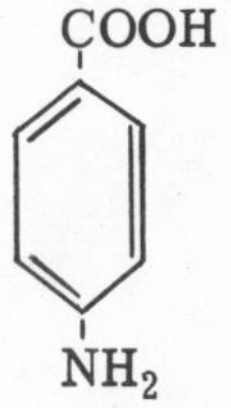

Para-aminobenzoic acid

Function. The function of this compound in animal nutrition is not clear at present. It may serve only as a precursor of folic acid, but may have additional functions also. Thus, it is regarded by some as an anti-graying factor in rats.

Source. Para-amino benzoic acid occurs in many plant and animal tissues, both in the free and combined forms. Good sources are liver, yeast, and the germ of seeds.

Requirements. None has been established.

PYRIDOXINE (VITAMIN B_6). Pyridoxine is a derivative of pyridine and thus is related structurally to nicotinic acid. At least two other compounds in nature have biological activity similar to that of pyridoxine, the 4-aminomethyl, and the 4-aldehyde derivatives, called pyridoxamine and pyridoxal, respectively. All are white crystalline solids, and are optically active.

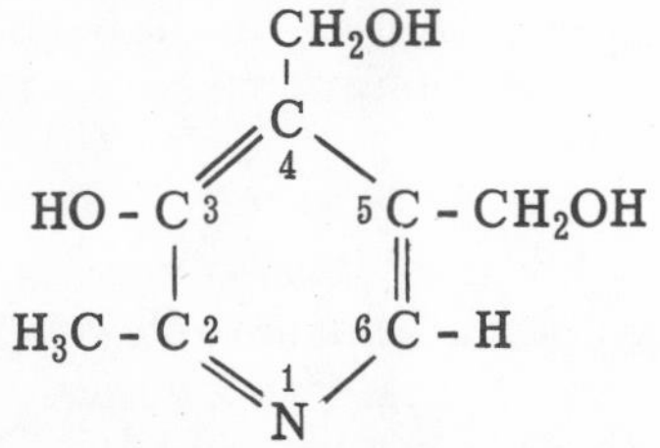

Pyridoxine
(2-Methyl-3-hydroxy-4, 5
(dihydroxymethyl pyridine)

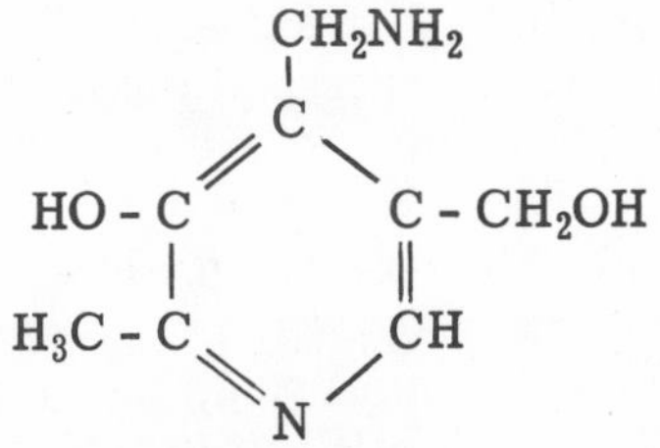

Pyridoxamine

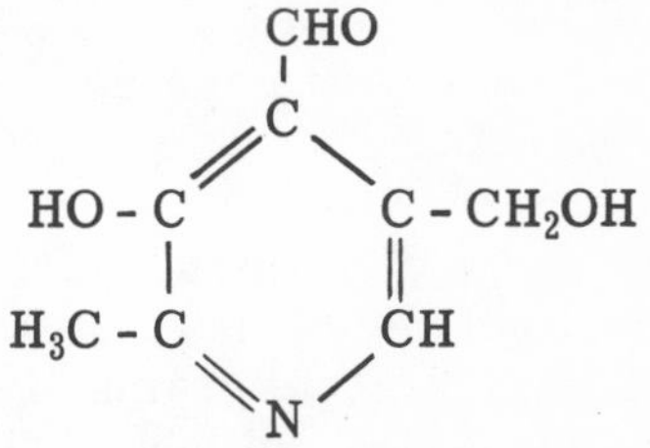

Pyridoxal

Function. This vitamin, either as the aldehyde or as the amine, serves as the coenzyme for decarboxylases (see p. 318), transminases (see p. 197) and possibly for enzymes involved in amino acid syntheses (pyridoxal phosphate serves as a coenzyme in tryptophan synthesis in *Neurospora crassa*). Deficiency of pyridoxine causes a dermatitis in rats. Other species that have been shown to need it are the dog, pig, chick and pigeon. In certain cases of pellagra in which all symptoms were not alleviated by the administration of nicotinic acid, thiamine and riboflavin, pyridoxine relieved the abdominal pain, weakness, nervousness and irritability of the patient.

Source. This vitamin is present in whole cereal grains, meats, milk and leafy vegetables. Dried brewer's yeast is an especially rich source.

Requirements. Chicks and hens need about 1.6 mg. per pound of feed; pigs need about 1.9-3.0 mg. daily, depending on body weight. No data are available on requirements in other species.

RIBOFLAVIN (VITAMIN B_2). This vitamin belongs to a class of water-soluble pigments called lyochromes. It is an orange-yellow crystalline solid, containing the chromogenic isoalloxazine (flavin) nucleus, and the pentose sugar, D-ribose.

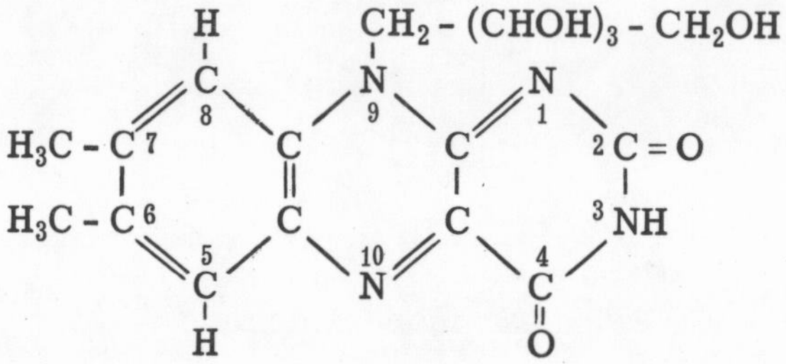

$$\text{Riboflavin structure: } CH_2-(CHOH)_3-CH_2OH$$

Riboflavin
(6, 7-Dimethyl-9-(D-ribityl)-isoalloxazine)

Function. Riboflavin is the coenzyme (see p. 98) in a series of "yellow enzymes" such as D- and L-amino acid oxidases, xanthine oxidase, cytochrome c reductase, etc., which catalyze the removal of hydrogen atoms from certain metabolites, and pass the hydrogen to an acceptor, such as cytochrome c or molecular oxygen (see p. 162). Since these reactions are vital, riboflavin is needed by all living cells.

In humans, a deficiency of riboflavin causes "ariboflavinosis", of which the characteristics are cheilosis (cracks and sores on the lips and at the corners of the mouth), glossitis (inflammation of the tongue), and eye disorders (inflammation, sensitivity to light). Riboflavin deficiency is also one of the contributing causes of pellagra.

In poultry, riboflavin deficiency causes "curled toe paralysis" in the chick, a condition in which extensive nerve degeneration takes place. Egg production drops in hens, and the eggs have a low hatchability. In rats and pigs, riboflavin deficiency produces a characteristic dermatitis, and often produces eye cataracts.

Source. Riboflavin is fairly widely distributed in plant, animal and microbial tissues. Some of the richest natural sources are eggs, milk, yeast, liver, meat, and fresh vegetables. Cereal grains are deficient in riboflavin, but legume seeds contain appreciable amounts. About 90% of the riboflavin in milk is in the free state, but that present in other animal and plant tissues is in conjugation with protein.

Most of the pure vitamin used commercially in vitamin concentrates is produced by a fermentation process using special riboflavin-producing microorganisms such as *Eremothecium ashbyii*. The pure vitamin is also prepared commercially by synthesis. The residues from the fermentation processes are used as supplements for poultry and livestock rations. Pure riboflavin is used in ton quantities for the enrichment of white flour and corn meal.

Requirements. The recommended daily allowances (see p. 329, Appendix) for different species are 1.4-2.5 mg. for adult humans, based on physiological state, 0.4-2.5 mg. for children based on age, 1.3 mg. for chicks, 1.0 mg. for hens, per pound of feed, and 3.2-8.3 mg. for pigs, depending upon their weight. Cattle synthesize adequate amounts of riboflavin in the rumen.

THIAMINE (VITAMIN B₁). Thiamin may be considered as a pyrimidine hydrochloride (see p. 109) condensed with a sulfur-containing heterocycle, thiazole. It is a white crystalline solid containing, per molecule, one molecule of water of crystallization.

Thiamine
(2-methyl-5-(4-methyl-5- -hydroxyethyl-thiazolium chloride)
methyl-6-amino-pyrimidine hydrochloride)

Function. This vitamin functions in the animal body as a coenzyme, *cocarboxylase* (thiamin pyrophosphoric acid ester - p. 100). The coenzyme is a part of carboxylase, and pyruvic acid oxidase, and as such functions in the breakdown of pyruvic acid in normal carbohydrate metabolism. When the body is deprived of adequate amounts of thiamine, pyruvic acid accumulates in the blood, lymph, and body tissues until toxic concentrations are reached. In humans, thiamine deficiency produces a disease called *beri-beri*. Two types are recognized, *dry* beri-beri, in which the muscles atrophy and there is paralysis of the extremities, and *wet* beri-beri, in which there is marked swelling of the extremities, accumulation of fluid in the body cavities, liver congestion, and dilatation of the heart. The wet type is more common in infants, but both types are observed in patients of all ages, and sometimes both types appear in the same individual. The nerve degeneration observed in many of these cases is apparently due to a concurrent vitamin A and riboflavin deficiency, based on studies with animals.

Beri-beri has been recognized as a human ailment since about 2500 B.C., when the Chinese described the condition. In spite of our knowledge as to its cause, the disease is still prevalent in China, India, Japan, and other Oriental countries (in 1947 there were 132 deaths per 100,000 population from this cause in the Phillipines, a rate second only to tuberculosis in that country). Thiamine deficiency in a less acute form has been observed clinically in this country.

Thiamine deficiency in poultry and in four-footed animals produces a disease called *polyneuritis*. In the advanced stages of the deficiency, the animals have paralytic seizures, which is typified in birds by a posture in which the head is pulled down upon the bird's neck, and in rats (Fig. 90) by spastic paralysis.

Source. Thiamine is widely distributed in plant, animal and microbial tissues. The richest plant sources are seeds. In cereal grains, the thiamine is concentrated in the embryo (germ). When such cereals are milled, most of the thiamine is lost in the by-products. This was first discovered in the pioneer experiments of Eijkman, who showed that rice polishings would cure the beri-beri produced by ingesting a diet high in polished rice. The practice of using polished rice, instead of whole rice, as the major food by many Oriental people, is responsible in part, at least, for the high incidence of beri-beri.

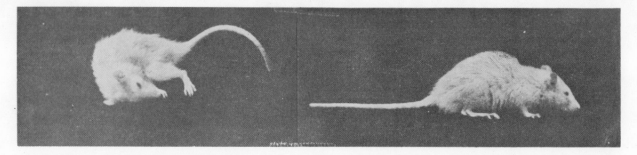

Figure 90.   Effect of thiamine deficiency in the white rat.   The spastic paralysis caused by ingestion of a
thiamine-deficient diet (left) was cured in 24 hours (right) by the administration of thiamine.
(From Smith and Munsell. U. S. Dept. Agr. Circ. No. 84 (1929)).

In the microbial kingdom, yeast is the richest source of this vitamin, and among
products of animal origin, eggs, lean pork, liver, and kidneys are good sources. Most
of the thiamine used in vitamin concentrates is synthesized commercially. The synthetic
product is used in ton quantities for the enrichment of white flour and corn meal.

Requirements.   The recommended allowances for thiamine (see p. 329, Appendix) are
1-2 mg. daily for human adults, 0.3-1.9 mg. daily for children, depending on age, 0.8
mg. per pound of feed for chicks, and 1.6-4.2 mg. daily, depending on weight, for pigs.

VITAMIN B_{12} (COBALAMINE).   Many microorganisms *(penicillium molds, streptomyces*
bacteria, etc.) synthesize a large number of vitamins, including the anti-pernicious anemia and growth-stimulating vitamin, B_{12}.   An interesting application of the need of certain
microorganisms for vitamins is the use of lactic acid bacteria for the microbiological determination of the vitamins riboflavin, choline, nicotinic acid, and B_6 in feeds and foods.
Also, an excellent method for the determination of B_{12} in feeds and foods is to test the
response of *L. Leichmanii* to various levels of this vitamin.   This microorganism requires B_{12} in the medium.

Function.   This vitamin functions in animals as a growth factor (it was originally called
A. P. F. - "animal protein factor"), and in humans as a growth factor and as the antiperni-
cious anemia factor.   It is probably a coenzyme in amino acid metabolism (see p. 222).
Injection of as little as 1 microgram daily of crystalline cyanocobalamine will restore the
low red cell blood count of a patient with pernicious anemia to normal levels, and alleviate the symptoms of the disease.   The vitamin is not as effective by mouth because
these patients lack "intrinsic factor" which occurs in the gastric juice, and protects and
aids the absorption of the vitamin.   The vitamin is also helpful in cases of sprue (p. 235)
and macrocytic anemias.   In children, growth stimulation has been obtained by the addition of vitamin B_{12} to ordinary diets.

The availability of inexpensive concentrates of vitamin B_{12} has been a big factor in
reducing the costs of poultry and livestock production, for it is now possible to balance
home grown grains and forage with cheap plant protein concentrates (soybean, cottonseed,
linseed, peanut, etc. meals) and obtain weight gains and feed efficiencies equal to those
obtained previously only with the more expensive animal protein concentrates such as
skim milk solids, meat and bone scraps, and tankage.

Structure.   Vitamin B_{12} has the most complex structure of all of the recognized vitamins.
The vitamin isolated from liver contains a cobalt atom centered in a porphyrin (p. 171)
type nucleus to both of which are attached ribose phosphate and benzimidazole.

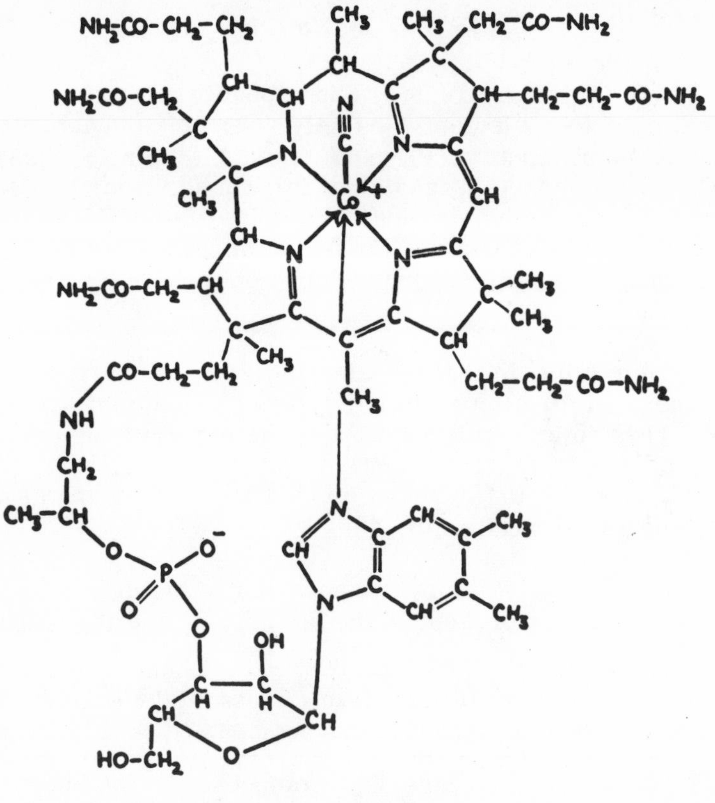

Vitamin B_{12} (cyanocobalamin)

The cyanide group can be replaced with Cl, SO_4, OH, SCN, NO_2, and other groups to produce analogs of the liver Vitamin B_{12}. Vitamin B_{12} itself has been named *cyanocobalamin*, Vitamin B_{12a} and Vitamin B_{12b} which are now known to be identical and to contain OH instead of CN are called *hydroxocobalamin*, and Vitamin B_{12c} prepared by nitrous acid treatment and containing a nitrite group is called *nitritocobalamin*. All of the analogs have about the same biological activity as cyanocobalamin, and can be converted to the latter by treatment with sodium cyanide at pH 5.

Source. The vitamin B_{12} used in animal feeds is obtained mainly as a by-product in the production of antibiotics, and is in the fermentation residue. Another source for animals is vitamin B_{12} from activated, dried sewage sludge. The vitamin B_{12} available in pure crystalline form for use in human medicine and diet supplements is prepared by purification of fermentation residues.

Requirements. No quantitative requirements have been established, but it is estimated that 1 microgram per day may be adequate in adult humans, and perhaps 5-10 micrograms per day are adequate, depending on age, in growing children.

Minerals in Nutrition

ESSENTIAL MINERALS. Animals, plants, and probably microorganisms, share in common a requirement for thirteen elements, namely, oxygen(O), carbon(C), hydrogen(H), nitrogen(N), calcium(Ca), phosphorus(P), potassium(K), sulfur(S), magnesium(Mg), iron(Fe), copper(Cu), manganese(Mn) and zinc(Zn). In addition, higher animals (compare plants, p. 136) also need five more elements, namely, sodium(Na), chlorine(Cl), iodine(I), cobalt(Co) and fluorine(F). The approximate levels of these 18 elements in the animal body, and the compounds in the animal body which contain the major share of these elements, are listed in Table 35.

It can be seen from Table 35 that the elements oxygen, carbon, hydrogen, nitrogen, and sulfur can be accounted for almost entirely as components of *water, proteins, lipids,* and *carbohydrates*. These four nutrient classes together make up over 95% of the total weight of the animal carcass. Small amounts of these five elements (O, C, H, N, and S) also occur in the body as minerals (carbonates, sulfates, etc.) and as vitamins (p. 226), hormones (p. 269), and as extractives (p. 284).

Most (90% or more) of the calcium and phosphorus in vertebrate animals is found in the skeleton. The remainder is present in the body fluids and the soft tissues. The other

Table 35. Approximate levels of essential elements
in the animal body

Element	Level (% of carcass weight)	Compounds of the body carrying most of the element
Oxygen	65.0	Water, proteins, lipids, carbohydrates
Carbon	18.0	Proteins, lipids, carbohydrates
Hydrogen	10.0	Water, proteins, lipids, carbohydrates
Nitrogen	3.0	Proteins
Calcium	1.5	$Ca_3(PO_4)_2$ (bones)
Phosphorus	1.0	$Ca_3(PO_4)_2$ (bones)
Potassium	0.35	Free as K^+
Sulfur	0.25	Cystine and methionine in proteins
Sodium	0.15	Free as Na^+
Chlorine	0.15	Free as Cl^-
Magnesium	0.05	$Mg_3(PO_4)_2$ (bones); free Mg^{++} (tissues)
Iron	0.004	Hemoglobin
Manganese	0.0003	Unknown
Copper	0.0002	Unknown
Iodine	0.00004	Thyroglobulin; thyroxine
Cobalt	Trace	Unknown
Zinc	Trace	Unknown
Fluorine	Trace	CaF_2 (teeth, bones)

(eleven) elements required by animals each make up only a fraction of one per cent of the animal carcass. The amounts of the elements iron, manganese, copper, iodine, cobalt zinc and fluorine present in the body, and required in the diet, are so small that these elements are often referred to as "trace minerals".

Function of Minerals; Requirements* and Deficiency Symptoms. The elements not entering the body as minerals, i.e., oxygen, hydrogen, carbon, nitrogen and sulfur, are components of nutrients whose chemical composition has been discussed in Chapters 2 to 5 inclusive. The "true" minerals serve various functions in the body. Some of these functions are discussed below.

CALCIUM. About 99 per cent of this element is deposited in the bones and the teeth of vertebrates; the other one per cent is in the blood, lymph, and soft tissues. About one-half of the calcium in blood serum is not ionized, indicating special functions.

Although calcium makes up only a small per cent of the body fluids, it is essential for the clotting of blood and lymph, for maintenance of the pH of the body fluids, and for the regulation of the irritability of the nerves and muscles.

Requirement. Any statements with regard to the requirement for calcium must include a recognition of the dependence of this requirement on (1) the phosphorus level of the diet (2) the magnesium level of the diet, (3) hormone levels in the body fluids (especially parathyroid hormone) and (4) the vitamin D level in the diet.

If the *phosphorus* level of the diet is too high, inefficient utilization of calcium may result, due to formation of poorly absorbed tricalcium phosphate. Most workers agree that the ideal ratio is in the range of 2:1 to 1:1 parts of calcium to phosphorus. *Magnesium* may to a limited extent be exchangeable with calcium; when a low magnesium diet is fed, *calcium increases* in the body fluids (compensating for lack of Mg?) and may even be deposited in the soft tissues. The *parathyroid hormone* (p. 274) mobilizes calcium from areas of reserve storage in the bones (for example, the trabeculae) and helps to maintain normal calcium levels in the blood and other body fluids. *Vitamin D* promotes absorption of calcium from the food; because of this action, the calcium:phosphorus ratio can exceed the limits given above, provided adequate amounts of this vitamin are in the diet. Vitamin D also promotes deposition of calcium in growing bone.

The requirements for calcium are increased during pregnancy and lactation in mammals, and during egg production in birds. As one would expect, the requirements of growing animals and children are higher per unit of body weight than for adults. Thus, adult humans need about one gram of calcium per day, whereas adolescent children require one to one and one-half grams per day. Since calcium is one of the minerals which is most likely to be deficient in the human diet, humans should ingest 2-3 glasses of milk daily, or its equivalent in cottage cheese, etc. to supply this mineral nutrient.

Non-lactating cows need 15-20 gm. of calcium per day (p. 330, Appendix) whereas lactating cows need 30 grams per day. Because of the heavy demands for calcium in the lactating animal, the cow usually goes into negative calcium balance (similar to negative nitrogen balance - see p. 223) during the early phases of milk production, and actually draws on calcium reserves in the skeleton. These depleted reserves are then replenished during the non-lactating periods. In the chicken, the needs for calcium for egg shell production are so high that the laying hen requires twice the amount of calcium in the feed as the growing chick.

---

* The mineral requirements of insects have not been studied. Based on their chemical composition, it is assumed that their qualitative requirements are similar to those of higher animals.

<u>Deficiency symptoms</u>. Lack of calcium in the diet of young growing animals can produce a disease known as *rickets* (p. 229). Here the term is used in its broadest sense* to include bone failures due to a deficiency of calcium, phosphorus, or vitamin D.

Extreme calcium deficiency causes sterility, enlargement of the joints, crooked legs, bone breaking tendencies, and in some cases even paralysis of the hind quarters in animals. There is a reduction of calcium in the blood and other body fluids, and when the level reaches a critical low level, the animal develops tetany (muscular spasms due to hyperirritability of muscles and nerves).

PHOSPHORUS. About 80 per cent of the phosphorus in vertebrates is contained in the bones and teeth. Another 10 per cent is present mainly as organic phosphates (see p. 284) in the muscles. The remaining phosphorus is distributed widely in the blood, lymph, and other body fluids, and in glandular tissues such as the liver.

Phosphates serve as important buffers of the blood, lymph, and body fluids (see p. 264). In the muscles, high energy phosphate bonds (see p. 283) provide the drive for metabolic changes. Phosphate is an important component of nucleoproteins (p. 108), of lipoproteins (p. 66) and of phospholipids (p. 45).

<u>Requirement</u>. The requirement for phosphorus is affected by the calcium to phosphorus ratio. As indicated above, excessive consumption of one of these two elements increases the excretion (or non-absorption) of the other. The intake of phosphorus should be one, to one and one-half times, that of calcium for maximum utilization (see Table 51, p. 330). ever, the relative need for calcium is increased in lactating animals and laying hens, and in these animals the calcium intake should be about twice that of the phosphorus intake.

A shortage of *phosphorus* is probably the most prevalent mineral deficiency in cattle and sheep, whereas a shortage of calcium is probably the most prevalent mineral deficiency in humans. This may be explained by the fact that the principal feed of ruminants, forage, is low in phosphorus, especially when grown in phosphorus-deficient soils; in the human diet, calcium is a limiting nutrient because the two principal types of foods eaten, namely, meat, and cereal grains, are quite low in this element.

<u>Deficiency symptoms</u>. Inadequate levels of phosphorus in the diet produce in growing animals rickets and other bone deformities similar to those observed with calcium-deficient diets. In adult humans and mature animals, phosphorus deficiency causes osteomalacia (softening of the bones).

MAGNESIUM. This element is closely associated with calcium and phosphorus, both in its distribution in the animal body, and in its metabolism. The total amount of magnesium in the body is small (0.05% - Table 35) and three-fourths of this is in the skeleton in combination with calcium and phosphorus (p. 280). In normal animals, the blood serum contains about 2.5 mg. of magnesium per 100 ml. (compare calcium, Table 36, p. 256); the soft tissues of the body actually contain a higher level of magnesium than of calcium.

In addition to its role in tooth and bone formation, magnesium is a specific activator for the enzyme phosphatase (p. 318) and also for enzymes concerned with carbohydrate, lipid and protein metabolism (pp. 154, 180, and 187 resp.)

---

* Young animals are usually in positive calcium balance, but in deficiency states the total retention of bone minerals may be too low to satisfy the needs for bone and tooth development. The reduced mineral content of the bones with consequent weakening gives lameness, fractures, misshapen bones (bow legs, beady ribs, etc.). These gross abnormalities are the same whether the poor bone formation results from lack of calcium, phosphorus, or vitamin D. However, the <u>histology</u> (microscopic structure) differs for each deficiency. Some workers confine the word "rickets" to the bone pathology found in early growth produced experimentally on a low phosphorus, high calcium diet deficient in vitamin D. Associated with this is a low blood inorganic phosphorus level, and an elevated blood phosphatase level. Other workers use the term more broadly as indicated above.

Requirement. The estimated magnesium requirement for growing animals and children is about 12-15 mg. daily per kilogram of body weight. The requirement for mature animals and humans is probably one-third to one-half of this amount. An excessive intake of calcium increases the requirement for magnesium, due to the mutual replacing action of these two mineral elements. Conversely, an excessive intake of magnesium leads to an increased urinary output of calcium.

Deficiency symptoms. Severe magnesium deficiency produces dilation of the blood vessels, hyperirritability of the nerves and muscles, and tetany in all animals studied (rat, calf, cattle). The occurrence of magnesium deficiency in cattle is usually associated with the turning of animals which have been wintering on maintenance rations into fresh lush grass pasture. The cattle carry no magnesium reserves to meet the demands of increased digestion and metabolism, and the serum magnesium levels drop to a low level, with the development of hyperirritability and tetany. This type of magnesium deficiency (observed in the United States, New Zealand, and the Scandinavian countries) is called "grass tetany".

A chronic (not acute) experimental deficiency of magnesium in calves was observed to produce extensive calcification of the vascular system, especially the aorta of the heart, and of the jugular vein. This would be expected, since low levels of magnesium cause increased levels of calcium to appear in the body fluids.

Magnesium deficiency has not been observed in humans; the human diet apparently carries adequate amounts of this mineral element.

POTASSIUM, SODIUM, AND CHLORINE. These three mineral elements will be considered together because of their close association in animal tissues. All are found almost entirely in the body fluids and soft tissues. However, potassium predominates in the *cellular* elements of the fluids, and soft tissues (red blood cells, muscle cells, etc.) (K:Na = 30:1), whereas sodium predominates in the interstitial (between cell) fluids (Na:K = 30:1). Both potassium and sodium are associated with chloride ion (together with smaller amounts of bicarbonate and protein anions). The potassium and sodium salts help to maintain the osmotic pressure relationships between cells and interstitial fluids, act as buffers to help maintain the acid-base balance in the body, and play important roles in water and carbohydrate metabolism. Studies with radioactive sodium indicate that each molecule of sodium chloride crosses the blood vessel walls about 100 times every 24 hours.

Chloride ion makes up about two-thirds of the anions of the blood, and passes with ease between the body cells and the interstitial fluids. The "chloride shift" (p. 264) is an important mechanism for releasing carbon dioxide from the cells for excretion by the lungs. Free hydrochloric acid is secreted by the border cells of the gastric mucosa, and performs important functions in gastric juice (p. 144).

Requirements for potassium. These have been determined for certain farm animals. Poultry and hogs need 0.157 and 0.15 per cent in the diet, respectively. Cattle need at least 30 grams daily. Most plants contain liberal amounts of potassium, and a deficiency of this mineral element has not been observed naturally in humans or animals.

Deficiency symptoms: potassium. Experimental potassium deficiency has been produced in rats, calves, pigs and dogs. In addition to growth retardation, these animals develop severe heart and kidney damage.

Requirements for sodium and chlorine. Sodium and chlorine (and also potassium) are easily absorbed from the intestinal tract and readily excreted by the kidneys. Fairly constant levels of these three elements are maintained in the body fluids and tissues by selective excretion. Most of the excess is excreted by the kidneys (normally about 90 per cent of the total), but during profuse sweating, large amounts are lost in the perspiration.

The National Research Council (p. 330, Appendix) recommends an intake of not less than 5 gm. of sodium chloride daily for mature humans. The average individual intake in this country is about 10-15 gm. per day, which is more than adequate except during profuse sweating; here an extra gram of salt should be consumed for each liter of water consumed in excess of the normal intake (3-4 liters per day).

Symptoms of a sodium and chlorine deficiency. Rats restricted to a diet containing only 0.002% sodium showed growth retardation, reproductive failure, and eye lesions. Continuance of this ration led to death. Chloride-deficient rats show similar symptoms except that they do not develop eye lesions, and the condition is not fatal. Lactating cows require more salt than that contained in their usual feeds; failure to supply extra salt leads to anorexia (failure of appetite), weight and milk production decline, and eventual death.

"Miner's cramps" in humans are believed to be caused by a combination of salt deficiency and heat prostration.

"TRACE MINERALS". IRON. The element iron is a component of several compounds which have important functions in the body. These compounds are hemoglobin, the oxygen-transporting chromoprotein of the blood, and iron-containing enzymes such as catalase, peroxidase, the cytochromes, cytochrome oxidase, and cytochrome peroxidase (see p. 262, 318). These compounds contain 0.1-0.4% iron. The spleen and intestinal wall also store an iron-proteinate, *ferritin*, which acts as a reserve for iron; ferritin contains about 23% of this metal. Ferritin is apparently concerned with the regulation of iron absorption. In the intestinal mucosa it reaches an equilibrium with the other iron reserves of the body, and governs further absorption, as indicated by the following scheme:

$$Fe^{++}(\text{gastrointestinal tract}) \longrightarrow Fe^{++}(\text{mucosal cells}) \rightleftharpoons Fe^{++}(\text{serum} \rightleftharpoons Fe(\text{Hb, Enzymes})$$
$$\Updownarrow \qquad\qquad\qquad \text{globulin)} \qquad \text{of body.}$$
$$Fe^{+++}(\text{Ferritin})$$

Requirements for iron. Information on the iron requirements of different species is limited at present to baby pigs and to humans. Both have requirements (recommended allowances) in the range of 6-15 mg. of iron daily (p. 330, Appendix). In the case of humans, the higher levels (12-15 mg.) are recommended for adolescents, and for women during the reproductive years; healthy men, and healthy women after the menopause, probable need less than 6 mg. of iron daily.

Deficiency symptoms. A deficiency of the mineral element, iron, causes *nutritional anemia*. In a severe iron deficiency, the hemoglobin content drops to one-third to one-sixth of normal (normal = 12-16 gm. per 100 ml). Other factors besides iron also can cause nutritional anemia. These factors are lack of copper, cobalt, protein, or folic acid.

Previous chapters have discussed the "dynamic equilibrium" existing in the amino acid pool (p. 187) and in the fatty acid pool (p. 180) of the body. An analogous pool exists for the red blood cells. The red cells are formed in the bone marrow (and in the spleen of younger animals), and are released into the blood stream; after circulating for 4 to 6 weeks, the red cells are destroyed. The hemoglobin in the discarded red blood cells is broken down, and the iron present is used to build *new* red blood cells in the bone marrow. Nutritional anemia results when the "dynamic equilibrium" is upset, either due to inability of the body to generate new red cells as fast as the old ones are destroyed, or to enlarge the blood supply to meet the demands of body growth.

Nutritional anemia produces certain characteristic symptoms such as pallor, shortness of breath due to reduced oxygen-carrying capacity of blood, fatigue, and lowered resistance to infection in humans. In suckling pigs at three or four weeks of age, severe anemia causes a subcutaneous edema which gives the animals a stocky appearance. Breathing becomes pumping in character, and a condition called "thumps", or spasmodic jerking of the diaphragm, develops. In many cases, the blood hemoglobin may drop to as low as 15 per cent of normal. Painting the sow's teats with a solution of ferrous sulfate (containing a small amount of copper sulfate) will prevent the disease in suckling pigs.

COPPER. In higher animals, copper plays an important role in hemoglobin formation, and is also an important constituent of several metalloprotein enzymes such as ascorbic acid oxidase, laccase, tyrosinase, polyphenol oxidase, etc. (see p. 318, Appendix). Its participation in hemoglobin synthesis is not clearly understood, for the element is not a component of hemoglobin.

In lower animals (lobster, snail, and other invertebrates) copper is a part of the major respiratory pigment, hemocyanin. Hemocyanin carries oxygen in these species in the same manner that hemoglobin carries oxygen in vertebrate animals. Hemocyanins contain 0.2-0.4 per cent copper, and have molecular weights ranging from about 300,000 to several million. Hemocyanins appear to be simple metalloproteins, and do not contain the porphyrin nucleus (compare hemoglobin - p. 262). They serve as a good food source of copper for higher animals and humans.

Most of the copper in higher animals is present in the red blood cells as the copper proteinate, *hemocuprein,* and in the liver as the copper proteinate, *hepatocuprein.* It is possible that these two metalloproteins serve as storage forms for copper in the body.

Requirements. The requirement for copper is approximately one-tenth of the requirement for iron. The suggested allowance for humans is in the range of 1-2 mg. of copper per day, for farm animals (daily), 50 mg. (cattle), 5 mg. (sheep), and 1 mg. (baby pigs). Chicks need about 1 mg. of copper per pound of feed. It has been found that a copper deficiency will develop in cattle and sheep if they graze on grass containing less than 8 p.p.m. of copper (dry basis). Copper-deficient soils producing forage with this low level of copper have been found in certain areas of the United States (Florida), Peru, Great Britain, Sweden, The Netherlands, Australia, New Zealand, and South Africa.

Deficiency symptoms. Copper deficiency produces nutritional anemia, as first shown by Hart and coworkers using rats restricted to a milk diet. Other symptoms also have been associated with a severe copper deficiency in farm animals: ventricular fibrillation (heart block), debilitating scours in cattle, spastic paralysis of rear legs and sometimes blindness in lambs, and diarrhea and poor quality wool in adult sheep. A copper deficiency also is one cause of graying of the hair in laboratory animals.

COBALT. Cobalt is a constituent of vitamin B_{12} (p. 241), making up about 4 per cent of the weight of this vitamin. In non-ruminants, vitamin B_{12} must be supplied preformed in the diet, for the tissues cannot synthesize the vitamin from dietary cobalt and carbon compound precursors. It has not been possible to demonstrate a requirement for cobalt in non-ruminants; rats and rabbits appear to grow normally on intakes of less than 0.3 micrograms (1 microgram = 0.000001 gram) per day.

The story is quite different for ruminants; dietary cobalt is essential for maintaining the appetite and hemoglobin level in sheep, cattle and goats. Its exact function in ruminants is not clearly understood, but most workers believe that it is essential for the health and maintenance of the mixed colonies of microorganisms in the rumen.

Requirements. The approximate minimum requirement for cattle is 0.3 mg. cobalt daily, and for sheep, 0.1 mg. of cobalt daily. Recommended allowances are 1 mg. of cobalt for cattle, and 0.1 mg. for sheep.

Pasturage or hay containing 0.07 p.p.m. or less of cobalt (dry basis) usually causes a cobalt deficiency in ruminants. Cobalt-deficient soils (and hence cobalt-deficient forage) are widely distributed in this country and in other parts of the world.

Deficiency symptoms. In ruminants, a cobalt deficiency causes a gradual loss of appetite (anorexia), unthriftiness, and emaciation (Fig. 91). Blood hemoglobin often drops to one-

Figure 91. Effect of cobalt deficiency on ruminant. Left picture shows heifer suffering from lack of appetite and anemia, with characteristic roughness of hair coat. Right picture shows same heifer after treatment with cobalt. (From Michigan Agr. Exp. Sta., E. Lansing, photo by Prof. C. F. Huffman. Reproduced from Recommended Nutrient Allowances Pamphlet No. 4 (1950), National Research Council, Washington, D.C.).

fourth the normal levels (normal: 12-15 gm. per 100 ml. of blood). The animals appear to die from starvation rather than acute symptoms of anemia.

Feeding excess amounts of cobalt to rats causes polycythemia (overproduction of red blood cells). Thus, cobalt is toxic when fed at moderately high levels.

MANGANESE. Manganese is required for the growth and development of bones and for reproduction in the species tested (rats, mice, chicks, rabbits, and pigs). It is an important activating ion in certain metalloprotein enzymes (arginase, phosphatase, certain peptidases).

Requirements. The amounts needed daily by several species are as follows: 25 mg. per pound of feed (chicks, poults), 15 mg. per pound of feed (laying hens), 0.3 mg. (rabbits), and 0.5-0.8 mg. (rats). The requirement for humans is probably less than 4 mg. per day, and the average diet furnishes this amount or more. Feeding excessive amounts of calcium or phosphorus decreases the absorption of manganese, probably by forming insoluble salts in the intestines.

Deficiency symptoms. Manganese deficiency causes reproductive failure in rats, rabbits, and mice, perosis (slipped tendon) in chicks, reduced hatchability of eggs with bone distortions in the hatched chicks, lameness and bone abnormalities in pigs and rabbits, and lowered arginase activity (liver) and lowered alkaline phosphatase activity (bones, blood) in rabbits.

ZINC. This element is a constituent of the enzyme, carbonic anhydrase (p. 242) which is found in the red blood cells, the pancreas, and the lining (mucosa) of the stomach. Carbonic anhydrase is involved in carbon dioxide elimination (p. 263), and may be concerned with HCl formation in the border cells of the stomach (p. 144). Zinc is also a constituent of crystalline insulin isolated from animal pancreas, and may play a role in carbohydrate metabolism.

Requirements. The requirement for zinc in different species is not well established. Hove and co-workers observed that 40 micrograms of zinc daily prevented deficiency symptoms in rats. The requirement in humans has been estimated at less than 12 mg. per day. Young pigs require 46 p.p.m. of zinc on a corn-soy ration (p. 330), lower amounts produce parakeratosis.

Deficiency symptoms. Experimental zinc deficiency produced growth retardation, poor fur development, and faulty intestinal absorption in rats, and parakeratosis (footnote 7 p. 330) in pigs.

IODINE. The mature animal body contains only a small amount of this element (less than 40 p.p.m.), but the element is essential for life. Except for a small amount of iodine present in the blood, most of the iodine is in the thyroid gland. Here it is present as the amino acid diiodotyrosine, and the amino acid hormone, thyroxine. These two compounds are combined in a complex with a globulin, and the conjugated protein is called *thyroglobulin*. Thyroxine contains 65 per cent iodine, and diiodotyrosine, 58 per cent. Another iodine compound in the thyroid is 3, 5, 3'-triiodothyronine. This is five times as potent as thyroxine, and is considered by some investigators to be the active thyroid hormone.

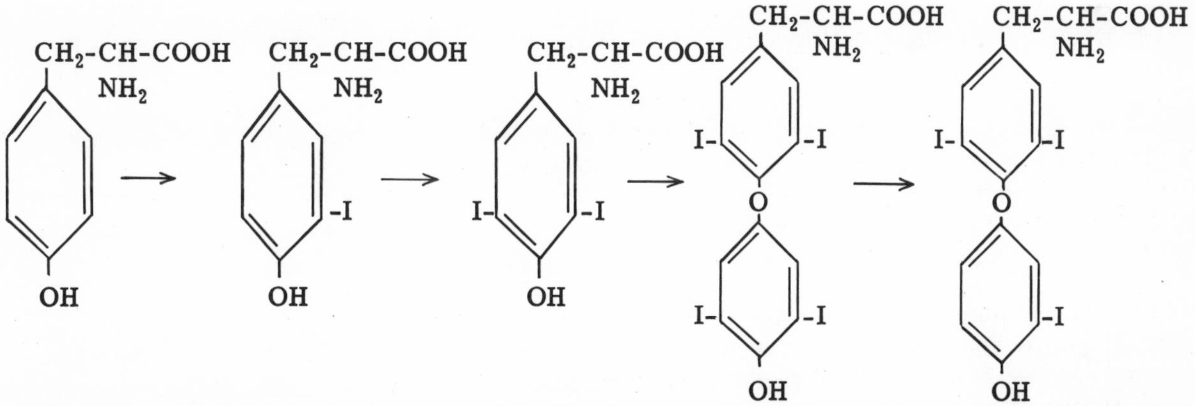

Tyrosine   Monoiodotyrosine   3, 5-Diiodotyrosine   Thyroxine   3, 5, 3' - Triiodothyronine

The primary function of iodine is as an important component of the thyroid hormones, which control the basal metabolic rate (p. 213) in the animal body. Removal of the thyroid gland early in life in all species causes marked stunting of physical, mental, and sexual development (see p. 275).

Requirements for iodine. Estimated daily requirements are 0.15-0.3 mg. (human adults), 0.2 mg. per 100 lb. of body weight (pregnant sows), and 0.5 mg. per pound of feed (chicks).

In the United States, the iodine-deficient areas are primarily in the Northwest and in the states surrounding the Great Lakes. Here the soils and plants are low in iodine. Humans in areas where sea food makes up an important part of the diet are not deficient in this mineral, since seafood is rich in iodine; the soils in areas near the oceans are also rich in iodine, and there is no problem in supplying iodine to farm animals grazing these areas.

The most practical way to supply iodine to both humans and farm animals in iodine-deficient areas is to add it to the salt. Iodized salt is available in stores, for both humans and farm animals; it contains 0.07-0.15 per cent potassium iodide stabilized with a reducing substance (such as D-glucose).

The iodine requirement is increased when *goitrogens* (agents tending to produce goiter, such as cabbage goitrogen (rabbits), soybean goitrogen (poultry)) are in the diet. Conversely, agents lowering the activity of the thyroid gland (thiourea, thiouracil) and agents supplying preformed thyroxine and diiodotyrosine (iodinated casein, other thyroproteins) would be expected to decrease the iodine requirement (see p. 275).

Deficiency symptoms. Inadequate levels of iodine in the diet of babies and preschool children produces cretinism, or physical and mental dwarfism, in older children and adults, lack of iodine can produce simple goiter (enlargement of the thyroid gland), or myxedema (lowered metabolic rate, change in body contour and facial features, with a lowering of mental activity).

In farm animals, iodine deficiency causes premature aging, mental and physical sluggishness, and a lowered metabolic rate. Simple goiter is also observed. There is an increased need for thyroxine during pregnancy and puberty, and goiters often develop during these periods.

Iodine-deficient young are born weak or dead, and in several species (calves, lambs, kids, and pigs) the goiter is very evident at birth. Pigs are also born hairless and edematous, with coarse skins. Birds and fish also show enlargement of the thyroid on iodine-deficient diets.

FLUORINE. In studies with rats, feeding diets extremely low in fluorine resulted in excessive tooth decay and reproductive failure, which could be prevented by the addition of small amounts of fluorine to the diet. Results of this nature have not been reported to date for other species. In children, controlled studies in several cities have demonstrated that the presence of one part per million of fluorine in the drinking water markedly reduces the incidence of dental caries. The incidence of caries in adult humans is apparently not affected by the ingestion of small amounts of fluorine. The reason for the reduction of caries in children is not clearly understood.

Toxicity. Fluorine is toxic when present at levels of more than 5 p.p.m. in the drinking water, and in the case of farm animals, at a level of 0.003-0.015 per cent in the dry rations. Fluorine is deposited in the bones and teeth as the mineral, fluoroapatite $(Ca_3(PO_4)_2)_3 \cdot CaF_2$. At toxic levels it produces mottling of the teeth, and malformations, abnormal outgrowths, etc. of the bones. Raw rock phosphate is often used as a source of calcium and phosphorus in the diet of farm animals; since it usually contains 3.5 to 4.0 per cent of fluorine, it must be defluorinated before use.

Chapter 13 | SPECIALIZED TISSUES

In the previous chapters, we have discussed the biochemistry of each of the six major nutrients. Analysis shows that these six nutrients are the major components of every living cell. However, the relative proportions of these nutrients may not be the same in all cells; thus, in animals and in multicelled plants, groups of cells have taken over certain specialized functions which are essential for the well-being of the total organism. In order to perform their function, these specialized cells may have an unusual distribution of the major nutrients in their make-up. A group of cells performing a special function is called a *specialized tissue*. A discrete functional part or member of the animal or plant body is called an *organ*, and may be composed of one or more specialized tissues.

Specialized Plant Tissues

The major organs of the plant are the roots, stems, and leaves. Each of these organs is composed of several types of specialized tissues. Unfortunately, relatively little is known regarding the chemical composition of these individual tissues. One difficulty is to separate a given tissue from closely associated tissues, so that it can be analyzed. New techniques need to be developed in this area. The major specialized tissues of the plant are discussed briefly below.

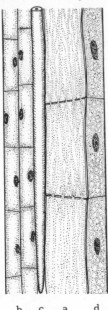

b   c   a   d

Figure 92*. Phloem cell types;
a, sieve tube;
b, parenchyma;
c, fiber;
d, companion cell.

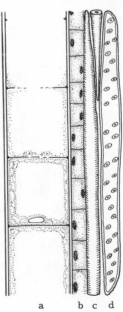

a   b c d

Figure 93. Xylem cell types;
a, vessel showing steps
in differentiation;
b, parenchyma;
c, fiber; d, tracheid.

*Figures 92-96 inclusive are reproductions of drawings from Cummins, Gries, Postlethwait and Stearns, Textbook of Intermediate Plant Science, Burgess Publishing Co., 1950.

CONDUCTING TISSUE. This tissue is concerned with the transfer of water, raw materials and food within the plant. There are two types of conducting tissue, the *xylem* and the *phloem*. (Figs. 92 and 93).

The *phloem* is a complex tissue which is responsible for the translocation of organic compounds (food). It consists of four types of cells: sieve cells, parenchyma, fibers, and companion cells. The *sieve* cells are the principal conducting elements of the phloem. The cells are arranged end to end, and the end walls are perforated, serving as sieve-like plates through which the cytoplasm of adjacent cells is continuous. Thus, a continuous path is provided for the movements of food. The walls of the sieve tubes are never lignified, and consist essentially of cellulose. Sieve tube cells contain cytoplasm, but no nucleus.

The four types of cells found in the *xylem* are: vessels (tracheae), parenchyma, fibers, and tracheids. Both vessels and tracheids are conducting elements for water and minerals from the roots to the upper portion of the plant. The vessels consist of a chain of cellular elements with the end walls out. The walls are made up of a mixture of lignin (see p. 314, Appendix) and cellulose, the pattern of lignification changing with the age of the tissues. Tracheids are elongated tubes with pointed ends, are pitted, and allow passage of fluids.

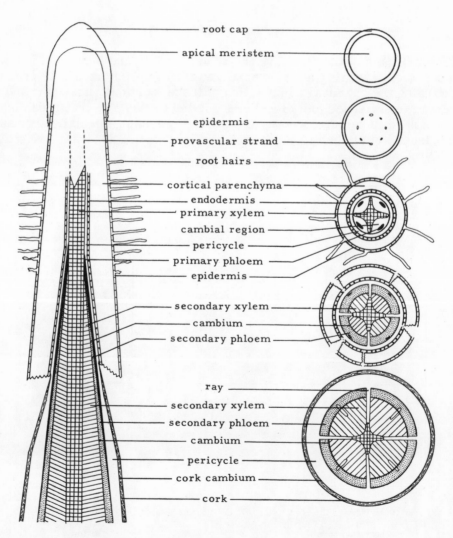

Figure 94. Diagram of the arrangement of tissues in a typical root tip.

MERISTEMATIC TISSUE. Any region of the plant composed of cells which have the ability to multiply themselves constitutes a meristem (see Fig. 94). In contrast to animals,
plants can carry on cell division only in certain special areas. These areas are (a) at the
extremities of the plant (apical meristems located at the tips of roots, stems, and buds),
(b) at the basal part of stem internodes (intercalary meristems), (c) in an area encircling
and parallel to the main axis of the stem (vascular and cork cambium-lateral meristems),
and of the root (pericycle-potential lateral meristem). The meristematic tissues in (a)
and (b) are responsible for elongation of plant tissues, whereas those in (c) are responsible for lateral enlargement. Thus, vascular cambium (Fig. 95) occurs between xylem
and phloem, producing phloem on its outer surface, and xylem on its inner surface; cork
cambium (Fig. 95) produces cork cells as a protective layer for the plant organ, and
pericycle (Fig. 94) produces lateral roots.

Meristematic cells are characterized by their lack of vacuoles, a very high concentration of protein (probably mainly enzymes), and by very thin walls containing very little
cellulose, but high levels of protopectin (p. 23). It is also in these cells that the auxin
content is at a maximum (see p. 286).

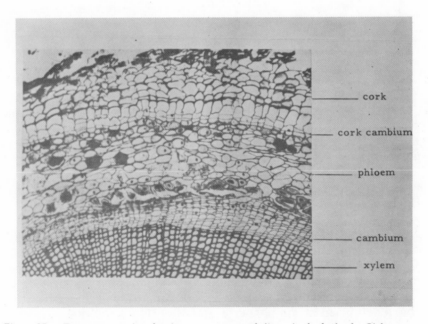

Figure 95.   Transverse section showing arrangement of tissues in the bark of a Ginko stem.

ABSORPTIVE AND PROTECTIVE TISSUE. This specialized tissue serves a protective
or an absorptive function (or both), depending on its location in the plant. It is subdivided
into three classes: epidermis, cork layer, and endodermis.

Epidermis. This is the outermost layer of cells covering a young plant, usually only one
layer of cells thick (Fig. 94). When serving a protective function, the epidermis sometimes undergoes limited thickening. In addition, in the above the ground parts, a layer
of cutin (cuticle) may be secreted which, because of its waxy nature, protects the plant
part against water loss, microbial invasion and mechanical injury.

Specialized epidermal cells facilitate the exchange of gases and the absorption of water and minerals. In the above-the-ground parts, gas exchange takes place mainly through pores called *stomata*. The extent to which water and minerals are absorbed by the stomata is not known, although it is probable that some absorption does take place by this pathway. Absorption can take place through any epidermal cell whose walls are sufficiently permeable. In the roots, (Fig. 94), there are specialized cell bodies called root hairs, which are an extension of the outer wall of an epidermal cell. The extension is an elongated tube which is not covered with cuticle and has excellent absorptive properties.

Chemically, the epidermis cells contain no chlorophyll (except in guard cells on either side of the stomata). The waxy cuticle layer on the above-the-ground epidermis is composed of high molecular weight alcohols, waxes, hydrocarbons, etc. (see p. 53). The epidermal cells of the root are similar, but contain no stomata and no cuticle. The root hairs have been shown to contain both cellulose and pectins.

Cork layer. In plants which slough off the epidermis as they mature, a special protective layer of cork is formed to replace it. This layer is made up of a sheath of suberized cork cells, a cork cambium, and a few parenchyma cells. Suberized cork cells (suberin) contain a high content of suberic acid. Since suberin is very impermeable to water, and is indigestible, it protects the plant against microbial invasion and water loss.

$$COOH$$
$$|$$
$$(CH_2)_6$$
$$|$$
$$COOH$$

Suberic acid

Endodermis. This specialized tissue is a constant structure of the root (see Fig. 94). It is a compact cell layer which is internal to the cortex and ensheathes the plant vascular system. The cell walls are irregularly thickened, and have a suberized strip (Casparian strip) which encircles the cell in a plane tangential to the axis of the plant. The suberized strip in this position makes it necessary for all substances entering the vascular system (xylem, phloem) to pass through the cytoplasm of the endodermal cells first. It is here that selective adsorption and absorption against an osmotic gradient takes place.

MECHANICAL TISSUE. This tissue provides support, elasticity, and flexibility to the plant. It is made up mainly of four cell types: collenchyma, sclerenchyma, tracheids, and vessels. Collenchyma (Fig. 96) are elongated cells which function as supporting tissue in young woody types of stems, and as the main supporting tissue in other plants ("strings" in celery, supporting tissue in stems of tomato, potato, geranium, etc.). Collenchyma fibers are usually composed of non-lignified cellulose. *Sclerenchyma* can be divided into two types, *fibers* and *sclereids* or "stone cells". The fibers are elongate cylindrical cells with pointed ends. Most of the plant fibers used commercially for textiles (see p. 296) and rope, are cells of this type. These fibers usually take the name of the complex tissue of which they form a part, for example, *xylem* fibers and *phloem* fibers. With the exception of a few plants (flax, ramie), the fibers are lignified cellulose. Flax and ramie fibers are almost pure cellulose. In the fibers of lignified cellulose, lignin (amorphous) gradually fills up the interstices in the cellulose microfibrils of the maturing plant.

Sclereids. Sclereids may be branched, round, columnar, or rod-shaped cells. They have thick, lignified (in some cases suberized or cutinized) walls. They provide rigidity and protection to nuts, fruits, and seeds.

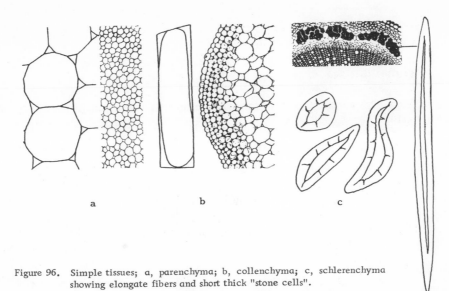

Figure 96.   Simple tissues; a, parenchyma; b, collenchyma; c, schlerenchyma
showing elongate fibers and short thick "stone cells".

<u>Tracheids and vessels</u>.   These types of mechanical tissue were discussed under *conducting* tissue.

<u>Storage and photosynthesis</u>.   Thin-walled parenchyma cells are a relatively unspecialized tissue of the plant (see Figs. 92, 93, 94 and 96).   They function for a large variety of purposes, depending upon the location and the nature of associated cells.   One important function is to serve as storage tissue in the root, stem, and leaf of the plant.   The cells also contain plastids, and under light stimulation, chlorophyll is produced, photosynthesis takes place, and food is manufactured in the exposed parts (stem, leaf) of the plant.

SECRETORY TISSUE.   Glandular tissue functioning primarily as secretory tissue is much more common in animals than in plants (see next section).   However, such tissues are found in certain plants.   Examples are the epithelial layer of the cotyledons of grasses, the nectaries of flowers, and lactiferous cells and ducts.   Extracellular enzymes are secreted by carnivorous, parasitic, and saprophytic plants, although this process may not necessarily be a function of specialized cells.   Epidermal hairs in certain plants secrete by-products of metabolism and could be classed as glandular tissue.   Some of these by-products of metabolism are very important commercially (rubber, essential oils - page 53, resins - page 301, and honey).

For further information regarding the physiology of plant tissues, the student is referred to textbooks in this area.

Specialized Animal Tissues

BLOOD: FUNCTION AND COMPOSITION.   The blood of animals may be considered as a "floating" tissue of the body.   It has many important specialized functions which are listed below:

1. Carries oxygen from the lungs (also gills, insect trachea), and nutrients from the intestinal tract, to the body cells.

2. Carries the waste products of metabolism from the body cells to the organs of excretion.

3. Serves as a buffer solution to maintain the pH of the body cells within narrow limits.

4. Carries antibodies and white blood cells, which help to protect the body against invasion by bacteria and viruses.

5. Regulates and maintains a constant osmotic pressure in body tissues.

6. Serves as a heat exchanger, preventing extremes in body temperature in warm-blooded animals.

7. Carries hormones from ductless glands to sensitive tissues.

<u>Composition.</u> The blood of higher animals is made up of formed elements (red blood cells, white blood cells, platelets) suspended in a straw-colored fluid called *plasma*. If fresh blood is drawn with a needle and a syringe, which have been made non-wettable by coating with a thin layer of paraffin or silicone grease, and the blood placed in a non-wettable centrifuge tube, it is possible to spin down the formed elements in either an

Table 36. Composition of human blood

Constituent	Normal Range (mg. /100 ml. of whole blood unless otherwise noted)
Total solids	19 - 23% (by vol.)
Formed elements (a, b, c)	40 - 50% (by vol.)
a) Red blood cells	4,000,000 - 5,000,000/cu·mm·
b) White blood cells	5,000 - 10,000/cu·mm·
c) Platelets	300,000 - 500,000/cu·mm·
Plasma	50 - 60% (by vol.)
Total proteins (plasma)	6.8 - 8.8 gm. /100 ml.
Albumin (")	4.6 - 6.7 gm. /100 ml.
Globulin (")	1.5 - 2.9 gm. /100 ml.
Fibrinogen (")	300 - 600
Prothrombin (")	20 - 30
Copper	0.05 - 0.25
Urea	20 - 30
Uric Acid	2 - 3.5
Creatinine	1 - 2
Creatine	3 - 7
Amino Acids (free)	30 - 48
Ammonia	.1 - 0.2
Glucose	70 - 120
Total fatty acids	290 - 420
Cholesterol	150 - 190
Lipid phosphorus	12 - 14
Inorganic phosphorus (plasma)	3 - 4 (as P)
Total acetone bodies (as acetone)	0.8 - 5.0
Bilirubin	0.1 - 0.25
CO_2 (arterial blood)	45 - 55 vols. /100 ml.
CO_2 (venous blood)	50 - 60 vols. /100 ml.
O_2 (arterial blood)	15 - 23 vols. /100 ml.
O_2 (venous blood)	10 - 18 vols. /100 ml.
Ascorbic acid	0.8 - 2.4
Lactic acid	5 - 20
Phenols (free)	1 - 2
Chlorides (as NaCl)	450 - 500
Sulfates, inorganic (plasma)	0.9 - 1.1 (as S)
Calcium (plasma)	9 - 11
Magnesium (plasma)	1 - 3
Sodium (plasma)	330
Potassium (plasma)	16 - 22
Iodine	8 - 15 micrograms/100 ml.

"angle" or "bucket" type centrifuge. The cells obtained in this way will occupy about 40-50% of the volume. The supernatant fluid will be straw-colored plasma. Cells and plasma can also be separated by centrifugation if the blood is drawn into an anticoagulant such as potassium oxalate or sodium citrate solution, which tie up calcium ions (see p. 259). A layering effect is observed in the packed, formed elements in the centrifuge tube; red cells constitute the bottom major layer, white cells form a thin white middle layer, and platelets form a thin white top layer. Most of the supernatant plasma can be removed with a glass tube by applying suction.

Table 36 shows the composition of normal human blood as it circulates in the vascular system. The same components in slightly different concentrations are found in the blood of most animals.

Whole blood contains about 20% total solids, about one-half of which is the chromoprotein, hemoglobin, and most of the remainder is plasma protein (mainly albumin and globulin). The *formed elements* are in the ratio of about 1:100:1,000 of white cells : platelets : red cells. Adult human females usually have a red cell count that is about one million per cubic millimeter lower than that of the male. If the total hemoglobin concentration (12-14 gm./100 ml. normal for males) shows a greater drop than the red cell count (Hb/r.b.c. "index" less than 1), then the human (or animal) has a hypochromic type of anemia. Conversely, if the Hb/r.b.c. index is more than 1, then the subject (or animal) has a hyperchromic type of anemia. If the total r.b.c. count drops but the "index" remains at 1.0, the patient has an orthochromic type of anemia. *Red cells* and *white cells* may exist in several different shapes, and a classification on the basis of the per cent of each type present (i.e., nucleated or macrocytic red cells, lymphocyte and neutrophile types of white cells) is helpful in the diagnosis of anemias, leucopenias, and leukemias. A normal *platelet* level is essential for proper clotting of the blood.

Blood plasma contains more than 50 different components, most of which are in trace amounts. The most abundant components are *albumins* (about 5%) and *globulins* (about 2%). Albumins serve an important function as colloids for maintenance of the proper exchange of fluid between blood and tissues. Alpha and beta globulins have the same function, and gamma globulins consist mainly of antibodies for certain bacteria and viruses. The trace proteins, *fibrinogen, prothrombin,* and certain activating globulins for prothrombin, are important factors in blood coagulation.

As can be seen from the table, blood plasma contains small amounts of all of the nutrients required by living cells, i.e., *glucose,* the 19 *amino acids, lipids, mineral ions,* and *vitamins.* It also contains appreciable amounts of oxygen (held in loose chemical combination by hemoglobin), and even larger amounts of carbon dioxide (also mainly in chemical combination).

Using very sensitive tests, it is possible to demonstrate the presence of hormones in the blood.

The major solid waste products in the blood of humans and most mammals are urea (20-30 mg. per 100 ml. of plasma), uric acid, creatinine, creatine, and acetone bodies.

THE HEMOSTATIC MECHANISM: VESSEL CONSTRICTION, BLOOD COAGULATION, CLOT LYSIS. The many vital functions performed by the blood and its components make it imperative that this fluid be maintained at a constant composition and volume in the closed vessel system. In the absence of surgical intervention, the severing of large arteries or veins leads to fatal hemorrhage, because the body has no hemostatic mechanism powerful enough to stop the flow of blood. In the ordinary course of living, both man and animals sever small arteries and veins, arterioles, venules, and arterial and venous capillaries. In these cases, the hemostatic mechanism usually stops the bleeding, otherwise minor cuts and scratches would prove fatal, as they often do in bleeding diseases of man and animals.

Vessel constriction. The large blood vessels cannot effectively seal themselves off by constriction; however, smaller vessels are apparently able to do this. It is probable that the *first stage* of hemostasis in the smaller blood vessels of mammals consists of a temporary constriction of the wall of the severed or otherwise injured vessel; this slows down or stops the loss of blood. The *second stage* consists of a firm coagulation of the blood, and a retraction of the blood clot in the lumen near the temporarily constricted part of the injured vessel. Following this second stage, dilatation of the vessel occurs, but the plugged condition of the injured area prevents further loss of blood.

Blood coagulation. The coagulation of blood is a beautiful example of delicately balanced protein interactions. Intravascular clotting is as dangerous to life as excessive bleeding, and the formation of a blood clot must therefore be confined to the point of bleeding only. The coagulation of blood may be divided into two major steps, the conversion of plasma prothrombin to thrombin, and the conversion of plasma fibrinogen to fibrin. The first step is by far the more complex. In Figure 97, the mechanism suggested by Seegers is outlined. In the first step, the conversion of prothrombin to thrombin is catalyzed or

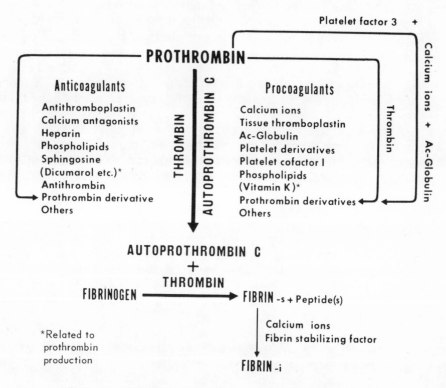

Figure 97. Mechanism of blood coagulation (according to Seegers).

retarded by procoagulants or anticoagulants. Prothrombin is a proenzyme containing within its structure two enzymes, thrombin and autoprothrombin C. Both of these enzymes are capable of catalyzing the conversion of prothrombin to thrombin. The initial release of the active enzymes is brought about by two major combinations of procoagulants: "extrinsic thromboplastin" and "intrinsic thromboplastin". Extrinsic thromboplastin is formed when there is damage to the tissues and tissue thromboplastin is released. This, together with activator globulin (Ac-globulin from plasma), and calcium ions makes a powerful activator of prothrombin. Injection of a purified thromboplastin made from brain or lung tissue into the blood stream of an animal causes widespread fatal intravascular clotting.

Intrinsic thromboplastin is formed by breakdown of the blood platelets. This releases several activators such as platelet factor 3. These, in conjunction with Ac-globulin, calcium ions, and certain cofactors in the plasma (for example, platelet cofactor I) also act together as a potent activator of prothrombin. Intravascular clotting, such as coronary thrombosis and cerebral thrombosis, is probably caused by the release of too much intrinsic thromboplastin.

Anticoagulants. Any agent which binds calcium will function as an anticoagulant. Examples are potassium oxalate, sodium citrate, and the chelating agent, ethylenediaminetetraacetic acid (EDTA). Two natural agents which circulate in the blood are heparin and antithrombin. Antithrombin is a protein associated with the albumin fraction of plasma.

Step 2. After sufficient amounts of thrombin are formed, this enzyme splits fibrinogen to soluble fibrin (fibrin-s) and small peptides. Autoprothombin C does not react with fibrinogen. To obtain a firm clot, calcium ions and an enzyme, fibrin-stabilizing factor (FSF), polymerize the soluble fibrin to insoluble fibrin (fibrin-i). The nature of some of the compounds involved in the coagulation of blood are discussed below.

Prothrombin. Prothrombin (bovine) has been prepared in highly purified form by Seegers and his coworkers. It is a glycoprotein containing 4 to 5 per cent of carbohydrate as hexose and glucosamine, and has a molecular weight of 65,000.

Thrombin. Thrombin is a glycoprotein and has a molecular weight of about 30,000.

Autoprothrombin C. This is a glycoprotein with a molecular weight of about 30,000.

Thromboplastin. This is a lipoprotein-nucleoprotein complex containing protein, lipid, nucleic acid and carbohydrate. It is released from injured tissues and is especially abundant in lung and brain tissues.

Activator Globulin (Ac-globulin). This is a plasma trace protein (9 mg. per 100 ml. plasma). It is a globulin but has not been prepared in pure form. It is required for rapid conversion of purified prothrombin to thrombin.

Platelet Cofactor I. (Antihemophilic factor). This is a beta-globulin in plasma which is effective in correcting the clotting defect of hemophilic plasma. In conjunction with a factor from platelets (platelet factor 3-water-insoluble factor in platelets and platelet fragments), it has an activating effect about equal to that of thromboplastin. Thus, when insufficient thromboplastin is released, platelets, together with this factor, can produce prothrombin conversion.

Platelet Cofactor II. This is a beta-globulin in plasma which is a trace protein (less than 1 mg. per 100 ml. of plasma). In the presence of platelets, it speeds up the conversion of prothrombin to thrombin. Its absence causes a bleeding disease which is unlike classical hemophilia.

Heparin. This compound is a polysaccharide containing alternate units of sulfated glucuronic acid and sulfamated glucose (Fig. 98).

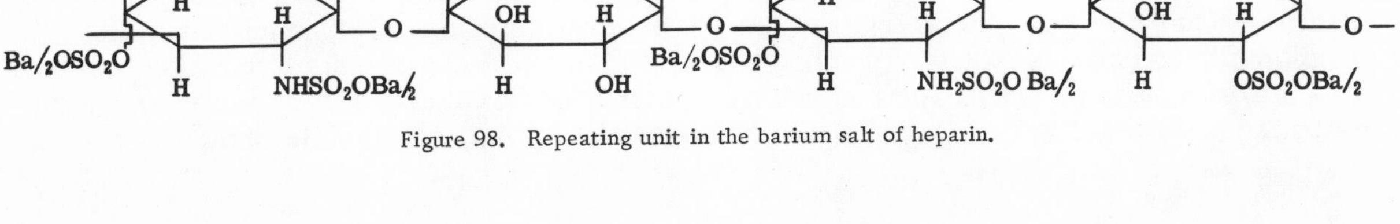

Figure 98. Repeating unit in the barium salt of heparin.

Heparin, in conjunction with a cofactor in plasma, blocks the conversion of pro-thrombin to thrombin. It has been isolated from liver, and is available in crystalline form. Because of its powerful anticoagulant properties, it is used to prevent the coagu-lation of freshly drawn blood, and to prolong the coagulation time *in vivo* in patients suf-fering from thrombosis. Warfarin (p. 290) and dicoumarol (p. 315) are also used.

Antithromboplastin. This is an ether-soluble lipid, which forms a complex with throm-boplastin, and renders it inactive. It has not been obtained in pure form.

Fibrinogen is a euglobulin (see p. 65) in plasma. With the electron microscope, human fibrinogen has been shown to consist of filamentous elements with an average length of 600 Å. and an estimated width of 30 or 40 Å.* The filaments appear to be nodular.

Fibrin is formed by the cleavage of a low molecular weight peptide from the fibrinogen molecule. This leaves an "activated fibrinogen" molecule which associates side by side, and end to end, with other activated molecules, to build the fibrin strands which form the network of the blood clot.

Clot Lysis. After the blood clot has served its purpose in preventing loss of blood, it is dissolved by an enzyme, fibrinolysin (plasmin). This enzyme is present in blood plasma as the inactive precursor or proenzyme, profibrinolysin (plasminogen). The factors which activate the proenzyme have not been isolated from plasma or serum. The plasma also contains at least one component (antifibrinolysin) which inhibits the enzyme. Fibri-nolysin from beef plasma has been shown to be similar in many respects to the protease, trypsin.

Lymph. Lymph circulates slowly in the lymphatic vessels, and is continuously returned to the blood via special lymphatic ducts. It is essentially a blood exudate, which serves as a "middleman" between the blood and tissues. The composition of lymph is essentially the same as plasma, except that the level of proteins is slightly lower, and the levels of nitrogenous waste products are slightly higher. Lymph is relatively free of formed ele-ments, and its coagulation time is therefore much slower than that of whole blood.

CHEMISTRY OF IMMUNITY. Immunity to infection is dependent on the action of the *white blood cells* (leucocytes), and on the action of *plasma antibodies*.

Action of leucocytes. The major leucocytes are the *polymorphonuclear leucocytes* (a type of granulocyte which originates chiefly in the hemopoietic tissues of bone marrow), and the *lymphocytes* (formed mainly in the lymph nodes and in the spleen). The former make up about 65% of the white cells, and the latter about 30%. They are nucleated cells.

Polymorphonuclear leucocytes have amoeboid motion, and move towards regions of lower pH. They also move toward a chemical, *leucotaxin*, which is liberated by injured or inflamed tissues. They are capable of passing through the capillary walls by a process called *diapedesis*. When the acidity due to release of organic acids during the development of inflammation approaches pH 6.7, these leucocytes lose their effectiveness, and the lymphocytes (macrophages-comparatively large cells) take over. Lymphocytes are less mobile, and operate mainly in the area where they originate (lymph nodes, liver, spleen, etc.).

The efficiency with which phagocytic white blood cells engulf and digest bacteria depends to a large extent on the content of specific substances (probably proteins) of the plasma called *opsonins*. Bacteria arouse the production of a specific opsonin, and the opsonin so alters the surface of the bacterium so that it is easily engulfed by leucocytes. The *opsonic index* of *serum* (plasma which has lost its fibrinogen and some of the other clotting factors through coagulation and removal of the clot), can be determined by divid-

* See page 102 for definition of Å unit.

ing the number of bacteria engulfed by a specific number of *normal* leucocytes in the test serum sample, by the number of bacteria engulfed by the same number of *normal* leucocytes in a normal serum sample.

Plasma antibodies. Opsonins may be considered as a type of antibody. They are specific proteins (usually associated with the gamma-globulin fraction of the plasma, but also extractable from tissues) which have been produced by the body in response to the injection or other entrance of a specific *antigen* into the tissues or blood stream. Antigens are foreign proteins usually carried in diluted form as an integral part of bacteria, molds, and protozoa, and in more concentrated form as toxins, pollens, viruses, etc. It is probable that any protein which is foreign to the animal or human body can act as an antigen and when injected will call forth an antibody response.

Antibodies have been subdivided into (1) *agglutinins* (cause the clumping together of cells carrying the antigen, such as foreign corpuscles, bacteria, etc.), (2) *antitoxins* (neutralize the toxin released by a specific pathogenic organism, or the toxin in venoms, etc.), (3) *hemolysins* and other *cytolysins,* which destroy cell membranes and cause liquefaction of the cell, and (4), *precipitins,* which form an insoluble compound specifically with the antigenic protein. These subdivisions overlap to a considerable degree.

Plasma Complement. In order for the antibody to react with its antigen, an additional factor occurring in blood plasma is required. This factor, called "complement", appears to be a complex globulin type of protein. It is non-specific, activating the reaction of any antibody with its antigen. The activation is not reversible, and the complement is "fixed" to the antigen-antibody. The reaction is therefore called "complement fixation". The reaction can be used to detect antibodies for syphilis by mixing (1) the patient's serum heated to destroy the natural complement, (2) an antigen that combines with syphilis antibodies, (3) just the right amount of guinea pig complement to (theoretically) exactly neutralize (fix) the syphilis antibodies and antigen present, and (4) a preparation of washed red blood cells mixed with a specific red blood cell hemolysin. If large amounts of syphilis antibodies are present, all of the complement is fixed, and none will be available to "fix" the red cells to the red cell hemolysin to cause liquefaction (hemolysis) of the red cells. Such a reaction would be classed as a "4 plus" Wassermann reaction for syphilis. A negative reaction would be one in which all of the red blood cells used in the test were hemolyzed.

ALLERGIES. Many humans are especially sensitive to certain proteins which they contact during the ordinary course of living. Absorption of small amounts of some food proteins directly through the intestinal wall is believed to be responsible for the *food allergies*. Sensitive individuals have the most trouble with egg, milk, wheat and shellfish proteins, and must avoid the food that produces the allergy. Foreign proteins entering via the mucous membranes of the respiratory tract also produce an allergy in sensitive individuals. "Hay fever" is caused by sensitivity to specific plant pollens (ragweed, rose, etc.); other types are caused by sensitivity to dandruff or dust from fur or feathers (horse fever, cat fever, etc.). Individuals may also develop skin allergies due to contact with such proteins as wool and fur.

Allergies are a form of *anaphylaxis,* or a condition of hypersensitivity to traces of foreign protein. True anaphylaxis is produced experimentally by the single injection of the antigen or foreign protein. If no further injections are given for about three weeks, the animal is hypersensitive, due to the formation of sensitizing antibodies instead of protective antibodies. At this time the injection of some of the antigen will produce *anaphylactic shock.* The more prominent symptoms are low blood pressure, constriction of the muscles of the bronchioles in the lungs, also of the muscles of the stomach, intestines, bladder, and uterus. The constriction of the bronchioles may cause fatal asphyxia. The most effective treatment is injection of the hormone, adrenaline (p. 269), which dilates the bronchioles, and raises the blood pressure. It is believed that in anaphylactic shock, histamine (p. 152) is released by the action of the antigen on the sensitizing antibody, and that this toxin is responsible for most of the symptoms. Desensitization to allergens is accomplished by the repeated injection of the allergen in small doses, so that the body can build *protective* antibodies instead of *sensitizing* antibodies.

BLOOD TYPES. Human blood may be classified into four types, based on its content of specific plasma antibodies called *isoagglutinins*, and specific antigens *(agglutinogens)* (in the red blood cell surfaces) which contain polysaccharide *haptens* A and B. A hapten is a prosthetic group attached to a protein, which determines the type of specific antibody produced by the hapten-protein (antigen). The red cell antigens do not react with the plasma antibodies of the same blood, or agglutination would result. Table 37 shows the Landsteiner (International) classification of blood types. In every case, an individual contains in his serum the antibodies for the antigens lacking in his erythrocytes, except in Groups

Table 37. Landsteiner (international) blood types

Red Cell Factors (Agglutinogens)	Plasma (or serum) Factors (Agglutinins)	Blood Type
None	a + b	O
A	b	A
B	a	B
AB	None	AB

O and AB. In Group O the agglutinogen is lacking in the red blood cells, and in Group AB the agglutinins are absent from the plasma. When bloods from individuals of different blood types are mixed, agglutination of the red blood cells of one (or both) of the bloods takes place. It is necessary, therefore, to use the patient's type of blood when he receives a blood transfusion.

The Rh factor. About 85% of the white population also carry in their red blood cells a specific antigen (agglutinogen) for which there is no corresponding antibody in the plasma. These individuals are said to be *Rh positive*. The other 15% of the population do not carry this antigen and are said to be *Rh negative*. Rh negative individuals can develop antibodies (plasma agglutinins) as a result of transfusions with Rh positive blood. Subsequent transfusions with Rh positive blood can then cause agglutination, which can be quite serious. The Rh factor, like the Landsteiner factors, is inherited as a simple Mendelian dominant, and an Rh negative mother may have a child which is Rh positive through inheritance from its father. During pregnancy the mother may become sensitized by the Rh antigen of the foetus, and the antibodies she produces may destroy the red blood cells of the foetus (erythroblastosis foetalis). In addition, the mother, after developing antibodies, could suffer a transfusion reaction if transfused with Rh positive blood.

Antibody content of adult human plasma. Serologists have examined the antibody content of mixed plasma (gamma globulin fraction) obtained from the Red Cross, and representing a cross section of the adult human population in the United States. Antibodies could be demonstrated for *all* of the common childhood diseases, and for many other diseases which are endemic in the United States.

FUNCTION OF HEMOGLOBIN IN THE TRANSPORTATION OF OXYGEN. The red blood cells are mainly responsible for the oxygen-carrying capacity of the blood. They contain a conjugated protein, hemoglobin, which is readily converted to oxyhemoglobin in the presence of atmospheric oxygen. Hemoglobin contains the pigment, heme, attached through its iron atom, to the protein, globin. It is believed that the point of attachment to the protein is at the imidazole ring of histidine. The reduced form (Hb) is hydrated, and the oxygenated form (HbO_2) has the water molecule replaced with an oxygen atom. Both the water and the oxygen molecules are readily displaced by carbon monoxide, which forms a poorly dissociated compound, carbon monoxide hemoglobin. This reaction is responsible for the toxic properties of carbon monoxide gas. All of these pigments are red.

| Heme | Hemoglobin (reduced form) | Oxyhemoglobin (oxygenated form) | CO-Hemoglobin | Methemoglobin I |

The iron atom in hemoglobin, oxyhemoglobin, and carbon monoxide hemoglobin is in the *ferrous* state. Certain drugs (aniline, chlorates, nitrophenols, etc.), oxidize the iron atom of hemoglobin to the *ferric* state, changing the compound to *methemoglobin*, a brown pigment. This pigment cannot be oxygenated.

Mechanism of oxygen transfer. The hemoglobin in 100 ml. of blood will combine with 20 ml. of oxygen when exposed to air. This is 100 times more oxygen than can be dissolved by an equal volume of distilled water. However, when the partial pressure of oxygen is lowered, the oxyhemoglobin begins to dissociate. Thus, at 80 mm. of oxygen pressure, 19 ml. of oxygen can be held by 100 ml. of blood. This is approximately the partial pressure of oxygen in arterial blood. At the partial pressure of oxygen in venous blood, (35 mm. of mercury pressure), the oxygen content drops to 12 ml. per 100 ml. of blood. In this manner hemoglobin takes up oxygen where it is present in good concentration (the lungs), and releases it where there is a demand for oxygen (the tissues).

Mechanism of transport of carbon dioxide. The chloride shift. The requirements for carbon dioxide transport are just the opposite to those for oxygen. High concentrations of carbon dioxide occur in the tissues where respiration is taking place, and this must be released to the atmosphere, where the concentration is negligible (.02-.03%). Venous blood contains 50-60 ml. of CO_2 per 100 ml. of blood. Arterial blood is about 10% lower (see Table 36). Here again the amount of CO_2 carried by the blood is much higher than could be carried by an equal volume of distilled water at the same partial pressure (45-47 mm. mercury pressure - venous blood). The CO_2 is carried as (1) HCO_3 - ion (with Na^+, K^+, and Ca^{++}), (2) as carbamates (united with the free amino groups of blood proteins*, especially with hemoglobin), and (3) as dissolved CO_2. Of the total amount of CO_2 liberated from the blood as it travels through the lungs, approximately 70% comes from bicarbonate ion, 20% from carbamates, and 10% from dissolved CO_2.

The conversion of bicarbonate ion to free carbon dioxide is an important reaction, as indicated by the fact that more than two-thirds of the CO_2 released in the lungs comes from blood bicarbonate. The decomposition of bicarbonate to CO_2 is catalyzed by an enzyme, *carbonic anhydrase*, which is found in the red blood cells. Since the bicarbonate of the blood is found mainly in the *plasma*, a mechanism is needed to bring the bicarbonate in contact with the red cell enzyme. This mechanism is known as the *"chloride shift"*. The "chloride shift" is explained in Figure 99. Plasma bicarbonate *enters* the red blood

* $Protein - NH_2 + CO_2 \rightleftharpoons Protein - N\overset{H}{-} C\overset{O}{=} OH + OH' \rightleftharpoons Protein - N\overset{H}{-} C\overset{O}{=} O^- + H_2O$
(Carbamate)

cell in exchange for chloride ions which *leave* the red blood cell and *enter* the plasma. Carbon dioxide is then released from the surface of the red blood cell in the lung capillaries.

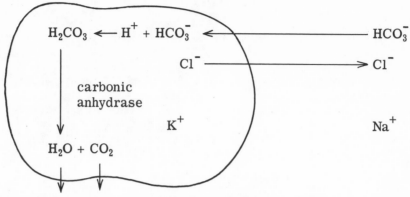

Figure 99.   The "Chloride Shift".

The bicarbonate ion which is transferred to the red blood cell as shown in Figure 99 must first be converted to carbonic acid before it is decomposed by carbonic anhydrase. The hemoglobin of the red blood cell plays an important role as a buffer in this conversion, for it helps to release carbonic acid in the lungs, and to convert carbonic acid to bicarbonate ion in the tissues.   This dual role played by hemoglobin and its oxygenated form is called the *Henderson Cycle* (Fig. 100 on the following page).

Oxyhemoglobin ($HHbO_2$) is a stronger acid than carbonic acid, but hemoglobin (HHb) is a weaker acid (less highly ionized).   When the blood circulates through the lungs, HHb is converted into the stronger acid, $HHbO_2$, which reacts with bicarbonate ion.

$$HHb + O_2 \;\; ----\!-\!> \;\; HHbO_2$$

$$(Na^+, \; K^+, \; etc.)HCO_3 + HHbO_2 \;\; ----\!-\!-\!> \;\; (Na^+, \; K^+, \; etc.)HbO_2 + H_2CO_3$$

$$H_2CO_3 \;\; \overset{\text{carbonic anhydrase}}{----\!-\!-\!-\!-\!-\!-\!-\!-\!>} \;\; CO_2 + H_2O$$

The reverse reaction occurs in the tissues; here the salt of oxyhemoglobin is changed to the salt of hemoglobin, and the carbonic acid reacts with it to form bicarbonate ion.

$$(Na^+, \; K^+, \; etc.)HbO_2 \;\; ----\!-\!-\!> \;\; (Na^+, \; K^+, \; etc.)Hb + O_2$$

$$(Na^+, \; K^+, \; etc.)Hb + H_2CO_3 ----\!> (Na^+, \; K^+, \; etc.)HCO_3 + HHb$$

Hemoglobin thus serves as an oxygen acceptor, oxygen donor, and buffer in these reactions, and its oxygen-carrying, and CO_2-fixing, and releasing functions constitute a cycle between the lungs and the tissues (Fig. 100).

<u>Buffer systems of the blood</u>.   The pH of the blood must be maintained within narrow limits or serious effects are observed.   The pH range of the blood is normally 7.35-7.45.   Symptoms of acidosis are observed if the pH falls below 7.35, with death of the animal at a pH of about 7.0.   Symptoms of alkalosis are observed if the pH rises above 7.45, with death of the animal at a pH of about 7.8.

A buffer system is most efficient at the pH at which *equal amounts* of the weak acid (or base) and its salt are present.   This pH is called the *pK value* of the buffer, and is

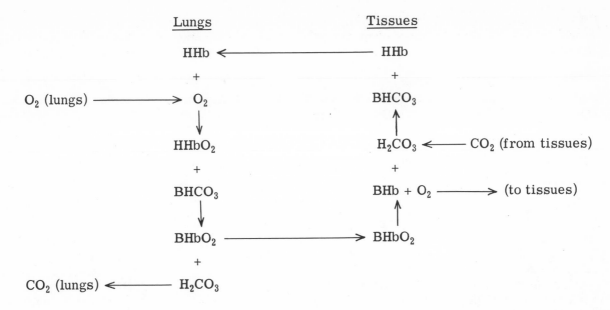

Figure 100.   The Henderson Cycle.

equal to the negative logarithm of the ionization constant of the weak acid (or base).
Mother nature has arranged a "defense in depth" with the blood buffers; the pK values
of the 5 major buffers of the blood are not the same, but serve to cover the range of
acidosis and alkalosis.   The main buffers and their pK values are listed below.

Buffer			pK
H_2CO_3	+	$B*HCO_3$	6.1
BH_2PO_4	+	B_2HPO_4	6.8
$HHbO_2$	+	$BHbO_2$	7.6
HHb	+	BHb	9.2
H-Protein	+	B-Protein	7.0

Glandular Tissues

THE DUCT GLANDS.   Two types of glandular tissues are found in the animal body (1)
those that empty their secretions into ducts *(duct glands)* and (2) those that empty their
secretions directly into the blood stream *(ductless glands)*.   The important duct glands
and their secretions are listed in Table 38.

Table 38.   The major duct glands in animals

Duct gland	Duct outlet(s)	External secretion
Brunner's and Lieberkuhn's glands	Intestinal wall	Intestinal juice
Gastric glands (chief and border)	Stomach wall	Gastric juice
Kidneys	Ureters (bladder)	Urine
Liver	Hepatic duct (gall bladder)	Bile
Mammary	Teats	Milk
Pancreas (acinous tissue)	Pancreatic duct (duodenum)	Pancreatic juice
Salivary glands	Mouth	Saliva
Sebaceous glands	Skin	Oil
Sweat glands	Skin	Sweat

* $B + Na^+$, K^+, Ca^{++}, etc.

Brunner's and Lieberkuhn's glands. These are located in the walls of the small intestine. They are present in greatest concentration in the duodenum, but also occur in the jejunum and ileum. The composition of their secretion is discussed on page 145.

Gastric glands. The gastric glands are essentially a collection of individual secreting cells, called the chief and the parietal (border) cells. The former secrete gastric juice rich in enzymes, the latter secrete gastric juice rich in hydrochloric acid. This is discussed in more detail on page 144.

Kidneys. The mammalian kidney serves as the chief outlet for excess water taken into the body, and for the end-products of nitrogen, mineral and vitamin metabolism. The diagram below (Fig. 101) illustrates the probable mechanism of secretion in a single secreting organ of the kidney. The kidney contains thousands of these individual secreting glands, with a system of duct vessels for collection of the urine secreted. The three major parts of the secreting organ (Fig. 101) are the *glomerulus* (filter), *Bowman's capsule* (collecting basin), and *uriniferous tubule* (absorber). A protein-free filtrate of the blood passes from the glomerulus into Bowman's capsule. It is estimated that in man as much as 75 to 150 *liters* of filtrate are produced by the kidney glomeruli in the two kidneys in a 24 hour period. The 24 hour output of urine, however, is only one to two liters under average conditions. This is due to the effective absorbing powers of the uriniferous tubule. As the blood filtrate passes from Bowman's capsule through the tubule, about 97% of the water, all of the glucose, and part of the chlorides, phosphates and other inorganic ions, are reabsorbed. The lining cells of the tubule at the same time add ammonia and certain other compounds (such as dyes, etc.) to the urine.

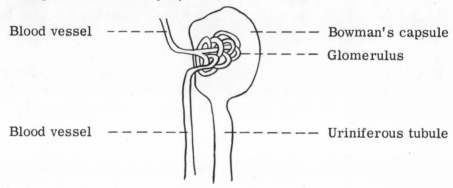

Blood vessel — — — — — — Bowman's capsule
                                      — — — — Glomerulus

Blood vessel — — — — — — Uriniferous tubule

Figure 101.   Secreting Gland of the Kidney.

Composition of Urine. As one would expect with a secretion which reflects the quantity and quality of food ingested, and any abnormalities in body metabolism, the urine varies widely in composition from day to day and from person to person. Table 39 gives the composition of "average" normal human urine. With many of the components, variations can be two-fold, and still remain in the range of normal. It is suggested that the student predict the variations one might encounter with different dietary regimens.

In addition to the components listed in Table 39, normal urine also contains small amounts of hormones, vitamins, proteins, pigments, purines related to uric acid, hippuric acid (glycyl benzoate-detoxification product for benzoic acid), glycuronates (-detoxification product of phenols), volatile fatty acids, fluorides and other inorganic ions, etc.

Normal urine has a yellow color due to the presence of a pigment called *urochrome*. Although urine is normally transparent, it may become cloudy because of the precipitation of phosphates. This often happens after the ingestion of a hearty meal; the increased

Table 39. Composition of "average" normal human
urine (24 hour collection)

Constituent	Amount (gm.)
Water	1200.0
Solids	62.0
Urea	30.0
Uric acid	0.8
Creatinine	1.4
Indican	0.01
Oxalic acid	0.02
Allantoin	0.01
Amino acid nitrogen	0.2
Purine bases	0.03
Phenols	0.2
Chloride as NaCl	12.0
Sodium	4.0
Potassium	2.0
Calcium	0.2
Magnesium	0.15
Total sulfur as S	1.0
Inorganic sulfates as S	0.8
Neutral sulfur as S	0.12
Conjugated sulfates as S	0.08
Phosphate as P_2O_5	3.0
Ammonia	0.7

alkalinity of the urine causes precipitation of the phosphates present. Normal urine has a faint aromatic odor which is not unpleasant. The unpleasant odor develops when micro-organisms convert part of the urea to ammonia, and cause other changes. Common preservatives for urine are chloroform, toluene and thymol. Refrigeration is also very effective.

Liver. The liver cells secrete a fluid called *bile,* which serves as a pathway for the excretion of certain dyes, and of certain lipids such as cholesterol, and also has important functions as an aid to digestion. The bile as it is secreted by the liver contains about 3% solids. This passes by way of the hepatic duct into the gall bladder. Here some of the water and inorganic salts are removed so that gall bladder bile contains about 14% solids. The entrance of food into the duodenum causes the gall bladder to contract and bile to flow through the common bile duct (in man) into the duodenum. The average composition of liver and gall bladder bile is given in Table 40.

Table 40. Composition of human bile

Component	Liver Bile (%)	Gall Bladder Bile (%)
Water	97.13	86.00
Bile salts	1.55	8.20
Mucin and pigments	0.49	2.25
Cholesterol	0.12	2.17
Fat, including lecithin	0.06	0.66
Inorganic salts	0.72	0.78

Mammary glands. The secretion of the mammary glands of mammals (including man) serves as the sole food of the mammal during the critical period of early growth. Breast feeding of human infants is becoming less popular as satisfactory formulas for feeding are developed. Nevertheless, the major ingredient of these formulas is still milk, usually cow's milk. The cow's milk is fortified with a source of carbohydrate (dextrimaltose, corn sirup, etc.) to compensate for the difference in lactose content of human and cow's milk (see Table 41).

Table 41. Average composition of milk from different species*

Kind of Milk	Water (%)	Protein (%)	Fat (%)	Lactose (%)	Mineral Matter (ash) (%)	Fuel value per 100 gm. (kilo cal.)
Human	87.5	1.4	3.7	7.2	0.2	68
Cow	87.0	3.5	3.9	4.9	0.7	69
Goat	87.0	3.3	4.2	4.8	0.7	70
Sheep	82.6	5.5	6.5	4.5	0.9	99
Reindeer	63.7	10.3	19.7	4.8	1.5	238

* Compiled by Food Composition Section, Bureau of Home Economics, U.S.D.A.

Milk has sufficient amounts of the nutrients that are essential for early growth and maintenance, provided that those factors lacking in milk were present in the diet of the mother, and that adequate amounts of the missing factors were stored in the offspring during gestation. The major nutritive essentials lacking in milk are *iron*, and *copper*, and the vitamins *thiamine, ascorbic acid*, and *vitamin D*.

Pancreas (acinous tissue). The acinous tissue of the pancreas is the major tissue of this organ as far as bulk is concerned. The acinous tissue surrounds smaller islands of tissue, called the Isles of Langerhans, which are ductless tissues secreting the hormone, insulin. The acinous tissue secretes pancreatic juice, a digestive juice rich in proenzymes for the digestion of proteins, lipids, and carbohydrates. The pancreas in adult humans secretes about 500-800 ml. of pancreatic juice in 24 hours. The composition of this secretion is described on page 145.

Salivary glands. In humans, three sets of glands are located in the mouth (see p. 140) (1) the sub-lingual (under the tongue), (2) the sub-maxillary (under the jawbone), and (3) the parotid (one duct opening in each cheek). The composition of saliva is discussed on page 143.

Sebaceous glands. These glands are distributed throughout the skin of the body of animals and humans. The secretion, which keeps the outer layers of the skin soft and pliable, is oily and contains fats, waxes (such as lanolin - see p.53), and cholesterol.

Sweat glands. These glands are distributed throughout the skin of those animals which are capable of perspiring, and are abundant in the skin of humans. Sweat closely resembles urine in its composition. In humans who are perspiring heavily, urine production by the kidneys is markedly reduced. Losses of sodium chloride via sweat can be so heavy that the human suffers from a salt deficiency (miner's cramps). Doctors recommend that salt tablets be taken with the water ingested by humans who are perspiring heavily.

DUCTLESS GLANDS. The ductless glands of the body, in contrast to the duct glands, pour their secretions *directly* into the blood stream. The active compounds in their secretions have been named *hormones*. A hormone is usually defined as an organic com-

Table 42. Major ductless glands in animals

Ductless Gland(s)	Internal secretion(s)
Adrenals	Adrenalin (medulla), steroids (cortex)
Duodenal glands	Secretin, cholecystokinin, enterogas-trone
Ovaries	Estrogens, progesterone (all steroids)
Pancreas (Isles of Langerhans)	Insulin (protein)
Parathyroids	Parathormone (protein)
Pituitary	Protein hormones (both lobes)
Testes	Androgens (steroids)
Thyroid	Thyroxine (amino acid)

pound which is produced in one tissue, and carried by the blood stream to another tissue, which it stimulates to activity. The major ductless gland tissues are listed in Table 42.

Adrenal glands. These glands are situated one above each kidney, and consist of two parts, the *medulla* (center part), and the *cortex* (outer shell). The medulla secretes a hormone, epinephrine (adrenalin) which is a derivative of phenylalanine and tyrosine.

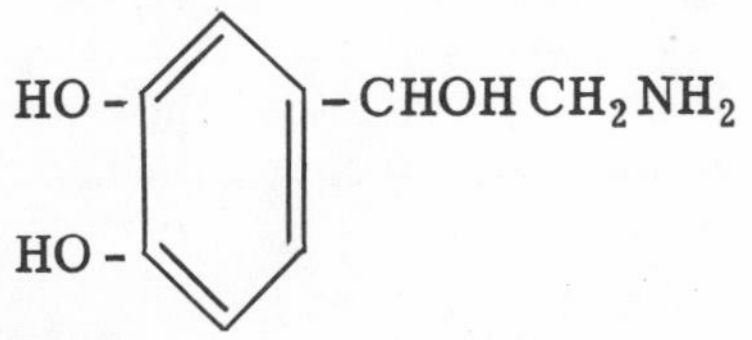

Norepinephrine (Noradrenalin) 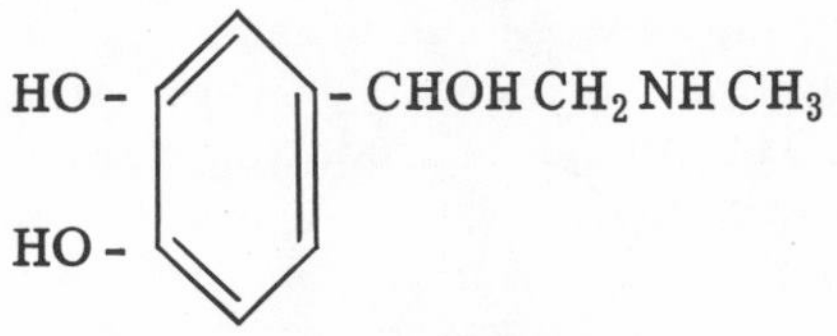   Epinephrine (Adrenalin)

Studies with radioactive isotopes have shown that epinephrine is synthesized from phenylalanine in the animal body (see p. 200). Norepinephrine is one-twentieth as potent as epinephrine as a hyperglycemic agent, but a more potent hypertensive agent. These two hormones stimulate the sympathetic nerves, and are apparently necessary for the transmission of nerve impulses in the sympathetic nerve system. Injection of epinephrine is followed by a rapid rise in blood pressure, caused by a constriction of the small arteries (arterioles). The hormone also causes relaxation of the bronchioles (see p. 262), increases salivation, raises the level of glucose by stimulating the liver to split glycogen (p. 156), and increases the basal metabolic rate (p. 213).

Adrenal Cortex. The outer shell, or cortex, of the adrenal glands produces more than 28 different steroid compounds; six of these have marked biological activity. Removal of

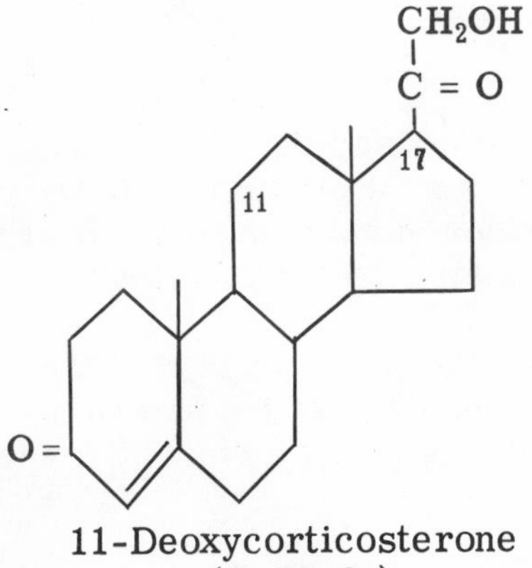

11-Deoxycorticosterone   Cortisone (17-Hydroxy-11-dehydro-
($C_{21}H_{30}O_3$)   corticosterone ($C_{21}H_{28}O_5$)

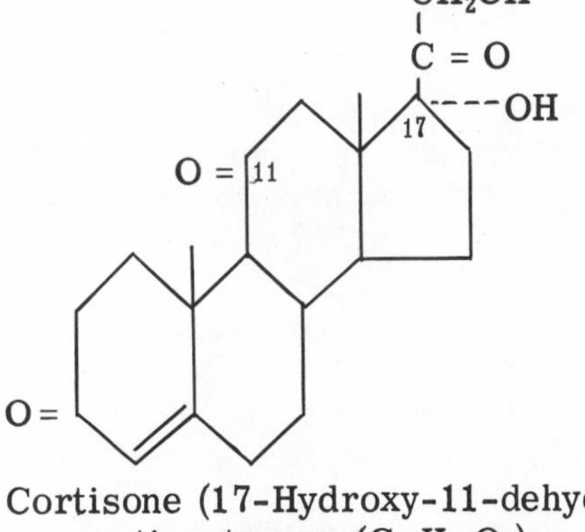

the adrenal medulla is tolerated by animals, but removal of the adrenal cortex decreases the ability of the animal to do work, or to withstand stresses of any kind (exposure to cold, fasting, exposure to disease organisms, etc.), upsets the salt balance of the body, so that excessive amounts of sodium and chloride ions are excreted in the urine, and upsets carbohydrate metabolism. The glycogen disappears from the liver, muscle weakness develops, and growth is inhibited. The ability of the various active cortical steroids to cure these symptoms varies. The two steroids which are the most potent in curing some of these symptoms are *11-deoxycorticosterone* and *cortisone* (17-hydroxy-11-dehydrocorticosterone), whose formulas are shown on the preceding page.

The most active cortical steroid for regulating salt metabolism, and for maintaining the life of adrenalectomized animals is *11-deoxycorticosterone*. In contrast, *cortisone* is relatively inactive as a regulator of salt metabolism, and when administered alone will not prevent the death of adrenalectomized animals. However, it is the most potent member of the group for improving the animal's ability to withstand stress, to store glycogen, and to do work. The other four active cortical steroids (corticosterone, 11-dehydrocorticosterone, 17-hydroxy-11-deoxycorticosterone, and 17-hydroxycorticosterone) resemble one or the other of the two cortical steroids discussed, except that they do not show as high a level of potency.

In humans, insufficient secretion of adrenal cortical hormones causes a condition known as *Addison's disease*. The disease is usually caused by tuberculosis or syphilis which attacks the adrenals. The use of 11-deoxycorticosterone has greatly prolonged the life expectancy of these patients, although they still cannot withstand the stresses of normal humans. It is possible that injections of *cortisone* will correct this deficiency, and clinical tests are now in progress to test its usefulness.

The most outstanding therapeutic use for cortisone in recent years has been for the treatment of *rheumatoid arthritis*, and other non-specific infections against which the body does not seem to have adequate defenses. Cortisone stimulates the body to fight these infections and inflammations, and its injection even relieves the pain associated with the inflammatory processes. Cortisone is now being manufactured by both chemical and microbiological synthesis, starting with inexpensive plant and animal steroids. Another hormone which is useful in the treatment of these diseases is a pituitary hormone, ACTH, which will be discussed later.

Duodenal glands. Secretin. The secretion of pancreatic juice is controlled by the hormone, secretin. This hormone is produced by the action of the HCl of the gastric juice on a proenzyme, prosecretin, which is present in the mucosa (lining) of the duodenum. When the acid chyme empties from the stomach into the first part of the duodenum, the release of secretin into the blood stream speeds up the flow of pancreatic juice into the duodenum. Secretin has been obtained in crystalline form (as the picrolonate). It is a polypeptide with a molecular weight of approximately 5,000, and contains about 36 amino acid units.

Cholecystokinin. This hormone, which was isolated by Ivy and coworkers, is apparently similar to secretin, for it is activated by HCl and exists as a proenzyme in the duodenal mucosa. The active hormone stimulates the gall bladder to contract in several animal species tested. The hormone has not been isolated in purified form.

Enterogastrone. This duodenal hormone is released when fat is present in the intestine. It inhibits the secretion of gastric juice, and the motor activity of the stomach. Although its chemical nature is unknown, it has been used in semipurified form with some success in the treatment of peptic ulcers.

Ovaries. The ovaries in the female animal and human secrete two types of hormones (1) the *estrogenic hormones,* which produce estrus and cause development or accentuation of femaleness, and (2) *progesterone,* which so affects the uterus that it is put in proper condition for the implantation and the nourishment of the fertilized ovum.

Estrogenic hormones. The parent substance of the estrogenic hormones is "Estrane" (see p. 50 for classification of steroids). The most potent natural estrongenic hormone is *estradiol,* which has two hydroxy groups and three ethylenic linkages.

Estrane

Estradiol
(Dihydroestrone)
(3-17dihydroxy-$\Delta^{1, 3, 5}$-estratriene)

Diethylstilbestrol

Dihydrodiethylstilbestrol
(Hexostrol)

Other estrogenic hormones produced by the ovary with one-third to one-tenth of the activity of estradiol are Estrone (theelin) : 3-hydroxy-17 keto$\Delta^{1, 3, 5}$-estratriene (1/6 as active), Estriol (theelol) : 3, 16, 17-trihydroxy-$\Delta^{1, 3, 5}$-estratriene (1/10 as active), Equilin (mare ovary) " 3-hydroxy-17-keto-$\Delta^{1, 3, 5, 7}$-estratetraene (1/3 as active), and Equilenin (mare ovary) : 3-hydroxy, 17-keto$\Delta^{1, 3, 5, 6, 8}$-estrapentaene (1/10 as active).

A synthetic coal-tar derivative, *diethylstilbestrol,* and its hydrogenated derivative, *dihydrodiethylstilbestrol* (see formulas above), are very active as estrogens. Diethylstilbestrol has about one-half the activity, and dihydrodiethylstilbestrol roughly the same activity, as estradiol. These synthetic compounds are effective orally (natural estrogens must be injected), and are inexpensive substitutes for the natural estrogens in the treatment of female disorders due to the lack of the natural hormones. It is indeed surprising that stilbestrol and its derivatives, when added in small amounts to cattle feeds, produce faster gains and increased feed efficiency in both sexes, without affecting the quality of the beef produced. Whether this is related to its estrogenic properties is not known. It has been found that estrogenic hormones are excreted in the urine of all mammals, both male and female, indicating that both sexes produce these substances, and that they are not limited to the female ovary. Their function in males is not known, but may be related to general body metabolism as indicated by the findings with cattle.

Progesterone. This steroid hormone is made in the corpus luteum (ovarian bed), and in the placenta, and is a derivative of the parent steroid, *pregnane* (see page 50).

Pregnane

Progesterone
(3, 20-Diketo-Δ^{4-5}-pregnene, <u>cis</u>)

It is related structurally to the steroid hormones of the adrenal cortex (p. 269). Progesterone has no estrogenic activity; it is quite specific for modifying the uterine sur- face so that nidation (implantation) of the fertilized ovum can occur, and pregnancy can be maintained through proper nourishment of the implanted ovum. It is injected clinically in an oil solution intramuscularly to prevent threatened abortion, and to correct certain dis- turbances of menstruation.

Progesterone is reduced in the body to pregnandiol (dihydroxy derivative of pro- gesterone), which is excreted in the urine as a derivative of glucuronic acid (p. 31). The use of deuterium-labeled cholesterol demonstrated that this sterol is the precursor of progesterone.

Testes. The testes of the male secrete a group of steroid hormones which have been named *androgens* (Gr. *andros*, male). The most potent of these is *testosterone*, which is a derivative of the parent steroid, *androstane* (p. 50).

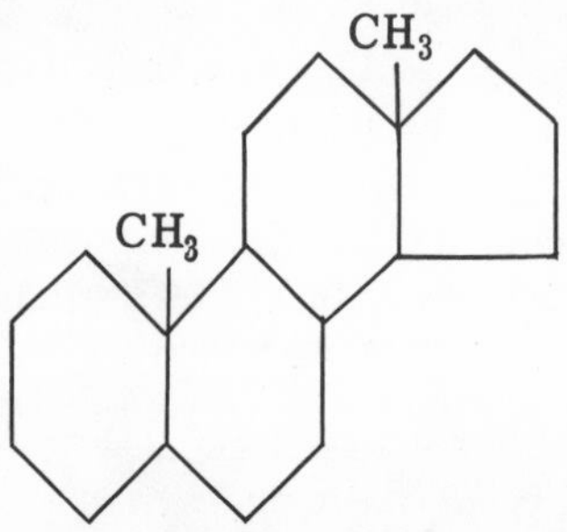

Androstane ($C_{19}H_{32}$)

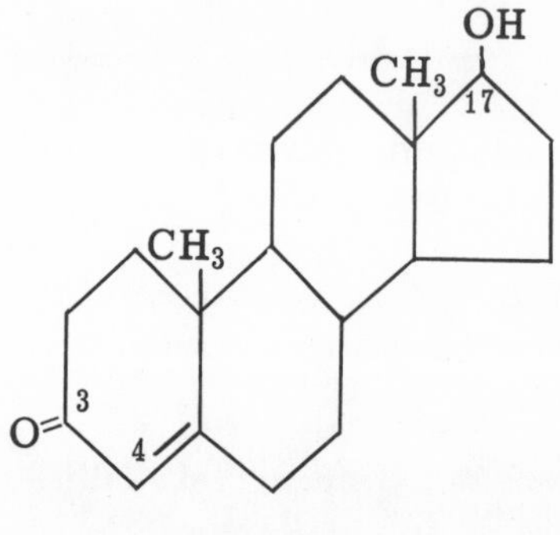

Testosterone
(3-Keto-17-hydroxy-Δ^4-androstene)

Other androgens produced by the testes are androsterone: 3-hydroxy-17 keto andro- stane, dehydroandrosterone : 3-hydroxy-17 keto-Δ^5 androstene, and adrenosterone : triketone produced by oxidation of 11-dehydro-17-hydroxycorticosterone.

These hormones control the development of the male genital organs, the production of spermatozoa, and the appearance of male secondary sex characteristics, in the same manner that the estrogenic hormones control the development of the female sex organs, and secondary sex characteristics.

Pancreas. The pancreas consists of two types of tissues - acinous tissue, which produces pancreatic juice (see duct glands, p. 265), and small islands of tissue embedded in the acinous tissue, known as the *Isles of Langerhans*. The islet tissue secretes a hormone, called *insulin*. Insulin is a protein with a molecular weight of 6,000. In the first study to show the complete sequence of amino acids in a pure protein, Sanger (see p. 60 for formula) demonstrated that insulin is built up of two open polypeptide chains, which are held together by -S-S-bridges of cystine.

Destruction of the islet tissue of the pancreas in animals or man produces a meta- bolic disease known as *diabetes mellitus*. The major symptoms of this disease are high fasting blood levels of glucose (150-400 mg/100 ml. of blood), with excessive excretion of glucose in the urine, and excessive oxidation of fatty acids with the piling up of acetone bodies (see p. 183), in the blood and urine. Weight loss is rapid in spite of the ingestion of adequate amounts of food, thirst is abnormal and large volumes of water are consumed to dilute out the glucose and acetone bodies in the urine; a gradual acidosis of the blood and tissues develops because the alkali reserves of the body are depleted, due to neutralization of acetoacetic and beta-hydroxybutyric acids before excretion. In untreated cases of diabetes, death occurs due to coma produced by extreme acidosis.

It is estimated that there are at least one million diabetics in the United States alone, who are dependent on daily injections of the hormone, insulin, for continued living. By following his physician's advice as to daily dosage (a diabetic with little or no functioning islet tissue needs 80-100 units of insulin daily), it is now possible for the diabetic to live out his normal life span with little limitations on his activities, except with respect to diet.

Insulin was first isolated in 1922 from the pancreas of dogs by Banting and Best at the University of Toronto, Canada. The pancreatic duct was tied off, causing atrophy of the acinous tissue of the pancreas. Insulin was then extracted from the pancreas. Previous attempts to isolate insulin had failed, because the proteolytic enzymes of the acinous tissue digested the insulin in the islet tissue before the insulin could be extracted. The methods of insulin manufacture have been greatly improved in the last 30 years. Beef and hog pancreas are the major sources of the hormone; the hormone is first extracted with acid-alcohol, which inactivates the proteases of the acinous tissue. Using standard methods of protein purification, a highly potent product is obtained.

In the pancreas, the insulin is apparently in the form of its zinc salt; the purified insulin from beef and hog pancreas is therefore converted into its zinc salt for drug use. Since insulin is a protein, it is attacked by the proteases in the digestive tract; it must therefore be injected to be effective. Fortunately for humans, insulin is not an antigenic protein (see p. 267); if antigenic, it would not be possible to inject bovine and porcine insulin into the blood stream of humans because of anaphylactic reactions.

Formerly, it was necessary for diabetics to inject insulin three times daily in order to maintain proper blood sugar levels. Now most diabetics need to inject insulin only once daily, usually in the morning before breakfast. By combining insulin (an acidic protein with an isoelectric point of 5.3) with protamine (a very basic protein with high isoelectric point - see p. 65), a salt, *protamine-insulin,* is obtained. This is very slowly absorbed on injection, and releases insulin slowly to the bloodstream, simulating the action of the normal pancreas.

Oral substitute for insulin. Diabetics who develop the disease in middle age or later can take a sulfanilamide derivative, tolbutamide*, by mouth and maintain satisfactory blood glucose levels. Its action is not clearly understood, but it may be destroying an insulin splitter (or inhibitor), thus allowing the diabetic to make more efficient use of his own insulin.

Hyperglycemic Factor (Glucagon). It was found that many preparations of commercial insulin contained small quantities of a factor which actually *increased* blood glucose levels, instead of decreasing them, as insulin itself does. This hormone, called *glucagon,* has been obtained in pure form and its amino acid sequence determined.

Insulin shock (hypoglycemia). Injection of excessive amounts of insulin produces hypoglycemia, which can lead to *insulin shock,* a state of coma (unconsciousness). Prompt administration of glucose by vein or mouth will alleviate the condition, which may otherwise prove fatal.

Metabolism of insulin. Small amounts of insulin are excreted in the urine, but most of the insulin is split by a proteolytic enzyme in the liver into a mixture of peptides which are excreted in the urine. This enzyme has been named "insulinase" by Mirsky and co-

* Sold commercially under the trade name "Orinase".

workers. A natural inhibitor of this enzyme, which seems to be a simple peptide, is also present in the liver. It is called insulinase inhibitor. It is possible that diabetes may be due in some cases to a low level of *insulinase inhibitor*, which in turn would permit excessive destruction by "insulinase" of the insulin produced by the pancreas of the diabetic. This was discussed in connection with the action of tolbutamide.

Alloxan diabetes. The compound, *alloxan*, when fed to animals, destroys the islet tissue of the pancreas, to produce a disease known as *alloxan diabetes;* this disease resembles diabetes mellitus in many respects.

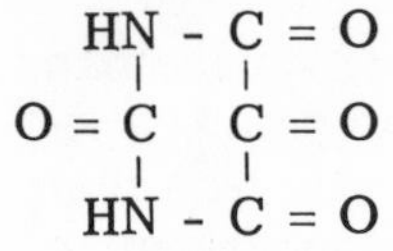

$$
\begin{array}{ccc}
HN & - & C = O \\
| & & | \\
O = C & & C = O \\
| & & | \\
HN & - & C = O \\
\end{array}
$$

Alloxan

Phlorhizin diabetes. A condition, resembling in certain respects diabetes mellitus, may be produced by feeding animals the drug, *phlorhizin,* a glucoside (see p. 16) present in the root and bark of many fruit trees.

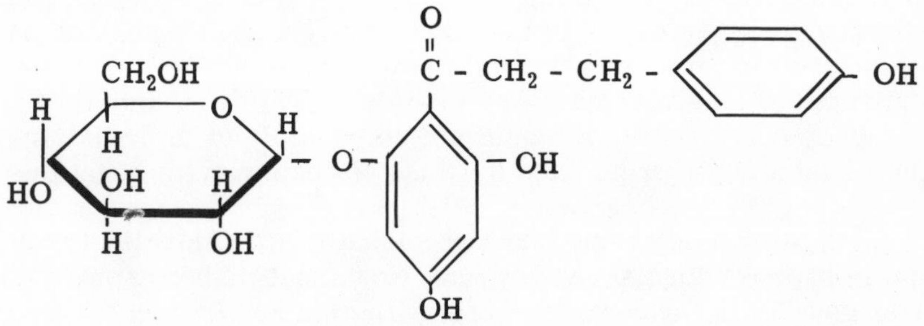

Phlorhizin

Phlorhizin actually produces a *renal glucosiuria* by affecting the secreting glands of the kidney (see p. 266) so that the resorption of glucose by the tubules is prevented. The blood sugar level is actually lower than normal, and the animal converts all metabolites (amino acids, certain fatty acids, carbohydrates, etc.) available in the blood into glucose to try to maintain the blood sugar level as near normal as possible.

Parathyroids. These are small bodies imbedded in, or closely associated with, the thyroid gland. Total removal, and in some animals, even partial removal, is fatal. The parathyroids secrete a protein hormone, called *parathormone,* which regulates the calcium, and possibly the phosphate level, of the blood. In its absence, blood calcium falls from its normal level of 9-11 mg. per 100 ml. of blood, to about one-half of this level. This produces a condition known as *tetany,* or hyperirritability of the muscles. Uncoordinated movements, or spasms, of the muscle occur, which when severe enough, cause death. Injection of calcium lactate will stop the spasms. The disease is sometimes observed in infants (infant tetany or "convulsions"), due to a low calcium level in the blood brought on by high fever, etc. Injection of parathyroid hormone promptly corrects the tetany. Parathormone has not been prepared in pure form yet, but the properties of purified preparations indicate that it is a protein.

Thyroid. The thyroid gland, located in the neck, secretes a hormone, thyroxine, which controls the rate of metabolism in the body. In the thyroid gland itself, thyroxine is bound, together with a probable precursor, diiodotyrosine, in a protein of high molecular weight (600,000 or higher), called *thyroglobulin*. Using radioactive iodine (I^{131}) as a tracer, it can be shown that thyroxine is mostly protein-bound (to plasma proteins) in the blood stream. Recent evidence indicates that 3,5,3'-triiodothyronine is five times more active than thyroxine, and may be the true peripheral hormone, with thyroxine a precursor. The formulas of these iodinated amino acids are shown on p. 249.

The thyroid gland takes about 80 times more iodine from the blood than do the other body tissues. When it has acquired between 20 and 30 mg. of iodine per 100 ml. of tissue, no more iodine is absorbed, and excess dietary iodine is excreted in the urine. Thyroxine (and/or 3,5,3'-triiodothyronine?) is then slowly released to the blood stream as it is needed, to maintain the normal basal metabolic rate (see p. 213), and to meet special demands for increased tissue oxidation.

In humans, two major types of thyroid dysfunction are observed, (1) subnormal functioning (hypothyroidism) and (2) overactivity (hyperthyroidism). *Hypothyroidism* may be caused by a dietary deficiency of iodine (common goiter, see p. 250), which in infants may cause cretinism, or mental and physical stunting. If the subnormal functioning is caused by inability of the thyroid to produce thyroxine even in the presence of normal amounts of dietary iodine, then the disease in its more severe form is called "myxedema". Here the patient becomes edematous and takes on a puffy appearance. Common goiter in adults and children responds quite well to ordinary iodized salt (sodium chloride containing potassium iodide), and the use of this in place of ordinary salt for table use has practically wiped out common goiter in the "goiter belt" (Great Lakes region of the United States). Cretinism and myxedema respond better to thyroxine than to iodine, because in these conditions the thyroid gland is no longer functioning normally.

Hyperthyroidism appears in a number of mild forms, but the most striking example of this condition is Grave's disease, or exophthalmic ("toxic") goiter. In Grave's disease, the basal metabolic rate is at least 20% above normal, and may be as high as 40% above normal. The patient has a rapid heart rate, a flushed face, usually protruding eyeballs (exophthalmos), insomnia, loss of weight in spite of normal food intake, and is unable to relax. Fatal termination in untreated cases is usually due to overstrain of the heart. In these patients, the thyroid contains too much thyroxine synthesizing tissue, and the standard treatment has been surgical removal of a large portion of the thyroid gland. Since iodine is almost selectively absorbed by the thyroid, a new therapy (both for Grave's disease and for cancer of the thyroid) is to feed or inject radioactive iodine (I^{131}) in measured amounts; the radioactive iodine collects in the thyroid gland, and the radiation destroys part of the tissue. Radioactive iodine is also used as a diagnostic tool in the determination of the various types of thyroid dysfunctions. Its rate of uptake by the gland gives valuable information on the functioning of this organ.

Thyroid inhibitors (Goitrogens). A number of compounds have been found to inhibit thyroxine production by the thyroid gland. Examples are the sulfonamides (p. 102), uracil (p. 109), 2-, and 6-propyl-2-thiouracil, and thiourea. Of these inhibitors, 2-, and 6-propyl-2-thiouracil appear to be the most potent, and have been studied intensively

$$N_3 = {}_4C - OH$$
$$HS - C_2 \quad {}_5CH$$
$$N^1 - {}^6CH$$

2-Thiouracil

$$NH_2$$
$$C = S$$
$$NH_2$$

Thiourea

$$N_3 = {}_4C - OH$$
$$HS - C_2 \quad {}_5CH$$
$$N^1 - {}^6C - CH_2CH_2CH_3$$

6-propyl-2-thiouracil

as thyroid depressants in humans and animals. Propyl thiouracil is being used in the treatment of human hyperfunction of the thyroid, especially Grave's disease, with considerable success. Goitrogens are also found in common foods such as yellow turnips, cabbage, peas, spinach, etc.

In vitro synthesis of thyroxine and diiodotyrosine. When casein and certain other proteins are treated with iodine in the presence of mild alkali (sodium carbonate), iodine is added to the tyrosine molecules, and small amounts of thyroxine are formed. The amount of thyroxine produced in this manner is related to the tyrosine content of the protein (for example, gelatin, which is low in tyrosine, does not yield thyroxine). Because this is an inexpensive way to produce a material rich in thyroxine, iodinated casein has been tested as a source of thyroxine to increase egg production in hens, and milk production in cows. Both egg production and milk production *can* be increased in this manner, but the practice is of doubtful value where the hens and cows are to be carried through more than one production period; overstimulation in this manner "burns them out", so that peak production cannot be maintained over several years.

Thyroxine and metamorphosis. In addition to its function of regulating metabolic rate in man and animals, thyroxine is responsible for the metamorphosis of salamanders, frogs, and similar species. The administration of thyroxine to tadpoles will quickly cause their change into frogs; if the tadpole is very tiny, frogs the size of flies can be produced. Conversely, removal of the thyroid gland from tadpoles prevents their metamorphosis into frogs, and they become giant tadpoles.

Pituitary. The pituitary is a small gland situated at the base of the brain; in the human adult it weighs only about 0.7 gm. In spite of its small size, it has often been referred to as the "master gland" of the body, because of its effect on the functioning of most of the other ductless glands. The pituitary gland has four main parts *(pars glandularis, pars nervosa, pars intermedia,* and *infundibulis* (stalk)); however, most biochemists refer to two parts, the *anterior lobe* (pars glandularis), and the *posterior lobe* (pars nervosa + pars intermedia). The infundibulis or stalk connects the pituitary with the brain.

Anterior lobe hormones. These hormones are called *trophic* hormones because they affect the functioning of other ductless glands or act directly on growth. They are apparently all proteins (or polypeptides) and are produced by individual specialized cells. Six anterior lobe hormones have been prepared in a state of purity or near-purity, namely, adrenocorticotrophic hormone (ACTH), follicle-stimulating hormone (FSH), luteinizing or interstitial-cell-stimulating hormone (ICSH), lactogenic hormone, growth-promoting hormone (GH), and thyrotrophic hormone. Other hormones which have been postulated as present in the anterior lobe include; pancreotrophic hormone, fat-metabolizing hormone, and diabetogenic hormone.

Adrenocorticotrophic hormone (ACTH). The complete molecular structure of ACTH isolated from sheep pituitaries has been determined by C. H. Li and coworkers. It is a straight chain molecule containing 39 amino acid residues. The ACTH molecule is known as a-corticotrophin. It is possible to break off 11 amino acids on the right side of the chain, leaving a residue with 28 amino acids, which has been called b-corticotrophin. b-Corticotrophin (molecular weight of about 3,000) still retains the biological activity.

ACTH stimulates the adrenal cortex to produce cortisone (see p. 269), and other steroid hormones. For this reason, it is effective in the treatment of rheumatoid arthritis and other metabolic disorders initiated by infectious agents.

Follicle-stimulating hormone (FSH). C. H. Li and coworkers have prepared this hormone in a state of relatively high purity. The hormone prepared from sheep pituitaries is a glycoprotein. It has the solubility properties of an albumin, an isoelectric point of 4.8, and contains about 13% carbohydrate (mannose and hexosamine).

This hormone exerts its effects on cells concerned with the production of ova and sperm. In the female, FSH stimulates the growth of the Graafian follicles of the ovary;

in the male, FSH stimulates the growth of spermatogenic tissue in the testes, without affecting the interstitial tissue. In the female, FSH appears to be synergistic with ICSH (see below), and to exert its effects only in the presence of this hormone.

Interstitial-cell-stimulating hormone (ICSH). Luteinizing hormone. C. H. Li and coworkers have isolated a relatively pure form of this hormone from sheep pituitaries. It has a molecular weight (osmotic pressure method) of about 40,000, and is a very water soluble glycoprotein. Its isoelectric point is 4.6, and the hormone contains 14.2% nitrogen and 10.3% carbohydrate (about equal amounts of mannose and hexosamine).

This hormone was long known as the luteinizing hormone, because it stimulates the development of the corpus luteum in the ovary. Now it is recognized as a hormone which stimulates interstitial cells in both the ovary and the testis. In the female it must act in conjunction with FSH. In the male, ICSH stimulates the interstitial cells (Leydig cells) of the testes, causing them to produce *androgens* (see p. 272). This hormone must therefore be one of the major factors in the initiation of puberty in human males. At levels too low to affect the Leydig cells, ICSH has been shown also to stimulate spermatogenic tissues to activity.

Growth-promoting hormone (GH). Li and Evans have isolated this hormone from beef pituitaries in highly purified crystalline form. It is a simple protein, with a molecular weight of about 42,000, and isoelectric point of 6.85. The protein, which has been obtained electrophoretically pure, is insoluble in distilled water. It contains 15.6% total nitrogen.

This hormone exerts its effects on the entire body. Continued injection will produce giants who show no distortion in the proportions characteristic of the species. Variations in the production of the growth hormone in humans is responsible for such dissimilar strains as the pygmies and the giant Watusi tribe in Africa. Diet may have been responsible originally for their difference in size, but adjustment has been made in level of secretion of GH so that the difference in growth potential is now inherited.

GH has been shown in experimental animals to increase bone growth, to produce a retention of nitrogen (positive nitrogen balance - p. 223), and to lower the R.Q. (p. 212).

In general, growth slows down as the animal or human approaches sexual maturity. It then ceases in most species shortly after sexual maturity has been attained (this is not the case with many species of fish; apparently there is no inhibitor of the free growth hormone acting at the time growth normally ceases in animals and humans. Growth hormone can be isolated from the pituitaries of mature, non-growing animals. Nevertheless, the *liberation* of growth hormone from the anterior pituitary is checked in some manner which is not understood at present.

Pathologically, hypofunction of the pituitary with decreased secretion of GH can produce one type of dwarf with normal intelligence but physically small, delicately formed, and with the features of a doll. These dwarfs, if they mature sexually, can produce children who will have normal stature. Another type of GH deficiency may give the *Frolich syndrome*, with sluggish growth, obesity and sexual infantilism.

A hyperpituitary condition in which excessive amounts of GH are produced in mature humans is called *acromegaly*. In this condition, which is usually caused by stimulation of the pituitary by tumor growth, the bones of the face and hands grow out of proportion to the rest of the tissues, causing distortion of the features.

Lactogenic hormone. (Prolactin). This hormone has been isolated in what appears to be a pure form from beef and sheep pituitaries. The products are proteins but are not identical from the two species. The sheep hormone has a molecular weight of about 24,000, is water-insoluble, absolute alcohol-soluble, contains 15.8% nitrogen, and has an iso-electric point of 5.7.

Lactogenic hormone stimulates milk secretion. Injection of this hormone causes lactation not only in the normal pregnant female, but also in the non-pregnant female, and in the hypophysectomized (pituitary removed) female. It can even cause some lactation in the *male* if injected after the male has been suitably conditioned with estrogenic hormone.

Thyrotrophic hormone. This hormone has not been isolated in a state of purity comparable to that of the other hormones discussed. The purest preparations indicate that the hormone is a glycoprotein with molecular weight of about 10,000, containing 12-13% nitrogen, and glucosamine as the carbohydrate component.

This hormone causes growth (enlargement) of thyroid cells, with increased production of thyroxine. Large doses injected into experimental animals lead to symptoms of hyperthroidism, even producing exophthalmus. There appears to be a balanced relation between the thyroid and anterior pituitary glands. The production of thyrotrophic hormone is depressed if there is excessive production or administration of thyroxine. Conversely, lowered production of thyroxine is followed by increased liberation of thyrotrophic hormone.

Posterior lobe hormones. Two major hormones have been isolated from the posterior lobe of the pituitary, *oxytocin* and *vasopressin*. Some workers believe that these hormones are a part of a larger molecule; however, the mild conditions under which they can be extracted from the ground tissue makes this seem improbable. These hormones have been isolated in pure form, and their structures proved by degradation and by total synthesis, by DuVigneaud and coworkers.

Oxytocin is a cyclic octapeptide with the structure shown below.

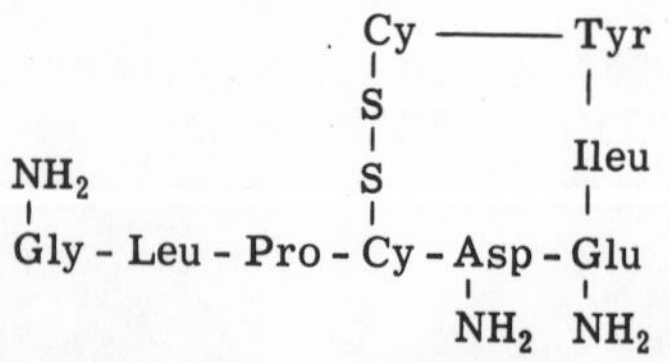

Oxytocin (amino acid pattern) 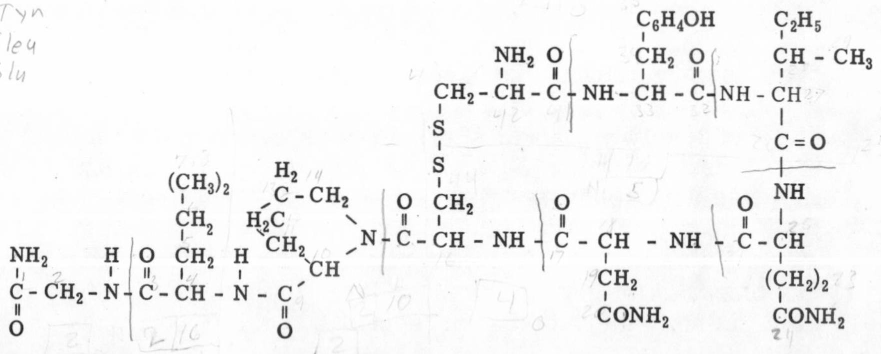   Oxytocin (full structure)

Oxytocin has as its outstanding properties the ability to contract uterine muscles (to a smaller extent, smooth muscles generally), and to act as a "milk let down factor" in nursing mothers. Oxytocin can be injected to hasten labor, and to facilitate extrusion of the afterbirth and involution of the uterus.

Vasopressin is a cyclic octapeptide with the structure shown on the following page. Beef vasopressin contains *arginine* in the side chain, whereas hog vasopressin contains *lysine* in place of arginine in the side chain.

```
                                                              C6H4OH    C6H5
                                                   NH2  O      CH2  O    CH2
                                                    |   ||      |   ||    |
                                             CH2 - CH - C - NH - CH - C - NH - CH
                                              |                                 |
                                              S                               C = O
            Cy ——— Tyr                NH2      |                                |
            |       |                  |       S                   O      O    NH
            S      Phe               C = N-H   |                   ||     ||    |
            |       |                  |      CH2 - CH - NH - C - CH - NH - C - CH
    NH2     S      Glu     NH2       N - H  CH2-CH2  |                |          |
     |      |       |       |         |        |     N - C = O       CH2        CH2
 Gly-Arg-Pro-Cy-Asp-Glu   C-CH2-NH-C-CH - NH - C = O               CONH2       CH2
              |    |       ||        ||                                          |
             NH2  NH2      O         O                                         CONH2

 Beef Vasopressin (amino acid pattern)          Beef Vasopressin (full structure)
```

It can be seen from the above formulas that oxytocin and vasopressin have similar structures, but different amino acid composition. Pure vasopressin has about one-tenth the activity of oxytocin as a uterine contractant, which may be related to similarity of structure; however, the outstanding biological properties of *vasopressin* are associated with its ability to restrain urine output (antidiuretic effect), and its ability to raise the blood pressure. Vasopressin is a specific hormone for the control of *diabetes insipidus*, a disease of humans in which the volume of urine excreted is enormously increased, although glucose is not excreted (as in diabetes mellitus). A major function of vasopressin is thus to restrain the loss of water from the kidney, for polyuria develops in experimental animals when the posterior lobe is removed.

Vasopressin has only a temporary effect on the blood pressure. Presumably it is one of several substances that normally help to regulate blood pressure. Thus, thyroxine, epinephrine, and a hormone-like protein, *renin*, also seem to function in this respect. Renin is a proteolytic enzyme secreted into the blood stream by the kidney, and splits a blood globulin to release a peptide, *hypertensin*. Hypertensin is a potent compound which raises the blood pressure by contraction of the small arteries, combined with increased heart action. Hypertensin is in turn destroyed by an enzyme, *hypertensinase*. Improper functioning of the renin system could conceivably produce hypertension, but this has not been demonstrated in any human cases. Another pressor substance produced in the body is *serotonin*, which has been isolated from blood serum. Serotonin is 5-hydroxy tryptamine.

```
HO -  /==\  - CH2 - CH2
      |  |           |
      |  |          NH2
      \==/
        |
        N
        |
        H
```

Serotonin

Other Specialized Tissues

In addition to blood and glandular tissues, which have been discussed at some length, there are several other specialized tissues in the animal body. The most important of these are *adipose* tissues, *bone* and *teeth*, *connective* tissues, *epithelial* tissues, *muscle* tissues, and *nervous* tissues. These will be discussed briefly on the following pages.

ADIPOSE TISSUES. Adipose tissue consists of a fascia matrix containing lobules or small clusters of fat-containing cells. It is widely distributed in the animal body, but is most abundant in the third major layer, or subcutaneous tissue, of the skin. Distribution of fat in the adult female rat was found to be independent of the diet fed, and is probably similar to that of other mammals and man. The distribution is as follows: subcutaneous tissue: 50%; genital region (ovaries, uterus): 20%; perirenal (around kidneys): 12%; mesenteric (between blood vessels in intestines): 10%; intermuscular: 5%; and omental (covering intestines): 3%. Adipose tissue may contain more than 90% triglycerides on a dry weight basis; the composition of the triglycerides will vary depending on the diet (see p. 218). Normal amounts of adipose tissue serve as a storehouse for potential energy to tide the animal over periods of starvation, and as a protective cushion for other body parts.

BONES AND TEETH. Both bone and teeth consist of an organic matrix (mainly proteins) in which crystals of mineral salts are deposited in large amounts. The mineral matter of dried, fat-free bone makes up about 60% of its weight. The mineral content increases to 70% for the cement layer, to 77% for the dentine layer, and to 96% for the enamel layer of teeth; the root of the tooth is similar in mineral content to bone (see Fig. 102 below).

The composition of the mineral matter of bones and teeth can be fairly accurately represented by the formula $3Ca_3(PO_4)_2 \cdot CaX_2$, where X is usually CO_3, but may also be F, SO_4, O, or $(OH)_2$. The bone and teeth microcrystals resemble the mineral, apatite, in both crystal habit and composition. Recent studies indicate, however, that a continuous series of solid solutions is present, all having the crystal lattice of apatite, but with

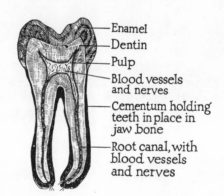

— Enamel
— Dentin
— Pulp
— Blood vessels and nerves
— Cementum holding teeth in place in jaw bone
— Root canal, with blood vessels and nerves

Figure 102.   Molar tooth cut lengthwise (U. S. Dept. of Agriculture).

variable ratios of calcium, phosphorus, hydrogen and oxygen. This crystal lattice can accommodate a large number of substitutes for the usual major elements, such as those listed under X above. It could also explain the ease with which calcium and phosphate ions from the blood are deposited in bones and teeth.

The *organic matrix* of bone and teeth is composed mainly of the proteins *collagen*, *osseoalbuminoid*, and *osseomucoid*. Osseoalbuminoid and osseomucoid are very similar in composition and properties to chondroalbuminoid and chondromucoid, respectively, which, with collagen, will be discussed in the next section.

The deposition of minerals in the organic matrix (calcification process), is dependent on (1) the levels of calcium and phosphorus in the blood, (2) the activity of bone phosphatase which makes organic phosphate available, (3) the ratio of Ca:P in the diet, (4) vitamin D (and ascorbic acid) and (5) activity of the parathyroid gland. These factors are all interdependent, and have been discussed in the chapter on minerals (see p. 242).

Studies with radioactive phosphorus have shown that there is a continual exchange with dietary minerals of mineral elements in the bones and teeth. The rate of exchange of injected radioactive phosphorus for enamel, dentin, and bone was in the ratio of about 1:16:100 in the cat.

The center of most bones in mammals and birds is filled with a fatty material called marrow. Marrow is rich in phospholipids, and is one of the major sites of red blood cell formation in adult animals and humans. Fish bones do not contain marrow.

Dental caries. Civilized man suffers greatly from dental caries or tooth decay. Many theories have been proposed to explain its cause, some of the more plausible being (1) production of acid by acid-forming bacteria, which causes progressive lesions in the teeth due to decalcification, (2) faulty tooth structure due to malnutrition, (3) pit formation during the growth process - the pits holding food particles and serving as fermentation vats. One of the most promising treatments for preventing dental caries is the frequent brushing of the teeth with dentrifices containing stannous fluoride, and for children, the addition of one part per million of the element, fluorine, as sodium fluoride, to the city water (see p. 250).

CONNECTIVE TISSUES. The function of connective tissues is to bind various parts of the body together, and in some cases to act as a supporting tissue. Examples of these functions are the binding of bone to bone by ligaments, the binding of bone to muscle by tendons, the binding of bone to bone (rib to sternum, vertebral cushions or pads) by cartilage, serving as second major layer of skin (collagen), as areolar fibers holding soft parts of body in place (elastin), and as the walls of blood vessels (elastin).

Tendons and ligaments. As shown by the data in Table 43 on a typical tendon (heel tendon), and typical ligament (neck ligament), collagen comprises more than three-fourths of the solids in tendon, whereas elastin comprises about three-fourths of the solids in ligament.

Table 43. Composition of representative tendon and ligament

Component	Tendon of Achilles (beef) (%)	Ligamentum nuchae (beef) (%)
Water	62.9	57.6
Inorganic material	0.5	0.5
Ether-soluble material	1.0	1.1
Coagulable protein	0.2	0.6
Mucoid protein	1.3	0.5
Elastin	1.6	31.7
Collagen	31.6	7.2
"Extractives"	0.9	0.8
Total solids	37.1	42.4

Collagen. Collagen is a fibrous protein (see p. 60) which is easily digested by pepsin but not by trypsin. The reason for this difference is that collagen is readily converted by treatment with acid or by boiling into another protein, *gelatin,* which is very water soluble and easily digestible by either pepsin or trypsin. Collagen is the major protein in *white fibrous tissue,* and is found in good quantity also in the organic matrix of bones and cartilage, and in skin.

Elastin. Elastin is also a fibrous protein. It is slowly digested by proteolytic enzymes, but is not converted to gelatin by boiling. Elastin is the major constituent of the *yellow elastic tissues* of the body. In addition to the ligaments, it is the major constituent of areolar fibers and the wall in blood vessels. It confers elasticity on these tissues. Both collagen and elastin are rich in the amino acid, glycine, which makes up about one-sixth of the weight of gelatin (see p. 317, Appendix).

Cartilage. The major constituent of cartilage is collagen, which has been discussed above. Another fibrous protein present in cartilage is *chondroalbuminoid*. Little is known about its nature except that it is an insoluble, but digestible, protein. Probably the most unique component of cartilage is the sulfate-containing glycoprotein, *chondro-mucoid*. This conjugated protein can be split by mild hydrolysis into protein (or peptides), and *chondroitin sulfuric acid,* whose formula is shown below. This acid is the repeating unit of the polysaccharide present in chondromucoid.

   Chondroitin sulfuric acid contains glucuronic acid, acetylated galactosamine, and sulfuric acid, connected by glycosidic (see p. 17) or ester linkages. It is similar to mucoitin sulfuric acid, the monomer in the polysaccharide from mucin of saliva, which contains acetylglucosamine instead of acetyl galactosamine, and contains only one sulfuric acid group. Removal of the sulfuric acid group from mucoitin sulfuric acid leaves *hyaluronic acid.* This acid is present as a polysaccharide polymer in vitreous humor, synovial fluid, umbilical cord, skin, etc. and is believed to function as a cementing material, holding cells together in a jelly-like matrix and serving as a lubricant and shock-absorber in the joints. An enzyme, *hyaluronidase,* depolymerizes the polysaccharide. Some bacteria contain this enzyme to aid in the penetration of the skin, which is cemented together with hyaluronic acid. Mature spermatozoa also contain relatively large amounts of hyaluronidase, which is believed to disperse the surface-cementing cells of the ovum, and permit the penetration of the ovum by the spermatozoon.

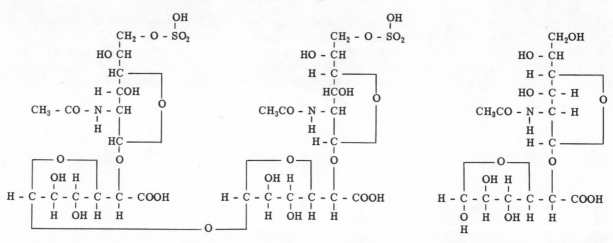

Chondroitin sulfuric acid monomer   Hyaluronic acid monomer

   At birth, the skeleton of animals and man is mainly cartilage; with increasing age, calcification and deposition of other minerals changes nearly all of the 200 bones in man to rigid high-mineral structures. Only ⅟ few sections of cartilage persist, such as the cartilage in the nose, cartilage connecting ribs to sternum, etc. Bone, then, may be considered as essentially calcified cartilage; in many species of fish, the transition from cartilage to bone never takes place, the skeleton remaining cartilaginous throughout life.

EPITHELIAL TISSUES. These tissues serve as a protective covering for the parts of the body exposed to the outside environment, such as the skin, and the lining of the respiratory tract. They also serve as a protective skin covering internally for the glandular organs and nervous tissues. As further protection to the animal, epithelial tissues produce dermal outgrowths such as nails and claws, hoofs and horns, and hair and feathers.

Epithelial tissues produce fibrous proteins (see p. 64) which are insoluble in all common solvents, and highly resistant to digestion by enzymes.

By far the greatest amount of research has been carried out on the composition of skin and hair. The major proteins of these epithelial tissues are classed as *keratins*. The keratin of hair and other dermal outgrowths has been called eukeratin by Block. It contains more arginine than the keratin of skin epidermis and related skin coverings, which he calls *pseudokeratins*. Both types of keratins are high in sulfur (about 3-5%), most of which is in the form of cystine. Thus, human hair contains about 16-21% cystine, wool about 8-11%, and feathers about 7-12%. The indigestibility of eukeratins is related to their fibrous nature, and especially to the rigidity of the peptide chains, which are held in a special configuration by the -S-S- linkages of the cystine. Reduction of these linkages to -SH groups, or simply grinding the protein in a ball mill (oxidation of the -S-S- groups?), markedly increases the digestibility of the eukeratin.

MUSCLE TISSUES. The body of man and higher animals contains approximately 500 different muscles, which are essential for blood and lymph circulation, motor activity of the digestive system, breathing, and locomotion. Muscle tissue is by far the most abundant tissue in the animal body. There are three main types of muscle tissue in the body, *skeletal, cardiac,* and *smooth*. The skeletal muscles provide power for movement and give form and substance to the extremities. The cardiac muscles form the walls of the heart. The smooth muscles are found in the eye, in the walls of the alimentary canal, and blood vessels, in the various ducts and channels that transmit fluid, and may comprise the bulk of an organ, as in the case of the uterus. Sometimes skeletal muscle is called *voluntary* muscle, and cardiac and smooth muscles are called *involuntary*. Also, since skeletal muscle shows cross-markings under the microscope, it is sometimes called *striated*, and smooth muscle, which lacks this characteristic, is called *nonstriated*.

Most of the chemical studies have been made on skeletal muscle; smooth muscle is similar in composition but tends to be somewhat lower than skeletal muscle in total proteins. Skeletal muscle contains about 25% total solids and 75% water. Of the 25% solids, about four-fifths is protein, and one-fifth is a mixture of many compounds (called muscle extractives). The major protein constituent is a euglobulin called *actomyosin* (formerly called myosin), with a molecular weight of about one to four million, and an isoelectric point of 5.5. This accounts for about two-thirds of the total protein. The remaining proteins are mainly a globulin, *globulin X,* and an albumin, *myogen,* present in a ratio of about 2:1. Red muscle fibers (but not white fibers) also contain a fraction of a per cent of a red pigment, *myoglobin,* which is similar to hemoglobin.

Actomyosin is the major protein concerned with muscle contraction. It is probably a complex resulting from the combining of two proteins "F-actin" and "a-myosin". In combination with adenosine triphosphate (ATP - see p. 166), which is closely associated with actomyosin in the muscle, muscle fibers shorten, or contract, when a nervous, or outside electrical stimulus, is applied. It is not known whether the coupling of actomyosin with ATP occurs during the contraction or the relaxation phase. At any rate, high energy phosphate bonds (p. 167) are consumed in the reaction, and must be replenished by oxidation of carbon compounds during the *recovery* stage after relaxation.

Muscle extractives. These can be divided into two classes, *nitrogenous,* and *non-nitrogenous*. The important nitrogenous extractives are creatine, creatine phosphate, purines (free and combined as nucleotides), carnosine, carnitine, anserine, adenylic acid, adenosinetriphosphate (ATP), inosinic acid, and traces of urea and creatinine. The structural formulas of some of these compounds are shown on the following page.

$$
\begin{array}{c}
\text{OH} \\
\text{NHP} = \text{O} \\
\text{HN} = \text{C} \quad \text{OH} \\
\text{N CH}_2\text{COOH} \\
\text{CH}_3
\end{array}
$$

Creatine phosphate (about 100 gm. in human body)

$$
\begin{array}{c}
\text{NH}_2 \\
\text{HN} = \text{C} \\
\text{N} - \text{CH}_2\text{COOH} \\
\text{CH}_3
\end{array}
$$

Creatine

$$
\begin{array}{c}
\text{H} \\
\text{N} \\
\text{HN} = \text{C} \\
\text{N} - \text{CH}_2 - \text{C} = \text{O} \\
\text{CH}_3
\end{array}
$$

Creatinine

$$
\begin{array}{c}
\text{H} \\
\text{H} - \text{C} - \text{N} \\
\| \quad\quad \text{C} - \text{H} \\
\text{C} - \text{N} \\
\text{CH}_2 \\
\text{H} \quad \text{O} \\
\text{CHN} - \text{C} - \text{CH}_2 \text{CH}_2 \\
\text{COOH} \quad\quad \text{NH}_2
\end{array}
$$

Carnosine
(Beta-alanyl histidine)

$$
\begin{array}{c}
\text{CH}_3 \\
\text{H} - \text{C} - \text{N} \\
\| \quad\quad \text{C} - \text{H} \\
\text{C} - \text{N} \\
\text{CH}_2 \\
\text{H} \quad \text{O} \\
\text{CHN} - \text{C} - \text{CH}_2 \text{CH}_2 \\
\text{COOH} \quad\quad \text{NH}_2
\end{array}
$$

Anserine
(Methyl carnosine)

$$(CH_3)_3 N - CH_2 \, CHOH \, CH_2 \, COOH$$
$$OH$$

Carnitine
(a betaine)

Creatinine, the anhydride of creatine, is excreted in relatively constant amounts in the urine (1-1.2 gm. per 24 hr., depending on total muscle mass, in man). Creatine, however, is rarely found in the urine of adults. Feeding experiments with isotopically labelled creatine and creatinine have proved that the *in vivo* conversion of creatine to creatinine is *irreversible*. Creatinine is therefore the *end-product* of creatine metabolism. Both creatine and creatinine phosphate are found in relatively high concentration in muscles. Creatine phosphate (a high energy phosphate - p. 167) apparently plays an important role in muscle metabolism, supplying energy for the resynthesis of ATP.

The functions of carnosine, anserine and carnitine in muscle are not known. It is interesting to note that carnitine has been found to be a vitamin (see p. 225), for *Tenebrio molitor* (the mealy worm).

The important *non-nitrogenous extractives* of muscle are glycogen, lactic acid, inorganic salts, hexose phosphates, lipids, and some water-soluble vitamins, especially inositol. Skeletal muscle is estimated to be capable of storing a maximum of 1.5% of glycogen. When an animal is slaughtered, glycolytic enzymes rapidly split the glycogen of the muscles to glucose.

NERVOUS TISSUES. About 85% of the total nervous tissue in the body is found in the brain, and most studies of composition have been made on brain tissue. Adult whole brain (mixed white and gray matter) has a high water content, about 77-78%, with human spinal cord somewhat lower (about 75%). The solid matter (about 22-25%) is composed mainly of proteins, lipids, and extractives. In adult whole brain solids, these are distributed about as follows: proteins, 38-40%, lipids 51-54%, and extractives (including inorganic salts), 8-9%.

Brain proteins. The major proteins isolated to date are a *globulin*, coagulation point 47°C., a globulin, coagulation point 70-75°C., and a fibrous protein, neurokeratin (a pseudokeratin similar to the keratin in skin epidermis - see p. 283). It has been suggested that the condition known as *sunstroke* may be due to the coagulation of the first globulin listed, which has a very low coagulation point. Temperatures above 47°C. are often encountered on the surface of the skull, but no one has devised a method of making measurements of internal brain temperatures in humans, so this interesting hypothesis has not been tested experimentally.

Lipids. The triglyceride content of brain tissue is very low. Most of the lipid material is present in the myelin sheaths, and consists of *phospholipids* (lecithins, cephalins, and sphingomyelins - p. 45), glycolipids (cerebrosides) (p. 48), and cholesterol (p. 51) and related sterols.

Extractives. Brain tissue contains about 1% of inorganic salts, mainly the sodium, potassium, calcium and magnesium salts of phosphoric and hydrochloric acids. It also contains free glucose, a trace of glycogen, lactic acid, and other intermediates of carbohydrate metabolism. The extract also contains free amino acids in proportions not like that found in serum. Glutamine, glutamic acid and aspartic acid predominate in the brain extract.

Metabolism of nervous tissue. The rate of uptake of oxygen in the brain tissue is 30-60 times greater than that in nerves (peripheral nerves, ganglia, plexuses). There are no significant stores of glycogen in nervous tissue, and both the brain and the other parts (spinal cord, nerves) must depend on direct utilization of the glucose, which is carried to them by the blood. Because of this dependence on blood glucose, the brain is one of the first parts of the body to be affected by a lowering of the glucose level (hypoglycemia). Normal fasting levels for blood sugar are 70-120 mg. per 100 ml. of blood; reduction to a level of about 40 mg. so inhibits the normal oxidative metabolism of the brain that the animal or human becomes unconscious (goes into a coma), which will be fatal if glucose is not supplied quickly.

Mechanism of transmission of nerve impulses. The actual impulse is an electric current which is initiated by some electrochemical process involving the cleavage of high energy bonds. Oxidative metabolism is not *immediately* required for nerve excitation, but is needed during the recovery period so as to restore the excitability of the nerve. In this respect, nerve discharge and muscle contraction are similar.

Chapter 14 | BIOCHEMICAL CONTROL OF ORGANISMS

New compounds, mostly organic in nature, have proved effective in the control of many plants, animals and microorganisms. A search for even more effective agents is always in progress. Some of these agents are described in this chapter.

PLANT HORMONES (AUXINS). The formulas for three growth hormones (auxins) commonly found in plants are shown below.

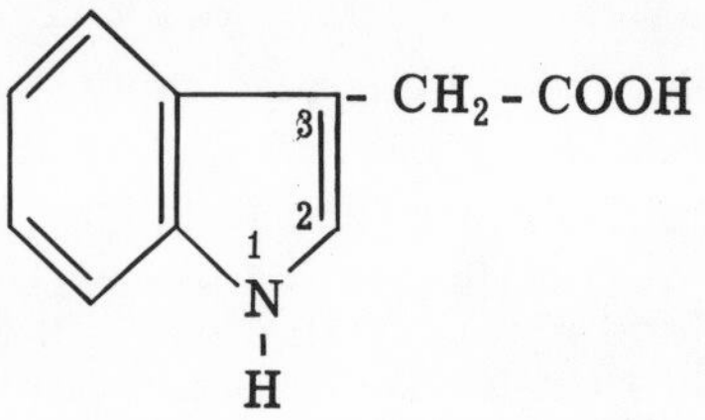

3-indoleacetic acid (IAA)   3-indoleacetonitrile 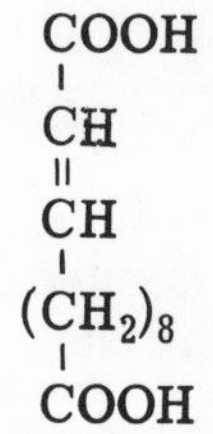   traumatic acid
(heteroauxin)

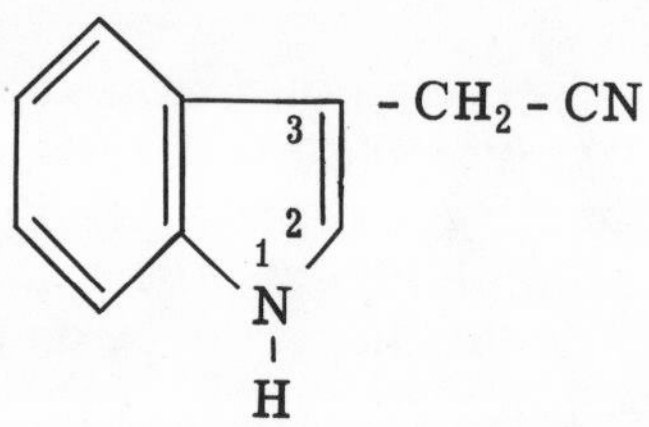

Other hormone substances have been reported to be present in plants, but their presence has not been verified. Plant hormones are believed to cause the following responses in plants: phototropism (bending toward light), geotropism (bending of stems away from, and roots toward, the center of gravity), bending produced by injury (mediated by traumatic acid), epinasty (downward bending of leaves), initiation of flowering, inhibition of sprouting, and the hastening of rooting.

Many synthetic organic compounds, related to the above compounds, exert similar effects. Thus, the methyl ester of naphthalene acetic acid, and also maleic hydrazide, inhibit the sprouting of potatoes and carrots. Most growth agents, natural and synthetic, hasten the rooting of cuttings. These agents are also used to prevent premature dropping of blossoms and fruit, and for production of seedless fruits (here applied to the flower). Although the natural and synthetic hormones produce normal and beneficial effects at high dilutions, when used in higher concentrations, they become effective herbicides (see below).

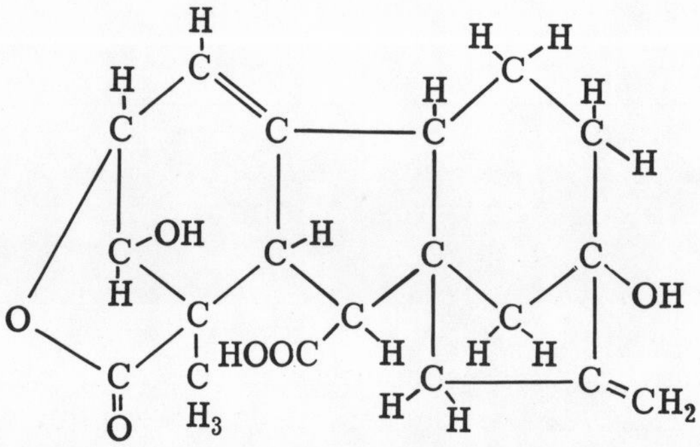

Gibberellic Acid (Gibberelin X, A_3)

GROWTH SUBSTANCES. The gibberelins. These growth substances were discovered
in Japan about 30 years ago, but it has only been in recent years that they have been studied intensively in this country. Gibberelins are produced by a fungus, *Gibberella fuji-
kuroi*. From this fungus, at least three gibberellins have been isolated. All are acids of
complex structure. The probable formula of one of the gibberelic acids is shown on the
preceding page.

Figure 103.   Effect of gibberellic acid on pea seedlings.   Treated
seedlings in right pot.

The gibberellins have been applied to a large number of plants and have been found
to produce a rather wide variety of responses. The most consistent and striking response,
however, is the ability of these substances to produce a marked elongation of the plant's
stems. In citrus trees, it has been found that this substance will cause the stems to
lengthen more than six-fold when compared with controls. In an experiment performed
by the author, a dilute solution of gibberellic acid was applied to five pea seedlings of
equal length just prior to planting them in a pot. At the same time, another five pea
seedlings of the same length as the experimental seedlings were planted in another pot.
At the end of four days, the seedlings that had been treated with gibberellic acid had
grown considerably more than those serving as control plants (see Fig. 103).

SELECTIVE HERBICIDES. The most effective herbicides discovered to date are certain
plant growth substances closely related to the naturally occurring plant hormones or auxins. The formulas for three growth hormones (auxins) commonly found in plants are
shown on p. 286.

A synthetic "plant hormone" which has found wide use in recent years as a herbicide
is 2, 4-dichlorophenoxyacetic acid, commonly known as "2, 4-D". Broad-leafed plants
(dicotyledonous types) are much more sensitive to this growth hormone than are mono-
cotyledons such as the grasses and cereals. It is therefore possible to apply it to lawns,
pastures, and grain fields for the control of broad-leafed weeds. 2, 4-D is usually applied as the non-volatile sodium salt, or as an amine derivative. The esters of this compound are not recommended, because they are volatile, and may be carried by the wind
to broad-leafed vegetables, shrubs and trees, which they injure.

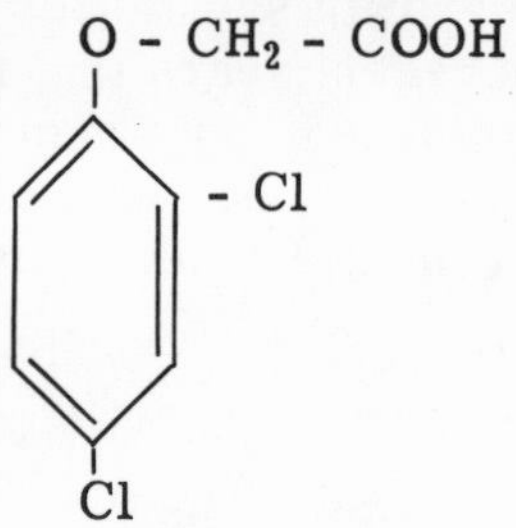

O - CH₂ - COOH

- Cl

Cl

2, 4-dichlorophenoxyacetic acid (2, 4-D)

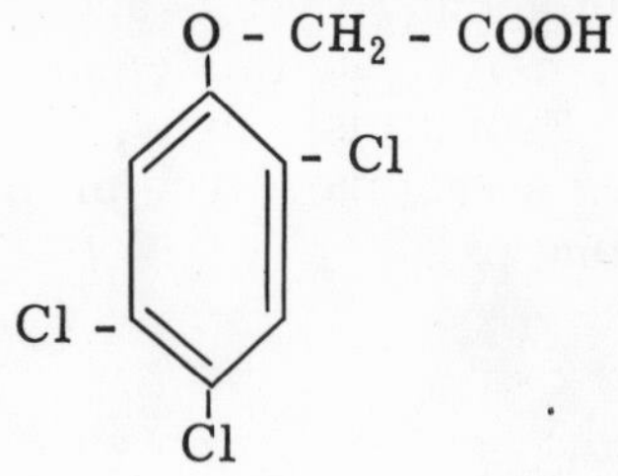

O - CH₂ - COOH

- Cl

Cl -

Cl

2, 4, 5-trichlorophenoxyacetic acid (2, 4, 5-T)

A compound closely related to 2, 4-D has been found to be very effective for the killing of resistant woody non-economic plants (brush and shrub types). It is 2, 4, 5, - trichlorophenoxyacetic acid (2, 3, 5-T).

FUNGICIDES. All fungicides tested to date are relatively non-selective, and are toxic to all forms of life. Some of the more effective organic fungicides contain mercury and chlorine. The formulas for four of these compounds are shown below.

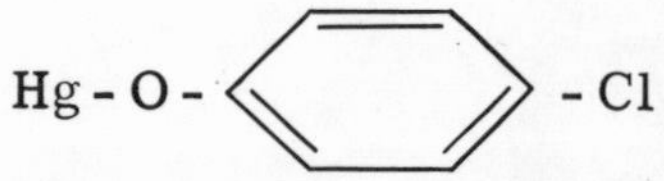

Hg - O - ⟨ ⟩ - Cl

hydroxymercurichlorophenol

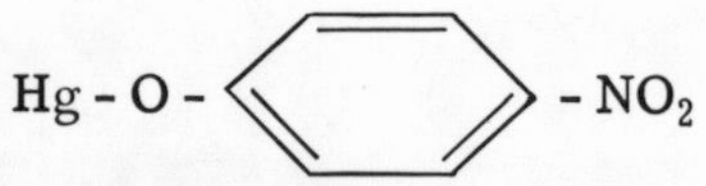

Hg - O - ⟨ ⟩ - NO₂

hydroxymercurinitrophenol

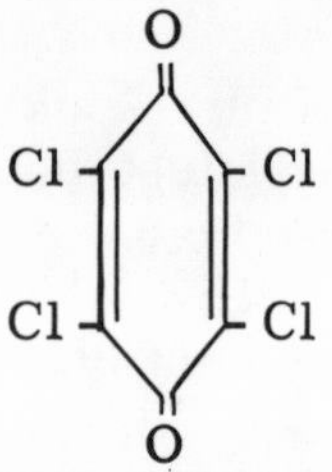

O

Cl   Cl

Cl   Cl

O

chloranil (tetrachloro-p-benzoquinone)

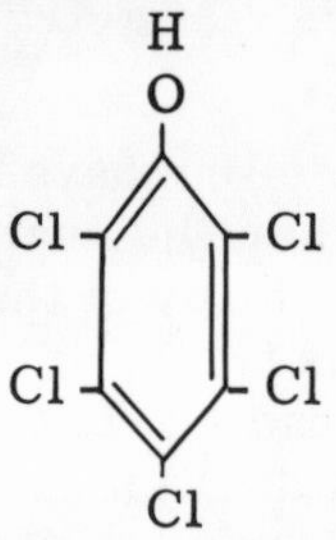

H
O

Cl   Cl

Cl   Cl

Cl

pentachlorophenol

For additional information on fungicides, the student is referred to textbooks on this subject.

Insecticides

Insecticides may be classified on the basis of their action: (a) contact poison, (b) stomach poison or (c) gaseous poison (fumigant). Several textbooks have devoted considerable space to the discussion of the many inorganic and organic insecticides. A few organic compounds which show outstanding action as insecticides are discussed below.

DDT. (2, 2-bis-(p-chlorophenyl)-1, 1, 1-trichloroethane). This compound was found to be an effective insecticide by a Swiss chemical company (Geigy, Inc.) during World War II, and was used widely by the U.S. Army, in their far-flung operations, to control insects, lice, malaria-carrying mosquitoes, etc.)

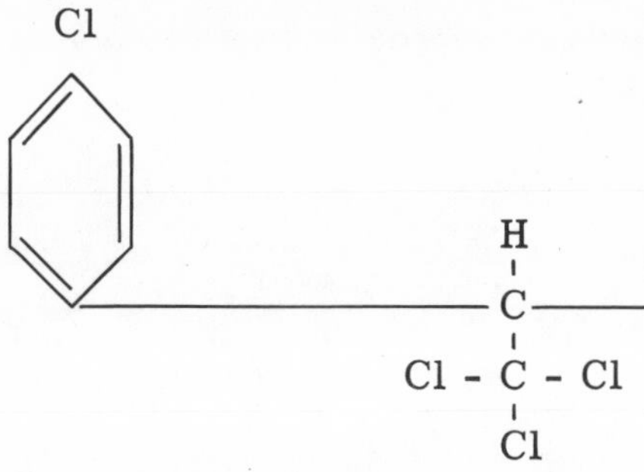

DDT (2, 2-bis-(p-chlorophenyl)-1, 1, 1-trichloroethane).

DDT acts both as a stomach and a contact poison, causing hyperirritability of the nervous system, with consequent death. It is a fat-soluble compound, and in oil or fat-solvents can be absorbed through the skin of higher animals, as well as insects. Since its effects are cumulative, care must be taken to avoid poisoning of animals, and to prevent accumulation of DDT residues in plant and animal tissues serving as human food.

DDT is marketed in the form of wettable powders, oil solutions, emulsifiable concentrates, aerosols, and dusts. The user must exercise judgment in the use of these forms for his particular needs. Adequate directions are supplied by the manufacturers.

Two compounds related to DDT have been found more useful than DDT in particular applications. TDE is more effective than DDT in controlling the corn borer, and methoxychlor is less toxic than DDT to higher animals.

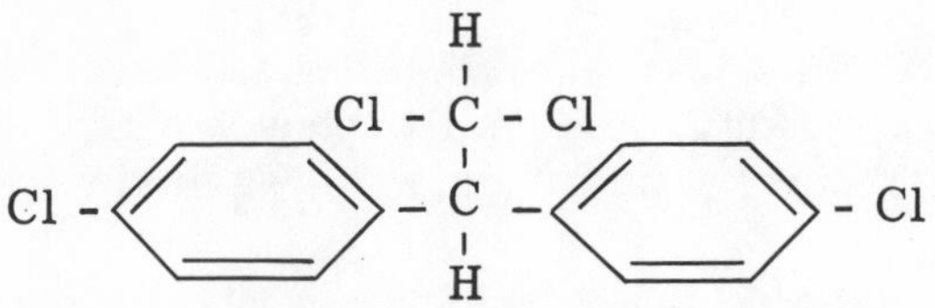

TDE

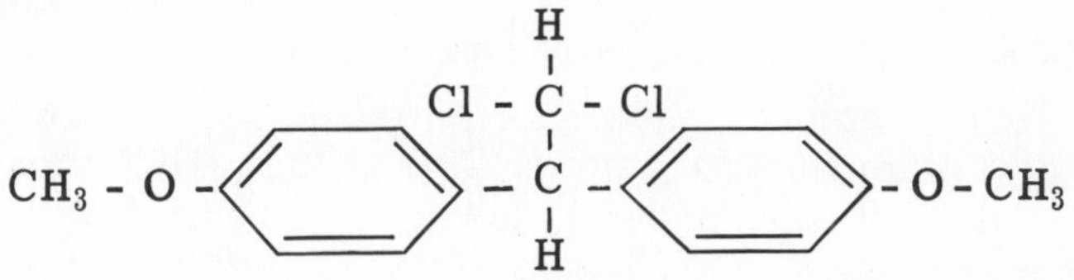

Methoxychlor

BHC (BENZENE HEXACHLORIDE). Another insecticide that has been found to be highly effective is benzene hexachloride, or more correctly, 1, 2, 3, 4, 5, 6-hexachlorocyclohexane.

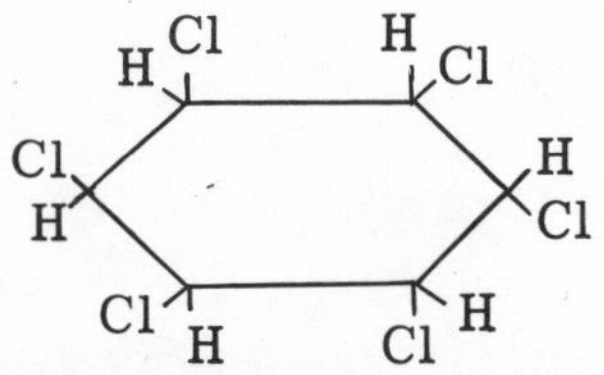

BHC (benzene hexachloride)

BHC may exist in 16 isomeric forms (space isomers). Of the limited number of isomers isolated in pure form to date, the gamma isomer is the most effective insecticide. The commercial form of highly purified (99+%) gamma isomer is called *lindane*. Lindane resembles DDT in its toxic properties, and the same precautions must be followed in using it. Lindane has a sufficiently high vapor pressure to act not only as a stomach and contact poison, but also as a fumigant.

Three other organic insecticides that are highly effective, although they are not so widely used as DDT and BHC, are *chlordane, tetraethylpyrophosphate (TEPP)* and *parathion,* whose formulas are shown below.

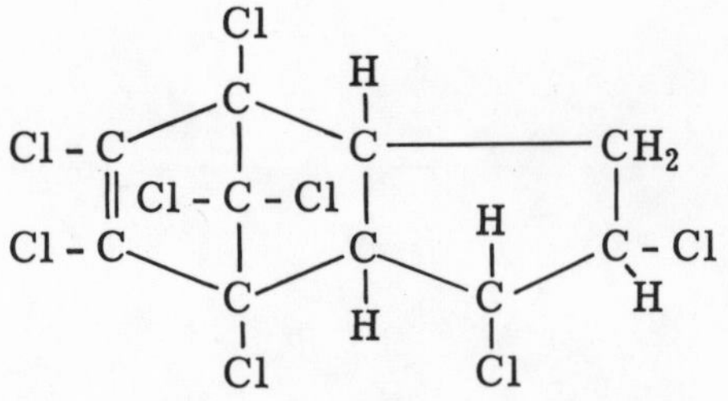

Chlordane
(1, 2, 4, 5, 6, 7, 8, 8 -octachloro-4, 7-methane, 3a, 4, 7, 7a-tetrahydroindane)

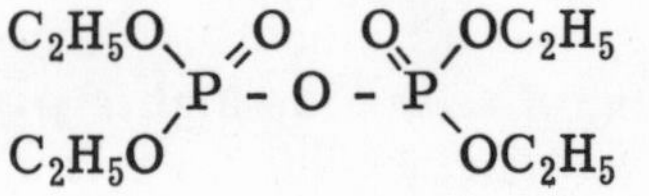

Tetraethyl pyrophosphate (TEPP) 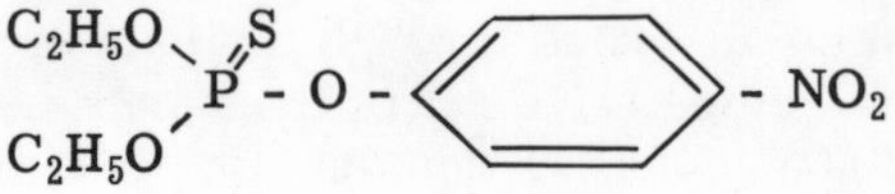   Parathion

TEPP and Parathion are two examples of compounds called "nerve gas" in World War II. They act as irreversible inhibitors (see p. 102) of the enzyme, choline esterase, in nerve endings, causing continuous nerve impulses with death of the animal or insect.

Rodenticides

Some of the important rodenticides are Warfarin, Antu, Red Squill, phosphorus, sodium fluoroacetate (FCH_2COONa), DDT, and strychnine. The formulas of Warfarin and Antu are shown below.

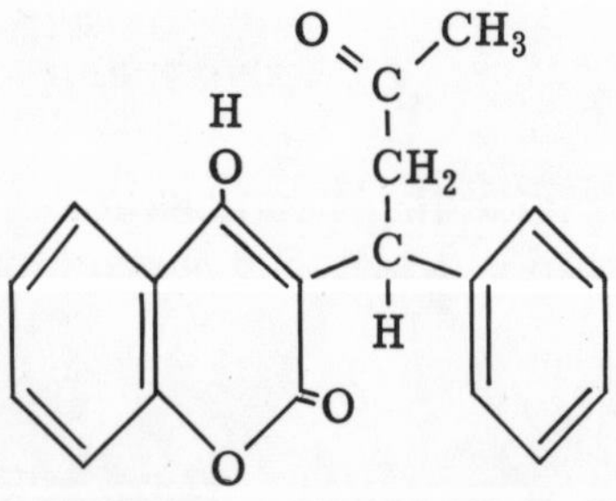

Warfarin 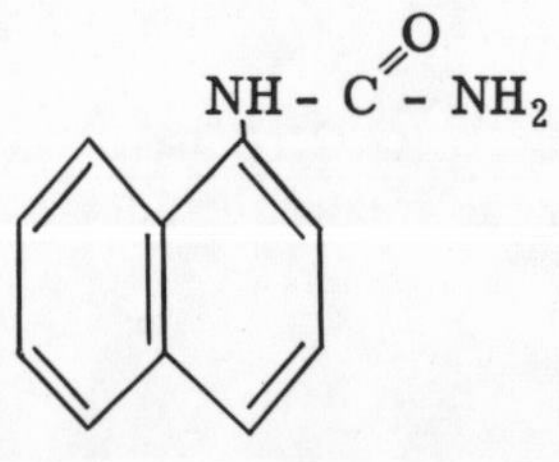   Antu (α-Napthylthiourea)

Red Squill and Strychnine are toxic alkaloids. DDT is not as effective as the others as a general rodenticide, but works well for mice, who track through the material, then clean their feet, and thus ingest enough DDT to kill them. All rodenticides are toxic to humans, and must be kept out of the reach of children.

One of the safest and most effective rodenticides tested to date is Warfarin, an anticoagulant closely related in structure and properties to dicoumarol (see p. 315). Warfarin is mixed with food palatable to the rodent (such as the rat). The drug is tasteless and relatively slow in action. As the rodent feeds on the bait, Warfarin gradually shuts off the supply of prothrombin from the liver (see p. 209) and the level of this vital clotting protein drops in the blood. In two or three days, the rodent's blood coagulation time becomes dangerously prolonged, and it succumbs to intestinal and lung hemorrhages. In the meantime, the animal's mates continue to feed on the bait, oblivious to its dangers.

An effective antidote for Warfarin poisoning in humans or pets is to administer a large dose of natural vitamin K (K_1) or its oxide (see p. 230); Vitamin K is antagonistic to Warfarin, dicoumarol, and related compounds and stimulates the liver to produce prothrombin at a rapid rate, thus correcting the prolonged coagulation time of the blood (see p. 258).

Antibiotics

Antibiotics have been described on page 135 as "toxic substances (from microorganisms) which inhibit or even kill the competing organisms". The antagonistic action of one organism toward another was termed "antibiosis" by DeBary in 1879. The known antiotics are produced exclusively by only one class of living organisms, namely, the microorganisms. It has been only in the last decade, since the discovery of the action of certain antibiotics on human pathogenic bacteria (see p. 135), that extensive research and development work have been carried out on antibiotics.

Several hundred antibiotics are described in the literature. About half of these have been obtained in sufficiently pure form to determine their elementary composition. The structure of only a small number has been determined. Most of the antibiotics which have been isolated are too toxic to use in humans as internal antibacterial agents.

The following antibiotics are used in human and veterinary medicine because of their high level of toxicity against certain undesirable microorganisms, combined with a relatively low toxicity towards humans and animals.

ANTIBIOTICS FROM BACTERIA. Streptomycetes. These are classified as bacteria, although they resemble molds because they grow in long thread-like filaments.

Streptomycin. This antibiotic was isolated from cultures of *Streptomyces griseus* by Waksman and coworkers in 1944. The combined efforts of many organic chemists and biochemists has resulted in the determination of the correct structure of this compound. It is a complex base made up of three fractions, N-methyl 1-glucoseamine, streptose, and streptidine, connected by oxide linkages.

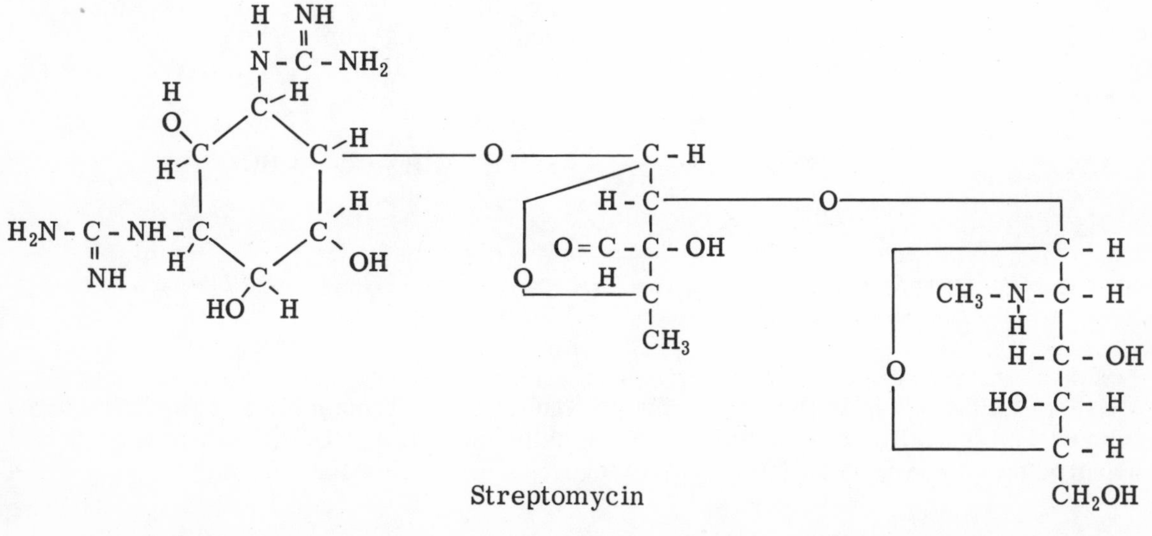

Streptomycin

By selecting superior strains of *S. griseus,* about 2 grams of streptomycin can be recovered per liter of medium. Many pharmaceutical companies in the United States and foreign countries manufacture streptomycin. It is one of the best antibiotics tested so far for the treatment of tuberculosis. One disadvantage of the drug is that prolonged use may lead to deafness.

Aureomycin and Terramycin (tetracycline). Aureomycin is produced by the soil micro-organism *Streptomyces aureofaciens.* Terramycin is produced by a closely related microorganism, *Streptomyces rimosus.* These antibiotics were isolated by microbiologists and biochemists in two different pharmaceutical companies, and are still produced exclusively by these companies. However, the structures of the two antibiotics are very similar, and the antibiotic properties are identical. For this reason, when the two compounds are used as growth stimulants in feeds (see p. 293), the Federal Food and Drug Administration has ruled that they must be listed on the feed tag as *tetracycline.*

Aureomycin and terramycin belong to a group known as "wide spectrum" antibiotics, because they are effective against so many different organisms. Bacteria are divided into two large groups, called gram-positive and gram-negative, which are based on their resistance to staining by certain dyes. Both groups of bacteria are sensitive to these antibiotics. In addition, the tetracyclines act against certain rickettsial diseases, such as typhus fever, Rocky Mountain spotted fever, etc., and against virus pneumonia. They are ineffective against fungal infections, bacteria of the *proteus* and *pseudomonas* groups, and the tubercle bacilli.

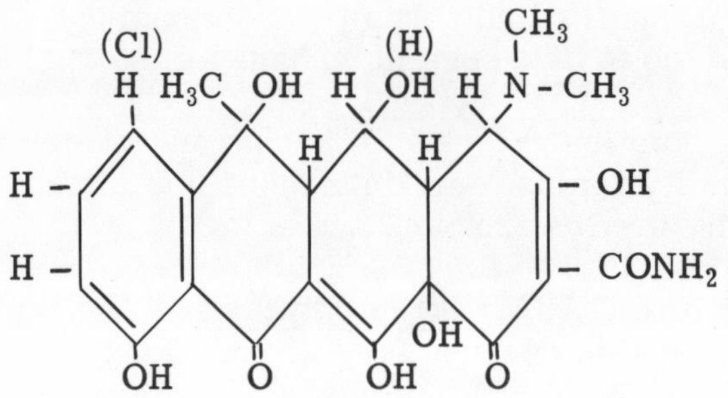

Terramycin (oxy-tetracycline)
Aureomycin (chlor-tetracycline, atoms in parentheses)

Chloromycetin (Chloramphenicol). This antibiotic is produced by *Streptomyces venezuela,* a microorganism which has been found in the soils of Venezuela, Illinois, and Japan, and which is probably distributed widely in soils. The formula for chloromycetin shows a relatively simple structure containing chlorine and a nitro group. The presence of a nitro group is unusual for compounds made by living organisms. The nitro group is re-

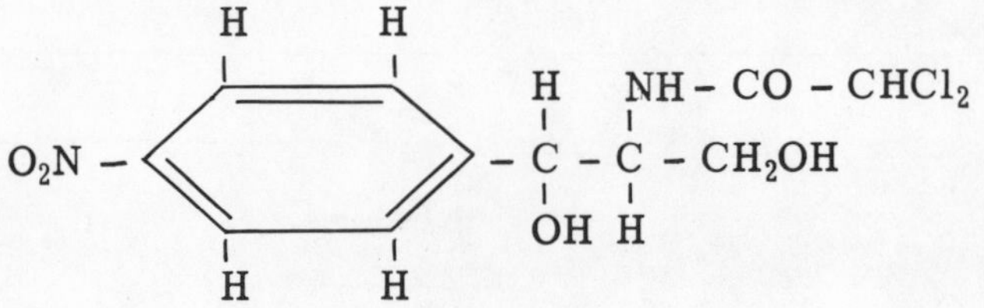

Chloromycetin

duced to an amino group in the animal body. One of the pharmaceutical companies has developed a practical method of synthesis for chloromycetin; it is the only antibiotic which is not produced by large-scale fermentation.

Chloromycetin is very effective as an antibiotic towards gram-negative bacteria, especially those producing intestinal diseases such as typhoid fever and dysentery. It is as effective as aureomycin and terramycin against typhus, Rocky Mountain spotted fever, and virus pneumonia. It differs from the latter, however, by showing poor activity towards gram-positive bacteria.

OTHER ANTIBIOTICS FROM BACTERIA. Several other antibiotics that have shown usefulness in certain therapeutic applications are bacitracin, carbomycin, erythromycin, neomycin, novobiocin, oleandomycin, polymyxin B, viomycin, and nystatin.

ANTIBIOTICS FROM MOLDS. Penicillin. The antibiotic action of penicillin was first recognized by Sir Roger Fleming in an agar plate containing colonies of a *penicillium* mold. Florey and associates at Oxford partially concentrated the antibiotic principle, and showed its effectiveness as an antibacterial agent in humans. During World War II, a joint research program between workers in England and this country confirmed Florey's findings, and led to the development by pharmaceutical companies in the United States of large-scale fermentation methods for the manufacture of this important antibiotic. Today more than 20 tons of pure penicillin are produced per month in the United States alone.

Penicillin is currently produced from a selected strain of *Penicillium Chrysogenum*. Fermentation tanks of 6,000 gallon capacity are filled with a liquid medium previously sterilized, and inoculated with the mold. "Submerged fermentation" is used, in which the mixture is aerated and stirred vigorously for a period of 3-4 days. The penicillin is extracted from the medium with butyl acetate. A typical nutrient medium for this *penicillium* contains a fermentable carbohydrate (lactose) 3%, corn steep solids (see p. 295) 3%, calcium carbonate 0.5%, sodium sulfate 0.1%, and phenylacetic acid 0.3%. The phenylacetic acid is added to produce a specific penicillin, *penicillin G*, which is the type used almost exclusively in clinical applications. By adding other precursors, more than 20 different penicillins have been produced. The formula for penicillin G is shown below.

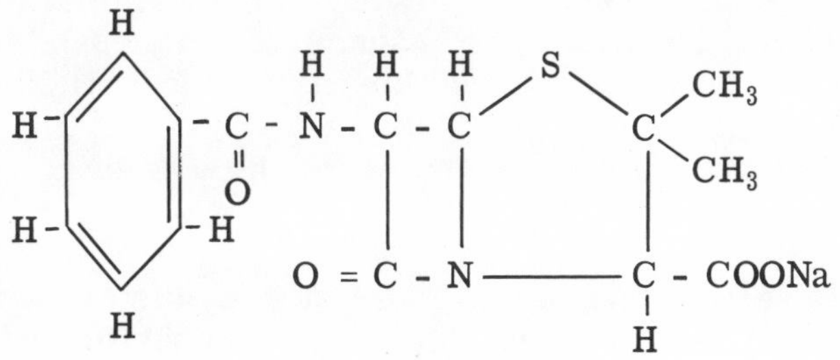

Penicillin G

Penicillin is very active against gram-positive bacteria, but it is not very effective against other microorganisms. The specific effect of penicillin, or for that matter, of other antibiotics, on bacteria, is not known. However, it has been observed that penicillin prevents cell division, and interferes with purine metabolism. Penicillin is specifically and irreversibly bound by gram-positive bacteria.

Penicillin-resistant strains of pathogenic microorganisms are beginning to appear. Fortunately, other antibiotics are available for use in these cases.

ANTIBIOTICS IN FEEDS. When streptomycin, aureomycin, terramycin or penicillin are incorporated into the feed of monogastric farm animals or immature ruminants at levels of 2-5 mg. per pound of feed, the growth rate is usually increased by 10-20 per cent. One theory for this effect is that they control (reduce) undesirable microrganisms in the intestinal tract.

Chapter 15 | INDUSTRIAL, DRUG, AND FOOD USES OF BIOCHEMICALS

Biochemical compounds have many important commercial uses. A large tonnage of carbohydrates, lipids, and proteins is processed daily for food, non-food, and drug uses. Smaller amounts of vitamins, hormones, enzymes, antibiotics and other biologically active biochemicals are also processed.

The government exercises rigid control over the production of biochemicals for food and drug uses in order to prevent misrepresentation in their sale, and to protect the health of the consumer. Before discussing food and drug uses of biochemicals, a brief description of these control activities will be given.

FOODS, DRUGS AND FEEDS; FEDERAL AND STATE CONTROL. The commercial production of human foods and feeds represents one of the largest segments of industry in the United States. Examination of the quantity, neatness and cleanliness of the canned goods counters, the fresh fruit and vegetable counters, and the meat counters of a typical small town supermarket invariably brings expressions of amazement from visitors from Europe and other parts of the world.

Almost every item of food for human consumption is processed in some fashion before it reaches the shelves of the food store. State agencies (Board of Health, Dept. of Agriculture) and Federal agencies (Pure Food and Drug Administration, U. S. Dept. of Agriculture) maintain a corps of inspectors who check the cleanliness and purity of foods which are processed for human consumption. Thus, meat processed by packing companies is inspected and stamped, fruit is checked for harmful insecticide spray residues, food plants are checked for cleanliness, etc. The Pure Food and Drug Administration also makes careful tests before giving its approval for the sale of new drugs for animals and humans.

The federal control over the manufacture and sale of animal feeds is not as rigid as that over the sale of human foods; however, this function is performed effectively by the individual states. In the author's state (Indiana), labeling laws control the sale of feeds, seeds and fertilizers to the farmer. The administration of these laws is delegated to the State Chemist, who is appointed by the governor. All feeds sold in the state must carry a tag showing, above the facsimile signature of the State Chemist, the minimum guarantee of nutrients. The tag usually shows (1) maximum moisture content of the feed, (2) minimum crude protein content, (3) minimum crude fat content and (4) maximum fiber content. If the feed is sold on the basis of its special vitamin, mineral or drug content, the levels of these ingredients must be indicated on the tag. For further details, the student is referred to the annual reports of the Indiana State Chemist* or to similar reports issued by other states.

USES OF CARBOHYDRATES IN FOODS. Unprocessed foods. Carbohydrates make up about 50-70% of the total dry weight of nutrients in the diet of man and most animals. Although carbohydrates are not essential in the sense that certain amino acids and fatty acids are, they nevertheless provide energy in the most economical form, and in addition provide roughage (in the form of cellulose, hemicellulose and other fiber materials), which give bulk to food residues, and aid intestinal peristalsis.

* Available from Bulletin Editor, Purdue Agricultural Experiment Station, Lafayette, Indiana.

Processed foods. Dry milled products. Cereal grains are milled to remove the germ
and outer horny layer of the endosperm. The degermed endosperm then serves as a raw
material for the preparation of such foods as flour, farina, corn meal, corn flakes, puffed
grains, and rolled oats. These foods have a high percentage of digestible carbohydrates.

Wet milled products. In the wet milling process, corn is steeped in a dilute sulfurous
acid solution at an elevated temperature. The corn steep liquor is drained off and concentrated for use in penicillin manufacture (p. 293). The steeped corn is then milled to
remove the germ, and the endosperm is ground with water. From the wet slurry, corn
starch is separated on special settling tables, and corn gluten is obtained by centrifugation. Corn starch is sold as such, and also used as the starting material for the preparation of corn syrup, and crystalline D-glucose (dextrose). The corn gluten is used as
a protein supplement in feeds for farm animals, and as a starting material for the preparation of zein, which is used for the preparation of a synthetic fiber, Vicara (see p. 302).

Sucrose. Sucrose (table sugar) is prepared commercially from the juice of the sugar cane,
and also from the juice of the sugar beet. The sugar cane stalks and the sugar beet root
are cooked with water, and the liquid extract separated from the bagasse and pulp, respectively. The extract is clarified and deionized, and evaporated *in vacuo* to a small
volume. Sucrose is crystallized out, and the mother liquor remaining, called *molasses,*
is used in human foods and animal feeds. Table grade sucrose is claimed to be the least
expensive chemically pure carbon compound.

Relative sweetness of sugars. Sucrose, and D-glucose (from corn starch) are used extensively as sweetening agents in the confectionery and baking industries. The relative
sweetness of several mono- and disaccharides is shown in Table 44.

Table 44. Relative sweetness of certain sugars
compared with sucrose

Sugar.	Relative Sweetness
D-fructose	170
Sucrose	100
D-glucose	74
D-xylose	40
D-galactose	32
Maltose	32
Lactose	16

Fermentations. Large quantities of carbohydrates are consumed by the industries which
carry out special fermentation reactions involving the actions of yeasts, bacteria, or molds.
Some of the major products produced by the fermentation of carbohydrates are CO_2 (usually converted to "dry ice"), ethyl alcohol, isopropyl alcohol, butyl alcohol, glycerol,
acetone, lactic acid, citric acid, acetic acid, propionic acid, butyric acid, mannitol,
and gluconic acid. All of the above products are isolated as C.P. (chemically pure)
compounds. In addition, the production of antibiotics by bacterial or mold fermentation
(see p. 293), consumes many tons of fermentable carbohydrates. The fermentation industry, using yeasts for the production of beers, wines and whiskeys, consumes large
quantities of carbohydrates in the form of cereal grains, sucrose, and molasses.

Pharmaceuticals. Crystalline D-glucose, manufactured from corn starch, is dissolved
in pyrogen-free (free of fever-producing agents) water to 5% (or higher) concentration,
sterilized in one liter special dispensing bottles, and sold in large quantities to hospitals,

where it is administered by vein to pre- and postoperative patients and to other patients, who are unable to take food by mouth.

Dextrans, polysaccharides with molecular weights of about 2-80 million, are prepared by fermentation of sucrose with *L-mesenteroides,* or enzyme preparations derived from this bacterium. The dextrans apparently have a branching structure similar to that of amylopectin (see p. 25). They can be partially degraded by acid hydrolysis to give products of lower molecular weight. A fraction with a molecular weight of about 100,000 has been used as an effective substitute for blood plasma, and was used with considerable success in the Korean war to replace lost blood and prevent shock in wounded soldiers. It should be pointed out that modified dextran solutions serve as a temporary substitute for blood plasma. The body must replace the lost blood, or doctors must provide it in a whole blood transfusion, in order to restore the blood picture to normal.

NON-FOOD USES OF CARBOHYDRATES. Natural and synthetic fibers. Two important natural fibers which have been used by man for centuries are cotton and flax. Cotton and linen fabrics are still major textiles. Cotton fiber now also serves as the raw material for the manufacture of several synthetic fibers. One of the first of these to be introduced to the public was *rayon.* Rayon was originally manufactured only from cotton linters, but can now be made also from purified wood pulp. The process is as follows:

$$\text{Pure cellulose (from cotton, wood)} \xrightarrow[\text{CS}_2]{\text{NaOH}} \left[C_6H_7O_2(OH)_2OC \begin{smallmatrix} \nearrow S \\ \searrow SNa \end{smallmatrix} \right]_n$$

Cellulose xanthate "viscose"

$$\xrightarrow[\text{(spinneret) into dilute H}_2\text{SO}_4]{\text{force viscose through small orifice}} \text{Rayon fiber} + CS_2 + Na_2SO_4 + H_2O$$

Acetate rayon. Cellulose contains alcoholic hydroxyl groups which are chemically active and can be acetylated (see p. 28). The ester produced can be spun into a fiber which is fire-resistant and has the properties of viscose rayon when woven into fabrics.

$$\text{Pure Cellulose} \atop \text{(cotton linters)} \atop \text{(wood cellulose)} \xrightarrow[\text{(H}_2\text{SO}_4\text{-trace)}]{\text{acetic acid, acetic anydride}} \text{Cellulose acetate } (+H_2O \xrightarrow[\text{off}]{\text{evap.}} \uparrow)$$

$$\text{Cellulose acetate-acetone solution} \xrightarrow[\text{into hot air chamber}]{\text{force through spinneret}} \text{cellulose acetate fiber}$$

Nitrocellulose lacquers. Cellulose can also be nitrated at the free alcoholic hydroxyl groups on carbons 2, 3, and 6 (see p. 21). The esterification with HNO_3 is carried out with H_2SO_4 (fuming or concentrated) as the dehydrating agent. In this reaction,

water is split out as follows: $(\text{-C-O} \lceil \text{H+H-O} \rceil NO_2 \xrightarrow{\text{conc. } H_2SO_4} \text{-C-O-NO}_2$

Nitrocellulose containing 10-12% of nitrogen is non-explosive (but highly inflammable) and is called *pyroxylin.* Nitrocellulose containing approximately three nitro groups per glucose molecule, and 12-13% nitrogen, is an explosive compound called *guncotton.*

Pyroxylin, which contains about 2 nitro groups per glucose unit, has found wide use in the lacquer industry. It is first partially depolymerized with dilute mineral acid under

under heat and pressure to make it more soluble in lacquer solvents. Then it is mixed with a softener (plasticizer), such as tricresyl phosphate or dibutyl phthalate, a suitable pigment is added, and the mixture is dissolved in a solvent such as butyl acetate (b.p. 127°C).

The resulting lacquer can be sprayed or brushed on a surface, and after the solvent has evaporated, a water, heat, and light-resistant film is left as a surface coating. Lacquers of this type have found wide use in the automobile industry as the outer protective coating on the metal surfaces of the car body.

Cellulose plastics. Celluloid. Historically, this was the first plastic manufactured in commercial quantities. John Wesley Wyatt manufactured the first plastic billiard balls with celluloid. Celluloid is prepared by mixing pyroxylin with a non-volatile plasticizer, camphor, and a volatile plasticizer, ethyl alcohol. By the process of extrusion molding, it is possible to shape rods, tubes, strips and sheets. In this process, the heated plastic is forced through special nozzles. The molded article is then "cured" by holding it at a temperature which will volatilize the alcohol but not the camphor. The molded article can be easily cut or machined on a lathe, and pieces can be cemented together by immersion of the ends in acetone, followed by the application of pressure until dry.

Cellophane. Cellophane is prepared by forcing viscose (cellulose xanthate, see above) through a long narrow slit, into the acid solution, whereby the regenerated cellulose is obtained in the form of a sheet. These sheets are washed free of acid, bleached, and treated with glycerol to impart pliability. Cellophane is used widely as a protective wrap for food, merchandise, etc.

Ethyl cellulose. This plastic is prepared from cellulose by treating the latter with ethyl chloride in the presence of alkali. The ethyl ether is produced (see p. 28).

$$-C-O\overline{H} \qquad Cl\overline{|}C_2H_5 \; --------\rightarrow \; -C-O-C_2H_5 \; + \; NaCl \; + \; H_2O$$

cellulose   ethyl chloride   ethyl cellulose

Tubes, strips, rods and sheets of ethyl cellulose are shaped by the process of *injection* molding (heated plastic forced at pressures of 2,000-5,000 pounds per square inch through branching channels into a cooled mold). Finished ethyl cellulose pieces can be machined easily. Ethyl cellulose is one of the toughest plastics known, and has one of the highest impact strengths.

Cellulose acetate. In the manufacture of plastics from this cellulose derivative, the cellulose acetate is mixed with a plasticizer (dimethyl or diethyl phthalate, or triphenyl phosphate, etc.) and shaped by injection molding. The product can be machined easily. Since cellulose acetate is not inflammable, it is used to manufacture "safety film", and this has replaced the inflammable movie film manufactured for years from celluloid.

For many years, cellulose acetate sheet was used as the center lamination in safety glass, but it has been displaced by polyvinyl butyral plastic. Nevertheless, several hundred plastic parts made from acetate plastic are still incorporated in modern automobiles.

USE OF CARBOHYDRATES IN THE PAPER AND BUILDING INDUSTRY. *Paper* is an interwoven web of cellulose fibers which has been treated with various sizes and fillers to give sheen, smoothness, and sometimes color. Cotton rags and wood are the two main sources of the cellulose fibers.

Wood. The cellulose skeleton of wood comprises about 75% of its dry weight, and gives it its structural strength. This product of our forests, which is mainly carbohydrate, is considered to be our most versatile building material.

The Concept of Chemurgy

Dr. W. J. Hale coined the term "chemurgy" to mean "chemistry put to work". It has become associated almost exclusively with the problem of obtaining useful new products of industrial value from farm crops, so should probably be called "farm chemurgy". Through the efforts of Dr. Hale and Wheeler McMillen, the Farm Chemurgic Council was created in 1935, and the Council has played a major role in stimulating national interest in farm chemurgy. One of the results of increased national interest in this field was the establishment of four regional research laboratories by Congress in 1935. The Southern (New Orleans, La), Northern (Peoria, Ill.), Eastern (Wyndmoor, Pa.) and Western (Albany, California) Regional Crop Utilization Laboratories conduct studies on the major crops, and agricultural wastes which are found in their respective regions. Research on farm chemurgy is stressed at these laboratories. In addition, many state agricultural experiment stations and industrial research organizations carry out research on crops of local interest. Students interested in this field are referred to books published by Hale, and by McMillen.

Industrial Uses of Lipids

About 13 billion pounds of fats (animal and vegetable combined) are produced annually in the United States. Approximately two-thirds of the annual production is used in human food products, and the other one-third is used for non-food purposes. The major vegetable fats produced are cottonseed, peanut, linseed, and soybean oils; the major animal fats are lard, beef and sheep tallow, and fish oils. Oils are also imported in moderate quantities from the following countries: Northern Europe (fish oil), Mediterranean countries (olive oil), South America (castor, linseed and rape seed oils), and the Orient and other tropical areas (coconut, palm and tung oils).

FOOD USES. Most of the food fats are used as table fats, shortening, and salad oils. Butter and oleomargarine are the most popular table spreads. Oleomargarine is manufactured almost wholly from soy and cottonseed oils by controlled hydrogenation to raise the melting point. The hydrogenated product is emulsified with skim milk, salted, and fortified with carotene.

Shortenings are used in cookery by the housewife and the baking industry. Hydrogenated vegetable oils (see p. 39) are popular because of their keeping qualities. Lard has improved in consumer demand because of special antioxidants (see p. 41) which are now added to increase its shelf life. Vegetable oils contain natural antioxidants which retard rancidity, whereas lard is lacking in these protective agents and in the unprotected state tends to become rancid on storage.

The most popular *salad oils* are corn, cottonseed, peanut and soybean oils.

NON-FOOD USES. The soap industry. A large proportion of non-edible fats and oils is used in the manufacture of glycerol and *soap*.

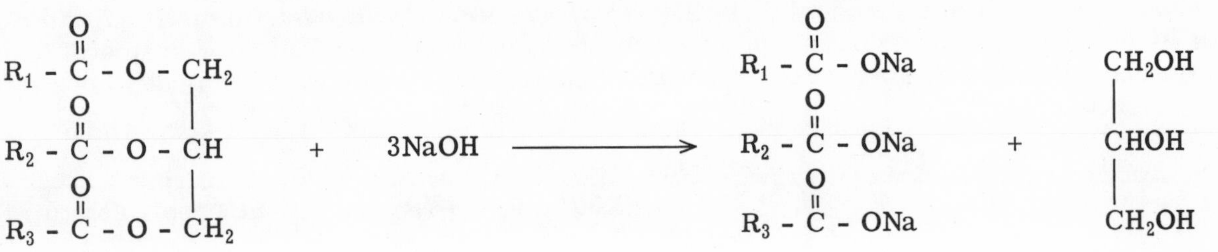

$$
\begin{array}{ccc}
R_1 - \overset{\overset{O}{\|}}{C} - O - CH_2 & & R_1 - \overset{\overset{O}{\|}}{C} - ONa \quad\quad CH_2OH \\
R_2 - \overset{\overset{O}{\|}}{C} - O - CH \quad + \quad 3NaOH \longrightarrow & R_2 - \overset{\overset{O}{\|}}{C} - ONa \quad + \quad CHOH \\
R_3 - \overset{\overset{O}{\|}}{C} - O - CH_2 & & R_3 - \overset{\overset{O}{\|}}{C} - ONa \quad\quad CH_2OH
\end{array}
$$

Animal or vegetable fat   Alkali   Soap   Glycerol

A *soap* may be defined as the salt of a higher (10 carbons or more) fatty acid. The soaps of the alkali metals (sodium, potassium, lithium) are water-soluble, whereas the soaps of the alkaline earth metals (calcium, magnesium, strontium) and of heavy metals (lead, etc.) are water-insoluble. The hard soaps used as toilet, flake, or powdered soaps, are the sodium salts of the higher fatty acids. The potassium soaps are softer, and are usually dispensed in water solution (liquid soap). The formation of alkaline earth metal soaps from household soaps in hard water (see below) decreases the effectiveness of the latter. Lead soaps and other insoluble soaps are used as lubricants in grease formulations.

Action of soap in pure and in hard water. The formula for sodium stearate, a typical ingredient of household soaps (Ivory, castille, etc.) is shown below. It can be seen from

$$
CH_3\ CH_2\ CH_2\ CH_2\ CH_2\ CH_2\ CH_2\ CH_2\ CH_2\ CH_2\ CH_2\ CH_2\ CH_2\ CH_2\ CH_2\ CH_2\ CH_2\ C\overset{\displaystyle \diagup O}{\underset{\displaystyle \diagdown O^-\ Na^+}{}}
$$

Sodium stearate

this formula that the salt end of the molecule is an ionic water-soluble group, whereas the hydrocarbon chain is a non-ionic fat-soluble group. When soap is added to an oil-water mixture, the ionic "head" stays in the water, and the hydrocarbon "tail" stays in the oil. These properties make soap a surface-active agent. Surface-active agents are substances which lower the surface tension of water, stabilize oil-water emulsions, and stabilize certain types of suspensions (for example - carbon particles in motor oil). Because of these properties, surface-active agents are widely used as cleaning agents.

The cleaning properties of soap are reduced if it is used with hard water. Hard water contains one or more of the following salts: the carbonates, bicarbonates, sulfates and chlorides of calcium, magnesium, iron and aluminum. If only carbonates and bicarbonates are present, the water is said to have *temporary hardness*, for these salts can be removed by boiling the water, or by careful addition of lime water.

$$
Ca(HCO_3)_2 \quad -----\overset{heat}{-----} \rightarrow \quad \underline{CaCO_3} + CO_2 + H_2O
$$

Calcium bicarbonate (soluble)   Calcium carbonate (insoluble)

$$
MgCo_3 \quad + \quad Ca(OH)_2 \quad ------ \rightarrow \quad \underline{CaCO_3} \quad + \quad \underline{Mg(OH)_2}
$$

Magnesium carbonate   Calcium hydroxide   Calcium carbonate   Magnesium hydroxide

(soluble)   (soluble)   (insoluble)   (insoluble)

If sulfates or chlorides of one or more of the four metallic elements listed above are present in the water, the water is said to have *permanent hardness*. This type of hardness can be removed only by distillation (conversion of the water to distilled water), or by passing the water through an ion-exchange agent (natural zeolite, or synthetic ion-exchange resins). The action of hard water ions on sodium and potassium soaps is shown below.

$$Ca^{++},\ Mg^{++},\ Fe^{++},\ Al^{+++}\ +\ R - C \begin{matrix}O\\\\\end{matrix} -ONa(or\ K) \dashrightarrow (R - C \begin{matrix}O\\\\\end{matrix})_2 - Ca,\ etc.\ + Na^+(or\ K^+)$$

(insoluble)

Use of fatty acids in synthetic detergents. During the past 20 years, synthetic detergents have been developed which are much more effective in hard water than the common soaps. The first of these to be offered for household use was one of the gardinols (sodium salt of sulfated alcohols).

$$CH_3(CH_2)_{11} - O - \overset{\overset{\displaystyle O}{\|}}{\underset{\underset{\displaystyle O}{\|}}{S}} - O - Na$$

Sodium lauryl sulfate (a gardinol).

The lauryl alcohol used in the manufacture of this detergent is obtained by hydrogenating lauric acid, which in turn is obtained from coconut or palm oil. The oil is either (1) saponified with alkali, and the soaps converted by acidification to the free fatty acids, or (2) heated with absolute methyl alcohol to produce two layers, a glycerol layer, and a methyl ester layer; these are easily separated. Free fatty acids are released by addition of water to the methyl esters, which decompose readily in the presence of water. Lauric acid is then separated from the other fatty acids released from the coconut or palm oil, by fractional distillation under vacuum.

Examples of other types of synthetic detergents are the monoglyceride fatty acid sulfates such as Vel and Syntex M, and the alkylaryl sodium sulfonates from petroleum such as Lanitol and Santomerse:

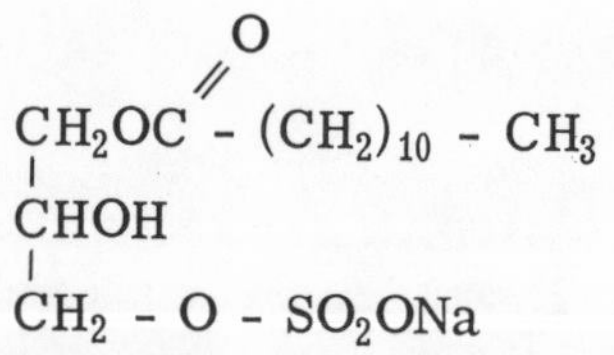

$$\begin{array}{l} CH_2OC \overset{\displaystyle O}{\|} - (CH_2)_{10} - CH_3 \\ CHOH \\ CH_2 - O - SO_2ONa \end{array} \qquad\qquad CH_3(CH_2)_n - \langle\!\bigcirc\!\rangle - SO_3Na$$

Sodium glycerol monolaurate sulfate 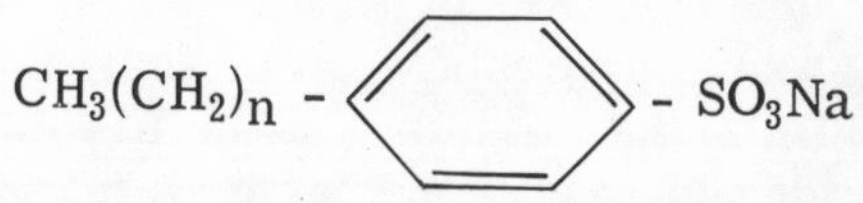   Alkyl aryl type sodium sulfonate

The synthetic detergents are so effective as emulsifying agents and sudsing agents that they must be diluted with sodium sulfate or a similar inert salt so that the housewife does not measure out excessive amounts into the dishpan or washer. Unlike ordinary soaps, their calcium and magnesium salts are soluble, and they are therefore more effective in hard water.

Commercial use of other fatty acid derivatives. The purified individual fatty acids are now prepared commercially in carload quantities from animal and vegetable fats and oils in this country, and production facilities have been developed in other countries. A mixture of free fatty acids is first obtained by saponification, or methyl alcohol exchange (see above), and the purified individual fatty acids are separated by fractional vacuum distillation. The fatty acids are converted into amides, aldehydes, alcohols, ketones, nitriles, amines, and quaternary ammonium compounds. The amides, nitriles, and ketones are used in lubricants, the alcohols for the manufacture of synthetic detergents, the amines as anionic-type detergents, and the quaternary ammonium compounds as disinfectants. At the present time, amines from fatty acids (for example, lauryl amine as the acetate salt) are being used for the flotation of most of the phosphate and potash salts mined in the United States.

Fatty acid derivatives

Fatty acid: $R - COOH$

$$R - \overset{\overset{O}{\|}}{C}NH_2$$
Amide

$$R - CO - R'$$
Ketone

$$R - \overset{\overset{O}{\|}}{C} - H$$
Aldehyde

$$R - C \equiv N$$
Nitrile

$$R - OH$$
Alcohol

$$R - CH_2 - NH_2 \cdot HOOCCH_3$$
Amine acetate

$$(R')_3 - N - \overset{\diagup Cl}{\underset{}{C}H_2} - R$$
Quaternary ammonium compound

Commercial uses for glycerol. Glycerol is obtained as a by-product in the manufacture of soap and free fatty acids. A large proportion of the output is used in the production of ester gum and alkyd resins for surface coatings (see below). Glycerol is also used extensively in the preparation of pharmaceuticals (cosmetics, drugs, etc.)

Use of fats and oil in the surface coating industry. Glycerol and drying oils are used in large quantities in the manufacture of surface coatings. A drying oil is a vegetable oil which contains a high percentage of unsaturated fatty acids. Examples of drying oils are linseed oil, fractionated soybean oil, dehydrated castor oil and tung oil. The fatty acid composition of the first three oils is shown in Table 7 (p. 37). Soybean oil was formerly separated into two fractions, a saturated fraction used in the preparation of surface coatings; now most of the oil destined for surface coatings is simply "heat bodied" with alkyd resins without previous fractionation.

The major ingredients of most oil-base paints and enamels are (1) drying oil, (2) resin, (3) pigment, and (4) a volatile thinner (turpentine or volatile saturated hydrocarbon). Outside paints usually contain little or no resin, but contain large amounts of mineral pigments which "chalk off" with weathering, thus exposing a clean new surface of paint. Inside paints contain moderate amounts of resins to give them body, but never contain the levels found in enamels. A high level of resin is used in enamels, and gives the enamel coat a fine lustre which is water-resistant and washable.

Oil-base varnishes are similar to enamels, except that they usually do not contain any pigment. One successful household varnish contains soybean oil as the drying oil, a mixture of phenol-formaldehyde resin and ester gum resin for body, and turpentine as the thinner.

The *resins* used in oil-base paints, enamels, and varnishes may be divided into three classes: (1) natural resins such as resin (abietic acid) from pine trees, and fossil resins (tropics), (2) modified natural resins such as glyceryl triabietate (ester gum) and pentaerythrityl tetraabietate, and (3) synthetic resins such as phenol-formaldehyde resins, terpene resins, alkyd resins, etc. In the latter group, alkyd resins are prepared by condensing phthalic or a similar dicarboxylic acid, with either glycerol itself, or with the mono- and diglycerides obtained by the partial hydrolysis of drying oils.

Essential oils. Essential oils such as those from citrus fruit, peppermint, spearmint, lemon grass, Dalmatian sage, lavender, goldenrod, French marjoram, rose, jasmine, anise, etc. are used in perfumes, cosmetics, chewing gum, as condiments, in soaps, medicinals and many other commercial items.

Industrial Uses of Amino Acids, Proteins and Enzymes

AMINO ACIDS. Purified amino acids are used mainly in the food and feed industry. Several million pounds of monosodium glutamate are produced annually by fermentation, from wheat gluten, and from Steffen's waste (from sugar beets) and used to enhance the flavor of soups, sauces, etc. consumed in this country*. In the Orient, this amino acid salt has been used for years to give a meat-like flavor to rice dishes. There it is called "Ajinomoto".

The amino acids most likely to be deficient in swine and poultry feeds are methionine and lysine. Methionine can be synthesized commercially at a cost which makes it feasible to use as a feed supplement. DL-methionine has already found a market as a supplement in corn-soybean rations for poultry. L-lysine can be synthesized by a process similar in many respects to that used to synthesize the monomers for nylon production, starting with furfural from corn cobs. It can also be prepared by a fermentation process. Since cereal grains are deficient in lysine, the quality of their protein is improved by supplementing with lysine. Thus, bread and other grain products would serve as better sources of balanced protein if supplemented with small amounts of lysine.

Amino acid mixtures in the form of protein hydrolysates are manufactured from nutritionally well-balanced proteins such as casein, fibrin, and lactalbumin, by several pharmaceutical companies. These hydrolysates (usually enzymatic) are administered intravenously to humans to correct cumulative deficits in chronic protein depletion, to prevent protein starvation after operations, and to supplement an inadequate oral intake of protein.

PROTEINS. Non-food uses.

1. Paint industry. Proteins (casein, corn gluten, soybean protein) are used as stabilizing agents in the preparation of water-in-oil and rubber-base paints (Kem-tone, Texolite, etc.). These paints contain a drying oil (or rubber latex), a detergent (see p. 300), a pigment, and a protein. The protein stabilizes the water-in-oil, or water-in-latex, emulsion formed when these paints are diluted with water to a viscosity suitable for spreading on a surface.

The prolamine, zein, obtained from corn, is used as a replacement for insect gum in the preparation of shellac.

2. Fibers. The two most important *natural* protein fibers are wool and silk. The first "synthetic" or modified protein fiber to attain commercial importance was Aralac, a fiber manufactured from casein. It has found wide acceptance as a replacement for part (or all) of the wool in felt hats. A fiber made from corn zein, called Vicara, has been manufactured as a substitute for wool in synthetic blends with such fibers as Nylon and Orlon. It is claimed that these blends can be woven into sweaters that have the physical characteristics of the finest Cashmeres.

* Available in grocery stores under the trade name "Accent".

3. <u>Leather</u>. Leather is an important modified protein product which is prepared by coagulating and denaturing the proteins (mainly collagen) in the skins of animals with tannic acid and chromium salts. The altered skins are very pliable, and are resistant to wear and to decomposition by climate and microorganisms.

4. <u>Paper and plastics</u>. Casein is used in ton quantities in the paper industry where it acts as a binding agent to hold fillers (such as clay) in the fiber mesh of the paper. It is also used extensively in the plastics industry, where it is molded into billiard balls, buttons, combs, fountain pens, etc.

<u>Food uses</u>. The mixed foods ingested by man, animals and poultry contain 15-25% by weight of crude protein. This nutrient is one of the most essential, and also one of the most expensive ingredients, of the diet.

Protein concentrates such as cottonseed, corn gluten, linseed, peanut and soybean meals, fish meal, meat tankage, etc., are sold by feed manufacturers to serve as protein supplements for animals on low protein feeds such as cereal grains, forages, etc.

ENZYMES. <u>Non-food uses</u>. Proteolytic enzymes from certain bacteria (for example, *bacillus mesentericus),* from molds (for example, *aspergillus oryzae),* or from the pancreas (see p. 150) are used in the dehairing and bating (plumping) of skins for the manufacture of leather. Dehairing compounds digest the collagen or connective tissue holding the hairs to the hide, and thus help to loosen the hair. Bating compounds prepare (plump and soften) the dehaired hide for the tanning process.

Amylases obtained from bacteria, malt, molds, and the pancreas, are used in the textile industry as desizing agents. Starch is added as a stiffening agent (size) to cotton fiber before the fiber is woven into cloth. The starch must be removed before the cloth is dyed, and this is done with an amylase preparation.

<u>Food uses</u>. The enzymes of microorganisms are important catalysts in the food and beverage industries. In bread making, yeasts produce a series of enzymes that ferment the sugars present with the production of alcohol and carbon dioxide. The carbon dioxide is the leavening agent which causes the bread to rise. In the fermentation industry, the enzymes of yeast produce industrial and beverage alcohol, and the enzymes of certain bacteria produce acetone, butanol, lactic acid, citric acid, etc. in industrial quantities from fermentable carbohydrate substrates.

The plant protease, papain, is used to tenderize meat, and the enzyme, rennin, obtained from the fourth stomach of the calf, is used in the manufacture of most cheeses. In cheese manufacture, rennin converts the calcium-casein of milk into calcium paracaseinate curd. The curd is then aged at the proper temperature and humidity, after inoculation with an appropriate mixture of microorganisms.

An interesting application of enzymes is in the manufacture of chocolate-covered cherries. A solid fondant is made with sucrose, and a small amount of sucrase (invertase) is mixed with the cooled product. Solid balls of fondant, containing a cherry, are formed, and dipped into melted chocolate. After a few days, the solid cream center changes to a clear liquid, due to the greater solubility of the glucose and fructose released from the sucrose by the action of the sucrase.

In the manufacture of fruit juices (apple juice, grape juice, etc.) pectinases are added to clarify the fresh product.

Clinical uses. The plant proteases, *papain* and *ficin,* from the papaya and fig trees respectively, are not inhibited by the secretions of intestinal worms (see p.102), and consequently have found wide use in deworming medicines for humans and animals. Both proteases readily digest worms.

Pepsin, trypsin, and defatted pancreas (pancreatin) are used clinically in the treatment of digestive disorders caused by a lack of these enzymes in the patient's digestive secretions. Trypsin has been used successfully in clearing away thick, purulent masses in surface infections, and in empyema associated with pleural pneumonia. The area cleaned by its digestive action heals much more rapidly than untreated areas.

Thrombin, the enzyme which clots fibrinogen (see p. 258), is manufactured from beef plasma, and is used topically (on the surface) to stop bleeding during operations and after tooth extractions.

APPENDIX 1 | BIBLIOGRAPHY

A Bibliography of Selected References

<u>General</u>

1. SELECTED TEXTBOOKS

Harrow and Mazur. *Textbook of Biochemistry*, W. B. Saunders Co., Philadelphia
(1962).
Hawk, Oser and Summerson. *Practical Physiological Chemistry*, McGraw-Hill Book
Co., N.Y. (1954).
Karlson. *Introduction to Modern Biochemistry*, Academic Press, New York (1965).
Rafelson and Binkley. *Basic Biochemistry*, Macmillan Co., N.Y. (1965).
West and Todd. *Textbook of Biochemistry*, The Macmillan Co., N.Y. (1961).
White, Handler and Smith. *Principles of Biochemistry*, McGraw-Hill Book Co.,
N.Y. (1964).

2. SELECTED GENERAL REVIEWS

Annual Review of Biochemistry, Annual Reviews, Inc., Palo Alto, California (1932-
current).
Annual Review of Physiology, Annual Reviews, Inc., Palo Alto, California.
Harvey Lectures, The Harvey Society, New York.
Physiological Reviews, American Physiological Society, Washington, D.C.

3. SELECTED GENERAL PERIODICALS (ENGLISH)

American Chemical Society Journal, (J. Am. Chem. Soc.).
American Journal of Physiology, (Am. J. Physiol).
Archives of Biochemistry and Biophysics, (Arch. Biochem.).
Biochemical Journal, (Biochem. J.).
Biological Abstracts, (Biol. Abs.).
Cereal Chemistry, (Cereal Chem).
Chemical Abstracts, (Chem. Abs.).
Federation Proceedings, (Fed. Proc.).
Journal of Agricultural and Food Chemistry, (J. Ag. Food Chem.).
Journal of Biological Chemistry, (J. Biol. Chem.).
Journal of Nutrition, (J. Nutrition).
Nature
Science, (Sci.).
Society for Experimental Biology and Medicine, Proceedings, (Proc. Soc. Expt.
Biol. Med.).

Chapter 1 (Introduction)

1. Chittenden. *The Development of Physiological Chemistry in the United States*, The Chemical Catalog Co., Inc. N.Y. (1930).
2. Steiner. *The Chemical Foundations of Molecular Biology*, D. Van Nostrand Co., N.Y. (1965).

Chapter 2 (Water)

1. Adolph, E. F. *The Metabolism and Distribution of Water in Body Tissues*, Physiol. Rev., 13, 336 (1933).
2. Gortner, R. A. *Outlines of Biochemistry*, 3rd Ed., John Wiley and Sons, Inc., N.Y. (1949).
3. Schmidt-Nielsen, K., and Schmidt-Nielsen, B. The Desert Rat, in *Twentieth Century Bestiary*, p. 109. Simon and Schuster, N.Y. (1954). Also: Physiol. Rev. 32, 135 (1952); Special Report 21, Dec. 1962, Missouri Agricultural Experiment Station, Columbia, "Comparative Physiology of Desert Mammals."

Chapter 3 (Carbohydrates)

1. Annual Review. *Advances in Carbohydrate Chemistry*, Academic Press, Inc., N.Y. (1945-current).
2. Gilman. *Organic Chemistry*, John Wiley and Sons, Inc., N.Y. (1943). Chapters by M. L. Wolfrom, A. L. Raymond and E. Heuser.
3. Pigman and Goepp. *Chemistry of the Carbohydrates*, Academic Press, Inc., N.Y. (1948).
4. Whistler and Smart. *Polysaccharide Chemistry*, Academic Press, Inc., N.Y. (1953).
5. Pigman. *The Carbohydrates*, Academic Press, N.Y. (1957).
6. Configuration of glucose. Hudson, C. S., J. Chem. Educ., 18, 353 (1941).
7. Carbohydrate Nomenclature. Chem. Eng. News, 26, 2 (1948) (May 31); and Science, 113, 314 (1951).

Chapter 4 (Lipids)

1. Lovern. *The Chemistry of Lipids of Biochemical Significance*, J. Wiley and Sons, N.Y. (1955).
2. Deuel. *The Lipids*, Vol. 1 (1951); Vol. 2 (1955). Interscience Publishers, Inc., N.Y.
3. Steroid Chemistry. Feiser, in Scientific American, p. 52 (January) 1955.
4. Chemistry and Metabolism of Phospholipids (Phosphatides). Federation Proceedings 16, 816-855 (1957).
5. Hanahan. *Lipide Chemistry*, J. Wiley and Sons, N.Y. (1960).

Chapter 5 (Proteins)

1. Annual review. *Advances in Protein Chemistry*, Academic Press, Inc., N.Y. (1944-current).
2. Greenberg. *Amino Acids and Proteins*, C. C. Thomas, Springfield, Illinois, (1951).
3. Haurowitz. *Chemistry and Biology of Proteins*, Academic Press, Inc., N.Y. (1950).
4. Fox and Foster. Introduction to Protein Chemistry, John Wiley and Sons, Inc., N.Y. (1957).

5. Neurath and Bailey. The Proteins, Vol. I., Parts A and B (1953); Vol. II, Parts A and B (1954), Academic Press, Inc., N. Y.
6. Bull. *Physical Biochemistry,* J. Wiley and Sons, N. Y. (1951).
7. Structure of Proteins. P. Doty, Scientific American, 197, pp. 173-184 (1957).
8. Structure of Insulin. Brown, Sanger and Kitai, Biochem. J., 60, 557 (1955).
9. Amino Acid Chromatography. Moore, Spackman and Stein, Analytical Chem., 30, 1185 (1958), and Spackman, Stein and Moore, Analytical Chem., 30, 1190 (1958).
10. Protein Chromatography. Phosphate Gel: Tiselius, Hjerten, and Levin. Archiv. Biochem. Biophys., 65, 132 (1956). DEAE - Cellulose Chromatography: Sober and Peterson. Fed. Proc. 17, 1116 (1958).
11. Amino Acid Assay Methods and Amino Acid Composition of Proteins. Block and Weiss: *Amino Acid Handbook,* C. C. Thomas, Springfield, Illinois (1956).
12. Microheterogeneity of Plasma Albumin. Sogami and Foster. J. Biol. Chem., 238, 2245 (1963).

Chapter 6 (Enzymes)

1. Annual Review. *Advances in Enzymology,* Interscience Publishers, N. Y. (1941-current).
2. Laidler. *Introduction to the Chemistry of Enzymes,* McGraw-Hill Book, Co., N. Y. (1954).
3. Neilands and Stumpf. *Outlines of Enzyme Chemistry,* J. Wiley and Sons, N. Y. (1955).
4. Sumner and Somers. *Chemistry and Methods of Enzymes,* Academic Press, Inc., N. Y. (1953).
5. Colowick and Kaplan. *Methods of Enzymology,* Academic Press, N. Y. (1956).
6. Sumner and Myrback (editors). *The Enzymes, Chemistry and Mechanism of Action.* Vol. I, Parts A and B (1950); Vol. II, Parts A and B (1952), Vol. I (Second edition, 1959). Academic Press, Inc., N. Y. (detailed treatise).
7. Northrop, Kunitz and Herriott. *Crystalline Enzymes,* Columbia University Press, N. Y. (1948).
8. Structure and Function of Certain Enzymes. Federation Proceedings, 16, 774-815 (1957).
9. Pfeiffer. Enzymes, in *The Physics and Chemistry of Life,* pp. 163-180, Simon and Schuster, Inc., N. Y. (1955).
10. Dixon and Webb. *Enzymes,* Academic Press, N. Y. (1964).

Chapter 7 (Nucleoproteins, Nucleic Acids and Nucleotides)

1. Davidson. *The Biochemistry of the Nucleic Acids,* John Wiley and Sons, Inc., N. Y. (1953).
2. Chargaff and Davidson. *The Nucleic Acids.* Vol. I and Vol. II Academic Press, Inc., N. Y. (1955).
3. Nucleic Acids. F. H. C. Crick, Scientific American, 197, pp. 188-200 (1957).
4. Reconstitution of active tobacco mosaic virus from inactive components. Fraenkel-Conrat and Williams: Proc. Nat. Acad. Sci. U. S., 41:690 (1955).
5. McElroy and Glass. *The Chemical Basis of Heredity,* Johns Hopkins Press, Baltimore (1956).

Chapter 8 (Biosynthesis of Proteins and Its Control by Genes)

1. Campbell. *Biosynthesis of Proteins,* Life Sciences No. 6, pp. 428-440, (1963). Pergamon Press, N. Y.

2. Steiner. *The Chemical Foundations of Molecular Biology*,   D. Van Nostrand Co.,
       N.Y. (1965).

Chapter 9 (Minerals, Soils, and Plant Nutrition)

1. Yearbook of Agriculture. *Soils and Men*, U.S.D.A., Washington (1938).
2. Frear. *Agricultural Chemistry,* Vol. 1. *Principles.* Vol. 2.
       D. Von Nostrand Co., N.Y. (1950-51).
3. *Hunger Signs in Crops.* The American Society of Agronomy and the National Ferti-
       lizer Association, Washington (1965).
4. Truog. *Mineral Nutrition of Plants. A symposium.* Univ. of Wisconsin Press,
       Madison (1951).
5. *Inspection Report 25. Inspection of Commercial Fertilizers.* Agricultural Experi-
       ment Station, Purdue University, Lafayette, Indiana. April, 1965.
6. Waksman. *Microbial Antagonisms and Antibiotic Substances.* The Commonwealth
       Fund, N.Y. (1945).

Chapter 10 (Digestion and Absorption)

1. Dukes. *The Physiology of Domestic Animals.* 7th Edition. Comstock Publ. Co.,
       Cornell University, Ithaca, N.Y. (1955).
2. *Feeds and Feeding.* 22nd Edition, Morrison Publ. Co., Clinton, Iowa. (1956).
3. Etheredge. *Health Facts for College Students.* 7th Edition. W. B. Saunders Co.,
       Philadelphia (1958).
4. Ross. *A Textbook of Entomology.* 2nd Edition. John Wiley and Sons, N.Y. (1956).
5. Metcalf, Flint, and Metcalf. *Destructive and Useful Insects. Their Habits and
       Control.* 3rd Edition. McGraw-Hill Book Co., N.Y. (1951).
6. *William Beaumont, Pioneer Physiologist: On the Centennial of His Death (1785-1853).*
       Stenn, F., J. Am. Med. Assoc., 152, 915-917 (1953).
7. Reiser, R., et al. J. Biol. Chem., 194, 131-138 (1952) (Intestinal absorption of
       triglycerides).

Chapter 11 (Metabolism)

1. Schoeinheimer. *The Dynamic State of Body Constituents.* Harvard Press, Cam-
       bridge, Mass. (1942).
2. Kamen. *Isotopic Tracers in Biology.* Academic Press, N.Y., (1957).
3. Greenberg. *Chemical Pathways of Metabolism.* Vol. 1 and 2, Academic Press,
       N.Y. (1954).
4. Hill and Whittingham. *Photosynthesis.* J. Wiley and Sons, N.Y. (1955).
5. Rabinowitch. *Photosynthesis and Related Processes.* Vol. I. Chemistry (1945).
       Vol. II. Kinetics. Part 1 (1951), Part 2 (1956). Interscience Publishers, N.Y.
6. Chapman, H. W., Gleason, L. S. and Loomis, H. E. *Plant Physiol.,* 29, 500-504
       (1954). (CO_2 deficiency in rapidly photosynthesizing corn plants).
7. Najjar. *Fat Metabolism.* Johns Hopkins Press, Baltimore (1954).
8. Lipman, F. *American Scientist,* 43, 37-47 (1955). (Coenzyme A and Biosynthesis).
9. McElroy and Glass. *Amino Acid Metabolism.* Johns Hopkins Press, Baltimore (1955).
10. Meister. *Biochemistry of the Amino Acids.* Academic Press, N.Y. (1965).
11. Hsia. *Inborn Errors of Metabolism.* Yearbook Publishers, Chicago (1959).
12. Ochoa, S.. *Fed. Proc.,* 15, 832-840 (1956). (Enzymatic synthesis of ribonucleic
       acid-like polynucleotides).

13. Frear. *Agricultural Chemistry. I. Principles*. D. Van Nostrand Co., N.Y. (1950). Animal and plant metabolism: Chapters VII-XIV, XVII, XVIII, XIX, XX.

Chapter 12 (Animal Nutrition)

1. Frear. *Agricultural Chemistry. I. Principles*. Chapter XVI. Energy Metabolism. D. Van Nostrand Co., N.Y. (1950).
2. Peters, J. P. and Van Slyke, D.D.. *Quantitative Clinical Chemistry*. The Williams and Wilkins Co., Baltimore, Md. 2 (1946). *Interpretations*. Chapter 1. Energy Metabolism.
3. Forbes, E. B. *Ann. Rev. Physiol.*, 5, 105 (1943). Energy Metabolism.
4. Brody. *Bioenergetics and Growth*. Reinhold Publishing Corp., N.Y. (1945).
5. Frear. *Agricultural Chemistry. II. Applications*. D. Van Nostrand and Co., N.Y. (1951). Nutrition of farm animals: Chapters XIII-XIX inclusive.
6. Rose, W. C.. *J. Biol. Chem.*, 217, 95 (1955). Amino acid requirements of man.
7. *Recommended Nutrient Allowances*. Humans: Publ. 1146 (1963); Comparative Nutrition of Farm Animals: Publ. 132 (1951); Poultry: Publ. 827 (1960); Swine: Publ. 1192 (1964); Dairy Cattle-Pamphlet No. 464 (1958); Beef Cattle: Pamphlet No. 1137 (1963); Sheep: Pamphlet No. 1193 (1964). National Research Council, 2101 Constitution Ave., Washington, D.C. In addition to tables of allowances, these publications have good descriptions of deficiency symptoms, and excellent bibliographies.

Chapter 13 (Specialized Tissues)

1. Cummins, Gries, Postlethwait and Stearns. *Textbook of Intermediate Plant Science*. Burgess Publishing Co., Minneapolis (1950).
2. Fulton. *Textbook of Physiology*. W. B. Saunders Co., Philadelphia (1955).
3. Bodansky and Bodansky. *Biochemistry of Disease*. The Macmillan Co., N.Y. (1952).
4. Best and Taylor. *The Physiological Basis of Medical Practice*. Williams and Wilkins Co., Baltimore (1955).
5. Albritton. *Standard Values in Blood*. W. B. Saunders Co., Philadelphia (1952).
6. Seegers, W. H.. *Coagulation of the Blood*. Adv. in Enzymology, 16, 23-103 (1955).
7. Sherry, S., Fletcher, A. P. and Alkjaersig, N.. *Fibrinolysis and Fibrinolytic Activity in Man*. Physiol. Rev., 39, 343-382 (1959).
8. Peters and Van Slyke. *Quantitative Clinical Chemistry. I. Interpretations*. Williams and Wilkins, Baltimore, Ed. 2 (1946). Acid-base chemistry of blood.
9. Pincus and Thimann. *The Hormones*. Vol. I (1948), Vol. II (1950), Vol. III (1951). Academic Press, N.Y.
10. Pincus. *Recent Progress in Hormone Research*. Annual Reports on Laurentian Conference, since 1947. Academic Press, N.Y.
11. Katchalsky and Difson. *Scientific American*. March, 1954 (p. 72). Muscle chemistry.
12. McElwain. *Biochemistry of the Central Nervous System*. Little, Brown and Co., Boston (1955).
13. Bourne. *Biochemistry and Physiology of Bone*. Academic Press, Inc., N.Y. (1956).

Chapter 14 (Biochemical Control of Organisms)

1. *Plant Growth Substances: Plant Life*, Simons and Schuster, N.Y. (1957). Chapter 1, pp. 3-41.
2. Frear. *Chemistry of Insecticides, Fungicides and Herbicides*. D. Van Nostrand Co., N.Y. Ed. 2 (1948).

3. Frear. *Agricultural Chemistry. Vol. 2. Applications.*   D. Van Nostrand Co.,
      N.Y. (1951). Pesticides: Chapters XX-XXII.
4. Raper. *Scientific American.* April, 1952 (p. 49). Antibiotics.
5. Waksman. *Microbial Antagonisms and Antibiotic Substances.* The Commonwealth
      Fund. N.Y. (1946).
6. Porter. *Bacterial Chemistry and Physiology.* J. Wiley and Sons, N.Y. (1946).

Chapter 15 (Industrial, Drug, and Food Uses of Biochemicals)

1. *Inspection Report 26. 1964 Inspection of Commercial Feeds in Indiana.*   Agricultural
      Experiment Station, Lafayette, Indiana. April, 1965.
2. Hale. *The Farmer Victorious.* Coward-McCann. N.Y. (1949).
3. Hale. *Chemi-Vision.* Destiny Publications, Merrimac, Mass. (1952).
4. McMillen. *New Riches From the Soil.* D. Van Nostrand, N.Y. (1946).
5. Frear. *Agricultural Chemistry. Vol. 2. Applications.* Chapter XXIV. Chemurgy.
      D. Van Nostrand, N.Y. (1951).
6. Furnas, C. C. *Roger's Manual of Industrial Chemistry.* Vol. 1 and 2. D. Van
      Nostrand Co., N.Y., 6th Ed. (1942).
7. Ralston. *Fatty Acids and Their Derivatives.* J. Wiley and Sons, N.Y. (1948).
8. Tauber. *Chemistry and Technology of Enzymes.* J. Wiley and Sons, N.Y. (1949).

APPENDIX 2 | FORMULAE

1. **CAROTENOIDS.** This is a group of yellow, orange, and red pigments found in green leaves. Their solubility and origin place them in the lipids class. Examples of carotenoids are alpha, beta and gamma carotenes, cryptoxanthin, luteol, and lycopene.

Beta carotene is the most potent precursor of vitamin A. It is about twice as potent as the alpha and beta forms, and cryptoxanthin. Luteol and lycopene are not precursors of vitamin A. Luteol is closely associated with beta carotene in the leaf chloroplast, and lycopene is the red pigment in peppers, tomatoes and watermelons. All contain a polyene chain of 18 carbon atoms and 9 double bonds. They differ in the type of chemical groups that are attached to the ends of the chain, as shown in the following formulae.

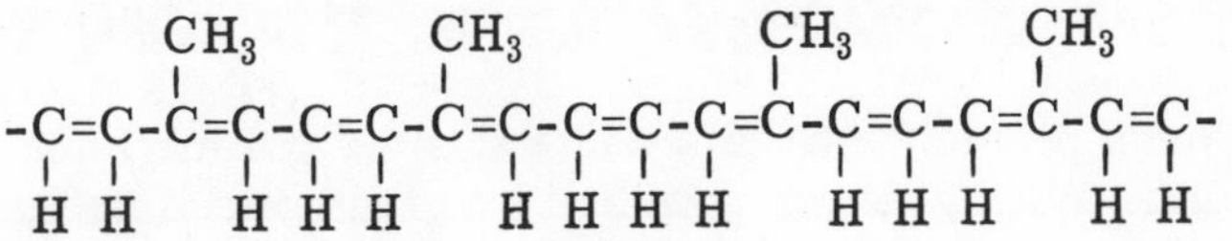

Methylated polyene chain

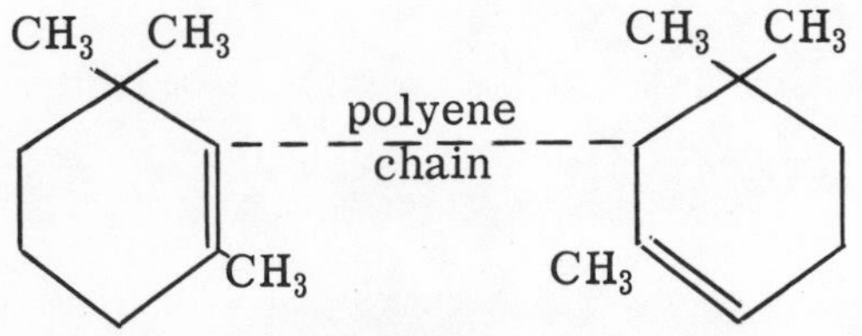

Alpha-carotene

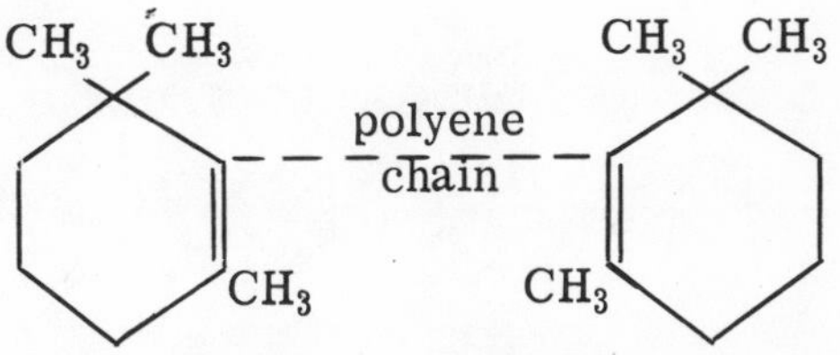

Beta-carotene

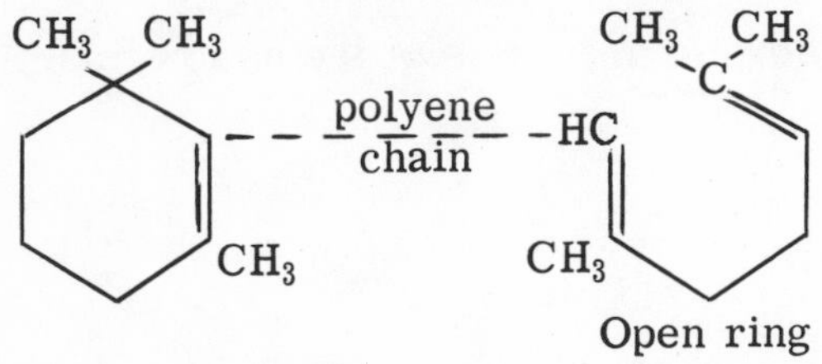

Gamma-carotene

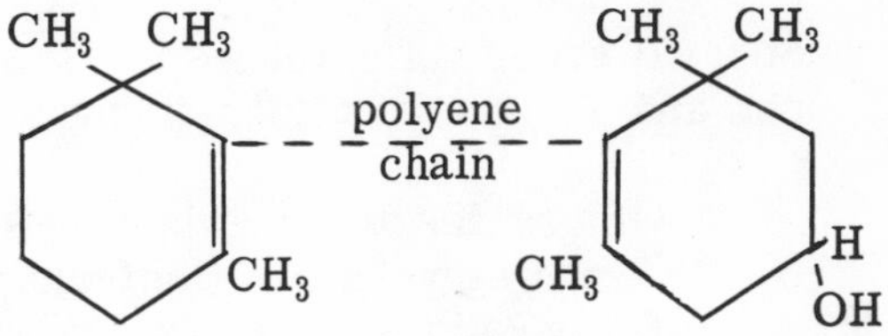

Cryptoxanthin

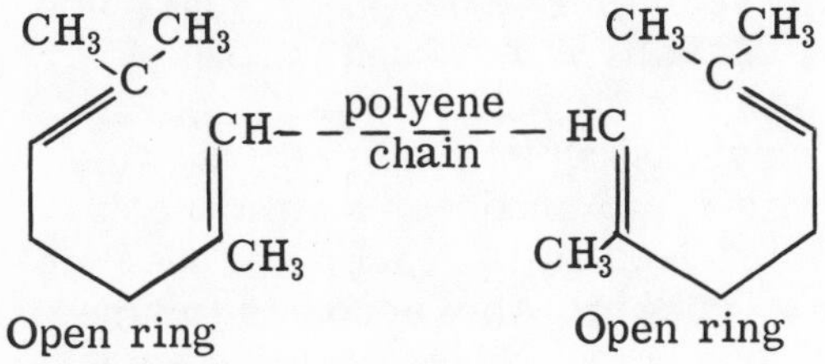

Lycopene

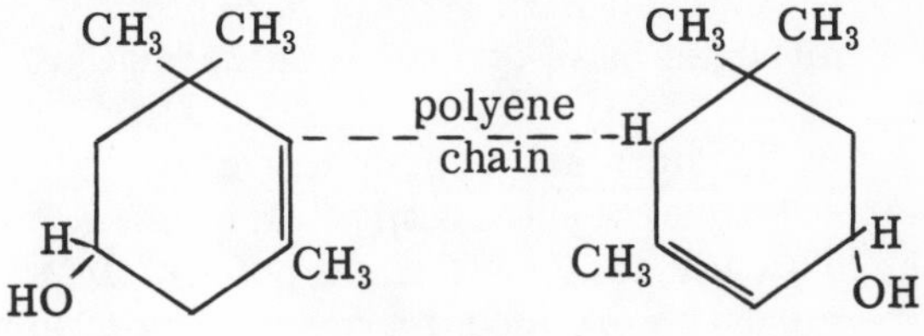

Luteol

2. WATER-SOLUBLE PLANT PIGMENTS. The beautiful blue, purple, violet, mauve, magenta, most of the reds, and pale yellow to ivory shades of color found in flowers and fruits, and in the spring and autumn leaves, are water-soluble pigments belonging to the anthocyanin or anthoxanthin groups. They contain the benzopyrylium and benzopyrone nuclei, respectively, as shown below.

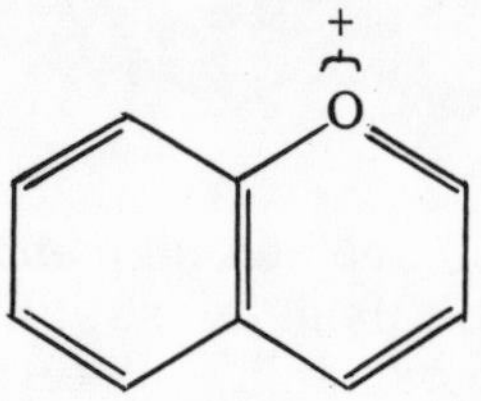

Anthocyanin
(benzopyrylium nucleus)

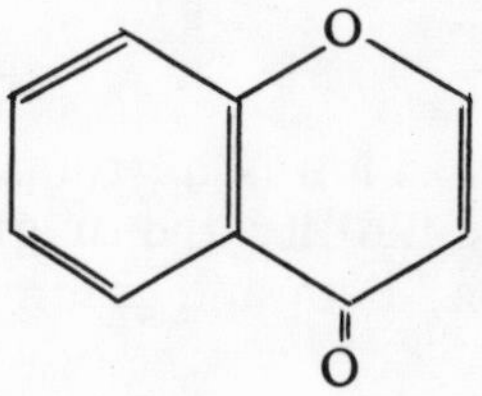

Anthoxanthin
(benzopyrone nucleus)

These pigments usually occur in the form of glycosides (see 17), which accounts for their solubility in water and easy extractability by aqueous solvents. They are found in the plant sap, and often as amorphous or crystalline solids in leaves, woody tissue, and fruits. Their color is sometimes masked by other pigments, such as chlorophyll.

Anthocyanins. These pigments have scarlet to blue colorations. A typical anthocyanidin is pelargonidin. With glucose attached by glycoside linkage to positions 3 and 5, it becomes the anthocyanin, *pelargonin*.

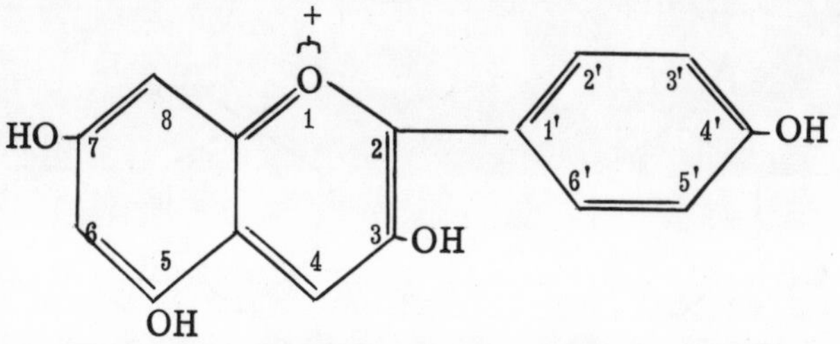

Pelargonidin (anthocyanidin)

Several groups of anthocyanins may be distinguished on the basis of the nature, number and position of attached sugars:

a. 3-Glucosides and 3-galactosides.
b. 3-Pentoseglycosides (including 3-rhamnosides).
c. 3-Diglycosides (disaccharide glycosides).
d. 3,5-Dimonoglucoside (most abundant type).
e. Anthocyanidin acylated with organic acids such as p-hydroxy benzoic acid.

An unusual anthocyanin is *betanin*, which gives the red color to beets. It contains a nitrogen base (probably the amino acid ornithine) in addition to a sugar group.

Anthoxanthins. These are glycosides of the benzopyrone nucleus. In slightly acid solution they are almost colorless. Treatment with alkali produces a yellow color. The aglycones and their potassium salts are yellow. Iron salts react with these pigments to produce a green or reddish brown color. This probably accounts for the darkening and precipitation observed when orange pekoe tea, which contains anthoxanthins, is brewed with hard water containing traces of iron.

Anthoxanthins may be divided into 5 modifications of the benzopyrone structure:

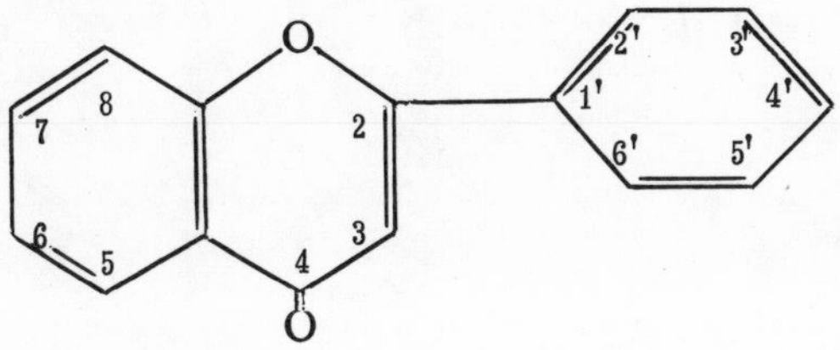

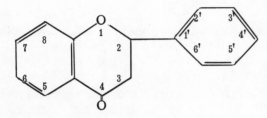

1. Flavone

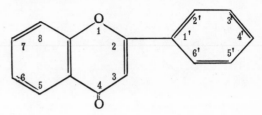

2. Flavonol (enol form)

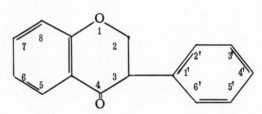

3. Flavonone

4. Isoflavone

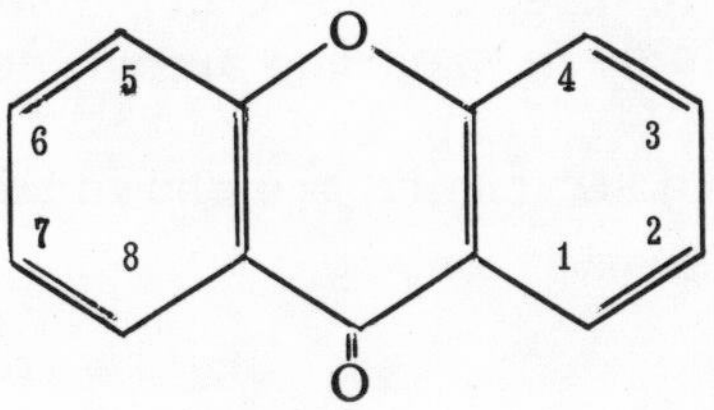

5. Xanthone

Apigenin (5, 7, 4'-trihydroxy-flavone) is found in the yellow dahlia, *Quercetin* (5, 7, 31, 41-tetrahydroxy-flavonol), is found in tea, *hesperidin** (5, 7, 3 trihydroxy-4'-methoxy flavanone) is found in grapes and oranges, *osajin* (5, 4'-dihydroxy iso-flavone) is found in the osage orange fruit, and *gentisin* (1, 7 dihydroxy-3-methoxy xanthone), is found in *Gentianaceae*. For further information regarding water-soluble plant pigments, the reader is referred to p. 350 of Reference 13 (Chapter 11), page 309 (Appendix).

3. MELANIN PIGMENTS. These red, brown and black pigments are formed by both plant and animal tissues. In animals they are found primarily in the hair and skin. They are quite inert. None are water-soluble, some are soluble in dilute acid, and all are soluble in dilute alkali. In both plants and animals, the building stone is the amino acid tyrosine. A partial mechanism of formation of melanin is given on p. 201. Formation of dopachrome (red) has been demonstrated with both plant and animal oxidases, using dopa as the substrate.

4. ALKALOIDS. These are complex nitrogen-containing compounds of plants which are related structurally, usually containing either pyridine, quinoline, or isoquinoline nuclei. Some alkaloids contain indole and imidazole groups.

* Vitamin P-increases capillary resistance in man - Biochem. J. 39, 271 (1945).

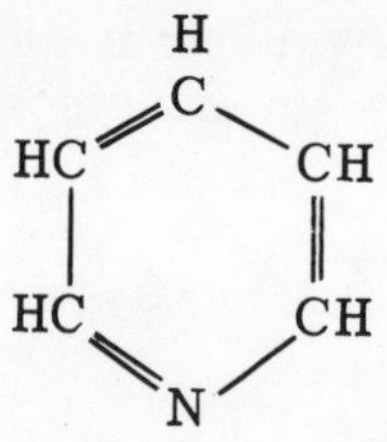

Pyridine 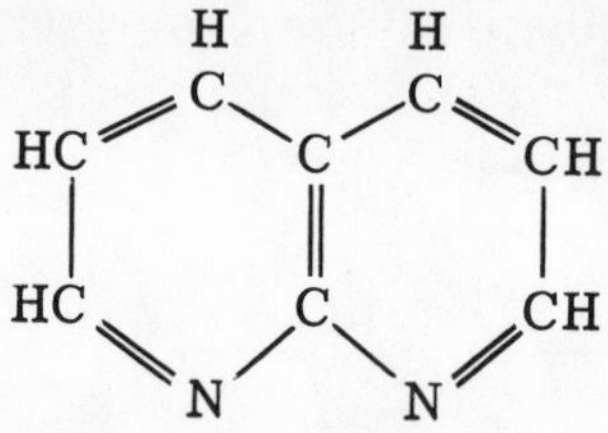   Quinoline 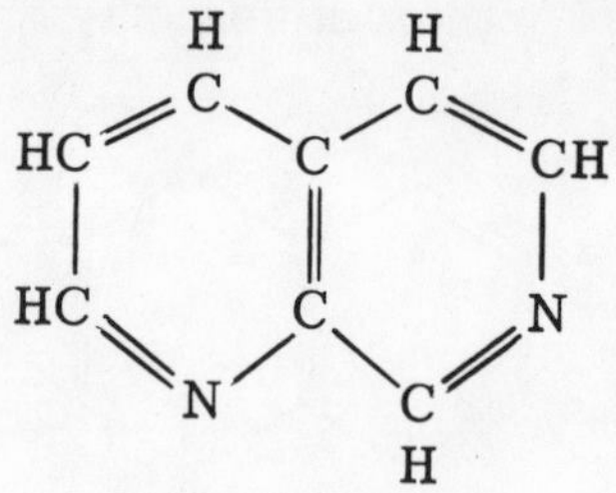   Isoquinoline

Although alkaloids occur quite widely in plants, the *Solanaceae* and *Papaveraceae* families are especially noted for their content of alkaloids.

The function of alkaloids in plants and the mechanism of synthesis is unknown. The alkaloid, nicotine, is synthesized in the roots of the tobacco plant, and then translocated to the leaves.

Most alkaloids are poisonous to animals if taken in large amounts. However, in small doses, atropine, cocaine, codeine, morphine, and quinine are important medicinals. Strychnine and nicotine must be administered with care; 60 milligrams of nicotine and a smaller quantity of strychnine are lethal to man.

Nicotine sulphate is used as in insecticide. Colchicine, another alkaloid, is used by geneticists to produce polyploidy in plant and animal cells.

The structures of nicotine and strychnine are shown below.

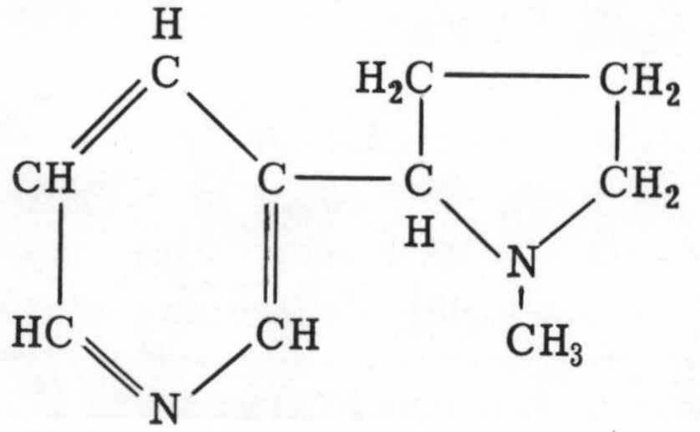

Nicotine 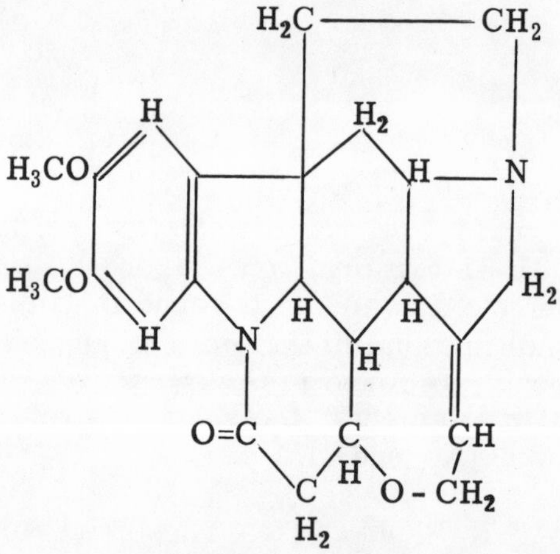   Strychnine

5. LIGNIN. Lignin is a high molecular weight amorphous polymer containing carbon, hydrogen and oxygen. In the plant, it is closely associated with cellulose, improving the tensile strength and hardness of the latter. Wood is composed mainly of a mixture of lignin and cellulose. Lignin is an undesirable constituent of paper and is removed by treating wood pulp with sodium bisulfite and sulfurous acid (sulfite process) or with sodium hydroxide.

Recent studies suggest that the aromatic amino acids, especially phenylalanine, serve as precursors of lignin in the plant. As the demands for phenylalanine decrease in the rapid growth phase, this amino acid is converted to p-hydroxy cinnamic acid and a methoxy derivative of the latter (ferulic acid), and these serve as monomer units in the formation of the lignin polymer.

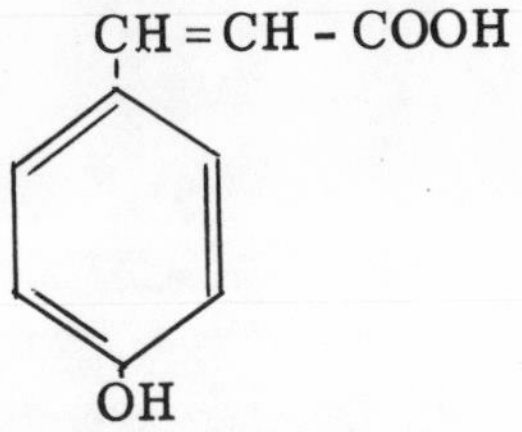

p-hydroxy cinnamic acid 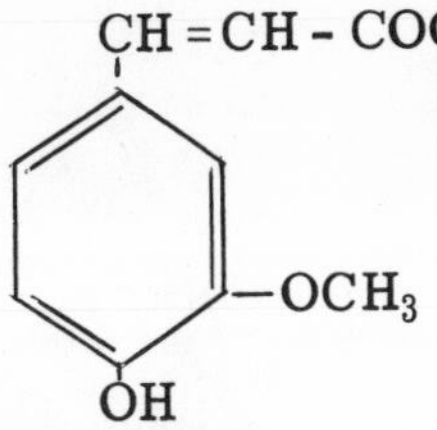   ferulic acid

Both monomer units have been isolated from lignin hydrolysates. Other compounds found in lignin hydrolysates contain the guaiacol, piperonyl or syringic group. These are designated as R_1, R_2 and R_3 in the formulae below. Their relationship to p-hydroxy cinnamic acid and ferulic acid is obvious.

$R_1(R_2, R_3)$ - CHOH-CHOH-CH$_2$OH

$R_1(R_2, R_3)$ - CHOH-CH$_2$-CHO

$R_1(R_2, R_3)$ - CHOH-CO-CH$_3$

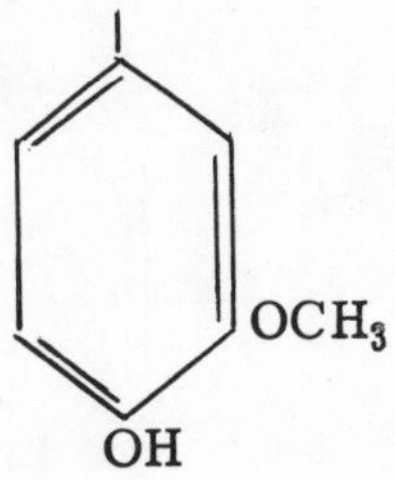

Guaiacol group (R_1) 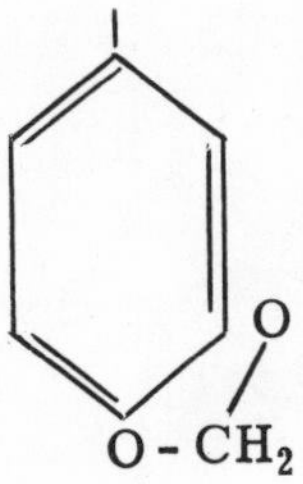   Piperonyl group (R_2) 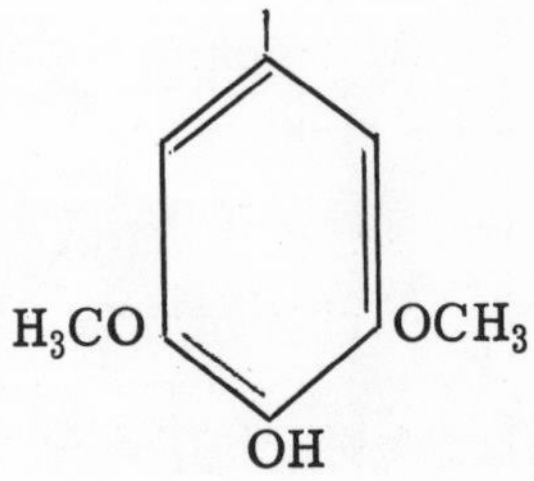   Syringic group (R_3)

6. FORMULA FOR DICOUMAROL.

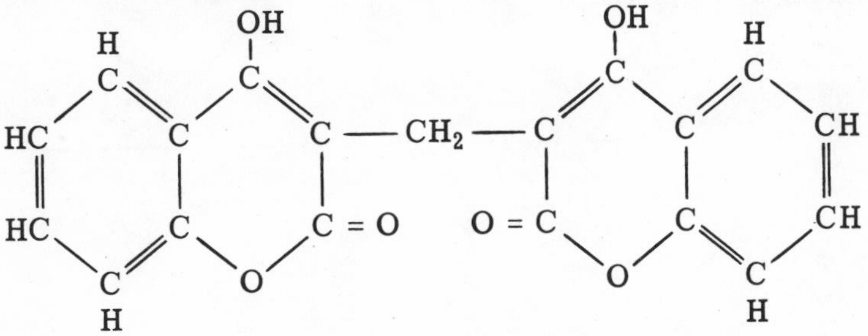

Dicoumarol

APPENDIX 3 | TABLES

Table 45. Amino acid composition of purified corn glutelin[1]

Amino Acid	Per Cent[2]	Amino Acid	Per Cent[2]
Alanine	9.77	Lysine	3.60
Arginine	5.51	Methionine	2.24
Aspartic Acid	7.33	Phenylalanine	7.21
Cystine	3.14	Proline	7.62
Glycine	5.06	Serine	4.36
Glutamic Acid	18.46	Threonine	3.72
Histidine	2.11	Tryptophan	0.92
Isoleucine	4.14	Tyrosine	4.94
Leucine	11.87	Valine	6.18

[1] Lloyd, N. E. and Mertz, E. T., Cereal Chem. 35 156 (1958).

[2] Grams per 100 gm. dry glutelin (16.1% N, 1.4% amide N).
Total recovery: 108.2 gm.

Table 46. Amino acid composition of selected proteins[1]

	Casein[2]	Gelatin[3]	Zein	Silk Fibroin[4]	Wool	Hemoglobin[5]	Wheat Gliadin
Alanine	3.0	7.9	9.9	30.2	4.0	9.7	1.9
Arginine	4.1	7.8	1.6	0.9	9.7	3.3	2.6
Aspartic Acid	7.1	4.9	3.3	2.1	6.7	10.0	1.6
Cystine	0.3	0.10	0.9	0.13	11.2	0.9	2.1
Glycine	2.7	15.7	0.4	37.3	6.8	4.3	--
Glutamic Acid	22.4	7.8	28.4	1.5	12.6	6.8	40.5
Histidine	3.1	0.8	1.2	0.3	0.8	8.0	1.8
Hydroxy proline	0.0	13.3	0.0	--	0.0	0.0	--
Isoleucine	6.1	1.4	7.3	0.8	4.4	0.3	4.7
Leucine	9.2	3.5	22.3	0.7	8.2	14.5	6.1
Lysine	8.2	4.8	0.1	0.5	2.8	10.2	0.7
Methionine	3.4	0.9	2.1	--	0.6	1.5	1.8
Phenylalanine	5.0	2.0	6.4	1.2	3.2	7.5	5.8
Proline	11.3	14.8	10.0	0.5	7.5	4.7	12.1
Serine	6.3	3.4	7.7	14.0	9.4	5.2	3.8
Threonine	4.9	1.7	2.7	1.3	6.5	5.8	1.9
Tryptophan	1.2	0.01	0.1	0.4	1.5	1.1	0.8
Tyrosine	6.3	0.6	5.0	9.9	5.1	4.1	2.9
Valine	7.2	2.7	2.6	2.7	5.1	10.6	2.4
Total	111.8	94.1	112.0	104.4	106.1	108.5	93.5

[1] Grams amino acid per 100 g. protein. Values for gelatin, wool and gliadin are average values from Block and Weiss (see p. 307, Appendix of this book).

[2] From p. 122, Hawk, Oser and Summerson (see p. 305, Appendix, this book).

[3] Also contains hydroxylysine: 0.8 gm./100 gm. crude protein.

[4] Schroeder, W. A. and Kay, L. M., J. Am. Chem. Soc. 77, 3908 (1955).

[5] Human adult. Van der Schaaf, P. C., and Huisman, T. H. S.,Biochim. et Biophys. Acta 17 81 (1955).

Appendix 3

Table 47. Outline of I.U.B. system for classification of enzymes*

Enzyme Commission Number	Systematic Name	Trivial Name	Active Groups And Cofactors	Reaction	Source
1 OXIDOREDUCTASES					
1.1 Acting on the $>$CHOH group of donors					
1.1.1 With NAD or NADP as acceptor (66)					
1.1.1.1 (C)	Alcohol:NAD oxido-reductase	Alcohol dehydrogenase	Zn^{++}	Alcohol + NAD= ald. or ketone + $NADH_2$	Yeast, some animal tissue
1.1.1.8 (C)	L-glycerol-3-phos-phate:NAD oxido-reductase	Glycerolphos-phate dehydro-genase		L-glycerol-3-phos-phate + NAD=dihy-droxy acetone phosphate + $NADH_2$	Animal tissues
1.1.1.37 (C)	L-malate:NAD oxido-reductase	Malate de-hydrogenase		L-malate + NAD= oxaloacetate + $NADH_2$	Animal, plant, microbial tissues
1.1.2 With a cytochrome as acceptor (4)					
1.1.2.3 (C)	L-lactate:cytochrome c oxidoreductase	Lactate dehydrogen-ase	F, H	L-lactate + oxid-ized cytochrome c = pyruvate + re-duced cytochrome c.	Yeast
1.1.3 With O_2 as acceptor (9)					
1.1.3.2 (C)	L-lactate:O_2 oxido-reductase (decarbo-xylating)	Lactate oxidase	F	L-lactate + O_2 = acetate + CO_2 + H_2O_2	Bacteria
1.1.99 With other acceptors (5)					
1.2 Acting on the aldehyde or keto group of donors					
1.2.1 With NAD or NADP as acceptor (20)					
1.2.1.12 (C)	D-glyceraldehyde-3-phosphate:NAD oxido-reductase (phos-phorylating)	Triose phos-phate de-hydrogenase	Zn^{++}	D-glyceraldehyde-3-phosphate + phosphate + NAD= 1,3-diphospho-D-glyceric acid + $NADH_2$	Most living cells
1.2.2 With a cytochrome as an acceptor (2)					
1.2.3 With O_2 as acceptor (4)					

* This is based on the Report of the Commission on Enzymes, International Union of Biochemistry Symposium, Vol. 20, Pergamon Press, New York (1961). Only a few examples are given in the above table, and the student should read the report for complete details. In the table above, column 1 shows the Enzyme Commission number, column 2 the systematic names authorized by the Commission, column 3 gives the trivial or common name, column 4 lists active groups and cofactors (F-flavoprotein, H-hemo-protein, Bt-bound biotin, S-sulfhydryl compound, Py-pyridoxal phosphate, M^{++}-activated by several different divalent metal ions, A-activated by a numer of anions), column 5 gives the reaction on which the systematic name is based, and column 6 shows a source (or sources) of the enzyme. A capital C in parentheses below the Commission number indicates that the enzyme has been prepared in crystalline form. The arabic number in parentheses after the sub-groups indicates the total number of enzymes in that sub-group in the year 1962.

Enzyme Commission Number	Systematic Name	Trivial Name	Active Groups And Cofactors	Reaction	Source
1.2.3.2 (C)	Xanthine:O_2 oxido-reductase	Xanthine oxidase	F, Mo^{++}, Fe^{++}	Xanthine + H_2O + O_2 = urate + H_2O_2	Animal tissues, milk, bacteria

1.2.4 With lipoate as acceptor (2)

1.2.99 With other acceptors (1)

1.3 Acting on the $>$CH-CH$<$ group of donors

1.3.1 With NAD or NADP as acceptor (5)

| 1.3.1.2 | 4,5-dihydro-uracil: NADP oxidoreductase | Dihydrouracil dehydrogenase | | 4,5-dihydro-uracil + NADP= uracil + $NADPH_2$ | Liver |

1.3.2 With a cytochrome as an acceptor (3)

| 1.3.2.2 | Acyl-CoA:cyto-chrome c oxido-reductase | Acyl-CoA dehydrogenase | F, Fe^{++} | Acyl-CoA + oxi-dized cytochrome c= 2,3-dehydro-acyl-CoA + re-duced cytochrome c. | Animal tissues |

1.3.3 With O_2 as acceptor (1)

1.3.99 With other acceptors (3)

1.4 Acting on the $>$CH-NH_2 group of donors

1.4.1 With NAD or NADP as acceptor (6)

| 1.4.1.2 | L-glutamate:NAD oxidoreductase (deaminating) | Glutamate dehydrogenase | | L-glutamate + H_2O + NAD= 2-oxoglutarate + NH_3 + $NADH_2$ | All com-plete cells |

1.4.3 With O_2 as acceptor (6)

| 1.4.3.2 | L-aminoacid:O_2 oxidoreductase (deaminating) | L-amino acid oxidase | F | L-amino acid + H_2O + O_2= 2-Oxo-acid + NH_3 + H_2O_2 | Liver, kidney, microbes |

1.5 Acting on the C-NH group of donors

1.5.1 With NAD or NADP as acceptor (5)

1.5.3 With O_2 as acceptor (3)

1.6 Acting on $NADH_2$ or $NADPH_2$ as donor

1.6.1 With NAD or NADP as acceptor (1)

1.6.2 With a cytochrome as acceptor (3)

1.6.4 With a disulphide compound as acceptor (3)

1.6.5 With a quinone or related compound as acceptor (4)

1.6.6 With a nitrogeneous group as acceptor (7)

1.6.99 With other acceptors (1)

1.7 Acting on other nitrogenous compounds as donors

1.7.3 With O_2 as acceptor (3)

1.7.99 With other acceptors (3)

1.8 Acting on sulphur groups as donors

1.8.1 With NAD or NADP as acceptor (2)

1.8.3 With O_2 as acceptor (2)

1.8.4 With a disulphide compound as acceptor (1)

| 1.8.4.1 | Glutathione:homo-cystine oxido-reductase | Glutathione-homocystine transhydro-genase | | 2 reduced gluta-thione + homocy-stine = oxidized glutathione + 2 homocysteine | Liver |

Enzyme Commission Number	Systematic Name	Trivial Name	Active Groups And Cofactors	Reaction	Source
1.8.5 With a quinone or related compound as acceptor (1)					
1.8.6 With a nitrogenous group as acceptor (1)					
1.9 Acting on heme groups of donors					
1.9.3 With O_2 as acceptor (2)					
1.9.3.1	Cytochrome c: O_2 oxidoreductase	Cytochrome oxidase (cytochrome a_3)	H, Cu^{++}	4 reduced cytochrome c + O_2 = 4 oxidized cytochrome c + 2 H_2O	Most cells
1.9.6 With a nitrogenous group as acceptor (1)					
1.10 Acting on diphenols and related substances as donors					
1.10.3 With O_2 as acceptor (3)					
1.11 Acting on H_2O_2 as acceptor (8)					
1.11.1.6 (C)	H_2O_2:H_2O_2 oxidoreductase	Catalase	H	H_2O_2 + H_2O_2 = O_2 + 2 H_2O	Most cells
1.98 Enzymes using H_2 as reductant (1)					
1.99 Other enzymes using O_2 as oxidant					
1.99.1 Hydroxylases (15)					
1.99.2 Oxygenases (9)					
2 TRANSFERASES					
2.1 Transferring one-carbon groups					
2.1.1 Methyltransferases (10)					
2.1.1.2	S-adenosylmethionine:guanidinoacetate N-methyltransferase	Guanidinoacetate methyltransferase		S-adenosylmethionine + guanidinoacetate = S-adenosylhomocysteine + creatine	Liver
2.1.2 Hydroxymethyl-, formyl- and related transferases (6)					
2.1.2.1	L-serine:tetrahydrofolate 5,10-hydroxymethyl transferase	Serine hydroxymethyltransferase	Py, Mn^{++}	L-serine + tetrahydrofolate = glycine + 5,10-methylene-tetrahydrofolate	Liver
2.1.3 Carboxyl- and carbamoyltransferases (3)					
2.1.3.3	Carbamoylphosphate: L-ornithine carbamoyltransferase	Ornithine carbamoyltransferase		Carbamoylphosphate + L-ornithine = orthophosphate + L-citrulline	Animal tissues, bacteria
2.2 Transferring aldehydic or ketonic residues (2)					
2.2.1.2 (C)	D-sedoheptulose-7-phosphate:D-glyceraldehyde-3-phosphate dihydroxyacetone transferase	Transaldolase		D-sedoheptulose 7-phosphate + D-glyceraldehyde 3-phosphate = D-erythrose 4-phosphate + D-fructose 6-phosphate	Liver, plants yeast
2.3 Acyltransferases					
2.3.1 Acyltransferases (20)					
2.3.1.9	Acetyl-CoA:acetyl-CoA C-acetyltransferase	Acetoacetyl-CoA thiolase		Acetyl-CoA + acetyl-CoA = CoA + acetoacetyl-CoA	Animal tissues

Enzyme Commission Number	Systematic Name	Trivial Name	Active Groups And Cofactors	Reaction	Source
	2.3.2 Aminoacyltransferases (1)				
	2.4 Glycosyltransferases				
	2.4.1 Hexosyl transferases (28)				
2.4.1.11	UDPglucose:glycogen α-4-glucosyltransferase	UDPglucose-glycogen glucosyl transferase	Mg^{++}, S	UDPglucose + (glycogen)$_n$ = UDP + (glycogen)$_{n+1}$	Animal tissues, yeast, bacteria
2.4.1.c	UDPgalactose: D-glucose 1-galactosyl-transferase	UDPgalactose-glucose galactosyltransferase		UDPgalactose + D-glucose = UDP + lactose	Mammary gland
	2.4.2 Pentosyltransferases (14)				
2.4.2.13	ATP:L-methionine S-adenosyltransferase	Methionine adenosyltransferase	Mg^{++}, M^{++}, S	ATP + L-methionine + H_2O = orthophosphate + pyrophosphate + S-adenosyl-methionine	Liver, yeast
	2.5 Transferring alkyl or related groups (5)				
	2.6 Transferring nitrogenous groups				
	2.61 Aminotransferases (19)				
2.6.1.2	L-alanine:2-oxoglutarate amino-transferase	Alanine aminotransferase (also glu-pyruvic transaminase)	Py	L-alanine + 2-oxoglutarate = pyruvate + L-glutamate	Animal, plant tissues
	2.6.2 Amidino transferases (1)				
	2.6.3 Oximinotransferases (1)				
	2.7 Transferring phosphorus-containing groups				
	2.7.1 Phosphotransferases with an alcohol group as acceptor (49)				
2.7.1.1 (C)	ATP:D-hexose 6-phosphotransferase	Hexokinase	Mg^{++}	ATP + D-hexose = ADP + D-hexose 6-phosphate	Animal tissues moulds, yeast
	2.7.2 Phosphotransferases with a carboxyl group as acceptor (5)				
	2.7.3 Phosphotransferases with a nitrogenous group as acceptor (5)				
2.7.3.2 (C)	ATP:creatine phosphotransferase	Creatine kinase	Mg^{++}	ATP + creatine = ADP + phosphocreatine	Animal tissues
	2.7.4 Phosphotransferases with a phospho- group as acceptor (10)				
	2.7.5 Phosphotransferases with regeneration of donors (4)				
	2.7.6 Pyrophosphotransferases (2)				
	2.7.7 Nucleotidyltransferases (24)				
2.7.7.12	UDPglucose:α-D-galactose-1-phosphate uridyltransferase	Hexose-1-phosphate uridyltransferase	Mg^{++}	UDPglucose + α-D-galactose 1-phosphate = α-D-glucose 1-phosphate + UDPgalactose	Animal tissues, yeast, bacteria
	2.7.8 Transferases for other substituted phospho-groups (3)				
	2.8 Transferring sulphur-containing groups				
	2.8.1 Sulphurtransferases (2)				
	2.8.2 Sulphotransferases (5)				
	2.8.3 CoA-transferases (4)				
3	HYDROLASES				
	3.1 Acting on ester bonds				
	3.1.1 Carboxylic ester hydrolases (20)				

Enzyme Commission Number	Systematic Name	Trivial Name	Active Groups And Cofactors	Reaction	Source
3.1.1.3	Glycerol ester hydrolase	Lipase	Ca^{++}	A triglyceride + H_2O = a diglyceride + a fatty acid	Pancreas, plants, moulds, bacteria
3.1.1.8	Acylcholine acyl-hydrolase	Cholinesterase		An acylcholine + H_2O = choline + an acid	Animal tissues, blood
3.1.2 Thiolester hydrolases (8)					
3.1.3 Phosphoric monoester hydrolases (19)					
3.1.3.1	Orthophosphoric mono-ester phosphohydrolase	Alkaline phosphatase	M^{++}	An orthophosphoric mono-ester + H_2O = an alcohol + H_3PO_4	Animal tissues, milk
3.1.4 Phosphoric diester hydrolases (9)					
3.1.4.5 (C)	Deoxyribonucleate oligonucleotido-hydrolase	Deoxyribo-nuclease	Mg^{++}	DNA + (n-1)H_2O = n oligodeoxy-ribonucleotides	Animal tissues
3.1.5 Triphosphoric monoester hydrolases (1)					
3.1.6 Sulphuric ester hydrolases (6)					
3.2 Acting on glycosyl compounds					
3.2.1 Glycoside hydrolases (36)					
3.2.1.1 (C)	α-1, 4-glucan 4-glucanohydrolase	α-amylase	Ca^{++}, A	Hydrolyzes α-1, 4-glucan links in polysacch. containing 3 or more α-1, 4-linked D-glucose units	Animal tissues, saliva, plants, moulds, bacteria
3.2.2 Hydrolyzing N-glycosyl compounds (6)					
3.2.3 Hydrolyzing S-glycosyl compounds (1)					
3.3 Acting on ether bonds					
3.3.1 Thioether hydrolases (1)					
3.4 Acting on peptide bonds (peptide hydrolases)					
3.4.1 α-aminopeptide aminoacidohydrolases (4)					
3.4.1.1	None	Leucine amino-peptidase	M^{++}	Splits off N-terminal amino acids in L-peptides. Best when leucine is N-terminal	Intestinal juice
3.4.2 α-carboxypeptide aminoacidhydrolases (3)					
3.4.2.1 (C)	None	Carboxypeptidase A	Zn^{++}	Splits off C-terminal amino acids from L-peptides. Can't handle proline or basic a.a.	Pancreatic juice
3.4.3 Dipeptide hydrolases (7)					
3.4.3.1	Glycyl-glycine hydrolase	Glycyl-glycine dipeptidase	Co^{++}	Splits glycyl- and sarcosyl-glycine	Animal tissues
3.4.4 Peptide peptidohydrolases (23)					
3.4.4.1	None	Pepsin		Endopeptidase	Gastric juice
3.4.4.4	None	Trypsin		Endopeptidase	Pancreatic juice
3.4.4.5	None	Chymotrypsin		Endopeptidase	Pancreatic juice

Enzyme Commission Number	Systematic Name	Trivial Name	Active Groups And Cofactors	Reaction	Source
3.4.4.13	None	Thrombin	Ca^{++}	Converts fibrinogen to fibrin	Plasma prothrombin
3.4.4.14	None	Plasmin		Converts fibrin to soluble products.	Plasma plasminogen

3.5 Acting on C-N bonds, other than peptide bonds

    3.5.1 In linear amides (18)

| 3.5.1.2 | L-glutamine amido-hydrolase | Glutaminase | A | L-glutamine + H_2O = L-glutamate + NH_3 | Animal tissues, protozoa, bacteria |

    3.5.2 In cyclic amides (7)

    3.5.3 In linear amidines (6)

| 3.5.3.1 (C) | L-arginine ureohydrolase | Arginase | M^{++} | L-arginine + H_2O = L-ornithine + urea | Animal tissues, plants |

    3.5.4 In cyclic amidines (12)

    3.5.99 In other compounds (2)

3.6 Acting on acid anhydride bonds

    3.6.1 In phosphoryl-containing anhydrides (12)

| 3.6.1.3 | ATP phospho-hydrolase | ATPase(myosin) | Ca^{++} | ATP + H_2O = ADP + ortho-phosphate | Muscle |

3.7 Acting on C-C bonds

    3.7.1 In ketonic substances (2)

3.8 Acting on halide bonds

    3.8.1 In C-halide compounds (1)

    3.8.2 In P-halide compounds (1)

3.9 Acting on P-N bonds (1)

4   LYASES

4.1 Carbon-carbon lyases

    4.1.1 Carboxy-lases (39)

| 4.1.1.22 | L-histidine carboxy-lyase | Histidine decarboxylase | Py, M^{++} | L-histidine = histamine + CO_2 | Animal tissues, bacteria |

    4.1.2 Aldehyde lyases (16)

| 4.1.2.b (C) | Fructose-1,6-diphosphate D-glyceraldehyde-3-phosphate-lyase | Aldolase | | Fructose 1,6-diphosphate = dihydroxyacetone phosphate + D-glyceraldehyde 3-phosphate | Muscle, moulds, yeast |

    4.1.3 Ketoacid-lyases (8)

4.2 Carbon-oxygen lyases

    4.2.1 Hydro-lyases (26)

| 4.2.1.2 (C) | L-malate hydro-lyase | Fumarate hydratase | | L-malate = fumarate + H_2O | Most cells |
| 4.2.1.11 (C) | 2-phospho-D-glycerate hydrolyase | Enolase | M^{++} | 2-phospho-D-glycerate = phosphoenol-pyruvate + H_2O | Most cells |

Enzyme Commission Name	Systematic Name	Trivial Name	Active Groups And Cofactors	Reaction	Source
	4.2.99 Other carbon-oxygen lyases (1)				
	4.3 Carbon-nitrogen lyases				
	4.3.1 Ammonia lyases (6)				
4.3.1.3	L-histidine ammonia-lyase	Histidase	S	L-histidine = urocanate + NH$_3$	Liver, bacteria
	4.3.2 Amididine-lyases (2)				
4.3.2.1	L-argininosuccinate arginine-lyase	Argininosuccinase		L-argininosuccinate = fumarate + L-arginine	Most cells
	4.4 Carbon-sulphur lyases (4)				
	4.5 Carbon-halide lyases (1)				
5	ISOMERASES				
	5.1 Racemases and epimerases				
	5.1.1 Acting on amino acids and derivatives (8)				
	5.1.2 Acting on hydroxyacids and derivatives (3)				
	5.1.3 Acting on carbohydrates and derivatives (7)				
5.1.3.2	UDPglucose 4-epimerase	Galactowaldenase	NAD, Mg^{++}	UDPglucose = UDPgalactose	Animal tissues, yeast, bacteria
	5.1.99 Acting on other compounds (1)				
	5.2 Cis-trans isomerases (4)				
5.2.1.3	All-trans-retinene 11-cis-trans-isomerase	Retinene isomerase		All-transretinene = 11-cisretinene	Retina
	5.3 Intramolecular oxidoreductases				
	5.3.1 Interconverting aldoses and ketoses (14)				
5.3.1.9	D-glucose-6-phosphate keto-isomerase	Glucosephosphate isomerase		D-glucose 6-phosphate = D-fructose 6-phosphate	Animal tissues, plants, yeast
	5.3.2 Interconverting keto- and enol- groups (1)				
	5.3.3 Transposing C=C bonds (3)				
	5.4 Intramolecular transferases				
	5.4.1 Transferring acyl groups (1)				
	5.4.2 Transferring phosphoryl groups (1)				
	5.4.99 Transferring other groups (1)				
5.4.99.2	Methylmalonyl-CoA CoA-carbonylmutase	Methylmalonyl CoA mutase	B$_{12}$	methylmalonyl-CoA = succinyl CoA	Animal tissues, bacteria
	5.5 Intramolecular lyases (1)				
6	LIGASES				
	6.1 Forming C-O bonds				
	6.1.1 Aminoacid-RNA ligases (11)				
6.1.1.7	L-alanine:sRNA ligase (AMP)	Alanyl-sRNA synthetase	M^{++}	ATP + L-alanine + sRNA = AMP + pyrophosphate + L-alanyl-sRNA	Liver

Enzyme Commission Number	Systematic Name	Trivial Name	Active Groups And Cofactors	Reaction	Source
6.2 <u>Forming C-S bonds</u>					
6.2.1 <u>Acid-thiol ligases (7)</u>					
6.2.1.1	Acetate:CoA ligase (AMP)	Acetyl-CoA synthetase	Mg^{++}, K^+	ATP + acetate + CoA = AMP + pyrophosphate + acetyl-CoA	Animal tissues, plants yeast, bacteria
6.3 <u>Forming C-N bonds</u>					
6.3.1 <u>Acid-ammonia ligases (3)</u>					
6.3.1.2	L-glutamate: ammonia ligase (ADP)	Glutamine synthetase	M^{++}	ATP + L-glutamate + NH_3 = ADP + orthophosphate + L-glutamine	Animal tissues, plants, moulds, bacteria
6.3.2 <u>Acid-aminoacid ligases (11)</u>					
6.3.2.a	L-histidine: β-alanine ligase (AMP)	Carnosine synthetase		ATP + L-histidine + β-alanine = AMP + pyrophosphate + carnosine	Animal tissues
6.3.3 <u>Cyclo-ligases (1)</u>					
6.3.4 <u>Other C-N ligases (5)</u>					
6.3.5 C-N ligases with glutamine as amino-N-donor (3)					
6.4 <u>Forming C-C bonds (4)</u>					
6.4.1.1	Pyruvate:CO_2 ligase (ADP)	Pyruvate carboxylase	Bt, Mg^{++}	ATP + pyruvate + CO_2 + H_2O = ADP + orthophosphate + oxaloacetate	Animal tissues, bacteria
6.4.1.2	Acetyl-CoA:CO_2 ligase (ADP)	Acetyl CoA carboxylase	Bt	ATP + acetyl-CoA + CO_2 + H_2O = ADP + orthophosphate + malonyl-CoA	Animal tissues, plants

Table 48. Energy expenditures under various conditions
of muscular activity*

	Calories per hour		
Form of activity	Per 70 kg. (average man)	Per kg.	Per pound
Sleeping	65	0.93	0.43
Awake lying still	77	1.10	0.50
Sitting at rest	100	1.43	0.65
Reading aloud	105	1.50	0.69
Standing relaxed	105	1.50	0.69
Hand sewing	111	1.59	0.72
Standing at attention	115	1.63	0.74
Knitting (23 stitches per minute on sweater) ...	116	1.66	0.75
Dressing and undressing..................	118	1.69	0.77
Singing	122	1.74	0.79
Tailoring	135	1.93	0.88
Typewriting rapidly	140	2.00	0.91
Ironing (with 5-pound iron)...............	144	2.06	0.93
Dishwashing (plates, bowls, cups, and saucers).	144	2.06	0.93
Sweeping bare floor (38 strokes per minute)....	169	2.41	1.09
Bookbinding..............................	170	2.43	1.10
"Light exercise".........................	170	2.43	1.10
Shoe making.............................	180	2.57	1.17
Walking slowly (2.6 miles per hour)	200	2.86	1.30
Carpentry, metal working, industrial painting..	240	3.43	1.56
"Active exercise"........................	290	4.14	1.88
Walking moderately fast (3.75 miles per hour) .	300	4.28	1.95
Walking down stairs......................	364	5.20	2.36
Stoneworking	400	5.71	2.60
"Severe exercise"	450	6.43	2.92
Sawing wood.............................	480	6.86	3.12
Swimming	500	7.14	3.25
Running (5.3 miles per hour)	570	8.14	3.70
"Very severe exercise"	600	8.57	3.90
Walking very fast (5.3 miles per hour)........	650	9.28	4.22
Walking up stairs........................	1100	15.80	7.18

* From Sherman, Chemistry of Food and Nutrition. 7th Ed., p. 189 (1946). By permission of The Macmillan Co., Publishers.

Table 49. Recommended daily allowances for
calories and protein[1]

Species	Calories	Protein (gm.)
Human		
Adult male (65 kg.)[2]	3, 200	65
Adult female (55 kg.)[3]	2, 300	55
Pregnant female (third trimester)	add 400	80
Lactating female (850 ml. daily)	add 1,000	100
Infants (on cow's milk)		
1-3 mos.	kg. x 120	kg. x 3.5
4-9 mos.	kg. x 110	kg. x 3.5
10-12 mos.	kg. x 100	kg. x 3.5
Children		
1-3 yr. (12 kg.)	1, 200	40
4-6 yr. (18 kg.)	1, 600	50
7-9 yr. (27 kg.)	2, 000	60
Boys		
10-12 yr. (35 kg.)	3, 500	70
13-15 yr. (49 kg.)	3, 200	85
16-20 yr. (63 kg.)	3, 800	100
Girls		
10-12 yr. (36 kg.)	2, 300	70
13-15 yr. (49 kg.)	2, 500	80
16-20 yr. (54 kg.)	2, 400	75
Chickens[4]		
0-8 weeks	kg. x 180	20
8-18 weeks	kg. x 180	16
Laying hens	kg. x 120	15
Turkeys[4]		
0-8 weeks	--	28
8-16 weeks	--	20
Breeders	--	15
Swine		
Growing, fattening pigs		
50 lb.	4, 300 (T.D.N. x 4.0)[5]	0.51[6] (16)[7]
100 lb.	7, 200	0.74 (14)
150 lb.	9, 600	0.88 (13)
200 lb.	10, 000	0.90 (12)
250 lb.	11, 000	1.00 (12)

[1] Based on National Academy of Sciences - National Research Council Publications 295, 301, 302, and Nutrient Allowances Publ. No. 3 (1950), 4 (1950) and 5 (1949), Washington, D. C.

[2] Cal. for men = 152 ($W^{0.73}$ where W = body wt. in kg. Must be adjusted to needs of individual.

[3] Cal. for women = 123.4 ($W^{0.73}$) where W = body wt. in kg. Must be adjusted to needs of individual.

[4] Calories estimated by author as "productive" energy needed in diet for growth or egg production. Add 70 x kg.$^{0.73}$ for basal metabolism (see p. 170). Protein expressed as per cent of feed.

[5] Product of grams total digestible nutrients needed, and estimated energy content of 4 Cal./gm.

[6] Pounds of crude protein.

[7] Per cent of air-dried feed.

CONTINUED ON NEXT PAGE

Species	Calories	Protein
Pregnant gilts and sows, breeding boars	8,000	1.0 (15)
Lactating sows	16,000	1.7 (15)
Sheep		
Bred ewes 6 wk. before lambing (130 lb.)	4,200[5]	0.23[8]
Ewes in lactation (130 lb.)	5,100	0.30
Fattening lambs		
50 lb.	2,200	0.17
90 lb.	3,600	0.20
Beef Cattle		
Heifers and steers		
400 lb.	12,700[5]	0.9[8]
1,000 lb.	19,000	0.9
Fattening Yearling Cattle		
600 lb.	20,800	1.3
1,100 lb.	31,700	1.7
Wintering Yearling Cattle		
600 lb.	14,500	0.8
900 lb.	16,300	0.8
Bulls, growth and maintenance		
600 lb.	18,000	1.3
1,800 lb.	25,200	1.4
Cows Nursing Calves, 1-3 mos.		
900 - 1,100 lb.	25,200	1.4

[8] Pounds digestible protein.

Table 50. Recommended daily allowances for vitamins[1]

Species	Vitamin A I.U.	Thiamin mg.	Riboflavin mg.	Niacin mg.	Ascorbic acid mg.	Vitamin D I.U.
Humans						
Adult male	5,000	1.6	1.6	16	75	--
Adult female	5,000	1.2	1.4	12	70	--
Pregnant female (3rd trimester)	6,000	1.5	2.0	15	100	400
Lactating (850 ml. daily)	8,000	1.5	2.5	15	150	400
Infants	1,500	0.3-0.5	0.4-0.9	3-5	30	400
Children						
1-3 yr.	2,000	0.6	1.0	6	35	400
4-6 yr.	2,500	0.8	1.2	8	50	400
7-9 yr.	3,500	1.0	1.5	10	60	400
Boys						
10-12 yr.	4,500	1.3	1.8	13	75	400
13-15 yr.	5,000	1.6	2.1	16	90	400
16-20 yr.	5,000	1.9	2.5	19	100	400
Girls						
10-12 yr.	4,500	1.2	1.8	12	75	400
13-15 yr.	5,000	1.3	2.0	13	80	400
16-20 yr.	5,000	1.2	1.9	12	80	400
Chickens[2]						
0-8 weeks	1,200	0.8	1.3	12	0	90
8-18 weeks	1,200	--	0.8	--	0	90
Laying hens	2,000	--	1.0	--	0	225
Turkeys[3]						
0-8 weeks	2,400	--	1.7	--	0	400
8-16 weeks	2,400	--	--	--	0	400
Breeders	2,400	--	1.5	--	0	400
Swine[4]						
Growing fattening pigs						
50 lb.	1.0 (mg. carotene)	1.6	3.2	19.2	0	288
100 lb.	2.0	2.6	5.3	26.5	0	477
150 lb.	3.0	3.4	6.8	34.0	0	612
200 lb.	4.0	3.8	7.5	37.5	0	675
250 lb.	5.0	4.2	8.3	41.5	0	747
Pregnant gilts & sows, breeding boars	15-18	3-3.8	7.2-9.0	30-37.5	0	540-675
Lactating sows	27-31	5.5-6.2	13.2-15.0	55-62.5		990-1,125

[1] See footnote 1, Table 49, p. 327. Sheep and cattle are not included here since rumen microorganisms and sunlight supply all needed vitamins except vitamin A or its precursor, carotene. The recommended daily level for ruminants is 6.0 mg. carotene per 100 pounds of body weight. This is five times the accepted minimum level for optimum growth, but leaves a slight margin of safety for reproduction.

[2] Pantothenic acid requirements are respectively down the list 4.2, 4.2, and 2.1 mg., choline 600 mg. for 0-8 wk. chicks, folacin 0.25 mg. and 0.11 mg. for 0-8 wk. chicks and laying hens, respectively. For 0-8 wk. chicks, vitamins B_{12} and K_1 are 0.004 and 0.18 mg./lb. of feed, respectively. All table values for birds = amount per lb. of feed.

[3] For 0-8 wk. poults, pantothenic acid 5 mg., choline 750 mg., and folacin 0.4 mg. All amounts per lb. of feed in table.

[4] Pantothenic acid requirements are (respectively reading down the list): 16, 23.8, 30.6, 33.8, 37.4, 27-33.8, and 49.5-56.2 mg. Pyridoxine for 50 lb. pigs is 1.9 mg., and Vitamin B_{12} is 16.0 and 26.5 micrograms for 50 lb. and 100 lb. pigs, respectively.

Table 51. Recommended daily allowances for minerals[1]

Species	Ca gm.	P gm.	K gm.	NaCl gm.	Mg. mg.	Fe mg.	Mn mg.	Cu mg.	I mg.	Co mg.	Zn p.p.m.	F p.p.m.
Humans												
Men	0.8	1.2[2]	-	5 (or less)	-	2	-	1-2[3]	0.1-0.3[4]	-	-	1[5]
Women	0.8	-	-	-	-	12	-	-	-	-	-	-
Pregnant (3rd trimester)	1.5	-	-	-	-	15	-	-	-	-	-	-
Lactating	2.0	-	-	-	-	15	-	-	-	-	-	-
Infants	0.6-1.0	-	-	-	-	6	-	-	-	-	-	-
Children	1.0	-	-	-	-	7-10	-	-	-	-	-	-
Boys 10-12 yrs.	1.2-1.3	-		-	-	12-15	-	-	-	-	-	-
Girls 10-12 yrs.	1.2-1.3	-		-	-	12-15	-	-	-	-	-	-
Chickens	(%)[6]	(%)[6]	-	(%)[6]								
0-8 wks.	1.0	0.6	-	0.5	220[6]	9[6]	25[6]	0.9[6]	0.5[6]	-	-	-
8-18 wks.	1.0	0.6	-	0.5	-	-	-	-	0.2	-	-	-
Laying hens	2.25	0.6	-	0.5	-	-	-	-	0.2	-	-	-
Turkeys	(%)[6]	(%)[6]	-	(%)[6]								
0-8 wks.	2.0	1.0	-	0.5	-	-	25[6]	-	-	-	-	-
8-16 wks.	2.0	1.0	-	0.5	-	-	-	-	-	-	-	-
Breeders	2.25	0.75	-	0.5	-	-	15[6]	-	-	-	-	-
Swine												
Growing, fattening pigs												
50 lb.	9.4	6.5	-	7.3	-	15[6]	18[6]	2.0[6]	0.1[6]	-	46[7]	-
100 lb.	15.6	10.8	2.5-5.0	12.0	-	15	18	2.0	0.1	-	-	-
150 lb.	17.0	10.2	-	15.4	-	15	18	2.0	0.1	-	-	-
200 lb.	18.7	11.2	-	17.0	-	15	18	2.0	0.1	-	-	-
250 lb.	20.7	12.4	-	18.8	-	15	18	2.0	0.1	-	-	-
Pregnant gilts, sows, breeding boars	16-20	11-14	-	14-17	-	15	18	2.0	0.1	-	-	-
Lactating sows	30-34	20-23	-	25-28	-	15	18	2.0	0.1	-	-	-
Sheep												
Bred ewes 6 wk. before lambing (130 lb.)	4.5	3.4	-	14	-	-	-	5	-	0.1	-	-
Lactating ewes (130 lb.)	6.5	4.8	-	14	-	-	-	5	-	0.1	-	-
Fattening lambs												
50 lb.	2.5	2.1	-	10	-	-	-	-	-	-	-	-
90 lb.	2.7	2.3	-	10	-	-	-	-	-	-	-	-

[1] See footnote 1, Table 49, p. 327.

[2] Phosphorus allowance should be about 1.5 times calcium allowance, except for pregnant women and children, where it should equal calcium allowance.

[3] One-tenth of iron requirement. In children, 0.05 mg./kg. body wt.

[4] About 0.002-0.004 mg. I/kg. body wt. in children and adults.

[5] One p.p.m. in drinking water protects against dental caries in humans.

[6] Per cent of feed, or amount per lb. of feed.

[7] Parts per million in a corn-soy ration. See Science 128, 1280-1281 (1958).

Species	Ca gm.	P gm.	K gm.	NaCl gm.	Mg. mg.	Fe mg.	Mn mg.	Cu mg.	I mg.	Co mg.	Zn p.p.m.	F p.p.m.
Beef Cattle												
Heifers & steers												
400 lb.	20	15	-	4	0.6[8]	-	-	-	0.3[9]	1	-	-
1,000 lb.	15	15	-	4	0.6	-	-	-	0.3	1	-	-
Fattening year- ling cattle												
600 lb.	20	17	-	4	0.6	-	-	-	0.3	1	-	-
1,100 lb.	20	20	-	4	0.6	-	-	-	0.3	1	-	-
Wintering year- ling cattle												
600 lb.	16	12	-	4	0.6	-	-	-	0.3	-	-	-
900 lb.	16	12	-	4	0.6	-	-	-	0.3	1	-	-
Bulls, growth, maintenance												
600 lb.	24	18	-	4	0.6	-	-	-	0.3	1	-	-
1,800 lb.	18	18	-	4	0.6	-	-	-	0.3	1	-	-
Nursing Cows												
900-1,100 lb.	30	24	-	26	-	-	-	-	-	-	-	-

[8] Grams per 100 lb. body weight.

[9] Estimated by author as 0.007 per cent of salt requirement.

Table 52.   Composition and energy value of selected foods[1]
(nutritive value of 100 grams, edible portion)

Food and description	Water %	Food energy Cal.	Protein Gm.	Fat Gm.	Carbohydrate Total Gm.	Carbohydrate Fiber Gm.	Ash Gm.	Calcium Mg.	Phosphorus Mg.	Iron Mg.	Vitamin A value I.U.	Thiamin Mg.	Riboflavin Mg.	Niacin Mg.	Ascorbic acid Mg.
A. Cereal Products															
1. Baked goods															
a. Bread: white, enriched	44.5	219	4.8	2.1	46.0	.3	2.6	185	158	2.9	140	.13	.17	1.9	0
Whole wheat	36.6	240	9.3	2.6	49.0	1.5	2.5	2.5	263	2.2	0	.30	.13	3.0	0
Rye, American	35.3	244	9.1	1.2	52.4	.4	2.0	2.0	147	1.6	0	.18	.08	1.5	0
b. Cake, plain	26.8	327	6.4	8.2	57.0	1.6	1.6	155	137	.4	120	.03	.08	.3	(0)
c. Cookies, plain	4.8	436	6.0	12.7	75.0	--	1.6	22	65	.6	(0)[2]	.04	.04	.5	(0)
d. Crackers, soda	5.7	420	9.6	9.6	72.7	.2	2.4	20	96	1.1	(0)	.06	.05	1.1	(0)
e. Crackers, graham	5.5	393	8.0	10.0	74.3	.8	2.2	20	203	1.9	(0)	.30	.12	1.5	(0)
f. Pie, Apple	47.8	246	2.1	9.5	39.5	.7	1.1	7	24	.4	160	.03	.02	.2	1
Custard	58.5	204	5.2	8.7	26.3	.0	1.3	125	116	1.2	230	.05	.16	.3	(0)
g. Rolls, enriched	28.5	309	9.0	5.5	55.1	.2	1.9	55	96	1.8	0	.24	.15	2.2	(0)
2. Breakfast cereals															
a. Corn flakes, enriched	3.6	385	8.1	.4	85.0	.6	2.9	11	58	2.2	(0)	.41	.10	2.2	(0)
b. Oatmeal, dry	8.3	390	14.2	7.4	68.2	1.2	1.9	53	405	4.5	(0)	.60	.14	1.0	(0)
c. Rice: flakes or puffed, enriched	3.5	392	5.9	.6	87.7	.5	2.3	21	116	1.8	(0)	.46	.08	5.5	(0)
d. Wheat cereals															
Farina, enriched	10.5	370	10.9	.8	77.4	.4	.4	28	112	1.3	(0)	.37	.26	1.3	(0)
Flakes or puffed, enriched	3.8	355	10.8	1.6	80.2	1.7	3.6	46	329	4.2	(0)	.56	.18	6.4	(0)
Shredded wheat	5.6	360	10.1	2.5	80.1	2.3	1.7	47	360	3.5	(0)	.22	.12	4.4	(0)
Whole meal, dry	8.2	344	12.7	1.7	75.3	2.2	2.1	46	392	3.4	(0)	.55	.15	4.4	(0)
3. All purpose enriched flour (wheat)	12.	364	10.5	1.0	76.1	.3	.43	16	87	2.9	(0)	.44	.26	3.5	(0)
4. Wheat germ	11.0	361	25.2	10.0	49.5	2.5	4.3	84	1096	8.1	(0)	2.05	.80	4.6	(0)
5. Other Cereals															
a. Barley, pearled, light	11.1	349	8.2	1.0	78.8	.5	.9	16	189	(2.0)	(0)	.12	.08	3.1	0
b. Corn:															
Corn, sweet, yellow, raw	73.9	92	3.7	1.2	20.5	.8	.7	9	120	.5	390	.15	.12	1.7	12
Corn meal, degermed, enriched, yellow	12.	363	7.9	1.2	78.4	.6	.5	6	99	1.1	300	.14	.05	1.0	(0)
Corn grits, degermed, enriched, dry	12.	362	8.7	.8	78.1	.4	.4	4	73	2.9	300	.44	.26	3.5	(0)
Tortillas	41.9	211	5.8	(2.8)	48.6	(1.4)	.9	111	184	2.2	210	.19	.06	1.0	--

[1] Based on U.S.D.A. Handbook No. 8, "Composition of Foods--Raw, Processed, Prepared", by B. K. Watt and A. L. Merrill, Washington, D. C. (1950).

[2] Parentheses indicate imputed value.

Table 52. Composition and energy value of selected foods - 2 - (cont'd)

Food and description	Water %	Food energy Cal.	Protein Gm.	Fat Gm.	Carbohydrate Total Gm.	Carbohydrate Fiber Gm.	Ash Gm.	Calcium Mg.	Phosphorus Mg.	Iron Mg.	Vitamin A value I.U.	Thiamin Mg.	Riboflavin Mg.	Niacin Mg.	Ascorbic acid Mg.
c. Macaroni, spaghetti, enriched, dry	8.6	377	12.8	1.4	76.5	.4	.7	22	165	2.9	(0)	.88	.37	6.0	(0)
d. Noodles, egg, enriched, dry	9.6	381	12.6	3.4	73.2	.4	1.2	22	199	2.9	200	.88	.37	6.0	(0)
e. Rice:															
Brown, raw, dry	12.0	360	7.5	1.7	77.7	.6	1.1	39	303	2.0	(0)	.32	.05	4.6	(0)
White, raw, dry	12.3	362	7.6	.3	79.4	.2	.4	24	136	.8	(0)	.07	.03	1.6	(0)
White, precooked, dry	7.6	382	8.8	.2	83.3	.4	.1	4	66	.8	(0)	.02	.02	.1	(0)
f. Tapioca, dry	12.6	360	.6	.2	86.4	.1	.2	12	12	(1.0)	(0)	(0)	(0)	(0)	(0)
B. Dairy Products															
1. Milk															
a. Whole, fresh	87.0	68	3.5	3.9	4.9	0	.7	118	93	.1	(160)	.04	.17	.1	1
b. Whole, dry	3.5	492	25.8	26.7	38.0	0	6.0	949	728	.6	1400	.30	1.46	.7	6
c. Condensed, unsweetened	73.7	138	7.0	7.9	9.9	0	1.5	243	195	0.2	400	0.05	0.36	0.2	1
d. Skim, dry	3.5	362	35.6	1.0	52.0	0	7.9	1300	1030	.6	(40)	.35	1.96	1.1	7
e. Buttermilk, cultured	90.5	36	3.5	.1	5.1	0	.8	(118)	93	.1	Trace	.04	.18	.1	1
2. Cream (20% fat)	72.5	204	2.9	20.0	4.0	0	.6	97	77	.1	830	.03	.14	.1	1
3. Ice cream, plain (typical formula)	62.1	207	4.0	12.5	20.6	0	.8	123	99	.1	520	.04	.19	.1	1
4. Cheese															
a. Cottage	76.5	95	19.5	.5	2.0	0	1.5	96	189	.3	(20)	.02	.31	(.1)	(0)
b. Cream	51.	371	9.0	37.0	2.0	0	1.0	68	97	.2	(1450)	(.01)	.22	.1	(0)
c. Cheddar, processed	40.	370	23.2	29.9	2.0	0	4.9	673	787	.9	1300	.02	.41	Trace	(0)
d. Swiss, processed	40.	355	26.4	26.9	1.6	0	5.1	887	867	.9	1390	.01	.40	.1	(0)
C. Dry Legumes, Nuts															
1. Legumes															
a. Beans, common or kidney	12.2	336	23.1	1.7	59.4	3.5	3.6	163	437	6.9	(0)	.57	.22	2.5	2
b. Beans, navy, pea bean, white marrow, etc.	11.5	338	21.4	1.6	61.6	4.0	3.9	163	437	6.9	0	0.67	0.23	2.2	2
c. Beans, lima	12.6	333	20.7	1.3	61.6	4.3	3.8	68	381	7.5	0	.48	.18	2.0	2
d. Chick peas	10.6	359	20.8	4.7	60.9	5.3	3.0	92	375	7.1	Trace	.55	.17	1.5	(2)
e. Cowpeas	10.6	342	22.9	1.4	61.6	4.2	3.5	77	451	6.5	30	.92	.16	2.2	2
f. Peas, split, without seed coat	10.0	344	24.5	1.0	61.7	1.2	2.8	33	268	5.1	370	.77	.28	3.1	2
g. Soybeans, whole	7.5	331	34.9	18.1	34.8	5.0	4.7	227	586	8.0	110	1.07	.31	2.3	Trace
2. Nuts															
a. Almonds	4.7	597	18.6	54.1	19.6	2.7	3.0	254	475	4.4	0	0.25	0.67	4.6	Trace
b. Peanuts, roasted	2.6	559	26.9	44.2	23.6	2.4	2.7	74	393	1.9	0	.30	.13	16.2	(0)
c. Pecans	3.0	696	9.4	73.0	13.0	2.2	1.6	74	324	2.4	50	.72	.11	.9	2
d. Walnuts, English	3.3	654	15.0	64.4	15.6	2.1	1.7	83	380	2.1	30	.48	.13	1.2	3

Table 52. Composition and energy value of selected foods – 3 – (cont'd)

Food and description	Water %	Food energy Cal.	Protein Gm.	Fat Gm.	Carbohydrate Total Gm.	Carbohydrate Fiber Gm.	Ash Gm.	Calcium Mg.	Phosphorus Mg.	Iron Mg.	Vitamin A value I.U.	Thiamin Mg.	Riboflavin Mg.	Niacin Mg.	Ascorbic acid Mg.
D. Eggs															
1. Eggs, whole, fresh	74.0	162	12.8	11.5	.7	0	1.0	54	210	2.7	1140	.10	.29	.1	0
2. Eggs, whole, dry	5.	592	46.8	42.0	2.5	0	3.6	190	767	8.8	3740	.34	1.06	.2	0
3. Egg white, fresh	87.8	50	10.8	0.	.8	0	.6	6	17	.2	(0)	0	.26	(.1)	0
4. Egg white, dry	3.	398	85.9	0.	6.3	0	4.8	48	135	1.6	0	0	2.05	.7	0
5. Egg yolk, fresh	49.4	361	16.3	31.9	.7	0	1.7	147	586	7.2	3210	.27	.35	Trace	0
6. Egg yolk, dry	3.	693	31.2	61.2	1.3	0	3.3	282	1123	13.8	5540	.50	.66	.1	0
E. Fats and Oils															
1. Bacon, medium fat, raw	20.	630	9.1	65.	1.1	0	4.3	13	108	.8	(0)	.38	.12	1.9	0
2. Butter	15.5	716	.6	81.	.4	0	2.5	20	16	.0	3300	Trace	.01	.1	0
3. French dressing	39.6	394	.6	35.5	20.3	.3	4.0	(0)	(0)	(0)	(0)	(0)	(0)	(0)	(0)
4. Lard	0.	902	0.	100.	0.	0	0	0	0	0	0	(0)	0	0	0
5. Margarine with vitamin A	15.5	720	.6	81.	.4	0	2.5	20	16	.0	3300	(0)	(0)	(0)	(0)
6. Mayonnaise (typical recipe)	44.7	384	1.1	36.8	13.9	(0)	3.5	9	30	.4	140	.02	.03	(0)	(0)
7. Oils, salad or cooking	0.	884	0.	100.	0.	0	0	0	0	0	0	0	0	0	0
F. Fruits															
1. Apples	84.1	58	.3	.4	14.9	1.0	.3	6	10	.3	90	.04	.03	.2	5
2. Apricots	85.4	51	1.0	.1	12.9	.6	.6	16	23	.5	2790	.03	.05	.8	7
3. Avocados	65.4	245	1.7	26.4	5.1	1.8	1.4	10	38	.6	290	.06	.13	1.1	16
4. Bananas	74.8	88	1.2	.2	23.	.6	.8	8	28	.6	430	.04	.05	.7	10
5. Berries:															
a. Blueberries	83.4	61	.6	.6	15.1	1.2	.3	16	13	.8	280	(.02)	(.02)	(.3)	16
b. Cranberries	87.4	48	.4	.7	11.3	1.4	.2	14	11	.6	40	(.03)	(.02)	.1	12
c. Raspberries, red	84.1	57	1.2	.4	13.8	4.7	.5	40	37	.9	130	.02	(.07)	(.3)	24
d. Strawberries	89.9	37	.8	.5	8.3	1.4	.5	28	27	.8	60	.03	.07	.3	60
6. Cantaloupe	94.0	20	.6	.2	4.6	.6	.4	17	16	.4	3420	.05	.04	.5	33
7. Grapefruit	88.8	40	.5	.2	10.1	.3	.4	22	18	.2	Trace	.04	.02	.2	40
8. Grapes (Concord)	81.9	70	1.4	1.4	14.9	.5	.4	17	21	.6	80	.06	.04	.2	4
9. Lemons	89.3	32	.9	.6	8.7	.9	.5	40	22	.6	0	.04	.04	.1	50
10. Limes	86.0	37	.8	.1	12.3	(.9)	.8	(40)	(22)	(.6)	0	(.04)	Trace	(.1)	27
11. Oranges	87.2	45	.9	.2	11.2	.6	.5	33	23	.4	(190)	.08	Trace	.2	49
12. Peaches	86.9	46	.5	.1	12.0	.6	.5	8	22	.6	880	.02	.03	.9	8
13. Pears	82.7	63	.7	.4	15.8	1.4	.4	13	16	.3	20	.02	.05	.1	4
14. Pineapples	85.3	52	.4	.2	13.7	.4	.4	16	11	.3	130	.08	.04	.2	24
15. Plums	85.7	50	.7	.2	12.9	.5	.5	17	20	.5	350	.06	.02	.5	5
16. Rhubarb	94.9	16	.5	.1	3.8	.7	.7	51	25	.5	30	.01	.04	.1	9
17. Tangerines	87.3	44	.8	.3	10.9	1.0	.7	(33)	(23)	(.4)	(420)	.07	—	(.2)	31
18. Watermelons	92.1	28	.5	.2	6.9	.6	.3	7	12	.2	590	.05	(.03)	.2	6
19. Fruit juices:															
a. Orange	87.5	44	.8	.2	11.0	.1	.4	19	16	.2	(190)	.08	.03	.2	49
b. Grapefruit	89.8	36	.5	.1	9.2	.1	.4	8	13	.3	Trace	.04	.02	.2	40

Table 52. Composition and energy value of selected foods – 4 – (cont'd)

Food and description	Water %	Food energy Cal.	Protein Gm.	Fat Gm.	Carbohydrate Total Gm.	Carbohydrate Fiber Gm.	Ash Gm.	Calcium Mg.	Phosphorus Mg.	Iron Mg.	Vitamin A value I.U.	Thiamin Mg.	Riboflavin Mg.	Niacin Mg.	Ascorbic acid Mg.
c. Grape (canned)	81.	67	.4	.0	18.2	--	.4	10	10	.3	--	.04	.05	(.2)	Trace
d. Pineapple (canned)	86.2	49	.3	.1	13.0	.1	.4	15	8	.5	80	.05	.02	.2	9
20. Dried fruit:															
a. Apples (small pieces)	3.	354	1.8	2.4	91.0	4.9	1.8	24	61	1.8	(0)	.07	.10	1.2	12
b. Apricots (sulfured)	24.	262	5.2	.4	66.9	3.2	3.5	86	119	4.9	7430	.01	.16	3.3	12
c. Peaches (sulfured)	24.	265	3.0	.6	69.4	3.5	3.0	44	126	6.9	3250	.01	.20	5.4	19
d. Prunes	24.	268	2.3	.6	71.0	1.6	2.1	54	85	3.9	1890	.10	.16	1.7	3
e. Raisins	24.	268	2.3	.5	71.2	--	2.0	78	129	3.3	50	.15	.08	.5	Trace
G. Meats, Poultry, Fish															
1. Beef:															
a. Chuck roast	65.	224	18.6	16.	0.	0	.9	11	167	2.8	(0)	.08	.17	4.5	0
b. Corned beef	54.2	293	15.8	25.	0.	0	5.0	9	125	2.4	(0)	.03	.15	1.7	0
c. Beef, chipped	47.7	203	34.3	6.3	0.	0	11.6	20	404	5.1	(0)	(.07)	(.32)	(3.8)	0
d. Hamburger	55.	321	16.	28.	0.	0	.8	9	128	2.4	(0)	.07	.14	3.8	0
e. Sirloin steaks	62.	254	17.3	20.	0.	0	.9	10	147	2.6	(0)	.07	.15	4.2	0
f. Rib roast	59.	282	17.4	23.	0.	0	.8	10	149	2.6	(0)	.07	.15	4.2	0
g. Round steak	69.	182	19.5	11.	0.	0	1.0	11	180	2.9	(0)	.08	.17	4.7	0
h. Rump roast	55.	322	16.2	28.	0.	0	0.8	9	131	2.4	(0)	0.07	0.14	3.9	0
2. Lamb:															
a. Leg roast	63.7	235	18.0	17.5	0.	0	.9	10	2.3	2.7	(0)	.16	.22	5.2	0
b. Shoulder roast	58.3	295	15.6	25.3	0.	0	.8	9	155	2.3	(0)	.14	.19	4.5	0
c. Rib chop	51.9	356	14.9	32.4	0.	0	.8	9	138	2.2	(0)	.13	.18	4.3	0
3. Pork															
a. Bacon (see part E)															
b. Ham, fresh	53.	344	15.2	31.	0.	0	.8	9	168	2.3	(0)	.74	.18	4.0	0
c. Ham, smoked	42.	389	16.9	35.	(.3)	0	5.4	10	136	2.5	(0)	.70	.19	4.0	0
d. Loin	58.	296	16.4	25.	0.	0	.9	10	186	2.5	(0)	.80	.19	4.3	0
e. Link sausage	41.9	450	10.8	44.8	0.	0	2.1	6	100	1.6	(0)	.43	.17	2.3	0
4. Veal:															
a. Cutlet (boned)	70.	164	19.5	9.	0.	0	1.0	11	200	2.9	(0)	0.14	0.26	6.5	0
b. Leg roast or steak	70.	173	19.4	10.	0.	0	1.0	11	199	2.9	(0)	.14	.26	6.5	0
5. Meat mixtures:															
a. Bologna	62.4	221	14.8	15.9	3.6	--	3.3	(9)	(112)	2.2	(0)	.18	.19	2.7	0
b. Frankfurters	60.0	257	14.2	20.5	2.7	--	2.7	8	100	1.5	(0)	.18	.19	2.8	0
c. Heart, beef, fresh	77.6	108	16.9	3.7	.7	0	1.1	9	203	4.6	30	.58	.89	7.8	6
d. Liver, beef, fresh	69.7	136	19.7	3.2	6.0	0	1.4	7	358	6.6	43,900	.26	3.33	13.7	31
e. Liver sausage	59.0	263	16.7	20.6	1.5	--	2.2	9	238	5.4	5750	.17	1.12	4.6	(0)
f. Tongue, fresh	68.	207	16.4	15.	.4	(0)	.9	9	187	2.8	(0)	.12	.29	5.0	(0)

Table 52. Composition and energy value of selected foods – 5 – (cont'd)

Food and description	Water %	Food energy Cal.	Protein Gm.	Fat Gm.	Carbohydrate Total Gm.	Carbohydrate Fiber Gm.	Ash Gm.	Calcium Mg.	Phosphorus Mg.	Iron Mg.	Vitamin A value I.U.	Thiamin Mg.	Riboflavin Mg.	Niacin Mg.	Ascorbic acid Mg.
6. Poultry															
a. Chicken, boned, canned	61.9	199	29.8	8.0	0.	0	2.4	14	148	1.8	(0)	.04	.16	6.4	(0)
b. Chicken, broilers	71.2	151	20.2	7.2	0.	0	1.1	14	200	1.5	(0)	.08	.16	10.2	(0)
c. Turkey, medium, fat	58.3	268	20.1	20.2	0.	0	1.0	23	320	3.8	Trace	.09	.14	8.0	(0)
7. Fish and shellfish															
a. Cod	82.6	74	16.5	.4	0.	0	1.2	10	194	.4	0	.06	.09	2.2	2
b. Haddock	80.7	79	18.2	.1	0.	0	1.4	23	197	.7	--	.05	.08	2.4	--
c. Oysters, meat only	80.5	84	9.8	2.1	5.6	--	2.0	94	143	5.6	320	.15	.20	1.2	--
d. Salmon, canned, Chinook	64.7	203	19.7	13.2	0.	0	2.4	154	289	0.9	230	0.03	0.14	7.3	(0)
e. Sardines, Atlantic type, canned in oil, drained	57.4	214	25.7	11.0	1.2	--	(4.7)	386	586	2.7	220	.02	.17	4.8	(0)
f. Shrimp, canned, drained	66.2	127	26.8	1.4	--	--	5.8	115	263	3.1	60	.01	.03	2.2	(0)
g. Tuna fish, canned, drained	60.0	198	29.0	8.2	0.	0	2.7	(8)	(351)	1.4	80	.05	.12	12.8	(0)
H. Sugars, Sweets															
1. Sugars															
a. Sugar, white, granulated or powdered	.5	385	(0.)	(0.)	99.5	(0)	--	--	--	--	(0)	(0)	(0)	(0)	(0)
b. Sugar, brown	3.	370	(0.)	(0.)	95.5	--	1.2	76	37	2.6	(0)	(0)	(0)	(0)	(0)
c. Sirup, corn	25.	286	(0.)	(0.)	(74.)	--	.6	46	16	4.1	0	0	.01	.1	(0)
2. Sweets															
a. Honey	20.	294	.3	0.	79.5	--	.2	5	16	.9	(0)	Trace	.04	.2	4
b. Jams, marmalade, preserves	28.	278	.5	.3	70.8	.6	.4	12	12	.3	10	.02	.02	.2	6
c. Jellies	34.5	252	.2	.0	65.0	0	.3	(12)	(12)	(.3)	(10)	(.02)	(.02)	(.2)	4
d. Molasses, cane (light)	24.	252	--	--	65.	--	6.3	165	45	4.3	--	.07	.06	.2	--
I. Vegetables															
Fresh															
1. Asparagus	93.0	21	2.2	.2	3.9	.7	.7	21	62	.9	1000	.16	.19	1.4	33
2. Beans, lima, green	66.5	128	7.5	.8	23.5	1.5	1.7	63	158	2.3	280	.21	.11	1.4	32
3. Beans, snap	88.9	35	2.4	.2	7.7	1.4	.8	65	44	1.1	630	.08	.11	.5	19
4. Beet greens	90.4	27	2.0	.3	5.6	1.4	1.7	118	45	3.2	6700	.08	.18	.4	34
5. Beets	87.6	42	1.6	.1	9.6	.9	1.1	27	43	1.0	20	.02	.05	.4	10
6. Broccoli	89.9	29	3.3	.2	5.5	1.3	1.1	130	76	1.3	3500	.10	.21	1.1	118
7. Brussels sprouts	84.9	47	4.4	0.5	8.9	1.3	1.3	34	78	1.3	400	0.08	0.16	0.7	94
8. Cabbage	92.4	24	1.4	.2	5.3	1.0	.8	46	31	.5	80	.06	.05	.3	50
9. Carrots	88.2	42	1.2	0.3	9.3	1.1	1.0	39	37	0.8	12,000	.06	.06	.5	9
10. Cauliflower	91.7	25	2.4	.2	4.9	.9	.8	22	72	1.1	90	.11	.10	.6	69
11. Celery	93.7	18	1.3	.2	3.7	.7	1.1	50	40	.5	0	.05	.04	.4	7

Table 52. Composition and energy value of selected foods - 6 - (cont'd)

Food and description	Water %	Food energy Cal.	Protein Gm.	Fat Gm.	Carbohydrate Total Gm.	Carbohydrate Fiber Gm.	Ash Gm.	Calcium Mg.	Phosphorus Mg.	Iron Mg.	Vitamin A value I.U.	Thiamin Mg.	Riboflavin Mg.	Niacin Mg.	Ascorbic acid Mg.
Fresh (cont'd.)															
12. Chard	91.8	21	1.4	.2	4.4	.9	2.2	105	36	2.5	2800	.06	.07	.4	38
13. Corn, sweet, yellow	73.9	92	3.7	1.2	20.5	.8	.7	9	120	.5	390	.15	.12	1.7	12
14. Cucumbers	96.1	12	.7	.1	2.7	.5	.4	10	21	.3	0	.03	.04	.2	8
15. Dandelion greens	85.8	44	2.7	.7	8.8	1.8	2.0	187	70	3.1	13,650	.19	.14	(.8)	36
16. Eggplant	92.7	24	1.1	.2	5.5	.9	.5	15	37	.4	30	.04	.05	.6	5
17. Kale	86.6	40	3.9	.6	7.2	1.2	1.7	225	62	2.2	7540	.10	.26	2.0	115
18. Lettuce, head	94.8	15	1.2	.2	2.9	.6	.9	22	25	.5	540	.04	.08	.2	8
19. Lettuce, leaf	94.8	15	1.2	.2	2.9	.6	.9	62	20	1.1	1620	.04	.08	.2	18
20. Mustard greens	92.2	22	2.3	.3	4.0	.8	1.2	220	38	2.9	6460	.09	.20	.8	102
21. Okra	89.8	32	1.8	.2	7.4	1.0	.8	82	62	.7	740	.08	.07	1.1	30
22. Onions, mature	87.5	45	1.4	0.2	10.3	0.8	0.6	32	44	0.5	50	0.03	0.04	0.2	9
23. Parsnips	78.6	78	1.5	.5	18.2	2.2	1.2	57	80	.7	0	.08	.12	.2	18
24. Peas, green	74.3	98	6.7	.4	17.7	2.2	.9	22	122	1.9	680	.34	.16	2.7	26
25. Pepper, green	92.4	25	1.2	.2	5.7	1.4	.5	11	25	.4	630	.04	.07	1.2	120
26. Potatoes	77.8	83	2.0	.1	19.1	.4	1.0	11	56	.7	20	.11	.04	1.2	17
27. Pumpkin	90.5	31	1.2	.2	7.3	1.3	.8	21	44	.8	(3400)	(.05)	(.08)	(.6)	8
28. Radishes	93.6	20	1.2	.1	4.2	.7	1.0	37	31	1.0	30	.03	.02	.3	24
29. Rutabagas	89.1	38	1.1	.1	8.9	1.3	.8	55	41	.4	330	.07	.08	.9	36
30. Spinach	92.7	20	2.3	.3	3.2	.6	1.5	81	55	3.0	9420	.11	.20	.6	59
31. Squash, summer	95.0	16	.6	.1	3.9	.5	.4	15	15	.4	260	.05	.09	.8	17
32. Squash, winter	88.6	38	1.5	.3	8.8	1.4	.8	19	28	.6	4950	.05	.12	.5	8
33. Sweet potatoes	68.5	123	1.8	.7	27.9	1.0	1.1	30	49	.7	7700	.09	.05	.6	22
34. Tomatoes	94.1	20	1.0	.3	4.0	.6	.6	11	27	.6	1100	.06	.04	.5	23
35. Turnip greens	89.5	30	2.9	.4	5.4	1.2	1.8	259	50	2.4	9540	.09	.46	.5	136
36. Turnips	90.9	32	1.1	.2	7.1	1.1	.7	40	34	.5	Trace	.05	.07	.5	28
Canned (solids and liquid)															
1. Asparagus	93.6	18	1.9	.3	2.9	.5	1.3	18	43	1.7	600	.07	.10	.9	15
2. Beans, lima	80.9	71	3.8	.3	13.5	1.3	1.5	27	73	1.7	130	.04	.04	.5	8
3. Beans, snap	93.5	18	1.0	.1	4.2	.6	1.2	27	19	1.4	410	.03	.04	.3	4
4. Beets	90.3	34	.9	.1	7.9	.5	.8	15	29	.6	20	.01	.02	.1	5
5. Corn, yellow	80.5	67	2.0	.5	16.1	.8	.9	4	51	.5	200	.03	.05	.9	5
6. Peas, green	82.3	68	3.4	0.4	12.9	1.4	1.0	25	67	1.8	540	.11	.06	1.0	8
7. Pumpkin	90.2	33	1.0	.3	7.9	1.2	.6	(20)	(36)	(.7)	3400	.02	.06	.5	--
8. Sauerkraut	93.2	16	1.1	.2	3.4	.7	2.1	36	18	(.5)	30	.03	.06	.1	16
9. Spinach	92.3	20	2.3	.4	3.0	.7	1.8	90	33	1.6	6790	.02	.10	.3	14
10. Tomatoes	94.2	19	1.0	.2	3.9	.4	.7	(11)	(27)	(.6)	1050	.06	.03	.7	16
11. Tomato juice	93.5	21	1.0	.2	4.3	.2	1.0	(7)	(15)	(.4)	1050	.05	.03	.8	16
12. Tomato puree	89.2	36	1.8	.5	7.2	.4	1.3	(11)	(37)	(1.1)	1880	.09	.07	1.8	28

INDEX